Values of fundamental constants

Quantity	Symbol	Value
Speed of light in vacuum	c_0	3.00×10^8 m/s
Gravitational constant	G	6.6738×10^{-11} N·m^2/kg^2
Avogadro's number	N_A	6.0221413×10^{23}
Boltzmann's constant	k_B	1.381×10^{-23} J/K
Charge on electron	e	1.60×10^{-19} C
Electric constant	ϵ_0	$8.85418782 \times 10^{-12}$ C^2/(N·m^2)
Magnetic constant	μ_0	$4\pi \times 10^{-7}$ T·m/A
Planck's constant	h	6.626×10^{-34} J·s
Electron mass	m_e	9.11×10^{-31} kg
Proton mass	m_p	1.6726×10^{-27} kg
Neutron mass	m_n	1.6749×10^{-27} kg
Atomic mass unit	amu	1.6605×10^{-27} kg

Other useful numbers

Number or quantity	Value
π	3.1415927
e	2.7182818
1 radian	57.2957795°
Absolute zero ($T = 0$)	-273.15 °C
Average acceleration g due to gravity near Earth's surface	9.8 m/s^2
Speed of sound in air at 20 °C	343 m/s
Density of dry air at atmospheric pressure and 20 °C	1.29 kg/m^3
Earth's mass	5.97×10^{24} kg
Earth's radius (mean)	6.38×10^6 m
Earth–Moon distance (mean)	3.84×10^8 m

PEARSON   ALWAYS LEARNING

Eric Mazur • Daryl Pedigo

Additional contributions from

Peter A. Dourmashkin • Ronald J. Bieniek

Practice of Physics

Part 2

Custom Edition for the University of Minnesota

Taken from:
Principles & Practice of Physics
by Eric Mazur and Daryl Pedigo

Cover Art: Courtesy of Photodisc/Getty Images.

Taken from:

Principles & Practice of Physics
by Eric Mazur and Daryl Pedigo
Copyright © 2015 by Pearson Education, Inc.
Upper Saddle River, New Jersey 07458

This special edition published in cooperation with Pearson Learning Solutions.

All trademarks, service marks, registered trademarks, and registered service marks are the property of their respective owners and are used herein for identification purposes only.

Pearson Learning Solutions, 501 Boylston Street, Suite 900, Boston, MA 02116
A Pearson Education Company
www.pearsoned.com

Printed in the United States of America

3 4 5 6 7 8 9 10 V092 16 15 14

000200010271907272

SL

ISBN 10: 1-269-92611-X
ISBN 13: 978-1-269-92611-9

Brief Contents

Getting the Most Out of *Practice*

The ideas of physics explain phenomena all around you—from static electricity in your laundry to how your smartphone knows your location. Some of these principles are straightforward, while others are not immediately obvious. Understanding physics requires not only understanding the concepts but also being able to *apply* these concepts to new situations. Transferring your knowledge to new situations requires advanced reasoning skills, such as judging which concepts are relevant to the problem at hand and then devising a plan to solve the problem. The *Practice* text puts the ideas you learned in the *Principles* text into practice. It teaches you how to make quantitative assumptions and use reason and strategy to solve problems. After you have read your assigned chapter in the *Principles* text, then turn to the corresponding chapter in your *Practice* text and work your way through the chapter.

Here's how the various parts of each chapter will help you become a competent problem solver:

Begin with the **Chapter Summary,** which highlights the major relationships covered in the chapter. Use it to refresh your understanding before you do your homework or as a quick study tool before class.

The **Review Questions** are designed to make sure you understand the primary points of each section. The answers to these questions are on the last page of the chapter. If you have difficulty answering the Review Questions, go back and re-read the appropriate *Principles* section.

You cannot determine whether the answer you obtain for a problem is reasonable if you have no idea what constitutes a reasonable magnitude for the answer. The **Developing a Feel** exercises help you develop both order-of-magnitude estimation skills as well as a "gut feeling" for the range of values appropriate for the physical quantities introduced in each chapter.

A series of **Worked Problems** provide detailed examples of how to approach, solve, and evaluate problems. Each Worked Problem is followed by a related **Guided Problem,** which guides you to solve a similar problem by yourself. The answers to the Guided Problems are on the last page of the chapter.

The **Questions and Problems** are designed as homework or review for examinations. They are provided in a range of difficulty levels, some with more conceptual emphasis and some with more quantitative emphasis.

Together, the *Principles & Practice of Physics* combine to create a learning tool that was developed with you, the student, at the center. We have worked hard to create accurate, physically plausible scenarios that will help you develop the type of problem-solving skills that will serve you not only in your physics course but also in your future career.

Eric Mazur
Harvard University

Daryl Pedigo
University of Washington

16

PRACTICE

Waves in One Dimension

PRACTICE

Chapter Summary

Representing waves (Sections 16.1, 16.2, 16.5)

Concepts A **wave** is a *disturbance* that propagates through material (the medium) or through empty space.

A **wave pulse** is a single isolated propagating disturbance.

The **wave function** represents the shape of a wave at any given instant and changes with time as the wave travels.

The **wave speed** c is the speed at which a wave propagates. For a mechanical wave, c is different from the speed v of the particles of the medium and is determined by the properties of the medium.

The **displacement** $\vec{D}$ of any particle of a medium through which a mechanical wave travels is a vector that points from the equilibrium position of the particle to its actual position.

In a **transverse** mechanical wave, the particles of the medium move perpendicular to the direction of the pulse movement. In a **longitudinal** mechanical wave, these particles move parallel to the direction of the pulse movement.

In a **periodic wave,** the displacement at any location in the medium is a periodic function of time. A periodic wave is **harmonic** when the particle displacement can be represented by a sinusoidally varying function of space and time.

Quantitative Tools If a wave travels in the x direction with speed c and $f(x)$ describes the form (shape) of the wave, then the y component D_y of the displacement of a particle of the medium is

$$D_y = f(x - ct) \tag{16.3}$$

if the wave travels in the positive x direction and

$$D_y = f(x + ct) \tag{16.4}$$

if the wave travels in the negative x direction.

The **wavelength** λ of a periodic wave is the minimum distance over which the wave repeats itself.

For a periodic wave of period T, frequency f, and speed c, the **wave number** k is

$$k = \frac{2\pi}{\lambda}. \tag{16.7}$$

The wavelength λ is

$$\lambda = cT, \tag{16.9}$$

the angular frequency ω is

$$\omega = \frac{2\pi}{T}, \tag{16.11}$$

and the wave speed is

$$c = \lambda f. \tag{16.10}$$

For a transverse harmonic wave of amplitude A and initial phase ϕ_i traveling in the positive x direction, the y component D_y of the displacement of a particle of the medium is

$$D_y = f(x, t) = A \sin(kx - \omega t + \phi_i). \tag{16.16}$$

Combining waves (Sections 16.3, 16.4, 16.6)

Concepts **Superposition of waves:** The resultant displacement of two or more overlapping waves is the algebraic sum of the displacements of the individual waves.

Interference occurs when two waves overlap. The interference is *constructive* when the displacements due to the two waves are in the same direction and *destructive* when the displacements are in opposite directions.

If the displacement at a point in space remains zero as a wave travels through, that point is a **node.** The displacement at other points typically varies with time. If the displacement at a point in space varies over the greatest range as a wave travels through, that point is an **antinode.**

Quantitative Tools If two harmonic waves of equal wavelength λ and equal amplitude A travel in opposite directions on a string, they produce a standing wave. The y component D_y of the string displacement at any position x along the string is given by

$$D_y = 2A \sin kx \cos \omega t. \tag{16.20}$$

The nodes occur at

$$x = 0, \pm \frac{\lambda}{2}, \pm \lambda, \pm \frac{3\lambda}{2}, \ldots \tag{16.22}$$

and the antinodes occur at

$$x = \pm \frac{\lambda}{4}, \pm \frac{3\lambda}{4}, \pm \frac{5\lambda}{4}, \ldots. \tag{16.24}$$

When a wave pulse (the *incident* wave) reaches a boundary where the transmitting medium ends, the pulse is *reflected*, which means it reverses its direction.

When a wave pulse is reflected from a fixed boundary, the reflected pulse is *inverted* relative to the incident pulse. When the reflection is from a boundary that is free to move, the reflected pulse is not inverted.

A **standing wave** is a pulsating stationary pattern caused by the interference of harmonic waves of equal amplitude and wavelength traveling in opposite directions.

Waves on a string (Sections 16.7—16.9)

Quantitative Tools For a uniform string of mass m and length ℓ, the **linear mass density** μ (mass per unit length) is

$$\mu = \frac{m}{\ell}. \tag{16.25}$$

The speed of a wave on a string under tension T is

$$c = \sqrt{\frac{T}{\mu}}. \tag{16.30}$$

The average power P_{av} that must be supplied to generate a wave of period T is

$$P_{av} = \tfrac{1}{2}\mu\lambda A^2\omega^2/T = \tfrac{1}{2}\mu A^2\omega^2 c. \tag{16.42}$$

Any function f of the form $f(x - ct)$ or $f(x + ct)$ that represents a wave traveling with speed c is a solution of the **wave equation:**

$$\frac{\partial^2 f}{\partial x^2} = \frac{1}{c^2}\frac{\partial^2 f}{\partial t^2}. \tag{16.51}$$

Review Questions

Answers to these questions can be found at the end of this chapter.

16.1 Representing waves graphically

1. What physical quantities are transported by a wave?
2. Classify each wave as longitudinal or transverse: the wave created when a whip is snapped, the wave represented by cars slowing down and speeding up in a traffic jam on a highway, water waves spreading out from the location where a stone is thrown into a pond, the wave created when a guitar string is plucked.
3. What is the difference between the wave speed c of a wave traveling along a rope and the speed v of a small segment of that rope?
4. For a given wave pulse, is it true that the wave function (a function of time) always looks the same as the displacement curve (a function of space)?

16.2 Wave propagation

5. You are sitting at the beach watching the waves. What is the difference between their frequency and their speed?
6. If the hand in *Principles* Figure 16.5 initially stretches the spring leftward rather than compresses it as shown, what happens to the wave speed?
7. Are waves always periodic? Are they always harmonic?
8. If you shake a rope at one end, slowly at first and then faster and faster, what changes about the wave you create in the rope? What remains the same?

16.3 Superposition of waves

9. In what sense is the constructive or destructive interference caused by two wave pulses a temporary phenomenon?
10. How are the values of kinetic energy and potential energy carried by any wave pulse related to each other?
11. When superposing waves, how are the wave functions combined?

16.4 Boundary effects

12. (*a*) How does a pulse reflected from a fixed boundary differ from the incident pulse? (*b*) How does a pulse reflected from a free boundary differ from the incident pulse?
13. Describe the graphical method for determining the shape of the reflected pulse when a wave pulse traveling along a string arrives at a boundary.

16.5 Wave functions

14. List all the variables required to describe a traveling harmonic wave.
15. What is the definition of *wave number*, and what is its purpose?
16. What is the direction of travel of the wave represented by the time-dependent wave function $D(x, t) = 3 \sin(5x - 2t)$?

16.6 Standing waves

17. What is an *antinode*?
18. What is the distance between a node and an adjacent antinode in a standing wave of wavelength λ?
19. Is the displacement of the medium in which a standing wave exists ever zero at an antinode?

16.7 Wave speed

20. An astronaut takes his ukulele out on a space walk. When he strums the strings in space, is the wave speed on each string higher than, lower than, or the same as on Earth?
21. A vibrating string is clamped at both ends, with one of the clamps being a tension-adjustment screw. By what factor must you change the tension in the string to double its frequency of vibration without changing the wavelength?
22. What is the *linear mass density* of a string or rope?

16.8 Energy transport in waves

23. Describe in words the relationship between power and wave properties expressed in Eq. 16.42.
24. When you shake the end of a string to produce a wave, what fraction of the energy you transfer to the string becomes kinetic energy associated with the motion of the string? What fraction becomes potential energy associated with the stretching of the string?

16.9 The wave equation

25. How does a partial derivative differ from an ordinary derivative?
26. A wave pulse moves along a stretched string. Describe the relationship among the speed at which the pulse moves, the pulse curvature, and the acceleration of small segments of the string.

Developing a Feel

Make an order-of-magnitude estimate of each of the following quantities. Letters in parentheses refer to hints below. Use them as needed to guide your thinking.

1. The longest wavelength possible for a standing wave on a guitar string (B, N)
2. The speed of transverse waves on a guitar string (A, R)
3. The speed of transverse vibrations in a telephone wire strung between two poles (C, I, L, T)
4. The frequency of a radio wave whose wavelength equals your height (D, J)
5. The longest wavelength possible for a standing wave around the circumference of a helium atom (O, S)
6. The wave number for a wave whose wavelength equals the circumference of Earth's orbit about the Sun (F, P)
7. The power involved in the vibration of a guitar string (A, H, M, R)
8. The ratio of the linear mass density of the thickest string on a guitar to the linear mass density of the thinnest string (K, Q, U, E, G)

Hints

A. What is the linear mass density of a typical guitar string?
B. What is a typical length for a guitar string?
C. What is the distance between the telephone poles?
D. At what speed do radio waves travel?
E. How does the linear mass density vary with wave speed?
F. What is the radius of Earth's orbit?
G. How do the two wave speeds compare?
H. What is the amplitude of the vibration?
I. What is the maximum vertical sag in the wire?
J. What is the relationship among wavelength, frequency, and speed?
K. What is the fundamental frequency played on each string?
L. What angle does the tensile force exerted on the wire make with the horizontal?
M. What is a typical frequency for a vibrating guitar string?
N. What is the node/antinode pattern on the string when it is vibrating?
O. What is the radius of a helium atom?
P. What is the relationship between wave number and wavelength?
Q. Do the two strings have equal tension?
R. What is a typical guitar string tension?

S. What is the node/antinode pattern in a standing wave that has the longest wavelength possible?
T. Is it possible to compute the vibration speed without knowing the mass of the wire?
U. How do the wavelengths of the fundamental (single-antinode) vibrations compare on the two strings?

Key (all values approximate)

A. 2×10^{-3} kg/m; B. 0.7 m; C. 2×10^1 m; D. the speed of light, 3×10^8 m/s; E. $\mu = T/c^2$; F. 2×10^{11} m; G. because the wavelengths are equal, c is proportional to f; H. 3 mm; I. 0.5 m; J. $\lambda f = c$; K. 1×10^2 Hz on the thickest string, 4×10^2 Hz on the thinnest string; L. 5×10^{-2} rad (sag height divided by half the wire length); M. 3×10^2 Hz; N. for the fundamental vibration, one antinode at the center and a node at each end; O. 1×10^{-10} m; P. $k = 2\pi/\lambda$; Q. yes, to a first approximation; R. 7×10^1 N; S. two nodes and two antinodes; T. yes, to a first approximation, mass appears in both numerator and denominator and so cancels; U. two strings of the same length, with the same fundamental node/antinode pattern, have identical wavelengths;

Worked and Guided Problems

These examples involve material from this chapter but are not associated with any particular section.
Some examples are worked out in detail; others you should work out by following the guidelines provided.

Worked Problem 16.1 Bobbing up and down

A passing speedboat sends out a wake that rocks a rowboat in which a physics student calmly fishes. She notices that the wake has a trough-to-peak height of 0.80 m and that the wave rocks the rowboat with a period of 1.5 s. The distance between crests is 1.7 m. What are (*a*) the wave speed, (*b*) the wave function, and (*c*) the maximum vertical speed of the rowboat?

❶ GETTING STARTED Our physics student has measured several parameters of the wave, and we need to calculate others. We begin with a sketch to help us visualize our ideas and approach (Figure WG16.1). We need to calculate three things: the wave speed, which is the speed at which the wave moves across the water surface, the wave function that describes the wave, and the speed at which the rowboat bobs up and down. In calculating this last value, we assume the boat rides lightly on the surface of the waves as opposed to riding low in the water; with this assumption the amplitude and speed of the boat's motion will match those of the water beneath the boat. For simplicity, we assume that the wave approximates a sine wave in determining the wave function.

Figure WG16.1

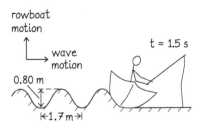

❷ DEVISE PLAN The wave speed can be found from the period and wavelength, $c = \lambda/T$ (Eq. 16.9). The rowboat's vertical speed is the speed of a water particle at the boat's location moving up and down in simple harmonic motion as the wave passes the location. Because the boat follows the vertical displacement of the water, the displacement curve for the boat should match that of the water. Because the motion of the water at a particular value of x along the wave is perpendicular to the direction along which the wave propagates (which we take to be the x axis), we take the displacement of the water surface (and the rowboat) to be along a y axis, making the wave function

$$y(x, t) = D(x, t) = A \sin(kx - \omega t).$$

Because the boat motion is up and down along the y axis, we can obtain the y component of the boat's velocity by taking the partial derivative of the boat's y coordinate with respect to time:

$$v_y = \frac{\partial y}{\partial t}.$$

We determine the maximum value this function can have to obtain the boat's maximum bobbing speed.

❸ EXECUTE PLAN (a) The wave speed is

$$c = \frac{\lambda}{T} = \frac{1.7 \text{ m}}{1.5 \text{ s}} = 1.1 \text{ m/s.} ✔$$

(*b*) The peak-to-trough height is twice the wave amplitude, which gives $A = \frac{1}{2}(0.80 \text{ m}) = 0.40 \text{ m}$. We know from Eqs. 16.7 and Eq. 16.11 that $k = 2\pi/\lambda$ and $\omega = 2\pi f = 2\pi/T$. Consequently, the wave function is

$$y(x, t) = A \sin\left(\frac{2\pi}{\lambda}x - \frac{2\pi}{T}t\right)$$

$$= (0.40 \text{ m}) \sin\left(\frac{2\pi}{1.7 \text{ m}}x - \frac{2\pi}{1.5 \text{ s}}t\right)$$

$$= (0.40 \text{ m}) \sin[(3.7 \text{ m}^{-1})x - (4.2 \text{ s}^{-1})t]. ✔$$

(*c*) Because the wave is sinusoidal, the x component of the boat's vertical velocity is

$$v_y(x, t) = \frac{\partial}{\partial t}A \sin(kx - \omega t) = -\omega A \cos(kx - \omega t).$$

No matter where the boat is located along the x axis, there is some instant t_{max} at which the bobbing speed reaches a maximum. This instant occurs when $|\cos(kx - \omega t_{max})| = 1$, and at that instant the bobbing speed is ωA:

$$v_{max} = \omega A(1) = \frac{2\pi}{1.5 \text{ s}}(0.40 \text{ m}) = 1.7 \text{ m/s.} ✔$$

❹ EVALUATE RESULT If you think about water waves moving across the surface of a lake, a wave speed of 1.1 m/s and a bobbing speed of 1.7 m/s both seem reasonable. We assumed that the boat moves with the water, so our results for the boat are based on the wave function, which describes how a water particle at position x moves along the y axis as the wave passes. The assumption seems reasonable for a small boat.

We also assumed that the wave caused by the wake of the boat is sinusoidal. The greatest possible bobbing speed for waves of any shape is given by assuming the boat is in free fall as it moves from a crest to a trough, which means that

$$v_{max}^2 < 2gh = 2(9.8 \text{ m/s}^2)(0.80 \text{ m}) = 16 \text{ m}^2/\text{s}^2$$

$$v_{max} < 4.0 \text{ m/s.}$$

The value we obtained, 1.7 m/s, appears to be in the right ballpark.

PRACTICE

Guided Problem 16.2 Human wave

A "people wave" is created by the crowd in a stadium when each person stands up just as one neighbor sits down and then sits down just as the other neighbor stands. A sophisticated crowd produces a "people wave" with each person approximately executing simple harmonic motion as they repeatedly stand and sit. (*a*) Estimate the frequency, wavelength, wave speed, and amplitude of such a wave, and use these values to construct a wave function that describes the wave. (*b*) What is the maximum speed of each person in the wave as she or he stands up and then sits down?

❶ GETTING STARTED

1. Describe the problem in your own words.
2. Assuming a sinusoidal wave, what is a generic expression for the wave function?

❷ DEVISE PLAN

3. Which of the asked-for values can you confidently estimate? Which ones do you have more uncertainty about? You might want to start with amplitude and wavelength.
4. In addition to amplitude and wavelength, what other quantities do you need in order to specify the wave function?
5. How can you determine the stand–sit speed of the wave "particles" (the people)?
6. How can you determine the maximum speed of each person?

❸ EXECUTE PLAN

❹ EVALUATE RESULT

7. Are your assumptions and estimates plausible? What errors are introduced by the uncertainty of your estimates?

Worked Problem 16.3 Musical wire

One end of a wire is attached to a wall, and the other end is strung over a pulley and attached to a block (Figure WG16.2). The distance from wall to pulley is 2.30 m, and the wire has a linear mass density of 1.3×10^{-3} kg/m. Plucking the horizontal section of the wire in specific ways can produce standing waves that contain specific numbers of antinodes: The first harmonic has one antinode, the second harmonic has two antinodes, and so on. What should the block's mass be in order that the third-harmonic standing wave (containing three antinodes) vibrates at frequency $f = 550$ Hz?

Figure WG16.2

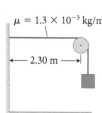

$\mu = 1.3 \times 10^{-3}$ kg/m

← 2.30 m →

❶ GETTING STARTED The tensile force exerted by the block on the wire provides the tension in the wire, and so we need to determine this force and then use the relationship between the tensile force and the gravitational force on the block to obtain the block mass needed to create the standing wave asked for. The number of antinodes is related to how many wavelengths of the traveling waves fit into the horizontal section of the wire. The third harmonic has three antinodes and is illustrated in Figure WG16.3. Thus we want to calculate what tension is required to create, along the horizontal section of the wire, a three-antinode standing wave vibrating at 550 Hz. We assume that the block moves negligibly when the wire is vibrating.

Figure WG16.3

❷ DEVISE PLAN We need to relate the frequency f, wavelength λ, and tensile force. Because the block is supported in equilibrium by the string, the tension (magnitude of tensile force) is $T = |\vec{F}^c_{sb}| = |\vec{F}^G_{Eb}| = m_b g$. Equations 16.10 and 16.30 permit us to relate the tension to wavelength and frequency, and we can determine λ from Eq. 16.21. For the third harmonic, there are three

antinodes and four nodes. The first node is at the wall; the fourth node (the one for which $n = 3$ in Eq. 16.21) occurs at $x = \ell$, where ℓ is the length of wire between the wall and the pulley. Knowing λ, we can solve Eq. 16.30 for the tension T and then equate T with the tensile force F exerted by the block to determine m_b.

❸ EXECUTE PLAN Substituting ℓ for x and 3 for n in Eq. 16.21, we get $\ell = \frac{3}{2}\lambda$. This tells us that the third harmonic has wavelength $\lambda = 2\ell/3$. Solving Eq. 16.30 for the tension gives us

$$c = \sqrt{\frac{T}{\mu}}$$

$$T = \mu c^2,$$

and from Eq. 16.10 we can rewrite this as $T = \mu(\lambda f)^2$. Because the tension is created by the tensile force exerted by (or on) the block, we have

$$m_b g = T = \mu(\lambda f)^2 = \mu(\tfrac{2}{3}\ell f)^2$$

$$m_b = \frac{4\mu(\ell f)^2}{9g}$$

$$= \frac{4(0.00130 \text{ kg/m})[(2.30 \text{ m})(550 \text{ Hz})]^2}{9(9.8 \text{ m/s}^2)} = 94 \text{ kg.} ✔$$

❹ EVALUATE RESULT Our result shows that we need quite a massive block to obtain the desired third harmonic. We know one has to increase the tension in a string to obtain a higher pitch (higher frequency) from it. Our algebraic expression indeed shows that the block's mass must be increased to increase the frequency f. We would also expect the required mass to be inversely proportional to g because if the gravitational pull were stronger, a block of smaller mass would be sufficient to create the required tension.

Our assumption that the block does not move is likely to be accurate given the mass of the block. We ignored the mass of the hanging portion of the wire in our calculation, but that seems reasonable considering the very small value for μ. The mass of the 2.30-m horizontal section is only 0.003 kg, so even a relatively long section of string has negligible mass relative to that of the block.

Guided Problem 16.4 Pitch-perfect guitar

A guitarist breaks the highest string on her guitar. If a new string is a steel wire of mass density 7.8×10^3 kg/m³ and radius 0.120 mm, what tension must the string be under if it is to produce the frequency 330 Hz as its fundamental (first harmonic, one antinode) frequency? The distance between the wire's two attachment points on the guitar is 640 mm.

① GETTING STARTED

1. Sketch the shape of the string oscillating at its fundamental frequency.
2. What variables affect the frequency?

② DEVISE PLAN

3. What equation relates the wave's frequency and wavelength to the tension?

4. How can you use the information that there is only one antinode in the standing wave to determine the wavelength of the traveling waves that interfere to produce this standing wave?
5. How can you determine the mass of the wire from the mass density of steel? How can you determine the wire's linear mass density from this?

③ EXECUTE PLAN

④ EVALUATE RESULT

6. Is your computed value of tension the right order of magnitude for the tension in a guitar string?

Worked Problem 16.5 Basic telephone service

Two children playing telephone use some string to connect two paper cups. To make the separation large enough, they use two strings of different linear mass densities connected at the center. String A has a linear mass density of 8.20×10^{-3} kg/m, and string B has a linear mass density of 5.90×10^{-3} kg/m. Consider a traveling wave that originates on string A, passes the junction at the center, and continues along string B. What is the ratio of the wavelength of this wave on string B to its wavelength on string A?

① GETTING STARTED We start with a sketch (Figure WG16.4), labeling the junction at the center by the letter J. We are asked to determine how the wavelength changes as a wave traveling from A to B passes the junction. The wavelength is related to the frequency and speed of the wave. Because the two strings have different linear mass densities, waves travel at different speeds in the two strings. We need to determine out how this change in speed affects the wavelength. We might also have to consider the tension in the strings because the tension affects the wave speed.

Figure WG16.4

$\mu_A = 8.20 \times 10^{-3}$ kg/m
$\mu_B = 5.90 \times 10^{-3}$ kg/m

② DEVISE PLAN The wave speed along a taut string is given by Eqs. 16.10 and 16.30, $\lambda f = c = \sqrt{T/\mu}$, where T is the tension in the strings and μ is its linear mass density. Neither the tension nor the frequency f in the two strings is specified. However, we can reasonably argue that the tension is the same in the two strings by considering what would happen if it were not. If the tension on the left were greater, then a free-body diagram of the junction would show a greater tensile force to the left than to the right, causing the junction to accelerate to the left. This would reduce the tension on the left and increase it on the right, ultimately leading to equilibrium at a new junction position.

To determine the frequency, we consider the vertical motion of the junction. The frequency at which the junction moves up and down is equal to the frequency of the incoming wave from A, which means that the junction end of string A produces the wave that goes into B with the same frequency. Therefore the frequency

of the wave *must* be constant throughout the joined strings. However, the wavelength does change because the wave speed changes due to the difference in linear mass densities.

We can solve Eq. 16.30 for the tension T in each segment, set the two tensions equal to each other, and use Eq. 16.10 to replace each c by its equivalent λf. The f values cancel, leaving us with the ratio of the wavelengths.

③ EXECUTE PLAN Solving Eq. 16.30 for the tension and then substituting λf for c from Eq. 16.10 give

$$T = \mu(\lambda f)^2.$$

Setting the tensions equal in the two strings, we have

$$T_A = T_B$$

$$\mu_A \lambda_A^2 f_A^2 = \mu_B \lambda_B^2 f_B^2.$$

Canceling the frequencies because they are the same in both segments gives us

$$\frac{\lambda_B}{\lambda_A} = \sqrt{\frac{\mu_A}{\mu_B}} = \sqrt{\frac{8.20 \times 10^{-3} \text{ kg/m}}{5.90 \times 10^{-3} \text{ kg/m}}} = 1.18. ✔$$

④ EVALUATE RESULT The relationship $c = \sqrt{T/\mu}$ tells us that the string that has the smaller linear mass density generates the greater wave speed c. Thus in one period of the motion the leading edge of the traveling wave moves a greater horizontal distance in the thinner string, which is B. This means that the distance between two adjacent crests is greater in B than in A; in other words, the wavelength is longer in B, which is consistent with our calculation. The 18% difference we obtained is reasonable: The mass densities differ by more than 30%, and we need to take the square root of these mass densities to obtain the wavelength.

Our assumption that the tension is the same in the two strings would be strictly valid only if no gravity were present. The gravitational force exerted by Earth causes both strings to sag, and the tension in the two strings must adjust differently to this sagging because the strings have different masses. However, the gravitational forces exerted on the strings are much smaller than the typical tension in a string telephone, and so our assumption should have a negligible effect on our answer.

PRACTICE

Guided Problem 16.6 At the junction

In Figure WG16.5, string B has twice the linear mass density of string A. When an incident wave described by the function $y_I(x, t) = A_I \sin(k_A x - \omega t)$ initially traveling left to right through string A hits the junction, some of the wave is reflected and the rest is transmitted into string B. What fraction of the incident wave power is reflected and what fraction is transmitted? (For simplicity, Figure WG16.5 does not show the reflected wave.)

Figure WG16.5

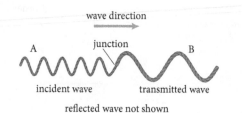

wave direction

junction

A

B

incident wave

transmitted wave

reflected wave not shown

❶ GETTING STARTED

1. Does the boundary at the junction behave as fixed or free?
2. The incident wave $y_I(x, t)$ is given. The reflected wave $y_R(x, t)$ must have an amplitude $A_R \neq A_I$, but what is the expression for its wave function? In writing your expression, consider direction of travel, inverted or upright amplitude, and so on.
3. The transmitted wave $y_T(x, t)$ has an amplitude $A_T \neq A_I$. What is an appropriate form for its wave function? Remember

that the wave number k_B, the number of wavelengths in 2π m of string B, may not equal k_A.)

❷ DEVISE PLAN

4. Wave power is proportional to the square of the wave amplitude by Eq. 16.42, $P_{av} = \frac{1}{2}\mu A^2 \omega^2 c$.
5. Where do the waves have the greater speed; in A or in B? Why?
6. Based on what you learned from the solution to Worked Problem 16.5, what is the relationship between the frequencies f_A and f_B (and thus the relationship between ω_A and ω_B)? What is the relationship between the tensions T_A and T_B?
7. What is the relationship between the wavelengths λ_A and λ_B? Between the wave numbers k_A and k_B?
8. The wave function and its slope (derivative) must be continuous everywhere, including at the junction, where superposition gives $y_I(x_J, t) + y_R(x_J, t) = y_T(x_J, t)$ and $\frac{\partial}{\partial x}[y_I(x, t) + y_R(x, t)]_{x=x_J} = \frac{\partial}{\partial x}[y_T(x, t)]_{x=x_J}$.

❸ EXECUTE PLAN

9. Take these derivatives to infer what the ratios A_R/A_I and A_T/A_I must be in order to ensure continuity.
10. The algebra is simplified if you choose the origin at the junction so that $x_J = 0$.

❹ EVALUATE RESULT

11. Does the sum of the transmitted and reflected power equal the incident power? If not, why not?

Worked Problem 16.7 A pulse on a rope

A certain transverse wave pulse traveling along a rope is described by the time-dependent wave function $f(x, t) = Ae^{-(kx - \omega t)^2}$, with wave number $k = 2\pi \text{ m}^{-1}$ and angular frequency $\omega = 2\pi \text{ s}^{-1}$. (a) Sketch the time-independent wave function at $t = 0$ and $t = 5.00$ s. (b) Sketch the pulse as a function of time (the displacement curve) at $x = 0$ and $x = 5.00$ m. (c) Show that the function given above satisfies the wave equation. (d) What is the wave speed of the pulse?

❶ GETTING STARTED We are given an equation for a particular wave pulse. We need to sketch the pulse at various positions and instants and then show that the given expression is a solution to the wave equation. Then we need to determine the wave speed of the pulse.

❷ DEVISE PLAN To make the sketches, we can make tables of values at various positions for the wave function of part a and various instants for the displacement curve of part b, and then plot the data. A graphing calculator would make this task easier, but we shall make one table just to get the idea.

Then we need to show that the given expression satisfies the wave equation

$$\frac{\partial^2 f}{\partial x^2} = \frac{1}{c^2}\frac{\partial^2 f}{\partial t^2}.$$

To do that, we can take appropriate derivatives of the given function, insert calculated values on both sides of the wave equation, and check that the values we get for the two sides are equal to each other.

The wave speed required for part d is given by the value of c in the wave equation.

❸ EXECUTE PLAN (a) First let us make a table of the wave function for the $t = 0$ case. Because the value of the amplitude A is not given, we divide $f(x)$ by A and compute only the exponential function.

x (m)	$f(x)/A$
−0.500	5.17×10^{-5}
−0.400	1.81×10^{-3}
−0.300	2.86×10^{-2}
−0.200	2.06×10^{-1}
−0.100	6.74×10^{-1}
0	1.00×10^{0}
0.100	6.74×10^{-1}
0.200	2.06×10^{-1}
0.300	2.86×10^{-2}
0.400	1.81×10^{-3}
0.500	5.17×10^{-5}

A similar calculation can be done for $t = 5.00$ s. The resulting plots for the pulse positions at these two instants are shown in Figure WG16.6. This exponential pulse is just a bump that travels to the right. In part a, $t = 0$, the peak is at $x = 0$, and in part b, $t = 5.00$ s, the peak has moved on to $x = 5.00$ m.

Figure WG16.6

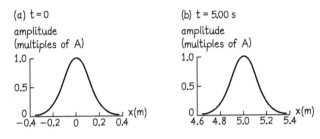

(a) t = 0
amplitude (multiples of A)

(b) t = 5.00 s
amplitude (multiples of A)

(b) The displacement curves $f(x = 0, t)$ and $f(x = 5.00\text{ m}, t)$ at the two positions given in the problem statement yield the graphs of Figure WG16.7a and b, where we have plotted $f(t)/A$ as a function of t. ✔

Figure WG16.7

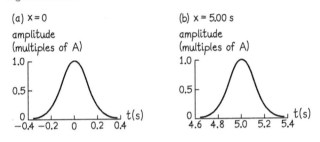

(a) x = 0
amplitude (multiples of A)

(b) x = 5.00 s
amplitude (multiples of A)

(c) Now, to confirm that the expression given for the pulse is a solution to the wave equation, we have

$$\frac{\partial^2}{\partial x^2} Ae^{-(kx-\omega t)^2} \stackrel{?}{=} \frac{1}{c^2}\frac{\partial^2}{\partial t^2} Ae^{-(kx-\omega t)^2}$$

$$-\frac{\partial}{\partial x}2k(kx - \omega t)Ae^{-(kx-\omega t)^2}$$

$$\stackrel{?}{=} \frac{1}{c^2}\frac{\partial}{\partial t}2\omega(kx - \omega t)Ae^{-(kx-\omega t)^2}$$

$$[-2k(kx - \omega t)]^2 Ae^{-(kx-\omega t)^2} - 2k^2 Ae^{-(kx-\omega t)^2}$$

$$\stackrel{?}{=} \frac{1}{c^2}\{[2\omega(kx - \omega t)]^2 Ae^{-(kx-\omega t)^2} - 2\omega^2 Ae^{-(kx-\omega t)^2}\}.$$

Eliminating the exponential factor gives

$$[-2k(kx - \omega t)]^2 - 2k^2 \stackrel{?}{=} \frac{1}{c^2}\{[2\omega(kx - \omega t)]^2 - 2\omega^2\}$$

$$2k^2[2(kx - \omega t)^2 - 1] \stackrel{?}{=} \frac{1}{c^2}2\omega^2[2(kx - \omega t)^2 - 1]$$

$$2k^2 \stackrel{?}{=} \frac{1}{c^2}2\omega^2.$$

This equation is true only if

$$c = \frac{\omega}{k},$$

which we know to be true from Eq. 16.11, $kc = \omega$. Our pulse function is indeed a solution to the wave equation. ✔

(d) The wave speed of the pulse is

$$c = \frac{\omega}{k} = \frac{2\pi\text{ s}^{-1}}{2\pi\text{ m}^{-1}} = 1.00\text{ m/s}. ✔$$

The values of ω and k are known to many significant digits, but we choose to report three because the other data are known to three significant digits.

4 EVALUATE RESULT We've demonstrated that this type of pulse is a solution to the wave equation. The speed is reasonable, if a bit slow. Also, the shape looks reasonable for a pulse on a rope.

Guided Problem 16.8 Superposed waves

Most of the waves in our everyday world, such as radio waves from a station's transmitter or sound waves from a plucked or bowed violin string, are not simple sine or cosine waves but rather a superposition of many different harmonic waves, as shown in Figure WG16.8 As an example, consider the wave function $f(x, t) = \sin(kx - \omega t) + (1.5)\sin(2kx - 2\omega t)$. You are

Figure WG16.8

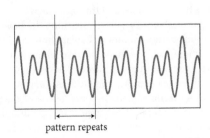

pattern repeats

informed that $k = 8.00\text{ m}^{-1}$ and that the frequency at which the pattern repeats is $f = 440$ Hz. (a) Sketch the wave as a function of time at $x = 0$ for three cycles on a suitable graph. (b) Show that this wave function is a solution to the wave equation, $(\partial^2 f/\partial x^2) = (1/c^2)(\partial^2 f/\partial t^2)$. (c) What is the speed of this wave?

1 GETTING STARTED

1. You'll need numerical values in order to complete parts a and c. List the values you know and those you need to determine.
2. What must be the value of ω to get the interference pattern to repeat at the specified frequency? What time interval elapses before the pattern starts to repeat itself?
3. For a fixed value of x, how many seconds would it take for the first term in the wave function to go through one cycle? How many seconds for the second term to go through one cycle?

2 DEVISE PLAN

4. Think through a simple consistent procedure to determine the displacement curve at the specified value of x for three cycles.

How do you determine how closely spaced the time values along your horizontal axis should be?

5. The procedure in Worked Problem 16.7 can be used to see whether the function satisfies the wave equation, but how can the wave speed be related to the quantities you know?

③ EXECUTE PLAN

6. Plot your data.

7. Write the wave equation and take the required partial derivatives of the wave function in its symbolic form (without the numerical values you have inferred for ω). Is it possible for the equation to balance? What does your answer to this question imply about the wave speed?

④ EVALUATE RESULT

Questions and Problems

For instructor-assigned homework, go to MasteringPhysics® (MP)

Dots indicate difficulty level of problems: • = *easy,* •• = *intermediate,* ••• = *hard;* CR = *context-rich problem.*

16.1 Representing waves graphically

1. Is it possible for the same medium to carry both a longitudinal and a transverse wave? If so, give an example. If not, explain why not. •

2. Suppose you have a light spring stretched out and one end is attached to a wall. With this setup, you can move the free end in any of three directions (x, y, z). If the spring lies along, say, the z axis, which type of wave—transverse or longitudinal—do you create when you move the free end along the z axis? Along the x axis? Along the y axis? •

3. Figure P16.3 is a snapshot at $t = 0.80$ s of a wave pulse traveling on a string. Construct (a) the wave function at $t = 1.1$ s and (b) the displacement curve for the position $x = 3.0$ m. Assume that the wave pulse was created at the origin at $t = 0$. ••

Figure P16.3

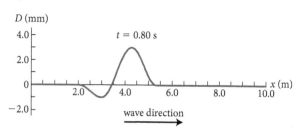

4. The graphs in Figure P16.4 show the displacement caused by a wave moving along a string at two instants, (a) t_1 and (b) t_2. Let v_{av} denote the average speed of a piece of string during the time interval between t_1 and t_2. Compare the wave speed c to v_{av} of a piece of the string at the position $x = a$. ••

Figure P16.4

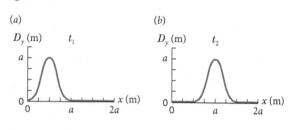

5. Figure P16.5 shows the displacement curve for the particle located at $x = a$ as a wave moves to the right along a string. If the wave advances a distance a each second, draw the wave function at the instant $t = 0$. •••

Figure P16.5

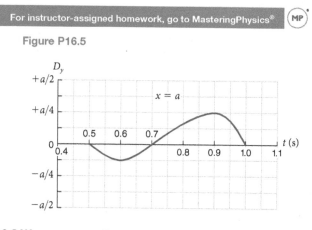

16.2 Wave propagation

6. Identical ropes were tied to two trees, and two men, A and B, started shaking the free ends at the same instant a short while ago (Figure P16.6). Which rope has the greater tension? Which man is shaking with the greater frequency? •

Figure P16.6

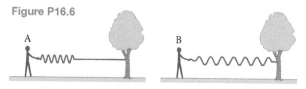

7. What is the definition of *frequency* for a nonharmonic periodic wave? •

8. You and a friend each have one rope. You tie the two ropes together and stand as far apart as possible, each holding one end of the new longer rope and pulling to put it under tension. You then begin moving your arm in such a way as to produce a harmonic wave with a wavelength of 1.0 m. Your friend looks at the waves as they reach her arm. Is it possible that she measures a wavelength of (a) 0.8 m, (b) 1.0 m, or (c) 1.2 m? ••

9. You are watching a ship being loaded with large crates. The ship is held in place by several long steel cables attached to the dock. At one point, a crate bumps one of the cables and sends a wave pulse along the cable. The pulse moves rather slowly up to the bow of the ship. A few minutes later another crate strikes the same cable, and this time the wave pulse shoots up along the cable very quickly, reaching the bow almost faster than your eyes can follow it. Explain how this is possible. ••

10. A harmonic wave is made to travel along a string when you move your hand up and down. The wave has a specific period T_1, wavelength λ_1, amplitude A_1, and speed c_1, and also causes a certain transverse speed $v(x, t)$ of the particles that make up the rope. If you repeat this up-and-down motion, this time completing the same motion twice as fast as before, what happens to the (a) period, (b) wavelength, (c) amplitude, (d) speed, and (e) transverse speed? •••

16.3 Superposition of waves

11. Water parks often have a pool with a wave-making machine at one end, consisting of a piston that pushes water back and forth. There are some places in the pool where the waves make inner-tube riders bounce up and down wildly, but other places where the water hardly moves. Explain what is happening. •

12. Suppose wave pulses in an aquarium are produced by a mechanical motor that moves a bob up and down at the surface. If the setup uses a 10-W motor and has a period of 1.5 s between bobs, how much kinetic energy is in each outgoing pulse? •

13. Figure P16.13 shows two waves in a rope approaching each other at instant $t = 0$. For any instant after $t = 0$, determine the maximum displacement that occurs (a) at $x = 0$, (b) at $x = 0.90$ m, and (c) anywhere along the rope. ••

Figure P16.13

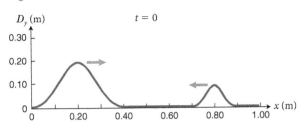

14. The two wave pulses in Figure P16.14 are traveling on the same string at $t = 1.0$ s. Sketch the shape of the string at this instant. ••

Figure P16.14

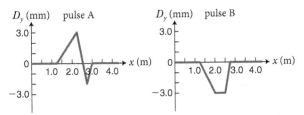

15. Suppose two waves, identical except for the direction of travel, approach each other in a medium that obeys Hooke's law. At certain instants, the waves interfere constructively at all positions. At one such instant, when their peaks align, determine the kinetic energy of the wave function that results from the superposition of both waves. •••

16.4 Boundary effects

16. A harmonic wave traveling along a light string approaches a splice to a heavier string, as shown in Figure P16.16. Which changes as the wave crosses the boundary: wavelength, frequency, both, or neither? •

Figure P16.16

17. A transverse wave in a swimming pool reaches the concrete side and is reflected. Determine whether the reflected wave is inverted. •

18. A rope is attached to a tree trunk and made taut, and then a pulse traveling rightward is sent along the rope. For each case depicted in Figure P16.18, determine whether or not the reflected pulse is depicted correctly. ••

Figure P16.18

(a)   (b)   (c)   (d)

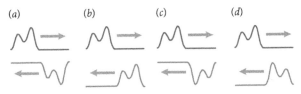

19. Figure P16.19 shows two strings of different linear mass densities at some instant. At some earlier instant, only one pulse existed on one of the strings. (a) Determine which string carried the initial pulse, and (b) sketch the approximate shape of the strings at the instant the initial pulse was created. ••

Figure P16.19

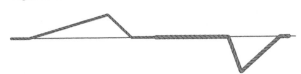

20. You shake the end of a taut string, creating two periods of a traveling sinusoidal wave, as shown in Figure P16.20. The string you are shaking (string 1) is connected to a second, much more massive, string (string 2). The wave speeds on the two strings differ by a factor of 2. (a) On the template, sketch the shape of the two strings a time interval $4T$ after the instant represented in Figure P16.20, with T the period of the original wave on string 1. Briefly explain how you determined the shape of the strings. (b) How do the periods of the waves on string 1 and string 2 compare? ••

Figure P16.20

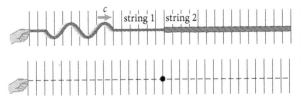

21. Figure P16.21 shows a pulse as it approaches a fixed end of a rope. Draw the shape of the rope halfway through the reflection (that is, when half of the pulse length is still moving to the right and the other half of the pulse has already been reflected). •••

Figure P16.21

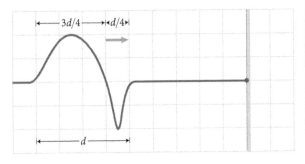

16.5 Wave functions

22. Walking along the beach, you notice that a new wave reaches the shore every 4.0 s, and you estimate the wave crests to be 2.5 m apart. At what wave speed c are the waves moving? •

23. While on a sailboat at anchor, you notice that 12 waves pass its bow every minute. If the waves have a speed of 6.0 m/s, what is the distance between two adjacent wave crests? •

24. Participating in a human rally wave at a football game, you have to stand up every 15 s. (a) What is the wave frequency? (b) If the stadium is oval and the inner circumference of the oval is 0.56 km, what is the wave speed? Assume that the main wave pulse spans 30 people and that the distance between the heads of any two adjacent people is 1.0 m. ••

25. (a) Plot the time-independent wave function for the traveling pulse described by the time-dependent wave function

$$D_y(x, t) = \frac{a}{b^2 + (x - ct)^2},$$

with $a = 5.0$ m³, $b = 1.0$ m, and $c = 2.0$ m/s for $t = 0, 1.0$ s, 2.0 s, and 3.0 s. (b) What is the wave speed c of this pulse? ••

26. What is wrong with each displacement curve in Figure P16.26 ••?

Figure P16.26

(a)   (b)   (c)

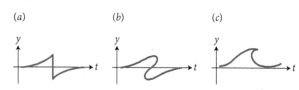

27. At $t = 0$, a wave pulse has a shape given by the time-independent wave function

$$f(x) = \frac{a}{b^2 + x^2},$$

where $a = 0.030$ m³ and $b = 2.0$ m. (a) If the pulse travels in the positive x direction at a wave speed of 1.75 m/s, write the time-dependent wave function $f(x, t)$ for this transverse wave. (b) Plot the time-dependent wave function $f(x, t)$ at $t = -0.50$ s and at $t = +0.50$ s over the range of x in which $f(x, t)$ is substantially changing. (c) Plot the displacement curve at $x = 2.0$ m. ••

28. A wave traveling along a string is described by

$$f(x, t) = a \sin(\pi bx + qt),$$

with $a = 30$ mm, $b = 0.33$ m⁻¹, and $q = 10.47$ s⁻¹. (a) Calculate the amplitude, wavelength, period, and speed of the wave. (b) Compute the y component of the displacement of the string at $x = 0.500$ m and $t = 1.60$ s. ••

29. A wave is described by the equation

$$f(x) = a \sin(bx),$$

with $a = 0.095$ m and $b = 2.25$ m⁻¹. (a) Calculate its wavelength. (b) If the wave has a speed of 17.0 m/s, what is its frequency f? (c) What is the angular frequency ω of the oscillation? ••

30. As an earthquake starts, you are standing 150 km (as the wave travels) from the epicenter. A geophysicist near the epicenter immediately telephones you to let you know that the transverse wave from the earthquake is on its way to you and that it is described by the equation

$$f(x, t) = a \sin(bx - \omega t),$$

where $a = 0.560$ m, $b = 0.0157$ m⁻¹, and a full wavelength passes any given location every 0.500 s. How long will it be before the ground you are standing on starts to shake? ••

31. The motion of a wave traveling along an x axis is given by

$$f(x, t) = a \sin[bx + qt],$$

with $a = 6.00$ m, $b = \pi$ cm⁻¹, and $q = 12.0$ s⁻¹. Determine the direction of travel and the wave speed. ••

32. A plucked violin string carries a traveling wave given by the equation

$$f(x, t) = a \sin[b(x - ct) + \phi_i],$$

with $a = 0.00580$ m, $b = 33.05$ m⁻¹, and $c = 245$ m/s. (a) If $f(0, 0) = 0$, what is ϕ_i? (b) Determine the simple harmonic period of a point on the string. ••

33. A wave that was produced by a harmonic oscillator and is traveling along a string is described by the equation

$$f(x, t) = a \sin[b(x - ct)],$$

with $a = 46$ mm, $b = 4\pi$ m⁻¹, and $c = 45$ m/s. Calculate the (a) wavelength, (b) angular frequency ω, (c) frequency f, and (d) period. ••

34. The amplitude of a wave traveling on a string is 0.250 m. The 80.0-Hz wave is traveling in the positive x direction at a wave speed of 17.5 m/s. (a) Determine its wavelength, and write the equation for its time-independent wave function. (b) For $t = 3.00$ s, compute the displacement and transverse velocity of the point on the string at $x = 1.25$ m, assuming an initial phase ϕ_i of zero. (c) Write the time-dependent wave function for the wave. (d) If the string displacement at $x = 1.25$ m is 0.210 m at $t = 3.00$ s, write the time-dependent wave function that uses the smallest possible value of ϕ_i. •••

16.6 Standing waves

35. Watching your fish swim in their tank, you notice that when one fish repeatedly jumps, it causes a standing wave given by the time-independent function

$$f(x) = a \sin(bx),$$

with $a = 0.015$ m and $b = 19.6$ m⁻¹. If the tank is 0.96 m long, determine the positions of the first three nodes, beginning with the node at one end of the tank. •

36. After tying one end of a rope to a stationary object, you flick the free end so as to cause a sinusoidal standing wave that has a maximum displacement of 0.50 m and a wavelength of 1.33 m. Write the time-dependent wave function in terms of the wave speed. •

37. When one end of a string is tied to a pole and the other end is moved with frequency f, the standing wave pattern shown in Figure P16.37 is created. What is the smallest frequency at which the string can be moved to produce any standing wave? ••

Figure P16.37

38. You have two string segments of equal length, segment 1 of linear mass density μ_1 and segment 2 of linear mass density $\mu_2 > \mu_1$. You splice the two together and then tie the combination tautly between two posts. You splice in such a way that, once attached to the posts, the length of segment 1 to the left of the splice is the same as the length of segment 2 to the right of the splice. When you pluck at a particular frequency, you set up a standing wave that has this pattern: nodes at the splice and where each segment is attached to its pole plus two more nodes in one of the segments and three more nodes in the other segment (eight nodes in all). What is the numerical value of the ratio μ_1/μ_2 ••?

39. A guitar string has a length of 0.650 m and a mass of 4.00×10^{-3} kg. (a) If it is kept under a tension of 126 N, what is the fundamental (smallest harmonic) frequency at which it vibrates? (b) At what other frequencies (higher harmonics) could it vibrate at this fixed length? ••

40. The equations for two waves traveling along the same string are

$$f_1(x, t) = a \sin(bx - qt)$$

and

$$f_2(x, t) = a \sin\left(bx + qt + \tfrac{1}{3}\pi\right),$$

with $a = 3.00 \times 10^{-2}$ m, $b = 4\pi$ m^{-1}, and $q = 500$ s^{-1}. (a) Calculate the amplitude and wavelength of the resultant displacement of the string at $t = 3.00$ s. (b) At $t = 1.70$ s, what is the displacement of the point on the string located at $x = 2.00$ m? ••

41. A string vibrates in a standing wave according to the function

$$f(x, t) = a \sin(bx)\cos(qt),$$

with $a = 6.00 \times 10^{-2}$ m, $b = \tfrac{1}{3}\pi$ cm^{-1}, and $q = 40\pi$ s^{-1}. What are the amplitude and wave speed of each of the component waves that form this standing wave? ••

42. A traveling wave on a long string is described by the time-dependent wave function

$$f(x, t) = a \sin(bx - qt),$$

with $a = 6.00 \times 10^{-2}$ m, $b = 5\pi$ m^{-1}, and $q = 314$ s^{-1}. You want a traveling wave of this frequency and wavelength but with amplitude 0.0400 m. Write the time-dependent wave function for a second traveling wave that could be added to the same string in order to achieve this. ••

43. You have a trough 3.60 m long. It is filled with water, and you want to create a standing wave such that a node occurs every 0.30 m. (a) What is the wavelength of this wave? (b) A leaf floating on the water 0.60 m from the one end of the trough is displaced a vertical distance $D_y = 10$ mm at $t = 3.2$ s, and the leaf's displacement has a period of 0.60 s. What is the resultant displacement of the standing wave? (c) Write the time-dependent wave function for the standing wave. ••

44. Two sinusoidal waves travel along the same string. Their time-dependent wave functions are

$$f_1(x, t) = a \sin\left(bx - qt - \tfrac{1}{4}\pi\right)$$

$$f_2(x, t) = a \sin\left(bx - qt - \tfrac{1}{3}\pi\right),$$

with $a = 5.00 \times 10^{-2}$ m, $b = 0.120$ m^{-1}, and $q = 180$ s^{-1}. (a) What is the phase difference between these two waves? (b) Write the time-dependent wave function for the wave created by the superposition of these two waves. (c) What is the displacement of the string at $x = 2.00$ m at $t = 1.70$ s? •••

45. Two sinusoidal waves travel in opposite directions along the same string. The wavelength and frequency are the same in both waves, and each has amplitude 0.0289 m. If one wave has a phase difference $\Delta\phi$ with respect to the other wave, what is the maximum displacement of the wave created by the superposition? •••

16.7 Wave speed

46. A piano wire has a linear mass density of 5.00×10^{-3} kg/m and is under 1.35 kN of tension. At what speed does a wave travel along this wire? •

47. Your professor uses a plastic chain 10 m long to demonstrate transverse waves in class. If you measure the speed of a traveling wave to be 15 m/s, and the professor measures the tension in the chain to be 100 N, what is the chain's mass? •

48. A large crane is being used to lower a 10,000-kg storage unit into place on a barge. If the cable that supports the unit from the end of the crane is 12 m long, and the linear mass density of the cable is 1.78 kg/m, how long does it take a wave to travel the length of the cable? •

49. A violinist is bowing one string to produce a certain note. List three ways in which she can produce a note of higher frequency, either while playing or by preparing the violin differently before she begins to play. ••

50. How long after the propellers at the back of an oil tanker start turning does the front of the ship start to move? ••

51. A wave traveling along a string has a speed of 24 m/s when the tension in the string is 120 N. What is the speed of the same wave if the tension is reduced to 100 N? ••

52. Two wires that have different linear mass densities, 0.45 kg/m and 0.29 kg/m, are spliced together. They are then used as a guy line to secure a telephone pole. If the tension is 300 N, what is the difference in the speed of a wave traveling from one wire to the other? ••

53. A string of linear mass density μ_1 fixed at both ends is replaced by a string of linear mass density $16\mu_1$. By what factor does the frequency of the fundamental standing wave change if the tension and wavelength remain what they were in the original string? ••

54. A 25.0-m steel wire and a 50.0-m copper wire are attached end to end and stretched to a tension of 145 N. Both wires have a radius of 0.450 mm, and the densities are $7.86 \times 10^3 \text{ kg/m}^3$ for the steel and $8.92 \times 10^3 \text{ kg/m}^3$ for the copper. (Note that these are mass densities, mass per unit volume, not linear mass densities, mass per unit length.) How long does a wave take to travel from one end to the other end of the combination wire? ••

55. A 100-m steel cable that helps support the Golden Gate Bridge is 72.0 mm in diameter and composed of 100 steel wires twisted together. Approximate this as a single uniform steel cable that has a mass density of $7.86 \times 10^3 \text{ kg/m}^3$. The wind generates in the cable a vibration that creates a wave that travels down the cable at 380 m/s. What is the tension in the cable? ••

56. One end of the wire in Figure P16.56 is anchored to the side of a building, and the other end is attached at an angle of 27° to a light horizontal bar from which a 75-kg sign hangs. The linear mass density of the wire is 0.067 kg/m. If the wind causes the sign to vibrate so that a wave travels along the wire, at what speed does the wave travel? •••

Figure P16.56

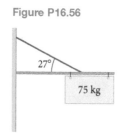

16.8 Energy transport in waves

57. A taut rope has a mass of 0.128 kg and a length of 3.60 m. What average power must be supplied to the rope to generate sinusoidal waves that have amplitude 0.200 m and wavelength 0.600 m if the waves are to travel at 25.0 m/s? •

58. Consider two waves X and Y traveling in the same medium. The two carry the same amount of energy per unit time, but X has half the amplitude of Y. What is the ratio of their wavelengths? Which wave has the longer wavelength? •

59. Transverse waves are being generated on a rope being held under constant tension. By what factor is the power required to generate the wave increased or decreased (a) if the length of the rope is halved, (b) if the amplitude and angular frequency are doubled, and (c) if the wavelength and rope length are doubled? ••

60. You hold one end of a string that is attached to a wall by its other end. The string has a linear mass density of 0.067 kg/m. You raise your end briskly at 12 m/s for 0.016 s, creating a transverse wave that moves at 31 m/s. (a) How much work did you do on the string? What are the wave's (b) energy, (c) potential energy, and (d) kinetic energy? ••

61. One end of a horizontal string that has a linear mass density of 3.5 kg/m is displaced vertically at a speed of 45 m/s for 6.7 ms. The pulse created by this motion travels down the string at 78 m/s. How much kinetic energy travels along the string? ••

62. A wave traveling along a string is described by the time-dependent wave function $f(x, t) = a \sin(bx + qt)$, with $a = 0.0268$ m, $b = 5.85$ m^{-1}, and $q = 76.3$ s^{-1}. The linear mass density of the string is 0.0456 kg/m. Calculate (a) the wave speed c, (b) the wave frequency f, and (c) the power P supplied by the wave. ••

63. An oscillator attached to a string transmits 350 mW of power down the string. The wave created by this motion has amplitude 0.0165 m and wavelength 1.80 m. If the string is under 14.8 N of tension, what is the wave speed? ••

64. A cord of linear mass density 0.360 kg/m is attached to a harmonic oscillator that has a maximum output of 200 W. (a) With the oscillator operating at this maximum power and the tension in the cord set at 30.0 N, a wave of amplitude 8.00×10^{-3} m is created. What is the minimum wavelength possible for a wave of this amplitude? (b) What is the power output of the oscillator if the wave generated has the same amplitude but double the wavelength you calculated in part a, and the tension is 15.0 N? •••

65. One end of a 9.00-m wire vibrates sinusoidally, creating a wave that travels in the positive x direction. The wave has a frequency of 60.0 Hz, a wavelength of 3.00 m, and an amplitude of 0.0725 m. (a) Write the time-dependent wave function that describes this wave. (b) If the mass of the wire is 1.20×10^{-2} kg, what is the power supplied to the wire to create this wave? •••

16.9 The wave equation

66. Show that $f(x, t) = e^{b(x - vt)}$, where b and v are constants, is a solution to Eq. 16.51, the wave equation. •

67. What keeps a surfer riding the crest of a wave from dropping down to the wave's base? ••

68. A string initially hanging vertically is displaced to the right with a speed of 25 m/s for 0.040 s, then returned to its original position in 0.010 s. This motion is repeated, with no delays, numerous times. The wave created by this motion travels down the string at 67 m/s and has a period of 0.050 s. (a) Write the time-dependent wave function for this pulse, and (b) show that this function is a solution to the wave equation (Eq. 16.51). ••

69. Show that if $f_1(x, t) = A_1\sin(k_1x - \omega_1t)$ and $f_2(x, t) = A_2\sin(k_2x - \omega_2t)$ are both solutions to the wave equation (Eq. 16.51), then $f(x, t) = f_1(x, t) + f_2(x, t)$ is also a solution. ••

70. (a) Show that the equations (i) $A\cos(kx + \omega t)$, (ii) $e^{-b|x - qt|^2}$, and (iii) $-(b^2t - x)^2$ all satisfy the wave equation (Eq. 16.51) provided that $A, k, \omega, b,$ and q are constants. (b) Calculate the speed of each wave of part a. •••

Additional Problems

71. Two children are holding a rope taut between them when one suddenly yanks the rope. (a) Does the child at the other end instantly get pulled? (b) Answer the same question for two children holding a rigid steel bar between them. •

72. A heavy rope is hanging by one end from the ceiling with a block hanging from the other end. Is the speed of a pulse in the rope greater at the top or the bottom of the rope? •

73. First you stretch a spring to twice its initial length and send pulse A from one end to the other. Then you stretch the spring to three times its initial length and send pulse B from one end to the other. How does the time interval needed for A to travel through the spring compare with the time interval needed for B to do so? ••

74. You pluck a guitar string so as to produce a standing wave for which $\lambda = 1.3$ m. What is the maximum value of the string's displacement at a position 0.500 m from the lower end of the string if the maximum resultant displacement of the wave is 0.75 mm? ••

75. Tossing rocks into the center of a pond, you notice that the ripples are evenly spaced 170 mm apart. If it takes 5.0 s for 15 ripples to pass a log sticking up out of the water, (*a*) what is the wave speed? (*b*) How long does it take a ripple to reach shore if the pond is 12 m in diameter? ••

76. When a person sings in the shower, certain notes seem louder than others. What's going on? ••

77. A standing wave is created on a string that is 1.75 m long. The wave has eight nodes counting the nodes at the two ends. (*a*) What is the wavelength? (*b*) What is the frequency if the wave speed is 130 m/s? (*c*) If the resultant displacement is 20.0 mm, write the time-dependent wave function that describes the standing wave, including units where appropriate. ••

78. Would water waves traveling along a trough on the surface of Mars travel faster than, slower than, or at the same speed as water waves traveling along a similar trough on the surface of Earth? (Hint: You'll need data from Table 13.1 on page 236 of the *Practice* volume.) ••

79. You hold one end of a horizontal string and raise your hand during a time interval of 0.18 s, doing 1.2 J of work on the string in the process. You then allow your hand to return to its original position. If the wave pulse you create travels along the string at 67 m/s and the linear mass density of the string is 0.0282 kg/m, what was the vertical speed of your hand? ••

80. Your friend wants to test your understanding of waves. She weaves together one end of two different ropes (one with greater mass density than the other, but each with the same radius and length) to make a single rope. Then she attaches one end of the combination to a pole. You are blindfolded and asked to hold the other end of the stretched rope. Your friend expects you to determine not only which end you are holding (the heavier or lighter rope), but also whether your friend used a fixed or free method of attachment to the pole. You think for a minute, then laugh and declare that you can even estimate the ratio of the linear mass densities! While she is speechless, you create a single wave pulse with your hand. ••• CR

81. Your job as assistant coach is to attach one end of several heavy, 10-m ropes to the trusses that support the gym ceiling, leaving the other end of each hanging free. The team is going to spend the afternoon climbing these ropes, but you begin to wonder about wave pulses traveling on such a rope. You could shake the free end of a rope back and forth once and measure how long it takes the pulse created by this motion to arrive at the top of the rope, but you are more of a calculation person. ••• CR

Answers to Review Questions

1. A wave transports energy and momentum but no matter, which means that for mechanical waves, each portion of the medium is at its original location after the wave passes through.
2. The traffic jam is longitudinal, and the other three are transverse.
3. The wave speed is the speed at which the wave moves along the rope. The speed of any small segment of the rope is the magnitude of the velocity at which that segment gets displaced from its equilibrium position as the wave passes through.
4. No, unless the pulse is symmetrical. In general, the displacement curve is the mirror image of the wave function.
5. The frequency is the number of wave crests that arrive each second, in units of hertz (Hz). The wave speed is how fast a wave travels in meters per second (m/s).
6. It remains the same. See Checkpoint 16.5.
7. Waves are not always periodic. A periodic wave is created only when the motion that causes the wave is repeated at regular intervals. A wave pulse is generally not periodic. Neither are waves always harmonic. A harmonic wave is created only when the motion that causes the wave is harmonic (that is, the motion is the particular type of periodic motion that yields a sine curve).
8. Assuming that you move your hand only vertically, the horizontal component of force you exert on the rope as you shake it remains constant and equal to the tension. The wave speed is therefore unaffected by whether you move your hand rapidly or slowly. Assuming that you move your hand up and down by the same distance each time, the amplitude of each pulse you create remains the same. Thus only the period, frequency, and wavelength of the wave change.
9. The interference is temporary in the sense that it occurs at only those instants and places where the pulses overlap. After the pulses move apart, they again have their original size and shape, and the interference no longer exists.
10. Wave pulses always carry equal amounts of kinetic and potential energy.
11. The wave functions are added algebraically at each point of overlap.
12. (*a*) The reflected pulse is inverted and left–right reversed. (*b*) The reflected pulse is left–right reversed but not inverted.
13. At each instant that the shape is desired, sketch a scale diagram of the wave pulse approaching the boundary and a reversed pulse (traveling in the opposite direction at the same speed) designed to arrive at the boundary at the same instant as the actual pulse. If the string beyond the boundary has a greater linear mass density (or if the boundary is a fixed end), the reversed pulse is drawn inverted. If the string beyond the boundary has a smaller linear mass density (or the boundary is a free end), the reversed pulse is drawn upright. Now superimpose the two pulses where they overlap by adding the displacements of each pulse at common positions. The result is an outline of the shape of the pulse at the chosen instant.
14. A complete description requires amplitude A; plus period T, frequency f, or angular frequency ω; plus wavelength λ, wave number k, or wave speed c; plus direction of motion.
15. The wave number of a harmonic wave is the number of wavelengths of the wave that fit in a length of 2π meters. The wave number is a conversion constant that is used to change distances in meters into unitless angles in the arguments of the sinusoidal functions that are used to describe harmonic waves.
16. The wave travels in the positive x direction. The relative sign of the position and time terms gives you this information.
17. An antinode is any point in a standing wave where the amplitude of the displacement attains its greatest value. These points occur halfway between nodes (positions of zero amplitude).
18. They are separated by a distance $\lambda/4$.
19. Yes. The antinodes cycle through all values of medium displacement, including zero.
20. The same. The wave speed depends on the tension and linear mass density of the strings, neither of which has changed.
21. You need to double the wave speed. This means quadrupling the tension, assuming that the string does not stretch (change its linear mass density).
22. Linear mass density is the mass per unit length of a string or rope, measured in units of kg/m.
23. The average power required to generate a wave is directly proportional to the linear mass density of the string and the wave speed and to the square of the amplitude and angular frequency of the wave.
24. Half of the energy transferred becomes kinetic energy and half potential energy.
25. A partial derivative is used for functions that contain more than one variable and is evaluated as an ordinary derivative with respect to one variable while all other variables are held constant.
26. The curvature of any location on the pulse increases as the acceleration of the string segments in the vicinity increases and decreases as the wave speed increases.

Answers to Guided Problems

Guided Problem 16.2 (*a*) A range of values is possible; for example, $f = 1/3$ Hz, $\lambda = 12$ m, $c = 4$ m/s, and $A = 1$ m give $f(x, t) = (1\text{ m}) \sin(\pi x/6 - 2\pi t/3 + \phi)$. (*b*) These values result in a vertical speed of 2 m/s for each participant.

Guided Problem 16.4 $T = 63$ N

Guided Problem 16.6 $\dfrac{A_R}{A_I} = \dfrac{k_A - k_B}{k_A + k_B}$ and $\dfrac{A_T}{A_I} = \dfrac{2k_A}{k_A + k_B}$, so 97.1% of the incident power is transmitted and 2.9% is reflected.

Guided Problem 16.8 (*a*) Figure GPS16.8

Figure GPS16.8

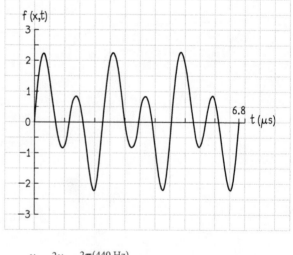

$(c)\ c = \dfrac{\omega}{k} = \dfrac{2\omega}{2k} = \dfrac{2\pi(440\text{ Hz})}{8.00\text{ m}^{-1}} = 346$ m/s

17

PRACTICE

Waves in Two and Three Dimensions

PRACTICE

Chapter Summary

Characteristics of waves in two and three dimensions (Sections 17.1, 17.4, 17.5)

Concepts A **wavefront** is a curve or surface in a medium on which all points of a propagating wave have the same phase.

A **planar wavefront** is a flat wavefront that is either a plane or a straight line.

A **surface wave** is a wave that propagates in two dimensions and has circular wavefronts. A **spherical wave** is a wave that propagates in three dimensions and has spherical wavefronts.

According to **Huygens' principle,** any wavefront may be regarded as a collection of many closely spaced, coherent point sources.

Diffraction is the spreading out of waves either around an obstacle or beyond the edges of an aperture. The effect is more pronounced when the size of the obstacle or aperture is about equal to or smaller than the wavelength of the wave.

Quantitative Tools If no energy is dissipated, the amplitude A of a wave originating at a point source decreases with increasing distance r from the source as

$$A \propto \frac{1}{\sqrt{r}} \quad \text{(surface wave)}$$

or

$$A \propto \frac{1}{r} \quad \text{(spherical wave)}.$$

The **intensity** I (in W/m^2) of a spherical wave that delivers power P to an area A oriented normal to the direction of propagation is

$$I \equiv \frac{P}{A}. \tag{17.1}$$

If a point source emits waves uniformly in all directions at a power P_s and no energy is dissipated, the intensity a distance r from the source is

$$I = \frac{P_s}{4\pi r^2}. \tag{17.2}$$

The intensity I_{surf} (in W/m) of a surface wave that delivers power P to a length L oriented normal to the direction of propagation is

$$I_{surf} \equiv \frac{P}{L}. \tag{17.3}$$

Sound waves (Sections 17.2, 17.5)

Concepts **Sound** is a longitudinal *compressional* wave propagating through a solid, liquid, or gas. The wave consists of an alternating series of *compressions* (where the molecules of the medium are crowded together) and *rarefactions* (where the molecules are spaced far apart). The frequency range of *audible* sound is 20 Hz to 20 kHz.

The speed of sound c depends on the density and elastic properties of the medium. In dry air at 20 °C, the speed of sound is 343 m/s.

Quantitative Tools The *threshold of hearing* I_{th} is the minimum sound intensity audible to humans. For a 1.0-kHz sound,

$$I_{th} \approx 10^{-12} \, W/m^2.$$

For a sound of intensity I, the **intensity level** β in decibels is

$$\beta \equiv (10 \, dB) \log\left(\frac{I}{I_{th}}\right). \tag{17.5}$$

Interference effects (Sections 17.3, 17.6)

Concepts Two or more sources emitting waves that have a constant phase difference are called **coherent sources.** If that constant phase difference is zero, the sources are said to be *in phase*.

Along **nodal lines,** waves cancel each other, and so the displacement of the medium is zero. Along **antinodal lines,** the displacement of the medium is a maximum.

The superposition of two waves of equal amplitude but slightly different frequencies results in a wave of oscillating amplitude. This effect is called **beating.**

Quantitative Tools When two waves of frequencies f_1 and f_2 result in **beating,** the **beat frequency** is

$$f_{beat} \equiv |f_1 - f_2|, \tag{17.8}$$

and the displacement D_x of the particles of the medium is

$$D_x = 2A \cos\left[2\pi(\tfrac{1}{2}\Delta f)\,t\right] \sin(2\pi f_{av}t), \tag{17.12}$$

where $\Delta f = |f_1 - f_2|$ and $f_{av} = \tfrac{1}{2}(f_1 + f_2)$.

The effects of motion on sound (Sections 17.7, 17.8)

Concepts The **Doppler effect** is a change in the observed wave frequency caused by the relative motion of a wave source and an observer.

A **shock wave** is a conical (wedge-shaped) disturbance caused by the piling up of wavefronts from a source moving at a speed greater than or equal to the wave speed in the medium.

Quantitative Tools If a source moving with speed v_s relative to the medium produces sound of frequency f_s, the **Doppler effect** causes an observer moving with speed v_o relative to the medium to observe the sound as having a frequency f_o given by

$$\frac{f_o}{f_s} = \frac{c \pm v_o}{c \pm v_s}. \tag{17.21}$$

The $\pm$ signs are chosen so that $f_o > f_s$ when the source and observer approach each other and $f_o < f_s$ when they move apart.

As a shock wave propagates at speed c, the angle θ it makes with the direction in which the source moves is given by

$$\sin \theta = \frac{c}{v_s} \quad (v_s > c), \tag{17.22}$$

where v_s is the speed of the source relative to the medium. The ratio v_s/c is the *Mach number*.

Review Questions

Answers to these questions can be found at the end of this chapter.

17.1 Wavefronts

1. Name two ways in which two- and three-dimensional waves differ from one-dimensional waves.
2. Which of the following factors plays a role in how much a wave's amplitude decreases as the wave travels away from its source: dissipation of the wave's energy, dimensionality of the wave, destructive interference by waves created by other sources?
3. Consider a sound wave, created at one end of a hollow pipe, that moves through the medium filling the pipe. How does the amplitude change as the wave travels away from the sound source inside the pipe? Ignore energy dissipation.

17.2 Sound

4. Are sound waves in air longitudinal or transverse?
5. What is the range of frequencies audible to humans who have normal hearing?
6. Describe a demonstration that shows that air is elastic.
7. In a sound wave, how do the locations of maximum and minimum medium displacement compare with the locations of maximum and minimum medium density?

17.3 Interference

8. Is the sound created by two sound waves passing a given position P always louder than the sound at P created by either wave alone?
9. Suppose your seat at a poorly designed concert hall is at a *dead spot*, which is a position where destructive interference destroys the sound coming from the stage. Is it a dead spot for all musical notes?
10. Picture two identical coherent wave sources placed side by side and sending out waves that interfere with each other, creating a moiré pattern. If the distance between the two sources is increased, does the number of nodal lines in the pattern increase, decrease, or remain the same?
11. Can destructive interference occur when waves emanating from three or more sources overlap?

17.4 Diffraction

12. What is Huygens' principle?
13. Why is it important that a bat use high-frequency waves to locate insects sonically?

14. Describe the relative extent of spreading of sound waves after they pass through a gap in a barrier. Consider three possibilities: The wavelength is (a) much smaller than the gap width, (b) comparable to the gap width, and (c) much greater than the gap width.

17.5 Intensity

15. A point source emits sound waves uniformly in all directions. How does the sound intensity I vary with distance from the source?
16. Increasing your distance from a point source of spherical waves by a factor of 10 reduces the intensity level β by how many decibels?
17. Explain why the units of intensity I differ for a ripple on the surface of a pond and for a sound wave from an emergency alert siren.

17.6 Beats

18. How is the beat frequency created by two interfering waves related to the frequencies of the waves?
19. One way to tune a piano is to strike a tuning fork (which emits only one specific frequency), then immediately strike the piano key for the frequency being sounded by the fork, and listen for beats. In making an adjustment, a piano tuner working this way causes the beat frequency to increase slightly. Is she going in the right direction with that adjustment?

17.7 Doppler effect

20. A train approaches as you wait at a crossing. Is the whistle frequency you hear higher than, lower than, or the same as the frequency you would hear if the train were stationary?
21. Which produces a greater frequency ratio f_o/f_s: a wave source approaching a stationary observer at a speed of $0.250c$ or an observer approaching a stationary source at a speed of $0.250c$?

17.8 Shock waves

22. Does the angle of a shock wave depend on the frequency of the sound emitted?
23. A boat travels through the water. If its speed increases, what happens to the angle of the bow wave it creates in the water?

Developing a Feel

Make an order-of-magnitude estimate of each of the following quantities. Letters in parentheses refer to hints below. Use them as needed to guide your thinking.

1. The wavelength of the sound wave traveling in air when you whistle (M, T)
2. The number of wavelengths of the musical tone A above middle C (440 Hz) in a standing wave that fills an auditorium (H, M, Q)
3. The width of the smallest object that can be located using sound in the range of human hearing (P, B, F)
4. The greatest distance at which you can just hear a large fireworks shell explode (A, C, I, R, S, U)
5. The power output of the warning horn on a freight train (G, J, N, R, E)
6. The maximum distance over which you can hear a train horn (E, R, L)
7. The ratio of the wavelength of a sound on your vocal cords to the wavelength of the same sound in air (D, K, O)

Hints

A. How much energy is released by a commercial fireworks shell?
B. Which end of the range of human hearing is more useful for detecting a very small object?
C. During what time interval is the energy released?
D. What is the length of a human vocal cord?
E. What is the intensity level β near the horn?
F. What is the frequency range of human hearing?
G. At what distance must the horn be heard?
H. What is the greatest dimension of an auditorium?
I. What fraction of the energy released goes into sound?
J. What must the intensity level β be inside an automobile approaching the tracks in order for the driver to hear the horn?
K. What is a typical frequency for the human voice?
L. What is the minimum intensity level β needed to hear this sound in an open field?
M. What is the speed of sound in air?
N. What must the intensity level β be outside the car?
O. What is the wavelength in air for this typical voice frequency?
P. What is the relationship between the width of the object and the wavelength of the sound wave being used to detect it?
Q. What is the wavelength for this tone?
R. How does the intensity I drop off with distance?

S. What fraction of the sound energy is absorbed or dissipated over great distances?
T. What is the frequency of sound emitted when you whistle?
U. What background noise level is appropriate?

Key (all values approximate)

A. 2 J; B. the smallest object requires the smallest possible wavelength for the sound wave, which means the highest possible frequency in the human-hearing range; C. 5 ms; D. 2×10^1 mm; E. 120 dB 1 m from horn; F. 2×10^1 Hz to 2×10^4 Hz; G. 1×10^2 m for a fast train, which may travel this distance in a few seconds; H. 6×10^1 m; I. taking into account energy to create light and kinetic energy of fragments—say, 1/2; J. above the intensity level of conversation or radio loudness—say, 65 dB; K. 2×10^2 Hz; L. 30 dB; M. 3×10^2 m/s; N. because the windows may be closed, allow a good margin—say, 80 dB; O. 2 m; P. wavelengths longer than the object's width diffract around the object instead of being reflected back to the detector; Q. 0.7 m; R. as $1/r^2$, because the wavefronts are spherical; S. say, another 1/2; T. 1 kHz; U. for a best case, 30 dB

Worked and Guided Problems

These examples involve material from this chapter but are not associated with any particular section.
Some examples are worked out in detail; others you should work out by following the guidelines provided.

Worked Problem 17.1 Minimal sound

Two small, spherical speakers simultaneously emit a note of wavelength λ. The speakers are a distance $10\lambda/3$ apart. If a microphone is moved along the line between their centers, at what positions does it detect (*a*) an unusually loud sound and (*b*) an unusually faint sound?

1 GETTING STARTED We know that the closer the microphone is to a speaker, the louder the sound it detects because the intensity I of the sound waves is greatest near the source. However, the question says *unusually loud*, which hints that we are being asked about the effects of constructive and destructive interference. We are asked for the positions where the microphone records very loud and very faint sounds, and so we draw a diagram that shows what we know and specifies a suitable reference position against which to measure distances. We choose this reference position to be the center of the left speaker, which we call speaker 1 (Figure WG17.1).

Figure WG17.1

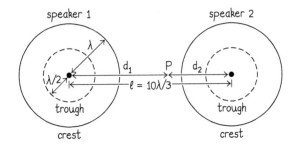

2 DEVISE PLAN Consider the arbitrary position labeled P in Figure WG17.1, which is on the line that connects the speaker centers. Constructive interference occurs at P when waves from the two speakers arrive at P in phase. To achieve this, the phase difference at P must be a multiple of one cycle: $0,\ \pm 2\pi,\ \pm 4\pi, \ldots$. Because there is one wavelength in each cycle, the number of wavelengths in distances d_1 and d_2 must differ by an integral number of wavelengths: $0,\ \pm\lambda,\ \pm 2\lambda, \ldots$. So, for constructive interference,

constructive interference: $\dfrac{d_1 - d_2}{\lambda} = n, \quad n = 0, \pm 1, \pm 2, \ldots$

$$d_1 - d_2 = n\lambda.$$

Destructive interference occurs in locations where the two waves are out of phase by $180° = \pi$ rad. Using the same argument as above, we can say

destructive interference: $\dfrac{d_1 - d_2}{\lambda} = n + \tfrac{1}{2}, \quad n = 0, \pm 1, \pm 2, \ldots$

$$d_1 - d_2 = (n + \tfrac{1}{2})\lambda.$$

We have to make sure that our values for d_1 and d_2 remain between the two speakers, which requires that $d_1 + d_2 = \ell$ and that $0 < d_1 < \ell$ and $0 < d_2 < \ell$.

3 EXECUTE PLAN
(*a*) Because $d_2 = \ell - d_1$, we have for constructive interference

$$d_1 - d_2 = d_1 - (\ell - d_1) = 2d_1 - \ell = 2d_1 - \tfrac{10}{3}\lambda = n\lambda$$

$$d_{1,n}^{\mathrm{con}} = \tfrac{1}{2}\big(n + \tfrac{10}{3}\big)\lambda, \quad n = 0, \pm 1, \pm 2, \ldots$$

Now we can substitute the first few values of n to obtain all the constructive-interference positions between the speakers:

$$d_{1,0} = \tfrac{1}{2}\big(0 + \tfrac{10}{3}\big)\lambda = \tfrac{5}{3}\lambda$$

$$d_{1,-1} = \tfrac{1}{2}\big(-1 + \tfrac{10}{3}\big)\lambda = \tfrac{7}{6}\lambda$$

$$d_{1,+1} = \tfrac{1}{2}\big(+1 + \tfrac{10}{3}\big)\lambda = \tfrac{13}{6}\lambda$$

$$d_{1,-2} = \tfrac{1}{2}\big(-2 + \tfrac{10}{3}\big)\lambda = \tfrac{2}{3}\lambda$$

$$d_{1,+2} = \tfrac{1}{2}\big(+2 + \tfrac{10}{3}\big)\lambda = \tfrac{8}{3}\lambda$$

$$d_{1,-3} = \tfrac{1}{2}\big(-3 + \tfrac{10}{3}\big)\lambda = \tfrac{1}{6}\lambda$$

$$d_{1,+3} = \tfrac{1}{2}\big(+3 + \tfrac{10}{3}\big)\lambda = \tfrac{19}{6}\lambda$$

$$d_{1,-4} = \tfrac{1}{2}\big(-4 + \tfrac{10}{3}\big)\lambda = -\tfrac{1}{3}\lambda$$

$$d_{1,+4} = \tfrac{1}{2}\big(+4 + \tfrac{10}{3}\big)\lambda = \tfrac{11}{3}\lambda.$$

These last two distances are not between the speakers, which are a distance $10\lambda/3 = 20\lambda/6$ apart, and so we discard them. Thus the positions between the speakers where the microphone detects unusually loud sounds are at these distances from speaker 1:

$$d_1^{\mathrm{con}} = \tfrac{1}{6}\lambda, \tfrac{2}{3}\lambda, \tfrac{7}{6}\lambda, \tfrac{5}{3}\lambda, \tfrac{13}{6}\lambda, \tfrac{8}{3}\lambda, \tfrac{19}{6}\lambda. \checkmark$$

(b) Using the same procedure, we discover that the distances from speaker 1 that produce destructive interference satisfy the expression

$$2d_1 - \tfrac{10}{3}\lambda = (n + \tfrac{1}{2})\lambda$$

$$d_{1,n}^{des} = \tfrac{1}{2}(n + \tfrac{23}{6})\lambda, \quad n = 0, \pm 1, \pm 2, \ldots$$

$$d_{1,0} = \tfrac{1}{2}(0 + \tfrac{23}{6})\lambda = \tfrac{23}{12}\lambda$$

$$d_{1,-1} = \tfrac{1}{2}(-1 + \tfrac{23}{6})\lambda = \tfrac{17}{12}\lambda$$

$$d_{1,+1} = \tfrac{1}{2}(+ 1 + \tfrac{23}{6})\lambda = \tfrac{29}{12}\lambda$$

$$d_{1,-2} = \tfrac{1}{2}(-2 + \tfrac{23}{6})\lambda = \tfrac{11}{12}\lambda$$

$$d_{1,+2} = \tfrac{1}{2}(+ 2 + \tfrac{23}{6})\lambda = \tfrac{35}{12}\lambda$$

$$d_{1,-3} = \tfrac{1}{2}(-3 + \tfrac{23}{6})\lambda = \tfrac{5}{12}\lambda$$

$$d_{1,+3} = \tfrac{1}{2}(+ 3 + \tfrac{23}{6})\lambda = \tfrac{41}{12}\lambda$$

$$d_{1,-4} = \tfrac{1}{2}(-4 + \tfrac{23}{6})\lambda = -\tfrac{1}{12}\lambda$$

$$d_{1,+4} = \tfrac{1}{2}(+ 4 + \tfrac{23}{6})\lambda = \tfrac{47}{12}\lambda.$$

Again we want only positions that lie between the speakers, which are $10\lambda/3 = 40\lambda/12$ apart. The last three values we just calculated are not on this center-to-center line, and so our destructive-interference positions are

$$d_1^{des} = \tfrac{5}{12}\lambda, \tfrac{11}{12}\lambda, \tfrac{17}{12}\lambda, \tfrac{23}{12}\lambda, \tfrac{29}{12}\lambda, \tfrac{35}{12}\lambda. \checkmark$$

❹ EVALUATE RESULT We expect constructive interference halfway between the speakers because the waves from the two speakers travel the same distance to reach this position. This distance is $\tfrac{1}{2}(\tfrac{10}{3}\lambda) = \tfrac{5}{3}\lambda = d_{1,0}^{con}$, and we see that this value does appear in our constructive-interference list.

We expect the spacings between constructive and destructive positions to be related to the wavelength in some simple way. In other words, the same type of interference should occur as the difference $d_1 - d_2$ changes by one wavelength. This is easiest to see with the constructive-interference positions. The midpoint between the speakers is a position of constructive interference. As we move from this midpoint toward speaker 2, d_1 increases and d_2 decreases. If d_1 increases by $\lambda/2$, d_2 decreases by $\lambda/2$, and the difference $d_1 - d_2$ changes by one wavelength. Thus positions of constructive interference should be a distance $\lambda/2$ apart, positions of destructive interference should be a distance $\lambda/2$ apart, and this is just what we see.

We expect destructive interference halfway between each pair of constructive-interference positions, which is just what we see—for example,

$$\tfrac{1}{2}[d_{1,+1}^{con} + d_{1,0}^{con}] = \tfrac{1}{2}\left[\tfrac{13}{6}\lambda + \tfrac{5}{3}\lambda\right] = \tfrac{23}{12}\lambda = d_{1,0}^{des}.$$

We made one assumption that can affect the accuracy of our answers. We assumed that the amplitude of the waves is constant along the line that joins the speakers, and this is not true. The closer you are to one speaker, the higher the amplitude of the wave coming from it and the lower the amplitude of the wave coming from the other speaker. Thus, positions where the phase difference is $\lambda/2$ are not positions where the crest of one wave cancels the trough of the other. This deviation from the ideal case causes both the constructive and the destructive interference to be less than complete. Nevertheless these are positions of unusually loud or faint sound.

Guided Problem 17.2 Dripping disturbance

A dripping faucet creates waves on the surface of a still pool of water in a stoppered sink. The drops enter the water at position P, and the crest-to-trough height of the waves 10 mm from P is 7.0 mm. (a) What is the amplitude of the waves 150 mm from P? (b) By what factor does the wave intensity 150 mm from P differ from the wave intensity 10 mm from P?

❶ GETTING STARTED
1. Describe what happens to the waves as they spread out.
2. What is the difference between a water wave spreading out in two dimensions and a sound wave spreading out in three dimensions?
3. Equation 17.1, $I = P/A$, is for three-dimensional waves. How does the denominator of the fraction change when you write the intensity equation for a two-dimensional wave?

❷ DEVISE PLAN
4. What unknown quantities do you need to determine?
5. What principles or methods can help you obtain these quantities?
6. How is energy related to a quantity you've studied in this chapter?
7. Which equations allow you to express the unknown quantities in terms of known quantities?

❸ EXECUTE PLAN

❹ EVALUATE RESULT
8. Are these results consistent with your experience with such water waves?

Worked Problem 17.3 Bottle music

When you blow across the mouth of a bottle, you can cause a standing wave in the air in the bottle, which makes a musical sound. Blowing harder can give a higher musical pitch, but that takes practice. Assume for any liquid height in the bottle that you can reliably obtain only the fundamental (first harmonic) and the next higher harmonic frequency by blowing. You have a beverage bottle 0.23 m in length, with an original liquid height of 0.20 m (before you drink any of the beverage). Given that the speed of sound in air is 343 m/s, what range of frequencies can you obtain as you slowly sip the liquid in the bottle?

❶ GETTING STARTED Sound waves are longitudinal waves, but standing waves in the bottle should form only for certain wavelengths, as for transverse standing waves on a string (see *Principles* Section 16.6). We must determine what standing wave patterns form in the air above the liquid in the bottle. The top surface of the liquid in the bottle (or the bottom of the bottle when the contents are consumed) acts as a fixed end because sound waves are longitudinal, and the displacement of air molecules is greatly reduced at the liquid or glass surface. Therefore we expect a node at this location. The top end of the bottle is open, and displacement of air molecules is not constrained at this end of the bottle. This corresponds to a free end for reflection, resulting in a displacement antinode near the top of the bottle. Now we just need to figure out how many wavelengths fit in the bottle to match these boundary conditions. The smallest number we obtain corresponds to the fundamental frequency.

❷ DEVISE PLAN We need to determine what fraction of a wavelength satisfies our boundary conditions. From the allowed wavelengths and the known speed of sound in air, we can then use the relationship $c = \lambda f$ to compute the frequencies.

One node in a standing wave pattern is separated from the next node by half a wavelength, so to get from one node to an adjacent antinode is a quarter of a wavelength. The fundamental pattern requires one-quarter wavelength to fit into the open space in the bottle. For each shorter wavelength that satisfies the same conditions, we need to add another half wavelength, adding an additional node and antinode so that there is still a node at the bottom and an antinode at the top of each pattern. Like the standing waves on a string, the patterns differ from each other by one-half wavelength. Unlike the standing waves on strings, the higher harmonics do not simply occur for every integer multiple of the half wavelength. Instead, the harmonics occur for odd integer multiples of one-quarter wavelength:

$$\frac{\lambda}{4}, \frac{3\lambda}{4}, \frac{5\lambda}{4}, \dots$$

Only the first two patterns are relevant for this problem. If the length of air in the bottle is ℓ, each pattern must fit into that length.

The first two patterns must satisfy

$$\ell = \frac{\lambda}{4} \quad \text{and} \quad \ell = \frac{3\lambda}{4}$$

$$\lambda = 4\ell \quad \text{and} \quad \lambda = \frac{4\ell}{3}.$$

The resulting frequencies are

$$f = \frac{c}{\lambda} = \frac{c}{4\ell} \quad \text{and} \quad \frac{3c}{4\ell}.$$

We must determine these frequencies for the range of lengths available.

❸ EXECUTE PLAN The minimum length of air in the bottle occurs before we take the first sip: It is the difference between the height of the bottle and the original height of the liquid. For this case we obtain frequencies

$$f_1 = \frac{c}{4\ell} = \frac{343 \text{ m/s}}{4(3.0 \times 10^{-2} \text{ m})} = 2.9 \times 10^3 \text{ Hz}$$

$$f_3 = \frac{3c}{4\ell} = 3f_1 = 8.6 \times 10^3 \text{ Hz}.$$

Any longer length ℓ will result in smaller frequencies, so the maximum frequency we can attain is just above 8500 Hz. The lower frequency limit will occur for the greatest value of the air column—that is, when the bottle is empty:

$$f_1 = \frac{c}{4\ell} = \frac{343 \text{ m/s}}{4(0.23 \text{ m})} = 3.7 \times 10^2 \text{ Hz}$$

$$f_3 = 3f_1 = 1.1 \times 10^3 \text{ Hz}.$$

The lowest possible frequency for these conditions is thus just over 370 Hz, giving a range of

$$370 \text{ Hz} < f < 8600 \text{ Hz}. \ ✔$$

❹ EVALUATE RESULT Many of us have produced tones by blowing across the mouth of a bottle, so it is reasonable that we obtain frequencies that can be heard. Both ends of this frequency range are well within the range of human hearing, although the upper limit is a pretty high note, perhaps reminiscent of a piccolo. Experience also tells us that longer bottles produce deeper notes, in agreement with our results.

Guided Problem 17.4 Bottle orchestra

Preparing to watch a ballgame on television, you raid the refrigerator for two 0.23-m-tall bottles of your favorite beverage for yourself and your roommate. After a few minutes the game is boring, so your roommate begins blowing across the top of his bottle. That looks like fun, so you decide to try it, too. Each of you has a bottle with a slightly different level of liquid, but the depth of liquid in each bottle is roughly 10^2 mm. What is the minimum difference in the heights of the liquid in the two bottles that will allow you to hear two different musical notes when you

and your roommate "play" your bottles simultaneously at their fundamental frequencies?

❶ GETTING STARTED
1. If the two bottles produce notes whose frequencies differ by just a few Hz, what pattern of sound do you expect to hear?
2. What is the lowest frequency note that humans can hear?
3. How is the fundamental frequency related to the depth of the liquid in the bottle?

PRACTICE

② DEVISE PLAN

4. Given the height of the bottle and the depth of the liquid, can you determine the frequency of the sound that forms a fundamental standing wave in the air in the bottle?

5. Examine Eq. 17.11, the immediate precursor to the beat equation (Eq. 17.12). Is there any difference in principle between the sine and cosine terms? Figure 17.27, the superposed displacement curves of two waves of slightly different frequencies, may help you answer.

6. What minimum difference in frequencies is needed so that either the sine or cosine term in Eq. 17.11 might represent a note that can be detected by the human ear?

7. Relate this minimum frequency difference to the minimum difference in the depths of liquid in the two bottles.

③ EXECUTE PLAN

④ EVALUATE RESULT

8. Is your result plausible? What are the two frequencies that can be heard if the average depth of liquid is 100 mm and the difference in the depths is your computed value?

9. You might try this experimentally, but realize that you may not have perfect hearing.

Worked Problem 17.5 Sharp cruising

Driving down a quiet street on a summer day with the car windows down, you see a convertible approaching from the opposite direction, with the driver playing her car stereo loudly. Having a well-trained musician's ear, you notice that the song you hear is in a key that is one semitone (the interval between adjacent notes on a piano) above the key in which the song is typically played. You also know that to shift any note by one semitone (from C to C-sharp, for instance, or from E-flat to E), the frequencies must be related by a factor of about 1.06. Assuming that both drivers are traveling at about the same speed, what is this speed?

❶ GETTING STARTED You know that if you are moving toward a stationary sound source, the frequency you hear is higher than the frequency you would hear if you were standing still. The same is true if a moving source approaches you, so both motion effects should contribute to a higher frequency. Thus we need to determine the common speed that gives us $f_o/f_s = 1.06$. The use of the word *about* in the problem statement should cause us to reduce the number of significant digits in our answer from three to two.

❷ DEVISE PLAN For a moving observer who is approaching a moving source, the change in frequency is given by Eq. 17.21:

$$\frac{f_o}{f_s} = \frac{c \pm v_o}{c \pm v_s}.$$

Under the assumption that the speeds of the two cars are equal, we can substitute $v = v_o = v_s$. We also must decide which signs to use, so we will pick the signs that produce a higher observed frequency due to motion of both the source and observer. Then, using the known speed of sound in air, we can solve for the single unknown v.

❸ EXECUTE PLAN

$$\frac{f_o}{f_s} = 1.06 = \frac{c + v}{c - v}$$

$$1.06(c - v) = c + v$$

$$0.06c = 2.06v$$

$$v = \frac{0.06c}{2.06} = \frac{0.06(343 \text{ m/s})}{2.06} = 10 \text{ m/s}. ✔$$

❹ EVALUATE RESULT The positive sign for v is consistent with our choices for signs in the numerator and denominator; a negative value for v would indicate some error in our thinking. This speed is reasonable for cars that are approaching each other on a quiet, therefore likely suburban, street (10 m/s = 22 mi/h).

Guided Problem 17.6 Cut to the chase

A motorist driving at 100 km/h is overtaken by a police car, siren blaring, chasing down a speeder (Figure WG17.2). The police car is moving at 136 km/h. What frequency does the motorist hear for the siren (*a*) before and (*b*) after he is passed if the frequency in the police car's reference frame is 1526 Hz?

Figure WG17.2

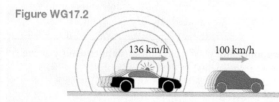

❶ GETTING STARTED

1. You have a sketch of the situation before the police car overtakes the motorist, so draw a sketch showing the situation after the police car has passed the motorist.

2. Can part *a* and part *b* be solved separately?

3. Keep in mind that both cars are moving relative to the air.

❷ DEVISE PLAN

4. What is the motional relationship between source and observer before the police car passes the motorist? After the police car passes?

5. Which Doppler equation is appropriate for each part of the motion?

❸ EXECUTE PLAN

❹ EVALUATE RESULT

6. Are your answers plausible? Does the frequency change the way you expect it to (that is, compare your answers with the general trend of frequency shifts when the source is approaching or receding)?

Worked Problem 17.7 Leaving a wake

A speedboat travels across the water of a shallow lake at 55 km/h, creating behind it a wake that spreads out from the line that bisects the boat along the boat's direction of travel. You estimate that the wake moves 1.0 m perpendicular to the bisector for every 3.0 m of forward motion of the boat. (a) How fast do the surface waves travel on the water? (b) At what water equivalent of a Mach number is the boat traveling?

❶ GETTING STARTED A wake is a shock wave that forms because the speed of the boat on the water surface is greater than the speed of the waves on the water surface. We're asked to determine (a) what this wave speed is and (b) how it compares with the speed of the boat.

❷ DEVISE PLAN Equation 17.22 relates the angle of a shock wave to the speed of the waves that create the shock wave and to the source speed:

$$\sin \theta = \frac{c}{v_s}.$$

We should be able to calculate the angle θ of the shock wave from the given distance information, and we know the boat speed v_s, so we can determine the wave speed c.

Mach numbers relate object speed to wave speed in a given medium. Once we have the wave speed, therefore, we can determine the "water Mach number" for the boat.

❸ EXECUTE PLAN
(a) The wake moves 1 m sideways for each 3-m forward motion of the boat, so the angle of the wake to the bisector of the boat should be given by

$$\tan \theta = \frac{1.0 \text{ m}}{3.0 \text{ m}} = 0.33 \qquad \theta = 18.4°.$$

Solving Eq. 17.22 for the wave speed gives

$$c = v_s \sin \theta = (55 \text{ km/h})\sin 18.4° = 17.4 \text{ km/h} = 4.8 \text{ m/s}. ✔$$

(b) Mach number is defined as the ratio of the speed of an object in a given medium to the speed of waves in that medium. The water Mach number is therefore

$$\frac{v_s}{c} = \frac{55 \text{ km/h}}{17.4 \text{ km/h}} = 3.2. ✔$$

❹ EVALUATE RESULT The answer to part a indicates that water waves spread across the surface at about 15 ft/s, a value that is not unreasonable. Part b shows that it is much easier to break the "water barrier" with a speedboat than to break the "sound barrier" with a jet airplane!

Guided Problem 17.8 Shocked, I say—shocked

A high-speed jet is flying across the Atlantic Ocean at an altitude of 15 km. It passes over a ship, and 34 s after it passes directly overhead, a sonic boom is heard by the ship's passengers. At what Mach number and speed is the jet flying?

❶ GETTING STARTED
1. Start with a diagram of the situation showing the relevant distances and the shock wave angle θ.
2. Do you need to make any assumptions?

❷ DEVISE PLAN
3. What information can help you determine the required unknowns?

4. How is the angle of the shock wave related to the speed of the jet?
5. Which equations allow you to express the unknown quantities in terms of known ones?

❸ EXECUTE PLAN

❹ EVALUATE RESULT
6. Can a jet travel this fast? If not, go back and check your work.

Questions and Problems

For instructor-assigned homework, go to MasteringPhysics® (MP)

Dots indicate difficulty level of problems: • = easy, •• = intermediate, ••• = hard; CR *= context-rich problem.*

17.1 Wavefronts

1. A neat trick for determining whether or not a train is coming is to press your ear to a railroad track. Why is this much more effective than listening for the train's sound carried by air? •
2. Suppose a material is stiffer in the x direction than in the y direction. Draw the wavefronts emanating from a point source embedded in this material and radiating in these two directions. ••
3. Your professor delivers a lecture. Does the amplitude of sound waves in the classroom decrease like $1/r$, where r is the distance from the professor to you? ••

4. A cannon is fired some distance away from you, and you wish to estimate that distance by determining how much sound energy enters your ear. (a) How does the sound energy depend on the distance between the cannon and your ear? (b) Now you use the dependence you described in part a to judge how far away the cannon is. First you estimate the distance assuming that none of the energy in the sound waves is dissipated (into, say, random motion of the molecules that make up the air), and then you repeat the estimate assuming that some of the sound energy is dissipated. Is your first estimate higher or lower than your second estimate? ••
5. One form of whispering gallery is an elliptical room where a person standing at one focus can hear quite clearly someone speaking very quietly at the other focus. Use your knowledge of ellipses to explain how this works. •••

17.2 Sound

6. How many octaves are there in the human audible-frequency range? •

7. Because the audible range in bats is about 10 kHz to more than 120 kHz, these animals are oblivious to normal human conversation, which is at frequencies of typically several hundred hertz. If you shout, though, you may in fact startle a bat. Why? ••

8. Standing waves (see Section 16.6) can form when the sound traveling in air inside a tube reflects from each end. Just as for waves on strings, the wavelength and tube length must satisfy some relationship in order for the standing wave to persist. Apply the arguments of Worked Problem 17.3 to determine the relationship between wavelength and tube length for the fundamental and the next two harmonics for standing waves in a tube that is open at both ends. ••

9. Sketch the three lowest-frequency harmonic wave function patterns for standing waves in the air in a tube that is open at both ends, (*a*) representing *displacement* nodes and antinodes and (*b*) representing *pressure* nodes and antinodes. Your sketches should be similar to *Principles* Figure 17.9c. ••

17.3 Interference

10. If the frequency of the sources in Figure P17.10 is increased, do the nodal lines get farther apart, get closer together, or remain unchanged? •

Figure P17.10

nodal lines

11. What happens to the nodal lines in Figure P17.10 if the phase of one of the sources is shifted by 180°? •

12. Are stable nodal lines formed by two sources that emit waves that have the same amplitude but different frequencies? ••

13. Speaker manufacturers often discourage placing speakers in front of curtains or drapes because having an uncovered wall behind the speakers often alleviates dead listening spots in the room. Explain why a wall helps. ••

14. How many nodal lines are created by two point sources that are separated by a distance equal to 2.5λ? ••

15. Vibration in a car can create concentric ripples on the surface of a cup of coffee sitting on the dashboard. What kind of waves are the ripples, and why are they circular? ••

16. Two sound sources emitting at the same wavelength λ are placed a distance d_s apart and a perpendicular distance d_m away from a row of microphones. Show that the distances Δx between those microphones that experience maximum variations in loudness are given by $\Delta x = d_m \lambda / d_s$ in the limit $d_m \gg d_s$. •••

17. Two coherent sources of water waves of frequency f are a distance d apart. (*a*) Far away from the sources, what are the angles between the nodal lines in the water and the perpendicular to the line joining the sources? (*b*) If you introduce a phase difference ϕ between the sources, how do the directions of the nodal lines shift? (Hint: For nodal destructive interference far from the sources, assume that the wavefronts from each source are parallel to one another and that their amplitudes are equal. Also see Worked Problem 17.1) •••

18. Three equally spaced, coherent sources of water waves of frequency f are in a line with a distance d separating each adjacent pair. Far away from the sources, what are the angles between the nodal lines in the water and the perpendicular to the line joining the sources? (Hint: For nodal destructive interference far from the sources, assume that the wavefronts from each source are parallel to one another and that their amplitudes are equal. Also see Worked Problem 17.1.) •••

17.4 Diffraction

19. When your mother shouted at you to come inside when you were a kid, how could you hear her when you were around a corner? •

20. The speaker in Figure P17.20 faces a narrow obstructing panel made of sound-absorbing material. A microphone is placed dead center behind the panel. Does the microphone pick up sound or not? ••

Figure P17.20

21. Two very small, coherent sources are separated by $d = 2\lambda$, where λ is the wavelength of the circular waves created by each source. (*a*) Use Huygens' principle to construct a dozen wavefronts from each source, six troughs and six crests. Mark antinodes with blue lines and mark nodes with red lines, starting each line at least two wavelengths from either source. (*b*) Repeat for the case when the two sources are not coherent, so that waves from one source are exactly one-half wavelength out of phase with waves from the other. (*c*) Compare your diagrams. Are the original antinodes still antinodes? Are the original nodes still nodes? ••

22. Phasors (see *Principles* Section 15.5) are useful for adding waves that are out of phase. For example, assume you have two sources, 1 and 2, that emit sound waves of the same frequency f. At your detector, the waves from source 1 have an amplitude of 1.00×10^{-8} m, and those from source 2 have an amplitude of 0.600×10^{-8} m and a phase of $+\pi/3$ relative to the phase of the source 1 waves. If the phase of the waves from source 1 is arbitrarily assigned to be $\phi_1 = 0$, what are the amplitude and phase of the combined waves? (Hint: It will help to draw the two waves as phasors.) •••

17.5 Intensity

23. A radio station has a power output of 140 W and is located 1.5 km from your house. The radio signal is emitted uniformly in all directions. What is the intensity I of the signal at your house? •

24. You measure the intensity of a sound wave to be 5.70 W/m². If the power output of the signal is 90 W and the signal is emitted in all directions, how far away from the source are you? •

25. One mosquito positioned 0.50 m from a decibel meter emits a sound that has an intensity level of 15 dB. What is the intensity level of the sound emitted by 100 mosquitoes at the same distance? •

26. If ten screaming children on the playground produce a sound for which the intensity level is 80 dB, how many children do you need to produce an 82-dB sound? •

27. A sound source at the center of a cubical room radiates uniformly in all directions. What is the difference in decibels between the intensity level at a ceiling corner of the room and the intensity level at the center of one of the walls? Ignore reflections. ••

28. At a distance of 3.0 m from your stereo system with two speakers, what power output must your stereo amplifier have in order for the intensity level to be 80 dB? Assume that all the energy from the amplifier goes into producing sound. ••

29. A satellite orbiting Earth at an altitude of 450 km emits a radio signal that has a power level of 12 W when it reaches Earth. The signal is beamed in such a way that it covers an area of 8.0 m² on Earth's surface. What power is received by a ground-based antenna if the surface area of the antenna is 400 mm²? ••

30. At a basketball game in an enclosed arena, you happen to sit next to a screaming baby. If the baby's yell arrives at your ear with an intensity level of 75 dB, and the music that reaches your ear from the loudspeakers during the teams' warm-up is at 80 dB, (*a*) what is the intensity I of the overall sound you hear and (*b*) what is the intensity level of the sound you hear? ••

31. The intensity level from a directional loudspeaker at your position at a political rally is 95 dB. (*a*) What is the intensity I of the sound in watts per square meter? (*b*) What is the power output of the loudspeaker if you are 20 m from the speaker and it emits sound into one hemisphere only? ••

32. You are on the design team for a new airport. The developer wants to build a hotel as close to the airport as possible. The intensity level of a large jet during takeoff is 140 dB at 50 m from the jet. The developer wants to build the hotel such that the intensity level heard by guests is not higher than 50 dB inside the hotel rooms and not higher than 125 dB in the parking lot of the hotel. (*a*) How far from the airport would you suggest the developer build the hotel? (*b*) What is the maximum allowable intensity I of the sound in the hotel rooms? ••

33. The intensity level at the front of a library reading room is 70 dB when 120 students are in the room and 20 dB when the room is empty. What do you expect the intensity level to be when 60 students are in the room? ••

34. A typical car horn has an intensity level of 90 dB at a distance of 1.0 m. (*a*) What is the intensity level of 16 cars all honking their horns at an intersection on a city street? (*b*) What is the power output of the combined horns at a distance of 5.0 m? (*c*) What is the intensity level three city blocks away? Assume 100 m for the length of each block. ••

35. On a whale-watching expedition, your underwater sound detector picks up a whale sound that has an intensity of 9.0 μW/m². (*a*) What is the intensity level β of this sound? (*b*) If your detector tells you that you are 2.3 km from the whale, what is the power of the emitted signal? (*c*) How many whales, emitting sound at the same intensity $I = 9.0$ μW/m², are needed to produce an intensity level of 100 dB at your location? ••

36. A frequency generator (a device that produces sinusoidal signals whose frequency and amplitude can be independently set) is used to power a horn. The frequency is set to 2000 Hz, and for a particular amplitude the sound intensity is measured to be 0.050 W/m² at a distance of 12 m. (*a*) What is the power output of the horn in this case? (*b*) If the power output is increased to 92 W, what is the new intensity reading? ••

37. Suppose that two coherent, spherical sound sources, 1 and 2, each generate the same amount of power P. The distance between the sources is 2λ. Point R is on a line of maximum destructive interference, and the distance between R and source 1 is equal to 9λ. Point Q is on a line of maximum constructive interference, and the distance between Q and source 1 is 6λ. Obtain expressions for the intensity at points R and Q. •••

38. Your bedroom is 8.0 m away from the living room. When requested by your parents to turn down your stereo, you do, and the intensity level where they are sitting in the living room drops from 50 dB to 45 dB. What is the change in the power of the sound emitted by your stereo? •••

17.6 Beats

39. If two superimposed frequencies differ by more than about 20 Hz, what do you hear? •

40. Two oboe players are next to each other on the stage. One is playing a 350-Hz note, and the other is playing a 355-Hz note. What is the beat frequency heard by the audience? •

41. Two tuba players in a marching band appear to your trained ear to be playing the correct note, 196 Hz, but there is an annoying warble that you interpret as being four beats per second. What are the frequencies of the notes played by the two tubas? •

42. The lowest frequency a certain sound receiver can detect is 760 Hz. If the receiver detects a frequency of 762 Hz that is then mixed with an unknown frequency, also detectable by the receiver, and you hear four beats per second, what is the unknown frequency? ••

43. You have four electronic audio generators, A, B, C, and D, all producing tones near 1200 Hz that are easily audible but not distinguishable by ear. When you increase the frequency of generator A a little, the beat frequencies between A and B, A and C, and A and D all increase. When you increase the frequency of generator B a little, the B-C beat frequency increases and the B-A and B-D beat frequencies decrease. Rank the generators by frequency, from lowest to highest. ••

44. One tuning fork vibrates at a frequency of 528 Hz, and a second one vibrates at 524 Hz, but you don't know which is which. After applying a small piece of modeling clay to the end of one fork, you notice that the beat frequency has increased. On which fork did you put the clay? ••

45. Three tenors are giving a concert at an outdoor amphitheater. What are the possible beat frequencies if tenor 1 holds a 262-Hz note while tenor 2 holds a 264.3-Hz note and tenor 3 holds a 258-Hz note? ••

PRACTICE

46. When two frequencies are added together, the beat frequency and the average frequency are an octave apart. What is the ratio of the original frequencies? ••

47. Two violin strings, each having a linear mass density of 0.0014 kg/m and under the same 100-N tension, have the same fundamental frequency of 660 Hz. If the tension in one of the strings is changed to 102 N, what is the beat frequency? ••

48. During a fire drill in your dormitory, you notice that the sound waves from the two alarms on your floor interfere with each other, and you hear five beats every two seconds. (a) If the average of the two frequencies is 3500 Hz, what are the frequencies of the two alarms? (b) If your room is 15 m from each alarm, what is the intensity I of the sound if the power output is 60 W for each alarm? ••

17.7 Doppler effect

49. What happens to the magnitude of the Doppler shift you hear in the whistle of a passing train if you increase the distance between you and the tracks? •

50. While driving down the road, you spot a friend standing on the sidewalk. You honk your horn at him while driving 70 km/h. Your horn emits a frequency of 360 Hz. What frequency does your friend hear (a) as you approach and (b) after you pass by? •

51. The electric bells at your school buzz with a frequency of 400 Hz. If you are late for class and riding your bike down a hill toward the school at a constant speed of 4.47 m/s, what is the frequency of the sound you hear? •

52. At the racetrack, you estimate that the whine of the cars changes by one octave as the cars pass. About how fast are the cars going? ••

53. How fast do you have to travel away from a stationary sound source in order for the frequency to be shifted by (a) 1%, (b) 10%, and (c) a factor of 2? ••

54. While you watch a parade, a band on a float passes you. You detect the frequency of a note played on a flute to be 352 Hz when the float is coming toward you and 347 Hz after the float passes you. At what speed is the float traveling? ••

55. You and a friend are riding bikes, you moving at 9.72 km/h and she moving at 7.20 km/h. She is behind you and turns on her electric horn, which has a frequency of 300 Hz. (a) What frequency do you hear? (b) What frequency is heard by a person who is standing alongside your route after you both have passed him? ••

56. While you are driving on a straight road at 97 km/h, a police car traveling in the opposite direction comes toward you with the siren blaring, and the frequency you hear is 310 Hz. Starting when the two of you are 200 m apart, it takes you 3.00 s to pass the police car. What is the frequency of the siren? ••

57. A car traveling west at 90 km/h along a road running parallel to a railroad track approaches a train traveling east at 65 km/h. If the train's whistle emits a frequency of 400 Hz, what is the frequency heard by the driver of the car (a) as the car approaches the train and (b) after the two vehicles have passed each other? ••

58. A foghorn that emits a frequency of 150 Hz is mounted on a buoy in the bay. If a ship approaches the buoy at 21.2 km/h, (a) what frequency does the captain of the ship hear? (b) Hearing the foghorn is a signal for the captain to slow his ship. After passing the buoy, the captain hears the horn again, but the frequency he detects is now 149 Hz. What is the new speed of the ship? ••

59. Two airplanes simulating a dogfight are headed right for each other, plane A moving at 285 km/h and plane B moving at 295 km/h. The electronic machine gun on A can emit 300 rounds per minute, with each round accompanied by a sound pulse. (a) How many pulses does the pilot in B hear during a burst that lasts 10 s according to observer A? (b) How long does the burst last for the pilot in B? ••

60. You stand in your yard and hold a battery-powered buzzer that is emitting a frequency of 560 Hz as a friend stands next to you. (a) What frequency does your friend hear if you throw the buzzer away from you with a speed of 18.0 m/s? (b) You and your friend now get on a flat railroad car that begins to travel at 12.0 m/s, and you throw the buzzer in the direction opposite the direction of the car's velocity. What frequency does your friend hear? (c) What frequency would a person standing alongside the tracks hear? ••

61. A dog whistle has a frequency of 21 kHz, which is above the high end of the audible range for humans. At what minimum speed and in what direction must you travel in order to just hear the whistle? ••

62. During trials of a new submarine, its speed is measured with an underwater sonar gun anchored to the ocean floor. The gun emits sound waves at a frequency f, and these waves reflect off the surface of the submarine and return to the source at a frequency $f' \neq f$. If the submarine is receding from the sonar gun at speed v, derive an expression for f' in terms of f, v, and c (the speed of the waves through water). •••

63. A device that both emits and receives sound waves is traveling at 80 km/h. The emitted waves have a frequency of 700 Hz. If the waves are reflected off a stationary flat surface in front of the device, what frequency is detected by the device? •••

64. Two students standing 54.9 m apart are tossing around footballs designed to whistle while they are airborne. (a) When student A throws her football toward student B at 16.0 m/s, it emits a frequency of 680 Hz. What frequency is heard by student B? (b) When student B throws his football toward student A at 15.0 m/s, it emits a frequency of 670 Hz. What frequency is heard by student A? (c) If the two footballs are thrown simultaneously, what is the beat frequency? •••

17.8 Shock waves

65. A supersonic jet airplane passing directly overhead creates a shock wave that makes an angle of 47° with the horizontal. What is the speed of the airplane? •

66. As a boat travels at 48.0 km/h across the surface of a still lake, the waves it creates in the water have a speed of 20.1 km/h. What is the angle of the shock wave created by the waves? •

67. A speedboat traveling at 73.0 km/h causes a shock wave that makes an angle of 14.3° with the path of the boat. At what speed are the waves moving through the water? •

68. Two jets flying at the same altitude pass over your head simultaneously, one traveling at Mach 1.5 and the other at Mach 2.5. Which plane's sonic boom do you hear first? ••

69. While attending an air show, you observe a fighter jet traveling horizontally at a speed of Mach 1.30. At the instant you hear the sonic boom, what is the angle between your line of sight to the jet and the horizontal? ••

70. Many years ago, test pilots accelerating through Mach 1 reported that the ride was pretty rough just before Mach 1 but smoothed out suddenly as Mach 1 was breached. How can you account for this? ••

71. Concerned about being disturbed by sonic booms, residents near an Air Force base located along a seacoast submit a petition asking that all jet aircraft from the base head out to sea before attaining Mach 1 and proceed inland only after they have reached supersonic speed. What do you think of the physics reasoning behind this idea? ••

72. A woman standing on the ground observes a jet directly overhead flying at an altitude of 20,000 m. If the jet has a speed of Mach 2 and its shock wave makes an angle of 30° with the horizontal, how long will it be until she hears the sonic boom? ••

73. At a pistol range, a microphone is placed between a shooter and the target so that when a bullet is fired we can hear its sonic boom. A bullet passes by the microphone at a speed of Mach 2.1. The microphone picks up the sonic boom 0.0021 s after the bullet passes above the microphone. (*a*) What is the angle of the shock wave? (*b*) What is the vertical distance between bullet and microphone? ••

74. A jet flying directly over you at an altitude of 3000 m produces a shock wave. If the angle of the shock wave is 42°, (*a*) how long will it be until the sonic boom reaches you, and (*b*) how far does the jet travel during this time interval? ••

75. At White Sands, New Mexico, a car powered by a rocket engine passes you while you are standing still. If you hear the sonic boom 0.045 s after the car passes and the angle of the shock wave is 37.0°, what is your perpendicular distance from the path of the car? •••

Additional Problems

76. What does an observer hear on the ground before and after a sonic boom caused by a jet passing overhead? •

77. Is a second sonic boom generated when a plane reaches a speed of Mach 2? •

78. Two test pilots are flying in a jet trainer going faster than Mach 1. Can the pilot in the front of the cockpit hear the pilot in back? ••

79. Two guitar strings, 1 and 2, plucked simultaneously produce standing waves described by ••

$$D_1 = A \sin(ax)\cos(bt)$$

$$D_2 = A \sin(qx)\cos(dt),$$

with $a = 14.5 \text{ m}^{-1}$, $b = 2512 \text{ s}^{-1}$, $q = 19.3 \text{ m}^{-1}$, and $d = 2575 \text{ s}^{-1}$. (*a*) What is the frequency of each wave? (*b*) What is the beat frequency of the combined wave?

80. A race car traveling at 350 km/h passes a spectator in the stands. If the spectator has an air horn that emits a sound of frequency 400 Hz, what is the range of frequencies of the sound heard by the driver of the car? ••

81. Which type of conic section (circle, ellipse, parabola, or hyperbola) is formed by the nodal-line pattern produced by two coherent wave sources? (Hint: For a given nodal line, the difference in distance between any point on it and the two sources is the same for all points.) ••

82. Why is the high-frequency "tweeter" on a stereo speaker usually much smaller than the low-frequency "woofer"? ••

83. You are standing beneath a Ferris wheel when two children riding in cars on opposite sides of the wheel both scream at 600 Hz. Your well-trained ears notice a beat frequency that is maximum when one child is moving directly toward you and the other is moving directly away from you. The Ferris wheel takes 24.0 s to complete one rotation, and its diameter is 27.0 m. You begin to wonder whether a Doppler shift could produce observable beats under these circumstances. ••• CR

84. You have tickets for an outdoor rock concert, fourth row from the stage. However, at that distance the intensity level is 100 dB, too loud to be enjoyable. You decide to move to a row where the intensity level is a more moderate 80 dB. Fortunately, turning around and counting the right number of rows back (assuming that the distance between rows is uniform), you see that the seats you want are available. ••• CR

85. You want to build a portable device that can detect pirate radio stations broadcasting at about 50 W of power a few miles from your beachfront home. You have a 0.60-m diameter bowl you might use as an antenna dish, but you are worried that your amplifier input will require a signal of at least 0.10 μW. ••• CR

86. Your car is third in line at a railroad crossing as a train moving at a constant speed approaches, with its whistle blowing constantly. To keep yourself from going crazy with the noise, you begin thinking about the relative difference between the frequency you hear and the frequency the engineer hears. Surely this must depend on the angle that your line of sight to the engine of the train makes with the perpendicular to the track. ••• CR

Answers to Review Questions

1. (1) The amplitude of two- and three-dimensional waves decreases as they propagate, even in the absence of energy dissipation. (2) Some interference effects that are not observed in one-dimensional waves occur in two- and three-dimensional waves.

2. Dissipation of the wave's energy leads to a decrease in amplitude as the wave travels, but even without dissipation, the dimensionality of the wave is important. Amplitude decreases as $1/\sqrt{r}$ in a two-dimensional wave and as $1/r$ in a three-dimensional wave.

3. The pipe circumference and thus its cross-sectional area are unchanged all along the pipe. Therefore the wave's amplitude remains constant because there is no change in the area over which the wave's energy is spread as the wave propagates from one end of the pipe to the other.

4. Sound waves in air are longitudinal.

5. The range is 20 Hz to 20 kHz.

6. Squeeze a plastic soda bottle that contains only air and has its cap screwed on tightly. You can decrease the volume only slightly because the compressional force you exert on the walls is transmitted to the air molecules inside. The air compresses elastically, exerting a force on the walls in the opposite direction.

7. Maximum and minimum medium densities occur at locations where the medium displacement is zero. Therefore the locations of maximum and minimum medium density are one-quarter wavelength away from (90° out of phase with) the locations of maximum and minimum displacement.

8. No. The sound is louder only if at P the interference between the two waves is constructive. If it is destructive, the sound when the two waves pass P is softer than the sound of either wave passing P alone.

9. No. A given position in the hall is dead for only certain frequencies because the relative phase of two waves coming to that position is determined by the ratio $\Delta r/\lambda$. Thus destructive interference occurs for only certain frequencies.

10. The number of nodal lines increases.

11. Yes. Any number of sources can be arranged such that wave maxima and minima overlap at certain locations. For example, a set of closely spaced collinear point sources creates constructive interference along a line perpendicular to the sources and destructive interference in other directions.

12. Huygens' principle is the model that considers wavefronts as a collection of closely spaced, coherent point sources, each of which creates new coherent waves that travel in all directions but, when superposed, cancel in all directions other than forward. The result can be used to sketch the shapes of additional forward-propagating wavefronts.

13. High frequencies correspond to short wavelengths, and wavelengths comparable to the size of the insect are needed for reliable location by reflected waves.

14. The amount of spreading depends on the size of the wavelength relative to the gap width: The longer the wavelength, the greater the extent to which the waves spread out. Thus in (a) very little spreading occurs, in (b) the spreading is quite noticeable, and in (c) the waves spread out in all directions, producing a pattern similar to that of a point source.

15. If we ignore dissipation, the intensity varies inversely with the square of distance from the source: $I \propto 1/r^2$ (Eq. 17.2). This is because the energy of the waves is constant regardless of the distance from the source, but the area over which this energy is distributed increases as the distance from the source increases.

16. The intensity I decreases by a factor of $(10)^2 = 100$ because of its $1/r^2$ dependence: $I = P/4\pi r^2$ (Eq. 17.2). Equation 17.5 for intensity level, $\beta = (10\ \text{dB})\log(I/I_{\text{th}})$, tells you that there is a 10-dB drop in intensity level β for each power-of-ten reduction in intensity I, and so the drop in intensity level is 20 dB.

17. In the case of ripples on a pond, as each ripple expands, the energy is spread over the circumference of a circle (formula $2\pi r$). This gives intensity units of W/m. An emergency warning siren is typically mounted on a tall pole, which allows the sound energy to spread out in all directions. In this case the energy carried by each wavefront is spread across the surface of a sphere (formula $4\pi r^2$). The intensity units are therefore W/m².

18. The beat frequency is the difference between the two wave frequencies.

19. No. As the tuning fork frequency and the piano key frequency approach equality, which is the tuner's aim, the beat frequency decreases.

20. The frequency is higher because of the Doppler effect for a moving source.

21. The ratio is greater for source approaching observer. Here's why. The source moving toward the stationary observer means that the observed frequency is higher than the emitted frequency and thus $f_o/f_s > 1$. Because $v_o = 0$, Eq. 17.21 becomes $f_o/f_s = c/(c \pm v_s)$. In order to have the fraction be greater than 1, you use a minus sign in the denominator: $f_o/f_s = c/(c - 0.250c) = 1.33$.

   The observer moving toward the stationary source means again $f_o > f_s$ and thus again $f_o/f_s > 1$. Because in this case $v_s = 0$, Eq. 17.21 becomes $f_o/f_s = (c \pm v_o)/c$. In order to have the fraction be greater than 1, you use a plus sign in the numerator: $f_o/f_s = (c + 0.250c)/c = 1.25$.

22. No. Equation 17.22, $\sin\theta = c/v_s$, contains no information about frequency.

23. As v_s in Eq. 17.22, $\sin\theta = c/v_s$, increases, $\sin\theta$ decreases, which means that θ decreases and the bow wave narrows.

Answers to Guided Problems

Guided Problem 17.2 (a) 0.90 mm; (b) $\frac{1}{15}$
Guided Problem 17.4 about 4 mm
Guided Problem 17.6 (a) 1.58×10^3 Hz; (b) 1.49×10^3 Hz
Guided Problem 17.8 Mach number 1.6 or 5.5×10^2 m/s

22

PRACTICE
Electric Interactions

PRACTICE

Chapter Summary

Electric interactions (Sections 22.1, 22.2, 22.5)

Concepts An **electric interaction** is a long-range interaction between objects that carry a surplus **electrical charge.** The electric force is sometimes called the *electrostatic* force because interactions between charged objects become more complicated for objects that are not at rest (see Chapter 27).

There are only two types of charge: **positive charge** and **negative charge.** Objects that carry like charges repel each other; objects that carry opposite charges attract each other. Any microscopic object that carries electrical charge, such as an electron or ion, is called a **charge carrier.**

The SI unit of charge is the **coulomb** (C), which is the magnitude of the charge carried by about 6.24×10^{18} electrons. It is also equal to the amount of charge transported in 1 s by a steady current of 1 ampere (see Chapter 27).

Quantitative Tools **Coulomb's law** states that if particle 1 carrying charge q_1 and particle 2 carrying charge q_2 are a distance r_{12} apart, the **electric force** $\vec{F}_{12}^E$ exerted by particle 1 on particle 2 is

$$\vec{F}_{12}^E = k\frac{q_1 q_2}{r_{12}^2}\hat{r}_{12},$$ (22.7)

where the unit vector $\hat{r}_{12}$ points from particle 1 to particle 2 and the constant k is

$$k = 9.0 \times 10^9 \, \text{N} \cdot \text{m}^2/\text{C}^2.$$ (22.5)

The **elementary charge** e is the smallest observed amount of charge and is equal to the magnitude of the charge carried by one electron:

$$e = 1.60 \times 10^{-19} \, \text{C}.$$ (22.3)

The charge q carried by any object comes in whole-number multiples of e:

$$q = ne \quad (n = 0, \pm 1, \pm 2, \pm 3, \ldots).$$ (22.4)

Movement of charge carriers (Sections 22.3, 22.4)

Concepts Charge carriers can flow through an **electrical conductor** but cannot readily flow through an **electrical insulator.** Charge carriers can be transferred from one nonconductor to another only by bringing the nonconductors into contact with each other, and the carriers remain near the spot at which they were deposited.

We **ground** an object by connecting it electrically to Earth. Grounding permits the exchange of charge carriers with Earth, a huge reservoir of charge carriers. A charged, conducting object that is grounded will retain no surplus of either type of charge, assuming no other nearby electrical influences.

An **ion** is an atom or molecule that has lost or gained one or more electrons.

According to the principle of **conservation of charge,** electrical charge can be created or destroyed only in identical positive-negative pairs, with the result that the charge of a closed system always remains constant.

Polarization, which is the separation of charge carriers in an object, allows neutral objects to interact electrically.

Charging by induction is a method of using a charged object to charge a neutral object without the two objects touching each other.

Forces due to multiple charges (Section 22.6)

Quantitative Tools The electric force exerted on a charged particle 1 by any number of other charged particles 2, 3, . . . is

$$\sum\vec{F}_1^E = k\frac{q_2 q_1}{r_{21}^2}\hat{r}_{21} + k\frac{q_3 q_1}{r_{31}^2}\hat{r}_{31} + \ldots.$$ (22.10)

Review Questions

Answers to these questions can be found at the end of this chapter.

22.1 Static electricity

1. Blow up a balloon, tie it closed, hold it next to your head, and let go. What is the interaction responsible for the balloon's fall? This interaction is between which two objects? Now rub the balloon against your hair until it sticks against your head when you let go. What is the interaction responsible for the balloon's behavior? This interaction is between which two objects?

2. Name two differences between the gravitational interaction and the electric interaction.

22.2 Electrical charge

3. What experimental evidence tells us there is more than one type of electrical charge?

4. You rub a balloon on a friend's hair, and the balloon clings to her head. You say her hair put charge on the balloon, and she says the balloon put charge on her hair. Which of you is right?

22.3 Mobility of charge carriers

5. How much charge can you produce *within* any closed system by any process?

6. You scuff your feet on the carpet and then a spark leaps from your fingertip when you touch a metal doorknob. What does this observation tell you about whether your body is an electrical conductor or an electrical insulator?

7. Classify each of the following as an electrical insulator or conductor: paper, paper clip, seawater, car tire, air.

8. Breaking a piece of wood involves breaking chemical bonds. Why doesn't this usually leave the resultant pieces charged?

22.4 Charge polarization

9. Describe the process by which an electrically neutral object can be attracted by an electrically charged rod.

10. Suppose early researchers in electricity had assigned electrons a positive charge and protons a negative charge. What would be different in the electric phenomena you have studied up to this point?

11. How is charge polarization similar in electrical insulators and conductors? How is it different?

12. Negatively charged object A attracts object B. (*a*) Which state or states are possible for object B: positively charged, neutral, negatively charged? (*b*) Negatively charged object C repels object D. Which state or states are possible for object D: positively charged, neutral, negatively charged?

22.5 Coulomb's law

13. Use Newton's third law and the experimental observation that the magnitude F_{AB}^E of the electric force exerted by a charged object A on a charged object B is proportional to the charge on B to argue that the magnitude of the electric force between the two *must* be proportional to the *product* of the charges (as opposed to, say, proportional to the *sum* of the charges or to one of the charges only).

14. If you double the charge on *each* of two objects, how much must you increase the distance between the objects to restore the force exerted on them to its original value?

15. In a carbon atom, where six electrons are located around a nucleus that contains six protons (and usually six neutrons), which force magnitude is larger, if either: that of the force exerted by an electron on the nucleus or that of the force exerted by the nucleus on an electron?

22.6 Force exerted by distributions of charge carriers

16. Consider some arrangement of charge carriers 1, 2, and 3. What is wrong with the expression

$$\Sigma \vec{F}_1 = k\frac{q_2 q_1}{r_{21}^2}\hat{r}_{21} + k\frac{q_3 q_1}{r_{31}^2}\hat{r}_{31} + k\frac{q_3 q_2}{r_{32}^2}\hat{r}_{32}$$

for the force exerted on carrier 1 by carriers 2 and 3?

17. Charged particle 1, carrying charge $+q$, is fixed at the origin of an x axis. Charged particle 2, carrying charge $-2q$, is fixed at $x = +2.0$ m. Where on the x axis should charged particle 3, carrying charge $+3q$, be placed so that the vector sum of forces exerted on particle 3 is zero: (*a*) $0 < x < 2.0$ m, (*b*) 2.0 m $< x < +\infty$, (*c*) $-\infty < x < 0$?

Developing a Feel

Make an order-of-magnitude estimate of each of the following quantities. Letters in parentheses refer to hints below. Use them as needed to guide your thinking.

1. The minimum magnitude for the electric force exerted on a tiny bit of paper lifted by attraction to a charged comb (C, O)
2. The magnitude of the electric force between a proton and an electron in an atom (R, S)
3. The magnitude of the electric force between a sodium ion and a neighboring chloride ion in a sodium chloride molecule (D, V, S)
4. The number of protons in a 1-liter bottle of cola (E, N, H, W)
5. The number of electrons in Earth (Y, T, M, J)
6. The magnitude of the electric force between you and a friend standing 10 m apart if each of you had 1% more electrons than protons (Z, H, K, W, A)
7. The percentage of Earth's electrons that, if transferred to the Moon, would create an electrical attraction equal to the gravitational attraction of these bodies (G, L, Y, U, results of number 5 above)
8. The amount of like charge on each of two identical pith balls hung by two 80-mm strings from a common point, if the two balls are at their equilibrium positions when the angle formed by the two strings is 40° (X, Q, I)
9. The maximum amount of like charge you can put equally on two pith balls you are holding without feeling their force of repulsion (B, F, P)
10. The charge-to-mass ratio q/m for two identical, isolated particles that would remain at rest if released from rest at any separation (X, G, U)

Hints

A. What is the magnitude of charge carried by 1% of a person's electrons?
B. What minimum gravitational force can you detect with your fingers?
C. To lift any object, what force must be overcome?
D. What is the separation distance between two neighboring ions in the crystal?
E. What is the main ingredient in cola?
F. How can you minimize the magnitude of the electric force between the pith balls?
G. If you equate the gravitational force and electric force expressions, what cancels?
H. What is the mass of a molecule of water?
I. What must the magnitude of the electric force be?
J. How many electrons are there for each proton in Earth?
K. What is the mass of a person?
L. What is the mass of the Moon?
M. What is the mass of a proton?
N. What is the mass of 1 liter of cola?
O. What is the mass of a tiny bit of paper?
P. What maximum distance can you create between your hands?
Q. What is the mass of a pith ball?
R. What is a typical separation distance between a proton and an electron in an atom?
S. What is the magnitude of the charge carried by an electron or a proton?

T. What fraction of this mass is due to protons?
U. What is the ratio of gravitational to electrical constants in the force expressions?
V. What charge does each ion carry?
W. How many protons are there in one molecule of water?
X. What is the vector sum of the forces acting on each object?
Y. What is the mass of Earth?
Z. What is the main ingredient in the human body?

Key (all values approximate)

A. 4×10^7 C; B. about 1/10 of the gravitational force exerted by Earth on a penny, which has a mass of 2×10^{-3} kg—thus 2×10^{-3} N; C. gravitational force; D. 2×10^{-10} m; E. water; F. hold them as far apart as possible; G. the separation distance; H. two H atoms plus one O atom, 3×10^{-26} kg; I. 4×10^{-4} N; J. one; K. 70 kg; L. 7×10^{22} kg; M. 2×10^{-27} kg; N. 1 kg; O. 10^{-5} kg; P. 2 m; Q. 1×10^{-4} kg; R. 5×10^{-11} m; S. 1.6×10^{-19} C, the elementary charge; T. half, because atoms have about equal numbers of protons and neutrons, and these two particles have nearly identical masses; U. with both constants in SI units, $G/k = 7 \times 10^{-21}$ C^2/kg^2; V. Na^+ and Cl^-, each with an elementary charge; W. ten; X. zero; Y. 6×10^{24} kg; Z. water

Worked and Guided Problems

These examples involve material from this chapter but are not associated with any particular section.
Some examples are worked out in detail; others you should work out by following the guidelines provided.

Worked Problem 22.1 Mutual attraction

We often feel what is called a "physical attraction" to other people. If this were literally true and due to the electric force between two persons, one of them would have to carry surplus positive charge and the other would have to carry surplus negative charge. Suppose you and a friend stand 1 m apart and feel an attractive electric force of 10 N between you. Estimate the fraction q/q_{body} for each of you, where q is the surplus charge of a given type in either body and q_{body} is all the charge of that type in the body.

❶ **GETTING STARTED** We begin with a sketch of the physical situation (Figure WG22.1).

Figure WG22.1

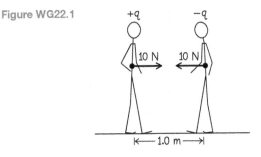

We first need to determine the amount of surplus charge q on each body that produces 10 N of force between the bodies, and to do this we must make some assumptions about where on each body that charge is located. We then need to estimate the number of charged particles of a given type in each body. These particles are the protons and electrons in the molecules of the body. Multiplying the number of particles by the elementary charge gives the charge q_{body} of that type in each body, and so we have the fraction we are asked to calculate. This solution will require many estimates.

❷ **DEVISE PLAN** We know the force magnitude and the separation distance between you and your friend. Let's assume you both have the same mass and equal amounts of surplus charge (though of opposite signs). Because it would be difficult to calculate the force if the charge were uniformly distributed throughout each body, we assume that all the charge in each body is concentrated at the body's center, with a center-to-center distance of 1 m. The human body is mostly water, H_2O (see Developing a Feel 6), and so dividing body mass by the mass of a water molecule gives us the number of water molecules in each body. Multiplying that number by the number of

protons or electrons in each molecule gives us the charge of each type in the body.

❸ **EXECUTE PLAN** We use Coulomb's law to solve for the magnitude of the surplus charge q needed to produce the 10-N force:

$$F = k\frac{|(+q)(-q)|}{r^2}$$

$$q = \sqrt{\frac{Fr^2}{k}} = \sqrt{\frac{(10\ N)(1\ m)^2}{9.0 \times 10^9\ N \cdot m^2/C^2}} = 3.3 \times 10^{-5}\ C.$$

To determine the change q_{body} of a given type in each body, let's use 60 kg as a reasonable value for your mass. Each H_2O molecule contains ten protons and eight neutrons, for a mass of 3×10^{-26} kg, making the number of water molecules in your body

$$\frac{60\ kg}{3 \times 10^{-26}\ kg/H_2O\ molecule} = 2 \times 10^{27}\ H_2O\ molecules\ in\ body.$$

Each of these molecules contains ten protons (and ten electrons), so the charge q_{body} of a given type (positive or negative) in the body is

$$q_{body} \approx (2 \times 10^{27}\ molecules)(10\ elementary\ charges/molecule)$$
$$\times (1.6 \times 10^{-19}\ C/elementary\ charge) \approx 3 \times 10^9\ C.$$

Thus the fraction of surplus charge is

$$\frac{q}{q_{body}} \approx \frac{3.3 \times 10^{-5}\ C}{3 \times 10^9\ C} \approx 1 \times 10^{-14}.\ ✔$$

This is approximately one surplus electron (or proton) for every 10 trillion (10^{13}) water molecules!

❹ **EVALUATE RESULT** It is hard to estimate whether or not this answer is reasonable because most people do not have a good feel for the magnitudes of various electric forces in our world. In reality, of course, attractive electric forces are not felt between humans. The actual fraction of surplus charge in your body is essentially zero under normal conditions. However, you can observe some consequences of surplus body charge when you rub your feet on a carpet, transferring charge to your body. You might get a trillion or so surplus elementary charges in this case, for a surplus charge fraction of about 10^{-16}. What gives you a shock when you then touch a metal doorknob is this surplus charge leaving your body.

Guided Problem 22.2 Electroscope

In Figure WG22.2, two identical 0.017-kg spheres are attached to nonconducting threads affixed to the ceiling. Initially, the spheres touch each other (*a*), but then an equal amount of charge is put on each (by touching them, for instance, with a charged rod not shown in the drawing) (*b*). If each thread is 120 mm long and the spheres come to rest at a separation $d = 93$ mm, what is the electrical charge on each sphere?

Figure WG22.2

(*a*)　　　　　　　(*b*)

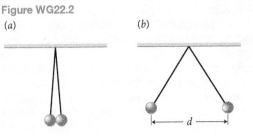

❶ GETTING STARTED

1. In what sense is this problem similar to Worked Problem 22.1? In what sense is it different?

2. Why do the spheres push apart but then come to an equilibrium configuration? What forces produce this motion?

❷ DEVISE PLAN

3. Draw the free-body diagram for each sphere. List any assumptions you make.

4. What quantity do you need to know to decompose the forces into components?

5. Choose a coordinate system, and then decompose the forces into x and y components.

❸ EXECUTE PLAN

6. Solve for the desired electrical charge q. Avoid solving for intermediate quantities if possible.

❹ EVALUATE RESULT

7. Think about how q should depend on the separation distance d. Does your algebraic answer reflect this expectation?

Worked Problem 22.3 Levitation

One possible way of levitating an object might be to use the forces associated with charged objects. For example, suppose you have two charged spheres fixed 0.50 m apart on a vertical pole. The lower sphere carries a fixed charge of $-3.0\ \mu C$, and the upper one carries a charge that can be adjusted. A 30-g sphere carrying a charge of $+8.0\ \mu C$ can move freely on the pole below the other two. You want this sphere to levitate (float) 1.0 m below the $-3.0\text{-}\mu C$ sphere. What should the charge on the upper sphere be adjusted to in order to achieve this feat?

❶ GETTING STARTED As usual, we begin with a sketch of the situation (Figure WG22.3). Let's label the upper fixed-position sphere A, the other fixed-position sphere B, and the movable sphere C. Let's use q_A for the unknown adjustable charge on sphere A. In order for sphere C to float at the specified position, we need to balance the electric and gravitational forces exerted on this sphere so that their vector sum is zero. We assume we're near Earth, so that g is a constant 9.8 m/s². The gravitational forces between C and B and between C and A are much smaller than the electric force between the pairs (you should verify this), and so the only forces we need to consider are the gravitational force exerted by Earth on C, the attractive upward electric force exerted by B on C, and the electric force exerted by A on C.

Figure WG22.3

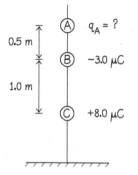

❷ DEVISE PLAN We want the vector sum of forces exerted on C to be zero. A free-body diagram is always helpful in force problems (Figure WG22.4). Because all the action is along a straight vertical line, we choose the reference axis to be a downward-pointing y axis. The gravitational force $\vec{F}^G_{EC}$ exerted on C is downward. Because the charges on B and C have opposite signs, these two particles attract each other, making the direction of the force $\vec{F}^E_{BC}$ upward. However, we don't know whether to make the force $\vec{F}^E_{AC}$ exerted by A on C attractive or repulsive (through the sign of q_A) because we do not yet know the magnitudes $\vec{F}^G_{EC}$ and $\vec{F}^E_{BC}$. In Figure WG22.4, we draw

the vector arrow for $\vec{F}^E_{AC}$ in the direction of our y axis, but we don't assume that its component along that axis is positive. It may point in the opposite direction, depending on the sign we calculate for q_A.

Figure WG22.4

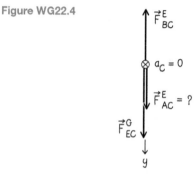

❸ EXECUTE PLAN For stable levitation ($a_C = 0$), we must have

$$\Sigma F_y = F^G_{ECy} + F^E_{BCy} + F^E_{ACy} = +F^G_{EC} + (-F^E_{BC}) \pm F^E_{AC} = 0.$$

We allow the final term to be either positive or negative because these are the only two options for the direction of $\vec{F}^E_{ACy}$. We can verify this by using the mathematical expression for the electric force (Eq. 22.7):

$$\vec{F}^E_{ACy} = k\frac{q_A q_C}{r^2_{AC}}(\hat{r}_{AC})_y.$$

Remembering that $\hat{r}_{AC}$ is the unit vector pointing from sphere A to sphere C, we see that $(\hat{r}_{AC})_y = +1$ in this coordinate system. The sign of the final term is thus determined by the sign of the unknown charge q_A. Thus

$$\Sigma F_y = +m_C g + \left[-k\frac{|q_B q_C|}{r^2_{BC}}\right] + \left[k\frac{q_A q_C}{r^2_{AC}}\right] = 0.$$

Solving for q_A and then substituting numerical values, we find

$$q_A = \frac{r^2_{AC}}{k q_C}\left(k\frac{|q_B q_C|}{r^2_{BC}} - m_C g\right) = \frac{r^2_{AC}}{r^2_{BC}}|q_B| - \frac{m_C g r^2_{AC}}{k q_C}$$

$$= \frac{(1.5\text{ m})^2}{(1.0\text{ m})^2}|-3.0 \times 10^{-6}\text{ C}|$$

$$- \frac{(0.030\text{ kg})(9.8\text{ m/s}^2)(1.5\text{ m})^2}{(9.0 \times 10^9\text{ N} \cdot \text{m}^2/\text{C}^2)(8.0 \times 10^{-6}\text{ C})}$$

$$= -2.4 \times 10^{-6}\text{ C}. \checkmark$$

This result shows us that we must put a negative charge on sphere A. This charge produces a force that is directed upward (attracting positively charged sphere C) and helps sphere B counteract the downward gravitational force exerted by Earth on C.

④ EVALUATE RESULT Do we expect q_A to be negative, which makes $\vec{F}^E_{AC}$ attractive (aimed upward)? If we make rough estimates of our known force magnitudes, we see that $F^G_{EC} \approx 3 \times 10^{-1}$ N and $F^E_{BC} \approx 2 \times 10^{-1}$ N. Thus Earth pulls C down more than sphere B pulls it up, which means sphere A needs to supply an upward force

to make the vector sum of the forces exerted on C be zero. With its negative $m_C g$ term, our expression for q_A correctly predicts the negative sign for q_A.

Is this system in stable or unstable equilibrium (see Section 15.4)? Does your answer to that question depend on the sign of q_A? As a further check of your understanding of the problem, re-derive the expression for q_A for the case where the charges on B and C have the same sign.

Guided Problem 22.4 Electron orbit

In the classical model of the hydrogen atom, a single electron orbits the single proton of the hydrogen's nucleus at a radius of 0.053 nm. (*a*) How fast is the electron moving? (*b*) How long does it take to complete one orbit?

❶ GETTING STARTED
1. Make a sketch showing the electron going around a circle and a proton fixed at the center of the circle.
2. Is the assumption that the proton is fixed justified?
3. What force or forces are exerted on the electron?

❷ DEVISE PLAN
4. Draw a free-body diagram for the electron.

5. Do you see any analogy between this problem and the topics discussed in Chapter 13?
6. What is the relationship between the electron's speed and the period of the orbit?

❸ EXECUTE PLAN

❹ EVALUATE RESULT
7. How does the electron's speed compare with the speed of light?

Worked Problem 22.5 Charge square

Four charged particles are arranged in a square as shown in Figure WG22.5. If $q = +3.9 \times 10^{-6}$ C and $a = 6.9$ mm, what is the vector sum of the forces exerted on particle D by the other three particles?

Figure WG22.5

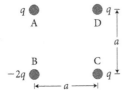

❶ GETTING STARTED This is an application of Coulomb's law, Eq. 22.7. We know all the charge magnitudes and the distances r_{AD} and r_{CD}, and we can use trigonometry to obtain the distance r_{BD}.

❷ DEVISE PLAN The first step is to draw Figure WG22.6, a free-body diagram of particle D. We can simplify the problem by choosing our axes to exploit symmetry, as shown. With the axes aligned this way, the force $\vec{F}^E_{BD}$ has no y component and the components F^E_{CDy} and F^E_{ADy} cancel each other. Thus all we need to calculate are the x components of the forces, which we get from Eq. 22.7.

Figure WG22.6

❸ EXECUTE PLAN The expression for the vector sum of the x components is

$$\Sigma F_{Dx} = F^E_{ADx} + F^E_{BDx} + F^E_{CDx}$$

$$= F^E_{AD} \cos 45° + (-F^E_{BD}) + F^E_{CD} \cos 45°$$

$$= 2F^E_{AD} \cos 45° + (-F^E_{BD})$$

$$= 2\left(k\frac{qq}{a^2} \right)\frac{\sqrt{2}}{2} - k\frac{(2q)q}{(\sqrt{2}a)^2}$$

$$= k\frac{q^2}{a^2}(\sqrt{2} - 1)$$

$$= (9.0 \times 10^9 \, \text{N} \cdot \text{m}^2/\text{C}^2)\frac{(3.9 \times 10^{-6} \, \text{C})^2}{(0.0069 \, \text{m})^2}(\sqrt{2} - 1)$$

$$= 1.19 \times 10^3 \, \text{N} = 1.2 \, \text{kN},$$

which means the vector sum of the forces exerted on D is a force of magnitude 1.2 kN directed along the positive x axis of our coordinate system. ✔

❹ EVALUATE RESULT Because two of the forces are repulsive and one is attractive, we expect to see terms of different signs in the algebraic answer. Reassuringly, we see that a *difference* of two terms is computed: the first term due to the two repulsive forces $\vec{F}^E_{AD}$ and $\vec{F}^E_{CD}$ and the second term due to the attractive force $\vec{F}^E_{BD}$. The computed force magnitude does seem large. However, the particles carry a sizable charge (remember, 1 C is a lot of charge) and they are close to one another.

Symmetry is a very powerful tool in approaching physics problems, and you should take advantage of it whenever possible.

PRACTICE

Guided Problem 22.6 Charge pyramid

Six ions are locked in a square pyramidal structure as shown in Figure WG22.7. The length of each side of the pyramid is $a = 0.13$ nm, and the sixth (shown in green) ion is at the center of the base of the pyramid. Calculate the vector sum of the electric forces exerted on the top ion if each of the six ions is missing one electron.

Figure WG22.7

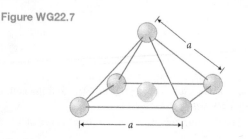

① GETTING STARTED

1. What causes the electric force experienced by the top ion?

2. Look for any symmetry you can exploit to make the problem simpler. Remember that this is a three-dimensional situation.
3. What is the amount of surplus charge on each ion?

② DEVISE PLAN

4. Which equations allow you to express the electric force experienced by the top ion in terms of known quantities?
5. Can the problem be reduced from three dimensions to two by an appropriate choice of coordinate axes?

③ EXECUTE PLAN

6. Write an algebraic expression for the electric force you are seeking, and then substitute known values to get a numerical result.

④ EVALUATE RESULT

7. Compare your numerical answer to the electric force between two protons a distance a apart.

Questions and Problems

For instructor-assigned homework, go to MasteringPhysics® Ⓜ

Dots indicate difficulty level of problems: • = *easy,* •• = *intermediate,* ••• = *hard;* CR = *context-rich problem.*

22.1 Static electricity

1. A piece of tape is pulled from a spool and lowered toward a 100-mg scrap of paper. Only when the tape comes within 8.0 mm is the electric force magnitude great enough to overcome the gravitational force exerted by Earth on the scrap and lift it. Determine the magnitude and direction of the electric force exerted by the tape on the paper at this distance. •
2. A baseball bat is placed on a table such that the narrow end of the bat hangs over the edge. Two freshly pulled strips of tape are hung from opposite sides of the overhanging end of the bat. The strips repel each other so that they hang in the air in an inverted V shape, with an angle of about 50° between the strips. Describe at least three things you could do to reduce the angle between the hanging strips. •
3. A plastic spring with spring constant $k = 450$ N/m has a relaxed length of 0.100 m. The spring is positioned vertically on a table, and a charged plastic 1.00-kg sphere is placed on the top end of the spring. Another charged object is suspended above the sphere without making contact. If the length of the spring is now 0.0950 m, what are the magnitude and direction of the electric force exerted on the sphere? ••

22.2 Electrical charge

4. Two small objects carry the same amount of charge, and the magnitude of the electric force exerted by one object on the other is 0.10 N when they are held 30 mm apart. If the force magnitude increases when the objects are released and free to move, are the objects of the same charge or opposite charge? •
5. How might the results from electrostatic experiments with tape strips described in *Principles* Section 22.2 differ from those actually observed if there were three types of electrical charges in the universe? ••

6. If you must do positive work to bring a charged balloon toward a negatively charged sphere, is the charge on the balloon positive or negative? ••
7. Suppose you have three identical, electrically neutral pieces of tape, A, B, and C. (*a*) Describe how you could make two of them repel each other. (*b*) Is it possible for all three to repel one another? ••
8. Suppose that in Figure P22.8, $|q_2| > |q_1| > 0$ but these particles may carry charges of the same or opposite type. A third particle carrying charge q_3 is to be placed in this system along the axis such that the vector sum of electric forces on the third particle is zero. In which region—I, II, or III—might this be possible if (*a*) q_1 and q_2 have the same sign and (*b*) q_1 and q_2 have opposite signs? (*c*) Under what circumstances can the third particle be placed in region I and have the vector sum of electric forces exerted on it be zero? ••

Figure P22.8

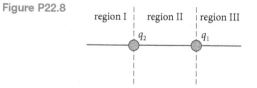

9. A salvage yard operator wants to make an electric force linkage for his wrecker crane as a safety device, so that when a vehicle being lifted is too massive, it will break the linkage before the force exerted by the vehicle topples the crane. His plan is to attach two metal plates to the crane cable as shown in Figure P22.9 and connect the plates to the crane's power system. There is to be a positive charge on one plate and a negative charge on the other, so that the two stick together because of the attractive electric force. Discharge is prevented by spraying a layer of plastic on each plate. He needs to know what diameter to make the plates so that they come apart when the vehicle being lifted has a mass greater than 2000 kg. On the micro level, the electric force is between a surface atom carrying surplus

positive charge on one plate and a surface atom carrying surplus negative charge on the other plate. The electric force for each atom pair has a magnitude of 2.3×10^{-12} N, and each atom occupies an area of 3×10^{-21} m². (*a*) Before doing any calculations, estimate the necessary plate surface area. Which is this surface area comparable to: that of a pinhead, a fingernail, a music compact disc, a dinner plate, or a manhole cover? (*b*) Calculate the necessary area. How accurate was your estimate as to which object the plate area is comparable to? ●●●

Figure P22.9

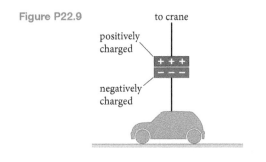

to crane

positively charged

negatively charged

22.3 Mobility of charge carriers

10. Which of the following phenomena are due to the electric interaction: (*a*) dissolution of salt in water, (*b*) surface tension in water, (*c*) the elliptical orbit of comets, (*d*) the binding of protons in an atomic nucleus, (*e*) "traction" between tires and pavement. ●

11. Technicians who repair electronic devices know that a spark can damage electronic chips. They therefore wear a wriststrap connected by a metal wire to the metal leg of a worktable that is electrically "grounded" to Earth. How does wearing such a strap help prevent damage? ●

12. You have two rods A and B, both made of a nonconducting material. Initially, neither rod is charged. A sphere carrying 100 units of surplus positive charge is placed close to the left end of rod A. One end of rod B is touched to the right end of rod A for some time interval and then removed. What is the final charge on rod B? ●

13. Some survivors of lightning strikes have reported feeling their hair standing on end shortly before the strike. What causes the hair to behave in this way? ●

14. A closed system consists of a neutron and a positron. The neutron eventually decays. After decay, what are the most likely particles in the system, and what is the charge in the system? (Use the principle of conservation of charge.) ●●

15. Two identical 500-mg paper clips, 1 and 2, dangle from two strings, the top ends of which are tied to the same nail. The clips are charged in such a way that the two strings hang with an angle of 32.0° between them. (*a*) Draw a free-body diagram for clip 1, which is to the left of clip 2. (*b*) What are the magnitude and direction of the electric force exerted by one clip on the other? (*c*) If the two clips were brought in contact with each other for an instant and then released, might they discharge into each other and no longer repel? ●●

16. A pith ball is suspended from a string, and when a rubber rod is brought close to the ball at $t = 0$, the ball is not noticeably affected by the rod. At $t = 5.00$ s the rod is turned around such that the opposite end is nearest the ball. Now the ball is attracted to the rod. At $t = 10.0$ s the rod and ball are brought into contact. Draw a charge-versus-time graph showing a plausible charge magnitude on the rod in the time interval from $t = 0$ to $t = 15$ s. ●●

17. At separation distance r_1, charged Ping-Pong balls A and B repel each other with an electric force of magnitude 0.40 N. At separation distance r_2, charged Ping-Pong balls A and C repel each other with a force of magnitude 1.4 N. Maintaining the separation distances r_1 and r_2, how should you arrange B and C around A (*a*) to create the maximum electric force exerted on A and (*b*) to create the minimum electric force exerted on A? ●●

18. A metal sphere is grounded via a single wire. One end of a plastic rod is given a positive charge and held near the sphere. (*a*) If the ground wire is removed while the rod and sphere are near each other but have not touched, is there an electric force between the two? Why or why not? (*b*) If the rod end is brought in contact with the sphere and then the ground wire is removed, is there an electric force between rod and sphere after they are separated? Why or why not? ●●●

22.4 Charge polarization

19. A rubber rod exerts no electric force on a small scrap of paper. After it is rubbed on cat fur for several seconds, the rod exerts an attractive force on the scrap. Is the force exerted by the fur on the same scrap attractive or repulsive? ●

20. Three small pieces of electrically neutral paper are placed far apart from one another on a table. One piece is given a negative electric charge, one is given a positive charge, and one is left neutral. They all look identical, and in order to tell which is which, a student runs a comb through her hair and waves the comb over each piece. She observes that one is strongly attracted to the comb; she labels this A. She observes that another is weakly attracted to the comb; she labels this B. The last piece, which is repelled by the comb; she labels C. Which piece is positive, which is negative, and which is neutral? ●

21. The electrically neutral metal rod in Figure P22.21 stands between two charged pith balls, and then a negatively charged rubber rod is scraped along the center of the metal rod. Draw the free-body diagram for each ball after the rubber rod is taken away. ●

Figure P22.21

22. A charged sphere with 1×10^8 units of negative charge is brought near a neutral metal rod. The half of the rod closer to the sphere has a surplus charge of 1×10^4 units. What is the magnitude of the charge on the half of the rod farther from the sphere? Is this charge positive or negative? ●

23. Near one end of an electrically neutral aluminum rod lying on a table made of nonconducting material, you hold a comb that is also made of a nonconducting material but carries a positive charge (Figure P22.23). Does a small steel sphere located near the other end of the rod roll toward the rod, roll away from the rod, or stay where it is if the sphere is (*a*) electrically neutral and (*b*) positively charged? ●●

Figure P22.23

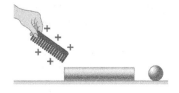

24. Two metal rods A and B are initially lying end to end on a wooden table and are touching each other. A sphere carrying surplus positive charge is brought close to the middle of rod A. While the sphere is still in place, the rods are pulled apart by someone wearing gloves made of a fabric that is an electrical insulator. Then the sphere is moved far away. (*a*) Do the two rods attract each other, do they repel each other, or is there no electric force between them? (*b*) Describe the surplus charge on each rod as positive, zero, or negative. ••

25. You have three pairs of spheres. Pair A consists of two conducting spheres, pair B of two nonconducting spheres, and pair C of one nonconducting sphere and one conducting sphere. If all spheres have the same charge q added to them and in each pair the two spheres are separated by the same distance d, rate the magnitude of the electric force between the two spheres of each pair when q is (*a*) positive on both spheres, (*b*) negative on both, and (*c*) positive on one sphere in the pair and negative on the other. ••

26. Metal sphere A is hung from the ceiling by a long, thin string and given a positive charge. An identical sphere B is suspended nearby with an identical string and given a *negative* charge that has the same magnitude as the charge on A. The two spheres are 50 mm apart when in equilibrium. If an identical sphere C carrying no surplus charge is placed between them, does the distance between A and B increase, decrease, or remain the same? ••

27. You are an astrophysicist working on a problem involving Saturn's rings and trying to figure out why the larger ice chunks in the rings stick to smaller chunks. You hypothesize that as the chunks come out of the shadow of Saturn into the sunlight, the outside of the larger chunks heats up sooner than the center and this temperature difference creates a nonuniform distribution of the charged particles in the larger chunks. (Charge polarization due to temperature differences is known as the "thermoelectric effect.") Then, even though the chunk is electrically neutral, it has a charge separation. The small ice chunks presumably heat up uniformly all the way through and hence are not affected. Explain why small chunks gradually stick to larger ones. •••

22.5 Coulomb's law

28. Suppose you have three identical metal spheres, A, B, and C. Initially sphere A carries a charge q and the others are uncharged. Sphere A is brought in contact with sphere B, and then the two are separated. Spheres C and B are then brought in contact and separated. Finally spheres A and C are brought in contact and then separated. What is the final charge on each sphere, in terms of q? •

29. Two electrons are separated by 1.50 nm. What is the magnitude of the electric force each electron exerts on the other? Is this force attractive or repulsive? •

30. Two particles carrying charges q_1 and q_2 are separated by a distance r and exert an electric force $\vec{F}^E$ on each other. If q_1 is doubled, what change must you make to one of the other variables in order to keep the magnitude F^E constant? There is more than one answer. •

31. A particle carrying a $-4.0\text{-}\mu$C charge is located at the origin of an xy coordinate system. What are the components of the electric force exerted on a particle carrying a $+1.0\text{-}\mu$C charge if that particle is located (*a*) at $x = 10$ m, $y = 0$ and (*b*) at $x = 0$, $y = -6.0$ m? •

32. (*a*) By what distance do two objects carrying 1.0 C of charge each have to be separated before the electric force exerted on each object is 1.0 N? (*b*) How much charge should be placed on each of two small objects separated by 1.0 m so that the electric force exerted on each is 1.0 N? •

33. In a chamber 0.300 m high, sphere 1 carrying charge $q_1 = 1.00\ \mu$C is suspended by a spring above a sphere 2 that carries charge q_2 and sits on the floor of the chamber (Figure P22.33). The relaxed length of the suspended spring is 70.0 mm, its spring constant is 30.0 N/m, and the mass of sphere 1 is 5.00 g. If sphere 1 comes to rest 0.200 m above the floor (and above sphere 2), what is the value of q_2? ••

Figure P22.33

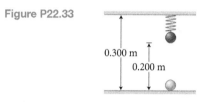

34. Two identical 9.60-g metal spheres (small enough to be treated as particles) are hung from separate 300-mm strings attached to the same nail in a ceiling. Surplus electrons are added to each sphere, and then the spheres are brought in contact with each other and released. Their equilibrium position is such that each string makes a 13.0° angle with the vertical. How many surplus electrons are on each sphere? ••

35. Suppose two particles carry a positive charge of 1.00 C for every kilogram of their mass. Compare the gravitational force and the electric force they exert on each other at a given separation. ••

36. Two metal spheres, one carrying a 6.0-μC charge and the other carrying a -24-μC charge, are initially 100 mm apart. They are brought in contact with each other and then moved back to their original positions. What is the numerical value of the ratio F_i^E/F_f^E, where F_i^E is the magnitude of the electric force between the spheres before they are brought in contact and F_f^E is the magnitude of that force after they are brought together and then moved back to their initial positions? ••

37. The device in Figure P22.37 is a so-called Newton's cradle. When you raise steel sphere 1 and then release it, its momentum is transferred to the other four steel spheres, and this momentum transfer causes sphere 5 to rise. When it falls, momentum is again transferred through the row of spheres, and sphere 1 rises and falls, and so on. Imagine modifying the device by positioning a charged wire in such a way that every time each end steel sphere rises, it touches the wire and acquires 10 units of charge. You lift sphere 1 and allow it to touch the wire for the first time and acquire 10 units of charge. You release the sphere and it hits the others, transferring its

Figure P22.37

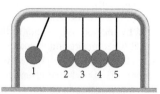

momentum and causing sphere 5 to rise. Sphere 5 touches the charged wire, descends, hits the row of spheres, and transfers its momentum so that sphere 1 rises again and touches the wire for the second time. How many units of charge does sphere 1 carry (*a*) just before it touches the wire this second time and (*b*) just before it touches the wire after one more round of this momentum-transfer motion? ••

38. Two 1.00-kg spheres carry identical charges and are placed a distance *d* from each other. (*a*) How large should the charge on each sphere be so that the repulsive electric force between them balances the attractive gravitational force between them? (*b*) What is the smallest mass that can balance in this way, given that the smallest possible charge is $e = 1.602 \times 10^{-19}$ C? (*c*) Why doesn't the distance between the balls affect this calculation? ••

39. A charged oil drop that has a mass of 5.00×10^{-12} kg and carries 10 elementary charges is centered 50 mm below the center of an oppositely charged sphere that has a radius of 5.0 mm. What charge should the sphere be given so that the electric force it exerts on the drop causes the drop to float in the air for an instant? Treat the drop as a particle. ••

40. In the Bohr model, a hydrogen atom consists of an electron orbiting a one-proton nucleus. (*a*) Derive an algebraic expression for the relationship between the electron's speed *v* and the radius R_{orbit} of its orbit. (*b*) Review the derivation of Kepler's third law in *Principles* Chapter 13 (page 310), and derive a corollary that relates the period *T* of the electron's orbital motion and the orbit radius R_{orbit}. ••

41. You scrunch up three same-size sheets of aluminum foil to form three balls 1, 2, and 3, and stick each one onto the end of a wooden stake (which allows you to transport the balls without touching them). You place the stakes holding balls 1 and 2 an arm's length apart and then give each ball charge *q*. Call the electric force between them $\vec{F}_{12}^{E}$. You then place charge $-2q$ on ball 3 and bring it first in contact with ball 1. Then you move it away from ball 1 and bring it in contact with ball 2. (*a*) Once you have moved ball 3 far away from balls 1 and 2, what is the magnitude, in terms of F_{12}^{E}, of the electric force between balls 1 and 2? (*b*) Has the direction of $\vec{F}_{12}^{E}$ changed? ••

42. (*a*) Draw and label the electric force exerted on each of the charged spheres in Figure P22.42 and compute their magnitudes. The centers of the spheres are separated by 0.11 m. (*b*) Repeat the problems, drawing to the same scale, if the charge on the left sphere is -6.30μC. ••

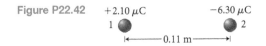

Figure P22.42 $+2.10 \mu$C -6.30μC
                  1   2
                  |←——— 0.11 m ———→|

43. Sphere A carries 6.0 nC of charge. It is placed 100 mm from sphere B, which carries 3.0 nC of charge. Assume the spheres are much smaller than their separation distance. (*a*) What is the magnitude of the electric force exerted on A? (*b*) Draw a figure showing the charges and the electric force vectors on each sphere. (*c*) Draw and label $\vec{r}_{AB}$ on your diagram. ••

44. You have two marbles, one carrying a uniformly distributed charge $q_p = +1.0 \mu$C and the other carrying a uniformly distributed charge $q_n = -0.50 \mu$C. (*a*) What is the magnitude of the electric force between them when they are held 100 mm apart? (*b*) What happens when the marbles are released and so are free to move? (*c*) If the marbles are metallic and share charge when they come in contact with each other, what is the magnitude of the electric force between them when they are again moved 100 mm apart, assuming no charge is transferred either to or from the surroundings of the two-marble system? ••

45. Two charged particles 3.0 m apart exert on each other an attractive electric force of magnitude 8.0×10^{-3} N. If the charge on the two particles sums to 6.0μC, what is the charge on each particle? ••

46. Determine the magnitude and direction of the electric force exerted by a 25-nC charged particle located at the origin of a Cartesian coordinate system on a 20-nC charged particle located at (2.0 m, 2.0 m). Draw a diagram illustrating the various quantities in your calculation. ••

47. The electric force between two identical positively charged ions is 3.7×10^{-9} N when they are 0.50 nm apart. How many electrons are missing from each of the original atoms? ••

48. Two particles 1 and 2, each carrying 71 pC of charge, are released from rest on a nonconducting, low-friction track. Particle 1 accelerates initially at 7.0 m/s^2. Particle 2, which has a mass of 0.49 mg, accelerates initially at 9.0 m/s^2. (*a*) What is the mass of particle 1? (*b*) What is the separation distance between the particles at the instant they are released? ••

49. Two identical lightweight conducting balls are suspended by thin strings of identical length from a common point. One of the balls is given a charge *q*, and both are constrained in their motion by only the tension in the strings, gravity, and air resistance. (*a*) Describe the behavior of the balls from the instant the first one is charged. (*b*) Determine *q* in terms of *m*, the mass of the balls, ℓ, the length of the strings, *d*, the final distance between the balls, and any necessary constants. •••

50. Suppose you want to use a repulsive electric force to launch a rocket. (*a*) How much charge do you need to create enough repulsion to bring a 100,000-kg rocket to escape speed (11,200 m/s) while the rocket travels 100 mm? Assume that two identical charged objects, one mounted on the rocket, are separated by an average distance of 1.0 m for the whole launch. (*b*) If each elementary charge requires adding mass equivalent to the mass of one hydrogen atom to the rocket, how much additional mass would be required? •••

51. Two metal spheres carry a charge and exert an electric force on each other. Sphere A carries $2n$ more surplus electrons than sphere B, where *n* is a positive integer. The two spheres are brought into electrical contact and then returned to their initial separation. Is the electric force between them increased, decreased, or unaffected? •••

52. (*a*) Prove that the repulsive electric force between two charged particles is a maximum when each particle carries charge $q/2$, where *q* is the sum of the charges carried by the two particles. (*b*) Explain why this is *not* true for the attractive electric force between charged particles. •••

22.6 Force exerted by distributions of charge carriers

53. Particle 1 carrying charge $+4q$ is fixed at the origin of a rectangular coordinate system, particle 2 carrying charge $-q$ is fixed $15.0°$ above the positive horizontal axis, and particle 3 carrying charge $-q$ is fixed $15.0°$ below the positive horizontal axis (Figure P22.53). Particles 2 and 3 are both 2.00 m from the origin. You must add two charged particles to the system in such a way that the vector sum of the electric forces exerted on particle 1 is zero. What quantity of which type of charge must each added particle carry, and at what locations must you place the particles? •

Figure P22.53

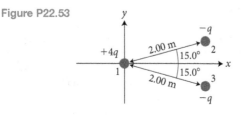

54. Particle 1 carrying $-4.0\ \mu C$ of charge is fixed at the origin of an xy coordinate system, particle 2 carrying $+6.0\ \mu C$ of charge is located on the x axis at $x = 3.0$ m, and particle 3, identical to particle 2, is located on the x axis at $x = -3.0$ m. What is the vector sum of the electric forces exerted on particle 3? •

55. Cesium chloride (CsCl) is a crystalline salt that forms in a cubic lattice structure, which you can imagine as a cube with Cs^+ ions at the eight corners and a Cl^- ion at the center. The edge length of the cube is 412 pm. Suppose that at the edge of a crystal, two cesium atoms have been stripped from adjacent corners of a cube, as shown in Figure P22.55. What is the vector sum of the electric forces exerted on the chloride ion by the six Cs^+ ions remaining in the cube? •

Figure P22.55

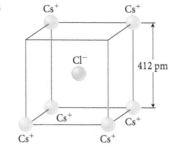

56. An xyz coordinate system contains three charged particles: particle 1, $q_1 = -5.0\ \mu C$, at (4.0 m, −2.0 m, 0); particle 2, $q_2 = 12\ \mu C$, at (1.0 m, 2.0 m, 0); and an electron at (−1.0 m, 0, 0). (a) Draw a diagram showing the vectors you need in order to determine the direction of the separate electric forces exerted on the electron by particles 1 and 2. (b) Calculate the vector sum of these two forces. ••

57. Particle 1 carrying charge q is at the origin of an xy coordinate system, particle 2 carrying charge $-2q$ is at (1, 0), and particle 3 carrying charge $3q$ is at (0, 1). What is the angle with respect to the x axis of the electric force exerted on a particle 4 carrying

charge q and located at (2, 0)? (Hint: Use simple geometry and ratios.) ••

58. Charged particles 1, 2, and 3 ($q_1 = 10.0\ \mu C$, $q_2 = -5.00\ \mu C$, and $q_3 = -3.00\ \mu C$) are arranged in an equilateral triangle in an xy coordinate system. Particle 1 is at (0, 0), particle 2 at (1.0 m, 0), and particle 3 at (0.50 m, $\sqrt{3}/2$ m). Determine the magnitude and direction of the electric force exerted on particle 3. ••

59. Four negatively charged particles each carry a charge q_n and form a square of side length d. A positively charged particle carrying a charge q_p is at the square's center. If the arrangement is in equilibrium (the vector sum of the electric forces on each particle is zero), what is the numerical value of the ratio q_p/q_n? ••

60. Particle 1 carrying $2.0\ \mu C$ of charge is fixed at the origin of a rectangular coordinate system, particle 2 carrying $-1.0\ \mu C$ is fixed $45°$ above the positive horizontal axis 2.0 mm from the origin, and particle 3 carrying $-1.0\ \mu C$ is fixed $45°$ below the horizontal axis 2.0 mm from the origin. Where in the system should you place a particle 4 carrying $-2.0\ \mu C$ so that the vector sum of the electric forces exerted on particle 1 is zero? ••

61. For the charge distribution in Figure P22.61, what is the ratio of the magnitude of the electric force exerted by particle 2 on particle 1 to the magnitude of the electric force exerted by particle 3 on particle 1? ••

Figure P22.61

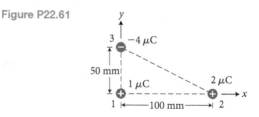

62. For the charge configuration shown in Figure P22.62, what is the vector sum of the electric forces exerted on particle 3? ••

Figure P22.62

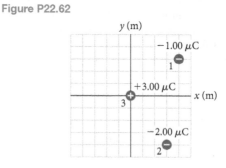

63. Two particles, each carrying charge $-q$, are fixed at opposite corners of a square, and a third particle, carrying charge $+q$, is fixed at a third corner (Figure P22.63). (a) Draw an arrow representing the vector sum of the forces exerted on a particle carrying charge $+q$ as it is placed first at position A, then at position B, and then at position C. (b) Sketch the trajectory of this particle if it is released at each of these three positions. ••

Figure P22.63

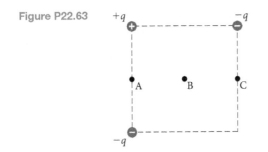

64. Two particles are located on the x axis of a Cartesian coordinate system. Particle 1 carries a charge of $+2.0$ nC and is at $x = -30$ mm, and particle 2 carries a charge of -2.0 nC and is at $x = 30$ mm. What are the magnitude and direction of the vector sum of the electric forces exerted by these two particles on particle 3, which carries a charge of $+5.0\ \mu$C and is located on the positive y axis 80 mm from the origin? ••

65. Particle 1 carrying charge $4q$ is fixed at the origin of an xy coordinate system, and particle 2 carrying charge q is fixed at $(0, 0.12$ m$)$. Particle 3 carrying $2.0\ \mu$C of charge can move along the y axis. This particle experiences zero electric force when at $y = 0.080$ m and an electric force of 126.4 N $\hat{\jmath}$ when at $y = 0.040$ m. What is the value of q? ••

66. Conducting spheres 1, 2, and 3 are placed at three corners of a square. Spheres 1 and 2 at opposing corners are very small and oppositely charged, and the magnitude of the charge on negatively charged sphere 1 is twice the magnitude of the charge on positively charged sphere 2. Sphere 3 is much larger than the other two and electrically neutral. (a) Draw the three spheres, showing the approximate distribution of charge on sphere 3. (b) Sketch a free-body diagram for sphere 2. ••

67. You are working as an engineer designing ink-jet printers. Your boss has come across a printer design that involves a charged drop of ink experiencing a force exerted by 100 small, fixed charged particles. As shown in Figure P22.67, the particles are arranged in a ring of radius 6.00 mm, and each carries a charge of 1.00 nC. The ink drop is released at a point 6.00 mm away from the plane of the ring and along the central axis running perpendicular to the plane of the ring. Your boss gives up on calculating the initial force exerted on the charged drop, but you take one look at the setup and realize you can do the calculation in less than a minute. (a) Explain how you can do the calculation so quickly, even though it involves 100 separate forces. (b) Determine the magnitude and direction of the initial force exerted on a drop that carries a charge of 8.00 nC. (c) If the printer adds to each drop of ink a charge equal to 1.00 C per kilogram of ink mass, what is the initial acceleration of each drop? •••

Figure P22.67   ink drop

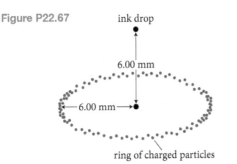

68. A 0.160-kg hockey puck modified to hold $+50\ \mu$C of charge is placed at one end of an ice hockey rink that is 61 m long. At the other end of the rink is a device capable of generating a charge of -0.10 C, but only for a short time interval. The coefficient of kinetic friction between ice and puck is $\mu_k = 0.015$. The puck is given a tiny nudge (just enough to get it moving but at a speed of nearly 0, which means you can ignore static friction), and then the charge generator is turned on for 100 ms. (a) Is the puck able to reach the generator? (b) If so, what is the puck's speed when it arrives at the generator? (For both parts, assume the 100-ms time interval is short enough to allow you to assume that the distance between the puck and the charge generator is constant.) •••

69. Two particles 1 and 2, each carrying 6.0 nC of charge, are located along an x axis, one particle at $x = -30$ mm and the other at $x = 30$ mm. Where along the y axis is a particle 3 carrying a charge of $+2.0$ nC if it experiences an electric force of 6.9×10^{-5} N $\hat{\jmath}$? •••

70. Figure P22.70 shows strips of transparent tape repelling each other. Use information given on the packaging of a roll of transparent tape to estimate what fraction of the atoms in either strip lose an electron in order to produce the repulsive effect. (Assume that the material of the tape is mostly carbon and hydrogen atoms present in a 1:2 ratio.) •••

Figure P22.70

Additional problems

71. If electrons move easily in electrical conductors, why aren't pieces of metal usually negatively charged on the bottom and positively charged on top, due to gravitational settling of the electrons? •

72. Metals are often good thermal conductors as well as good electrical conductors. In fact, usually the better a metal is as a thermal conductor, the better it is as an electrical conductor. Give a physical explanation for this. •

73. Suppose a glass rod is rubbed on wool. When held 35.0 mm above a 0.20-g scrap of paper, the rod lifts the paper with an initial acceleration of 0.14 m/s^2. Calculate the magnitude and direction of the electric force exerted by the rod on the scraps. •

74. Three identical conducting spheres, A, B, and C, are given different initial charges. Sphere A, which initially carries 12 units of negative charge, is brought in contact with sphere B, which initially has 4 units of negative charge. Then sphere B is brought into contact with sphere C, which is initially neutral. What is the final charge ratio A:C? •

75. Particle A carrying a 4.0-μC charge is located at $y = 3.0$ m on the y axis of an xy coordinate system, and particle B carrying a 6.0-μC charge is located at the origin. What are the magnitude and direction of the electric force exerted (*a*) on A and (*b*) on B? •

76. Protons and neutrons are made up of particles called quarks. The particles known as up quarks carry a charge of $2e/3$, and those known as down quarks carry a charge of $-e/3$. How could you assemble a proton from up and down quarks to account for its charge? How could you assemble a neutron? ••

77. Three charged particles are arranged along a line as in Figure P22.77. If particle 2 experiences zero electric force, what is the charge on particle 3? ••

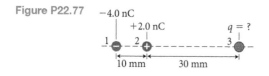

Figure P22.77

78. Four identical charged particles are constrained along an x axis. Identify one possible configuration of the particles that would leave one of them at rest at the origin when the others are fixed in place. No two charged particles can be at the same location. ••

79. (*a*) A particle carrying charge $+q$ is located at the center of a square with sides of length ℓ. Given four particles, two carrying charge $+q$ and two carrying charge $-q$, how should you place them at the four corners of the square, with one particle at each corner, such that the vector sum of the electric forces exerted on the center particle is zero? (*b*) If you leave the corner particles in the arrangement determined in part *a* but move the center particle to the midpoint of one side of the square, what are the magnitude and direction of the vector sum of the forces exerted on this particle? ••

80. A small charged sphere hanging from a thin string next to an oppositely charged plate experiences a 2.3-N attractive electric force (Figure P22.80). If the string makes an angle of 3.6° with the vertical, what is the mass of the sphere? ••

Figure P22.80

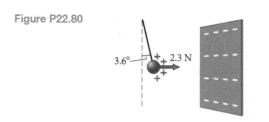

81. The accelerometer in a certain video game controller is constructed as shown in Figure P22.81. A block made of material that is an electrical conductor is grounded by a small stretched spring and is constrained to sliding along a rail. A nonconducting, positively charged block is fixed in position on the rail. When the magnitude of the electric force between the blocks is 0.100 N, the spring makes a 45.0° angle with the wall and is stretched 3.00 mm from its equilibrium position. What is the spring constant? Ignore friction. ••

Figure P22.81

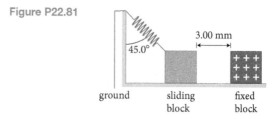

82. An anti-hydrogen atom, A, is composed of one positron orbiting one antiproton just as a regular hydrogen atom is composed of one electron orbiting one proton. The difference is that each antiparticle has the usual mass but an opposite charge of its regular counterpart. Atom A is placed in a closed container with a neutron. What is the most likely charge of the system after the neutron decays? (Hint: Use charge conservation.) ••

83. All life on Earth is based on one of many two-polymer systems, each made up of a protein and a nucleic acid. In a cell, these polymers are, for the most part, charge-balanced, with the nucleic acid in any pair carrying a negative charge and the protein carrying an equal amount of positive charge. Consider a distribution of eight of these polymers, where the eight proteins sit together near the center of the cell and the nucleic acids are spread out along the circumference of a circle with the radius equal to one-quarter of the cell diameter, centered on the proteins. If seven of the eight nucleic acids are at $\pi/4$, $\pi/2$, $3\pi/4$, π, $3\pi/2$, $7\pi/4$, and 2π rad, where on the circle must you place the eighth acid to give the system a balanced charge distribution? (Hint: Begin by making a sketch.) ••

84. In a simplistic model of the hydrogen atom, the electron orbits the proton in a circle of radius 53 pm. What is the orbital period of the electron, in seconds, if the force responsible for the proton-electron attraction is (*a*) gravitational and (*b*) electric? ••

85. (*a*) About how many electrons are there in a copper penny, which has a mass of about 0.003 kg? (*b*) If you could isolate these electrons, how much charge would you have? (*c*) Estimate the magnitude of the electric force it would require to bring one more electron to within 1.0 nm of these electrons, assuming they are combined to form one small charged object. (*d*) Based on this force magnitude, do you think it would be possible to combine this amount of negative charge? ••

86. Earth exerts an electric force on small charged objects located near its surface. The effect can be modeled by assuming Earth is a particle at the center of Earth carrying a charge of -6.76×10^5 C. (*a*) What is the magnitude of the electric force exerted by Earth on an electron at its surface? Is this force attractive or repulsive? (*b*) How does this force magnitude compare with the magnitude of the gravitational force exerted by Earth on the electron? (*c*) How much negative charge would you have to put on a penny in order for the repulsive electric force exerted by Earth on the penny to cancel the attractive gravitational force exerted by Earth on the penny? (*d*) How many electrons would you have to add to the penny to achieve this? ••

87. Four particles, each carrying a charge of 3.0 nC, are located at the corners of a square that has a side length of 50 mm. The charge on the particle at the lower left corner is positive, and the other three particles are negatively charged. (*a*) Draw a free-body diagram showing the electric forces exerted on the particle at the upper right corner. (*b*) Determine the magnitude and direction of the vector sum of the electric forces exerted on this particle. ●●

88. A small sphere 1 carrying charge *q* is fixed a few meters above the Moon's surface next to a spaceship. An astronaut holds a charged sphere 2 a couple of meters above sphere 1, almost but not quite directly over sphere 1. Sketch the trajectory for sphere 2 when the astronaut drops it if the charge on sphere 2 is (*a*) *q*, (*b*) 9*q*, and (*c*) −*q*. ●●●

89. Someone has challenged you in a friendly bet that, given a set of six charged spheres with three carrying positive charge and three carrying negative charge, you can't place any three of them in a line (a board with a groove in it serves the purpose) and have them be in translational equilibrium. You determine which of the three spheres are the positively charged ones and call them 1, 2, and 3. By comparing the electric force exerted by sphere 1 on sphere 3 with the electric force exerted by sphere 2 on sphere 3, you rank 1 as smaller than 2, placing them in the groove several hundred millimeters apart, temporarily blocking them from moving. You can release them only when the third sphere is in place, but there are so many things to consider! ●●● CR

90. While assembling part of an electric generator, you realize that two pieces were not properly labeled. One piece is a nonconducting block, and the other is a conducting block, but without labels you don't know which is which. Because you had counted on the parts being properly labeled, you do not have a multimeter, batteries, or other standard electrical tools. All you have is your wool sweater, some nonconducting styrofoam "peanuts" used in packaging, and some string. You are about to go for help when you realize that your knowledge of static electricity should be enough. ●●● CR

91. Working on a system to collect solar energy, you are trying to move some charged particles through the open interior of a uniformly charged ring. A colleague vaguely remembers Newton's and Priestley's argument that no electrostatic force is exerted on a charged particle inside a uniformly charged sphere. He suggests that the same must be true for a charged ring, and so you can send the charged particles through any part of the ring interior without the particles feeling an electric force and being deflected by it. You are skeptical, wondering if there might at least be a restriction on the path over which you send the particles such that they experience no electric force. ●●● CR

Answers to Review Questions

1. The gravitational interaction between the balloon and Earth makes the balloon fall. After charging, the electric interaction between your hair and the balloon dominates. (Friction between your hair and the balloon is the source of the force that opposes the gravitational interaction between the balloon and Earth.)

2. The electric interaction is much stronger than the gravitational interaction. The electric interaction can be attractive or repulsive, while the gravitational interaction is only attractive.

3. A charged object can interact in different ways with a second charged object, either repelling or attracting that object. This means there are different possibilities for the type of charge on the second object.

4. Without further information, it's impossible to say who is right. Positive charge carriers moved from an object A to an object B or negative charge carriers moved from B to A have the same effect. However, because we know that plastic combs become negatively charged when rubbed through hair, and the hair acquires positive charge, we could speculate that the hair transfers electrons to the balloon.

5. Zero. Charge can only be moved from one place to another or created or destroyed in equal positive and negative portions. Because charge is a conserved quantity, the amount of charge in a closed system is constant.

6. The surplus charge causing the spark entered your body at your feet but interacted with the knob at your fingers. That the charge migrated tells you that your body is a fair electrical conductor.

7. Paper is an electrical insulator; to see this for yourself, insert a slip of paper between two batteries in a flashlight and turn on the switch. A paper clip is metal and thus an electrical conductor. Seawater is an electrical conductor because of the presence of dissolved ions. Tires are rubber and so electrical insulators, just as the rubber insulation on electrical power cords is. Air is usually an electrical insulator, but as with most other electrical insulators, a sufficient electric force exerted on a volume of air can cause a breakdown, or spark, and then charge carriers can flow through the air, making it an electrical conductor in the breakdown region.

8. Breaking wood leaves two pieces of similar material. There's no reason the symmetrical result (same material on both sides of the break) should leave a positive charge on one piece and a negative charge on the other. It is usually in the breaking of bonds in *dissimilar* materials that a surplus of charge is left behind on the two materials.

9. The charged rod attracts opposite charges and repels like charges on the neutral object, causing the object to become polarized. An oppositely charged region forms near the rod, while a like-charged region forms farther away. The proximity of the oppositely charged region causes the object to be attracted (weakly) to the rod.

10. There would be no difference. Opposite charges would still be opposite and attract, and like charges would still be like and repel.

11. Polarization is accomplished by bringing an already charged item near the object to be polarized. In each case the polarization effect creates regions of surplus charge in the object, with the region of charge opposite to those on the charged item forming closest to the charged item. In a conductor, some electrons are free to move throughout the material, and it is these mobile electrons that move from one part of the object to another as the object becomes polarized. In an insulator, electrons are not free to move through the material, but rather the electron cloud in each atom shifts slightly toward or away from the charged item (depending on the sign of its surplus charge). The effect of many superposed atomic cloud shifts creates thin regions of surplus charge on the surface of the insulating object.

12. (a) Positively charged or neutral; (b) negatively charged only.

13. The magnitude F^E_{AB} is proportional to the charge on B, experimentally. Likewise, the magnitude F^E_{BA} is proportional to the charge on A. Because Newton's third law tells you that these two forces must be equal in magnitude, they must both be proportional to both the charge on A and the charge on B. The only way to make this happen is for the product $q_A q_B$ to appear in the expression for the force. Note that the sum $q_A + q_B$ does not reproduce the proportionality behavior; doubling q_B does not double the sum.

14. Doubling both charges without changing the distance would increase the force exerted on each by a factor of 4. Doubling the distance would compensate for this factor of 4, because the force is inversely proportional to the square of the distance.

15. The magnitude of the force exerted on either partner in the interaction pair is identical, as is always the case with any interaction.

16. The last term does not involve charge carrier 1 and therefore has nothing to do with the force exerted on 1. This term should be omitted from the expression.

17. Because particles 1 and 2 carry charges of opposite types, the situation requires that particle 3 not be placed between 1 and 2 in order that the directions of the two forces oppose each other. To obtain equal magnitudes for the two forces, particle 3 must be placed closer to the particle with smaller charge (particle 1). Thus the answer is (c).

Answers to Guided Problems

Guided Problem 22.2 Let α be the angle that each thread makes with respect to vertical. Then

$$Q = d\sqrt{\frac{mg\tan\alpha}{k}} = (0.093\text{ m})\sqrt{\frac{(0.017\text{ kg})(9.8\text{ m/s}^2)(0.4203)}{9.0\times10^9\text{ N}\cdot\text{m}^2/\text{C}^2}}$$

$$= 2.6\times10^{-7}\text{C},$$

where $\alpha = \sin^{-1}\left(\dfrac{d}{2\ell}\right) = \sin^{-1}\left(\dfrac{93\text{ mm}}{2\times120\text{ mm}}\right) = 22.80°$, and $\tan\alpha = 0.4203$.

Guided Problem 22.4

(a) $v = e\sqrt{\dfrac{k}{mR}}$

$$= (1.6\times10^{-19}\text{ C})\sqrt{\frac{9.0\times10^9\text{ N}\cdot\text{m}^2/\text{C}^2}{(9.1\times10^{-31}\text{ kg})(5.3\times10^{-11}\text{ m})}}$$

$$= 2.2\times10^6\text{ m/s};$$

(b) $T = \dfrac{2\pi R}{v} = \dfrac{(2\pi)(5.3\times10^{-11}\text{ m})}{2.2\times10^6\text{ m/s}} = 1.5\times10^{-16}\text{ s}.$

Guided Problem 22.6 The force on the top ion points upward, away from the central base ion, and has magnitude

$$F = ke^2\left[\frac{1}{h^2} + \frac{4}{a^2\sqrt{2}}\right] = 6.6\times10^{-8}\text{ N, where } h = \frac{a}{\sqrt{2}}.$$

23

PRACTICE
The Electric Field

PRACTICE

Chapter Summary

Electric fields (Sections 23.1–23.3, 23.5)

Concepts In the field model of long-range interactions, interacting object A fills the space around itself with a **field** (or **interaction field**). When an object B is placed in this field, the field acts on B. If A and B have mass, the field is a *gravitational field*; if they are charge carriers, it is an *electric field*.

A **test particle** is one whose mass and/or charge is so small that the particle does not perturb the objects generating the field being measured.

The direction of the **electric field** at a given location is the same as the direction of the electric force exerted on a positive test particle at that location.

Quantitative Tools If a test particle located at position P and carrying charge q_t experiences a force $\vec{F}_t^E$, then the **electric field** $\vec{E}$ (N/C) at P is

$$\vec{E} \equiv \frac{\vec{F}_t^E}{q_t}. \tag{23.1}$$

If the source particle is at position $\vec{r}_s$ and carries charge q_s, the electric field it creates at any position P is

$$\vec{E}_s(P) = k\frac{q_s}{r_{sP}^2}\hat{r}_{sP}, \tag{23.4}$$

where $\hat{r}_{sP}$ is a unit vector pointing from the source particle to P and $k = 9.0 \times 10^9$ N·m²/C².

Principle of **superposition of electric fields:** The combined electric field $\vec{E}$ created by a system of particles that carry charges $q_1, q_2, \ldots$ is

$$\vec{E} = \vec{E}_1 + \vec{E}_2 + \cdots = \sum k\frac{q_i\hat{r}_{iP}}{r_{iP}^2}. \tag{23.5}$$

Electric dipoles (Sections 23.4, 23.6, 23.8)

Concepts A *uniform electric field* has a constant magnitude and direction at all locations; a *nonuniform electric field* can vary in magnitude and/or direction from one location to another. A uniform electric field gives a charged particle a constant acceleration.

An **electric dipole** consists of equal quantities q_p of positive and negative charge separated by a small distance.

When an electrically neutral object is placed in an electric field, the field causes the object's positive and negative charge centers to separate, producing an **induced dipole.**

Quantitative Tools The **dipole moment** $\vec{p}$ (C·m) of a dipole is

$$\vec{p} \equiv q_p\vec{r}_p, \tag{23.9}$$

where $\vec{r}_p$ is the vector from the center of negative charge to the center of positive charge.

The torque $\sum\vec{\tau}$ produced on a dipole by a uniform electric field is

$$\sum\vec{\tau} = \vec{p} \times \vec{E}. \tag{23.21}$$

The **induced dipole moment** $\vec{p}_{ind}$ of a neutral atom placed in an external electric field that is not too large is

$$\vec{p}_{ind} = \alpha\vec{E}, \tag{23.24}$$

where α is the **polarizability** of the atom.

For positions far from an electric dipole, the electric field due to the dipole is inversely proportional to the cube of the distance r from the dipole. In particular, at distant points along the bisector axis (x axis)

$$E_y \approx -k\frac{p}{|x^3|}, \tag{23.10}$$

and at distant points along the dipole separation axis ($+y$ axis)

$$E_y \approx 2k\frac{p}{y^3}. \tag{23.13}$$

Electric fields of continuous charge distributions (Section 23.7)

Concepts **Charge density** can be linear (λ, C/m), over a surface area (σ, C/m^2), or throughout a volume (ρ, C/m^3).

Quantitative Tools The electric field due to a set of infinitesimal source particles of charge dq_s is

$$\vec{E} = k \int \frac{dq_s}{r_{sP}^2} \hat{r}_{sP}.$$

(23.15)

See the Procedure box on page 414.

Linear, area, and *volume charge densities* are

$$\lambda \equiv \frac{q}{\ell}$$

(23.16)

$$\sigma \equiv \frac{q}{A}$$

(23.17)

$$\rho \equiv \frac{q}{V}.$$

(23.18)

A uniformly charged rod of length ℓ carrying charge q oriented along the y axis and centered at the origin produces an electric field

$$E_x = \frac{kq}{x\sqrt{\ell^2/4 + x^2}}$$

along the x axis.

A uniformly charged ring of charge q and radius R oriented with the plane of the ring perpendicular to the z axis and the ring center at the origin produces an electric field

$$E_z = k\frac{qz}{(z^2 + R^2)^{3/2}}$$

along the z axis.

A uniformly charged disk of surface charge density σ and radius R oriented with the disk face perpendicular to the z axis and the disk center at the origin produces an electric field

$$E_z = 2k\pi\sigma\left[1 - \frac{z}{(z^2 + R^2)^{1/2}}\right]$$

along the z axis.

Outside a solid sphere of radius R carrying a uniformly distributed charge q, the electric field produced by the sphere is

$$E_{\text{sphere}} = k\frac{q}{r^2},$$

where $r > R$ is the distance from the sphere's center. This field is the same as the field that would be produced if all the charge were concentrated at the sphere's center.

Review Questions

Answers to these questions can be found at the end of this chapter.

23.1 The field model

1. What is the physics definition of *field*?
2. What are the two major reasons for introducing the field concept?
3. When two charged Ping-Pong balls, A and B, are held a small distance apart, which ball is the source of the electric field that acts on ball B?
4. What is the difference between a scalar field and a vector field? Give an example of each type.
5. What is a vector field diagram, and how is it useful?

23.2 Electric field diagrams

6. How can a charged test particle be used to determine the electric field at a point P caused by a charged source object S located nearby?
7. A positively charged styrofoam pellet is placed in the electric field surrounding a charged sphere. If the charge on the pellet is changed from positive to negative, what happens to the magnitude and direction of the sphere's electric field at the pellet's location?
8. A negatively charged test particle is placed at position P in an electric field, and it experiences an electric force directed to the west. What is the direction of the electric field at point P?

23.3 Superposition of electric fields

9. Balloon 1 is charged and taped to a board, and a pushpin is inserted at a different location on the board. The electric field at the pushpin due to balloon 1 is measured to have magnitude E_1. Balloon 1 is removed and the process is repeated with balloon 2, taped at a third location. The electric field at the pin due to balloon 2 is measured to have magnitude E_2. If both balloons are present, is the magnitude of the electric field at the pin equal to $E_1 + E_2$?

23.4 Electric fields and forces

10. An electron initially moving horizontally near Earth's surface enters a uniform electric field and is deflected upward. What can you say about the direction of the electric field (assuming no other interaction)? What can you say about the direction of the electric field if the electron is deflected downward?
11. A uniform electric field is directed to the right. Sketch the trajectory of a proton and an electron launched straight up in this field.
12. Is it possible for a dipole that is initially moving in a straight line to be deflected by a uniform electric field?
13. An electron is traveling in circular motion at constant speed due to the effect of an electric field. Is it possible for the electric field to be uniform?

23.5 Electric field of a charged particle

14. If the charge on particle 2 in *Principles* Figure 23.23 were doubled, what aspects of the electric field at point P would change: the magnitude, the direction, or both?
15. A delicate instrument is two paces away from a highly charged metallic sphere. If you want to reduce the magnitude of the electric field at the instrument to 1% of its present value, how many paces away from its present position must you move the instrument?

23.6 Dipole field

16. Which is greater, the magnitude of the electric field a distance r from a small sphere carrying charge q or the magnitude of the electric field a distance r from a small electric dipole of dipole moment qd, where d is the dipole separation and $r \gg d$?
17. What is the definition of *dipole moment*?
18. An electric dipole is fixed at the origin of a coordinate system, and an electric field detector can be moved anywhere along the surface of an imaginary sphere of radius R that is centered on the origin. The radius of this sphere greatly exceeds the dipole separation, $R \gg d$. As the detector is moved over the spherical surface, what is the ratio of the largest and smallest magnitudes of the electric field it detects, $E_{maximum}/E_{minimum}$?

23.7 Electric fields of continuous charge distributions

19. A hemispheric shell made of a material that is an electrical insulator has a radius R and a charge q distributed uniformly over it. It is placed in the $z \geq 0$ region of an xyz coordinate system, centered about the z axis, with its base resting on the xy plane. Write the expression for the charge dq on an infinitesimally thin ring portion of the shell of width $Rd\theta$, where θ is the angle from the z axis to the ring.
20. What is the distinguishing radial dependence of the electric field (*a*) around a charged particle (charge distributed in no dimensions), (*b*) around a long uniformly charged wire (charge distributed in one dimension), and (*c*) around a large uniformly charged sheet (charge distributed in two dimensions)?

23.8 Dipoles in electric fields

21. What are the SI units of polarizability?
22. The magnitude of the electric field due to a permanent dipole decreases as the cube of distance r from the dipole: $E \propto 1/r^3$. The electric force exerted by the dipole on a charged particle placed in the electric field of the dipole is also proportional to $1/r^3$: $F_{dp}^E \propto 1/r^3$. How does the force exerted by the charged particle on the dipole depend on r?
23. What are the similarities and differences between permanent and induced dipoles?

Developing a Feel

Make an order-of-magnitude estimate of each of the following quantities. Letters in parentheses refer to hints below. Use them as needed to guide your thinking.

1. The electric field magnitude 0.1 nm from a proton (P, B)
2. The electric field magnitude 1 m from a ball of 10^6 electrons (I)
3. The charge-to-mass ratio for a sodium (Na^+) ion (G, P)
4. The charge-to-mass ratio for either of two identical particles whose gravitational and electric interactions cancel each other (E, R)
5. The volume charge density of a hydrogen nucleus (F, K, P)
6. The surface charge density on a 200-mm length of a freshly pulled strip of transparent tape (D, H, M, Q, U)
7. The linear charge density on a rubbed plastic rod that is 300 mm long (C, H, L, Q, T)
8. The electric field strength 0.1 m from the long axis of the plastic rod of Question 7 (Answer to Question 7, A)
9. The magnitude and direction of the uniform electric field required to "float" a proton near Earth's surface (N, P, S)
10. The electric dipole moment of a water molecule (J, O)

Hints

A. Is this location close or far enough from the rod to use an approximation for the magnitude of $\vec{E}$?
B. What is 0.1 nm in meters?
C. What is the mass of the rod?
D. What is the mass of the tape strip?
E. If you equate the gravitational and electric force expressions, what factor cancels?
F. What is the radius of a hydrogen nucleus?
G. What is the mass of a sodium ion?
H. What fraction of this mass is due to protons?
I. What is the charge on the ball?
J. How should you model the charge distribution?
K. What is the formula for the volume of a sphere?
L. What is the number of electrons in the rod?
M. What is the number of electrons in the strip?
N. What is the mass of a proton?
O. What is the separation of the centers of charge?
P. What is the charge of a proton in coulombs?
Q. What fraction of the electrons is redistributed during charging?
R. What is the ratio of the gravitational constant to the proportionality constant in Coulomb's law?

S. If the electric field points upward, what is the direction of the electric force it exerts on the proton?
T. What is the length along which the surplus charge is distributed?
U. What is the surface area of the strip?

Key (all values approximate)

A. No, which means you must use the expression in the Chapter Summary: $E_x = kq/x(\ell^2/4 + x^2)^{1/2}$; B. 1×10^{-10} m; C. 0.1 kg; D. 1×10^{-4} kg; E. the factor for the distance between the particles; F. 1×10^{-15} m; G. 4×10^{-26} kg; H. half, assuming the atoms contain equal numbers of protons and neutrons; I. -2×10^{-13} C; J. there is an imbalance of about one elementary charge, so the dipole consists of one "surplus" proton centered between the H atoms and one surplus electron centered on the O atom; K. $V = 4\pi r^3/3$; L. 3×10^{25}; M. same as the number of protons, 3×10^{22}; N. 2×10^{-27} kg; O. 5×10^{-11} m, because of the bonding angle of 105° between the H atoms; P. $+2 \times 10^{-19}$ C; Q. about one in 10^{12} (see *Principles* Section 22.3); R. $G/k \approx 7 \times 10^{-21}$, with both constants in SI units; S. upward; T. 0.2 m, or two-thirds the length of the rod; U. 0.002 m^2

Worked and Guided Problems

Procedure: Calculating the electric field of continuous charge distributions by integration

To calculate the electric field of a continuous charge distribution, you need to evaluate the integral in Eq. 23.15. The following steps will help you evaluate the integral.

1. Begin by making a sketch of the charge distribution. Mentally divide the distribution into small segments. Indicate one such segment that carries a charge dq_s in your drawing.

2. Choose a coordinate system that allows you to express the position of the segment in terms of a minimum number of coordinates (x, y, z, r, or θ). These coordinates are the integration variables. For example, use a radial coordinate system for a charge distribution with radial symmetry. Unless the problem specifies otherwise, let the origin be at the center of the object.

3. Draw a vector showing the electric field caused by the segment at the point of interest. Examine how the components of this vector change as you vary the position of the segment along the charge distribution. Some components may cancel, which greatly simplifies the

calculation. If you can determine the direction of the resulting electric field, you may need to calculate only one component. Otherwise express $\hat{r}_{sP}$ in terms of your integration variable(s) and evaluate the integrals for each component of the field separately.

4. Determine whether the charge distribution is one-dimensional (a straight or curved wire), two-dimensional (a flat or curved surface), or three-dimensional (any bulk object). Express dq_s in terms of the corresponding charge density of the object and the integration variable(s).

5. Express the factor $1/r_{sP}^2$, where r_{sP} is the distance between dq_s and the point of interest, in terms of the integration variable(s).

At this point you can substitute your expressions for dq_s and $1/r_{sP}^2$ into Eq. 23.15 and carry out the integral (or component integrals), using what you determined about the direction of the electric field (or substituting your expression for $\hat{r}_{sP}$).

These examples involve material from this chapter but are not associated with any particular section. Some examples are worked out in detail; others you should work out by following the guidelines provided.

Worked Problem 23.1 Charge square

Four charged particles are arranged in a square as shown in Figure WG23.1, with $q = 3.9 \times 10^{-4}$ C and $a = 6.9$ mm. Determine the magnitude and direction of the electric field at the center of the square.

distance $a\sqrt{2}$ and contributing an electric field $\vec{E}_2$ to the center (Figure WG23.2).

Figure WG23.1

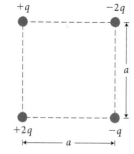

Figure WG23.2

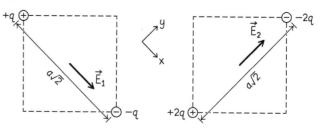

① GETTING STARTED We use the superposition principle, expressed in Eq. 23.5, on the individual electric fields created by the four particles to determine the electric field at the center.

② DEVISE PLAN We could calculate the electric field due to each particle and then add the components to get the field at the square's center. However, we can simplify the problem by exploiting the symmetry of the configuration. One way to use that symmetry is to separate the four particles into two pairs: $+q/-q$ having separation distance $a\sqrt{2}$ and contributing an electric field $\vec{E}_1$ to the center and $+2q/-2q$ having separation

Each of the two fields is produced by a pair of charged particles carrying charges of equal magnitude but opposite signs, with the fields pointing away from the positively charged particle and toward the negatively charged particle. Note in Figure WG23.2 that we have aligned the axes of our coordinate system in a way that facilitates the calculation of components. Because we seek the electric field at the center of the square, we know that the magnitudes E_1 and E_2 are related by a factor of 2 (that is, $2E_1 = E_2$) due to the similarities of distance and charge. All we have to do is add the electric field vectors $\vec{E}_1$ and $\vec{E}_2$ to obtain the electric field at the center.

③ EXECUTE PLAN For the $+q/-q$ pair, the electric field at the square's center is

$$\vec{E}_1 = k\frac{q}{r_{+q}^2}\hat{r}_{+q} + k\frac{(-q)}{r_{-q}^2}\hat{r}_{-q}$$

$$= k\frac{q}{(\frac{1}{2}a\sqrt{2})^2}\hat{\imath} + k\frac{(-q)}{(\frac{1}{2}a\sqrt{2})^2}(-\hat{\imath})$$

$$= 4k\frac{q}{a^2}\hat{\imath}.$$

For the $+2q/-2q$ pair, we note that $\vec{E}_2$ is produced along the y direction by particles that carry charges that are twice as large as in the $+q/-q$ pair. We can therefore infer that

$$\vec{E}_2 = 8k\frac{q}{a^2}\hat{\jmath},$$

which means that the electric field at the center of the square is

$$\vec{E} = \vec{E}_1 + \vec{E}_2 = 4k\frac{q}{a^2}\hat{\imath} + 8k\frac{q}{a^2}\hat{\jmath}.$$

The magnitude of this electric field is

$$E = \sqrt{E_x^2 + E_y^2} = \sqrt{\left(\frac{4kq}{a^2}\right)^2 + \left(\frac{8kq}{a^2}\right)^2} = 4\sqrt{5}k\frac{q}{a^2},$$

and its direction is

$$\theta = \tan^{-1}\frac{E_y}{E_x} = \tan^{-1}\frac{8kq/a^2}{4kq/a^2} = \tan^{-1}2 = 63°.$$

Substituting values yields

$$\vec{E} = \frac{4\sqrt{5}(9.0 \times 10^9 \text{ N} \cdot \text{m}^2/\text{C}^2)(3.9 \times 10^{-4} \text{ C})}{(0.0069 \text{ m})^2}$$

$$= 6.6 \times 10^{11} \text{ N/C},$$

at 63° above the positive x axis as oriented in Figure WG23.2. ✔

④ EVALUATE RESULT The electric field we obtained is large, but the charge on these particles is large and the separation distance is small. The direction makes sense because it points approximately along the line that connects the two particles carrying a charge $\pm 2q$.

Guided Problem 23.2 Charge triangle

Three particles form an equilateral triangle with side length a. Two of the particles carry a positive charge $+q$, and the third particle carries a charge $-2q$. What are the magnitude and direction of the electric field at the center of the triangle?

① GETTING STARTED

1. Draw a diagram showing the particles, charges, and distances.
2. Locate the center of the triangle.
3. What causes the electric field at the center? Account for all sources that contribute to this field.
4. Is there any symmetry you can use to simplify your work?

② DEVISE PLAN

5. Must you work with vectors to solve this problem? You know that particles carrying the same type of charge repel each other

and particles carrying opposite types of charge attract each other. Be sure to take this aspect of the interaction into account in your diagram.

③ EXECUTE PLAN

6. What are the relevant distances to the center of the triangle?

④ EVALUATE RESULT

7. Does your answer behave in a physically plausible way when the side lengths or charge magnitudes are varied?

Worked Problem 23.3 Torqued dipole

Figure WG23.3 shows an electric dipole located near a fixed charged particle A that carries charge $+q_A$. The dipole charge is q_D. (a) What torque does the electric force exerted by A create about the dipole's midpoint? (b) Sketch a graph showing how the torque caused by $\vec{F}_{AD}^E$ changes as the dipole separation d increases while the distance a between particle A and the dipole remains constant.

Figure WG23.3

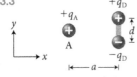

① GETTING STARTED The positive pole of the dipole is repelled by A, and the negative pole is attracted to A. This combination of attraction and repulsion causes a torque about the dipole midpoint that tends to rotate the dipole clockwise. The right-hand rule tells us that this torque is directed into the page. The two electric forces

exerted on the dipole are not parallel to each other because the electric field created by A is directed radially outward.

② DEVISE PLAN One way to approach this problem is by brute force: Calculate the electric force exerted by A on one pole of the dipole, determine the torque caused by it about the dipole midpoint, do the same for the other pole, and then add the torques to get their vector sum. If we think of the dipole and particle A as a system, however, all the interactions are internal: The system is isolated. This means the vector sum of torques on the system about a chosen reference point is zero. The dipole midpoint is the reference point specified in the problem statement, so we choose it as the origin of our coordinate system. The torque on the dipole is the negative of the torque on particle A. Because the *Principles* volume derives a formula for the magnitude, at any position, of the electric field created by a dipole (Eq. 23.8, which using our symbols for variables is $E = -kq_Dd/[a^2 + (d/2)^2]^{3/2}$), we can solve this problem.

❸ **EXECUTE PLAN** To keep track of the dipole variables in our calculations, we label them with subscript D.

(a) From Eq. 23.1 we know that the electric force exerted by the dipole on particle A is

$$\vec{F}_{DA}^E = q_A \vec{E}_D. \tag{1}$$

From Eq. 23.8, the electric field surrounding the dipole at the position of particle A (on the x axis) is

$$\vec{E}_D = -k \frac{q_D d}{[a^2 + (d/2)^2]^{3/2}} \hat{j}. \tag{2}$$

The torque on A about the midpoint of the dipole is

$$\vec{\tau}_{DA} = \vec{r}_{DA'} \times \vec{F}_{DA}^E = (-a\hat{i}) \times q_A \left(-k \frac{q_D d}{[a^2 + (d/2)^2]^{3/2}} \hat{j} \right).$$

By remembering that $\hat{i} \times \hat{j} = \hat{k}$ (out of the page) and that the torque on the particle is equal and opposite to the torque on the dipole, we obtain the torque that the force F_{AD}^E causes on the dipole:

$$\vec{\tau}_{AD} = -\vec{\tau}_{DA} = -k \frac{q_A q_D a d}{[a^2 + (d/2)^2]^{3/2}} \hat{k}. ✔ \tag{3}$$

(b) Figure WG23.4 shows the magnitude of this torque as a function of d, with a held fixed. At $d = 0$, the torque is zero. For small values of d ($d < a$), the torque increases almost linearly as d increases because the denominator is nearly equal to a^3. As the dipole separation approaches $d = \sqrt{2}a$, the torque reaches a maximum value. For larger values of d, the denominator is dominated by the

d term and is nearly equal to d^3. This means that the torque decreases almost quadratically as d increases in this region, as illustrated in Figure WG23.4.

Figure WG23.4

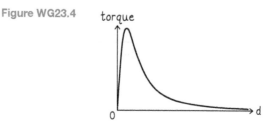

torque

❹ **EVALUATE RESULT** Equation 3 says that if $q_A > 0$, the torque on the dipole is in the negative z direction—that is, into the page. This information combined with the right-hand rule of Section 12.4 means that the dipole should rotate clockwise. This is what we expect because a positively charged particle A causes the top of the dipole to rotate away from A and pulls the bottom of the dipole toward A.

We could also check the result by using the brute force method mentioned above. The direction of the torque for $q_A < 0$ is also as we expect, twisting the dipole counterclockwise. The electric force exerted on the particle is in the downward y direction, as we see by substituting Eq. 2 into Eq. 1. In what direction is the electric force exerted by the particle on the dipole? Does this result make sense? We have seen from Eq. 3 that as the dipole separation d gets large, the torque magnitude decreases. Why is this?

Figure WG23.4 shows that there is a maximum torque. Why is this? Think about what happens to the lever arm of the torque as the dipole separation decreases.

Guided Problem 23.4 Interacting dipoles

The centers of the two dipoles in Figure WG23.5 are separated from each other by a center-to-center distance a. Both dipoles have a dipole charge q_p and a dipole separation d. What are the magnitude and direction of the electric force exerted by one dipole on the other?

Figure WG23.5

❶ **GETTING STARTED**

1. For a dipole aligned along a y axis, Eq. 23.11,

$$E_y = k \frac{q_p}{[y - (d/2)]^2} - k \frac{q_p}{[y + (d/2)]^2},$$

gives the magnitude of the electric field at any position on the y axis (the dipole's axis). How can you use this equation to determine the electric forces exerted by one dipole on the

two poles of the other dipole? (Hint: A useful approach is to model one dipole as a set of source particles for an electric field and the other as a set of two oppositely charged test particles in that field. You need to identify the source particles and test particles so that you do not double count.)

❷ **DEVISE PLAN**

2. Can you take advantage of any symmetry in the problem?
3. How can you keep track of the various relevant distances in your diagram? Be careful not to use the same symbol to represent two different things.

❸ **EXECUTE PLAN**

❹ **EVALUATE RESULT**

4. Does the electric force in your result point in the direction you expect? Consider the relative sizes of the various terms in your result.
5. What happens to the force as the center-to-center distance a from one dipole to the other becomes much greater than the dipole separation d in each dipole?

Worked Problem 23.5 Electric field created by a straight charged rod

A charged rod of length ℓ has a uniform linear charge density λ. What are the magnitude and direction of the electric field at a point P that is a distance a from one end of the rod and lies along the rod's long axis?

❶ GETTING STARTED First we make a diagram displaying the given information (Figure WG23.6). This problem is similar to examples in the *Principles* volume for a continuous charge distribution. However, in this problem we are not given the charge q carried by the rod; all we know is the charge per unit length. Nonetheless, we should be able to use similar techniques to obtain the electric field.

Figure WG23.6

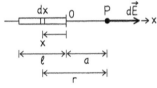

❷ DEVISE PLAN We can determine the electric field $\vec{E}$ created by a continuous charge distribution by dividing the rod into a large number of small segments and then summing their contributions $d\vec{E}$ to the electric field:

$$\vec{E} = \int d\vec{E} = \int k \frac{dq}{r^2} \hat{r}_P,$$

where dq is the charge on any segment and r is the distance from that segment of the rod to P. To keep track of the contributions from the various segments we will draw a diagram. From symmetry, we know the electric field points along the rod's long axis.

❸ EXECUTE PLAN We draw a diagram that shows one rod segment dx and all the variables needed for our calculation (Figure WG23.7).

Figure WG23.7

For convenience, we choose the x axis to be along the rod's axis and locate the origin of this axis at the right end of the rod. If we choose the positive x axis to the right, $\hat{r}_P = \hat{i}$ and $d\vec{E} = \hat{i}\, dE$ is the electric

field created by segment dx centered at position x. Remembering that the coordinate x represents a signed quantity (the position), we see from Figure WG23.7 that the distance r from any segment to P is $a - x$ in our coordinate system. The charge dq on the segment is $dq = \lambda dx$. The electric field at P is thus

$$\vec{E} = \hat{i}\int_{-\ell}^{0} k\frac{\lambda dx}{(a-x)^2} = k\frac{\lambda}{a-x}\Big|_{-\ell}^{0}\,\hat{i}$$

$$= k\left[\frac{\lambda}{a} - \frac{\lambda}{a-(-\ell)}\right]\hat{i}.$$

$$= k\lambda\left[\frac{1}{a} - \frac{1}{a+\ell}\right]\hat{i}. \checkmark$$

❹ EVALUATE RESULT We first want to make sure our expression gives the correct direction for the electric field. If the charge on the rod is positive, the electric field at P should point to the right because that is the direction a small positively charged test particle would move. This is in the positive x direction for our coordinate system. For positive λ, the factor in front of $\hat{i}$ is indeed positive, meaning the component of the electric field in the x direction is positive, as expected.

If the rod length ℓ is much greater than the distance a from the rod end to P, we can assume ℓ is effectively infinite. As ℓ approaches infinity, the term $1/(a + \ell)$ inside the square brackets drops out and the electric field magnitude becomes $E = k\lambda/a$; that is, the field magnitude for positions very close to the rod is independent of ℓ.

As we move P closer and closer to the right end of the rod (a goes to zero), the electric field becomes infinite. At the right end of the rod, P is presumably right on top of a charged particle (zero separation), so the electric field should become very large because of the $1/r^2$ dependence of Coulomb's law. Note also that as ℓ approaches zero, the electric field becomes zero—which is what we expect because there is no charge on a rod of zero length.

Guided Problem 23.6 Electric field created by a curved charged rod

A thin semicircular rod of radius R carries a charge q uniformly distributed along its length. What are the magnitude and direction of the electric field at the center of the arc formed by the rod?

❶ GETTING STARTED
1. Draw a sketch with the rod as a half circle and the given quantities placed appropriately.
2. How do you deal with the effects of a continuous charge distribution when the direction from the point of interest to one segment of the charge distribution is different from the direction from the point of interest to another segment?

❷ DEVISE PLAN
3. How are you going to determine the contributions to the electric field from different segments of the rod?

4. What is the most natural variable to use in doing the integration required in this circular arc problem? How can an angular measure be related to the lengths of various rod segments?
5. What simplifications, if any, does the symmetry of the half circle allow you to make? Think in terms of the components of the vectors at the position of interest (center of the arc).

❸ EXECUTE PLAN

❹ EVALUATE RESULT
6. Is the direction of the electric field you obtained plausible?
7. Does your expression behave in a physically plausible way when you vary either R or q?

Worked Problem 23.7 Dipole corrections

In any direction far away from a dipole, the electric field surrounding the dipole decreases approximately as the inverse cube of distance. For a dipole with dipole charge q_p, dipole separation d, and dipole moment magnitude $p = q_p d$, what is the first level of correction to this inverse-cube approximation (a) at any position on the dipole axis that is an intermediate distance (neither very close nor very far) from either end of the dipole and (b) at any position on the perpendicular bisector of the dipole axis that is an intermediate distance from the dipole?

❶ GETTING STARTED Figure WG23.8 shows the dipole along with the information given in the problem statement and labels for the electric fields at an arbitrary location along the dipole axis ($\vec{E}_\parallel$)

Figure WG23.8

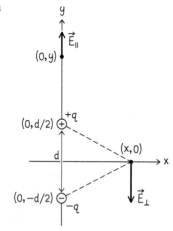

and at an arbitrary location on the perpendicular bisector ($\vec{E}_\perp$). *Principles* Section 23.6 derives the expression for the nonzero components of the electric fields along the dipole axis (Eq. 23.12) and perpendicular to it (Eq. 23.8):

$$E_\parallel = E_y = k\frac{q_p}{y^2}\left[\left(1 - \frac{d}{2y}\right)^{-2} - \left(1 + \frac{d}{2y}\right)^{-2}\right]$$

$$E_\perp = E_y = -k\frac{q_p d}{[x^2 + (d/2)^2]^{3/2}}$$

(Remember that E_x is zero in both cases.) We then saw how these equations yield the approximations $E_\parallel = E_y \approx 2kq_p d/y^3$ (Eq. 23.13) and $E_\perp = E_y \approx -kq_p d/x^3$ (Eq. 23.10) when the distance from the dipole is much greater than the dipole separation d ($y \gg d/2$ and $x \gg d/2$). We just have to make the approximations more accurate, keeping in mind that the corrections for the two cases may differ slightly from each other because the expression for $E_\perp = E_y$ in the x direction is different from the expression for $E_\parallel = E_y$ in the y direction.

❷ DEVISE PLAN The approximations $E_\parallel = E_y \approx 2kq_p d/y^3$ and $E_\perp = E_y \approx -kq_p d/x^3$ were obtained using only the first-order term in a binomial expansion. To make the approximations more accurate, we need to take the next term in the expansion into account. The expansion is $(1 + z)^n = 1 + nz/1! + n(n-1)z^2/2! + n(n-1)(n-2)z^3/3! + n(n-1)(n-2)(n-3)z^4/4! + \cdots$. We hope to get by with just the terms through z^2 because the long-range expressions used only $1 + nz$, but we'll go to the z^3 term in case there is an exact cancellation.

❸ EXECUTE PLAN (a) Consider first the electric field $\vec{E}_\parallel$ along the dipole axis, given by Eq. 23.12. Noting that $n = -2$ in this

equation and using the expansion of $(1 + z)^n$ to the z^3 term with $z = d/2y$, we have

$$\left(1 \pm \frac{d}{2y}\right)^{-2} \approx 1 \pm (-2)\frac{d}{2y} + \frac{(-2)(-2-1)}{2}\left(\frac{d}{2y}\right)^2$$

$$\pm \frac{(-2)(-3)(-4)}{6}\left(\frac{d}{2y}\right)^3$$

$$= 1 \mp \frac{d}{y} + \tfrac{3}{4}\frac{d^2}{y^2} \mp \tfrac{1}{2}\frac{d^3}{y^3}.$$

Substituting this expression into Eq. 23.12, we see that the first-level correction for intermediate distances is

$$E_\parallel = E_y \approx k\frac{q_p}{y^2}\left[\left(1 + \frac{d}{y} + \tfrac{3}{4}\frac{d^2}{y^2} + \tfrac{1}{2}\frac{d^3}{y^3}\right)\right.$$

$$\left. - \left(1 - \frac{d}{y} + \tfrac{3}{4}\frac{d^2}{y^2} - \tfrac{1}{2}\frac{d^3}{y^3}\right)\right] = k\frac{q_p}{y^2}\left(2\frac{d}{y} + \frac{d^3}{y^3}\right)$$

$$= 2k\frac{q_p d}{y^3}\left(1 + \frac{d^2}{2y^2}\right). \checkmark$$

This result is similar to Eq. 23.13, $E_{\parallel y} \approx 2kq_p d/y^3$, except that now we have the additional factor $[1 + d^2/2y^2]$. It is good that we kept terms through $z^3 = (d/2y)^3$ because the z^2 term cancels in the difference.

(b) We carry out a similar calculation for intermediate distances from the dipole along the perpendicular bisector. We start by writing Eq. 23.8 in the form

$$E_\perp = E_y = -\frac{kq_p d}{[x^2 + (d/2)^2]^{3/2}} = -\frac{kq_p d}{x^3}\left(1 + \tfrac{1}{4}\frac{d^2}{x^2}\right)^{-3/2}.$$

Using the same expansion procedure we used to obtain a first-level correction for $E_\parallel$, we see that the first-level correction for this direction is

$$E_\perp = E_y \approx -\frac{kq_p d}{x^3}\left[1 + (-\tfrac{3}{2})\tfrac{1}{4}\frac{d^2}{x^2}\right]$$

$$= -\frac{kq_p d}{x^3}\left(1 - \tfrac{3}{8}\frac{d^2}{x^2}\right). \checkmark$$

It is gratifying to note that in both cases the correction term ($1 + d^2/2y^2$ for $E_\parallel$, $1 - 3d^2/8x^2$ for $E_\perp$) is on the order of $(d/y)^2$ or $(d/x)^2$. We expect that these two cases should bracket the actual correction for arbitrary directions at intermediate distances, because the electric field contribution from each charged particle is spherically symmetrical, suggesting significant dependence on distance but not so much on direction.

❹ EVALUATE RESULT If we let either x or y get very large relative to d (that is, at locations very far from the dipole), then $d/x \to 0$ and $d/y \to 0$. At these locations, our expression for $E_\parallel$ becomes Eq. 23.13 and our expression for $E_\perp$ becomes Eq. 23.10. The plus sign in front of the $(d^2/2y^2)$ term in the correction for $(E_\parallel)_y$ is plausible. To see why, imagine holding a positively charged test particle at a location on the dipole axis far beyond the positive end—for instance, at location $(0, y)$ in Figure WG23.8—and then moving the test particle closer and closer to the dipole. As you do this, the magnitude of the repulsive force exerted by the dipole's positive end on the test particle increases more rapidly than does the magnitude of the attractive force exerted by the more distant negative end.

Guided Problem 23.8 Cathode ray tube

A cathode ray tube uses an electric field to steer electrons to various locations on a screen. In Figure WG23.9, an electron fired from the "electron gun" passes between two parallel plates, and the uniform vertical electric field between the plates deflects the electron's trajectory in the y direction. As the electric field magnitude is varied, the electron can be directed to hit the screen anywhere vertically from top to bottom. (A separate set of plates controls the horizontal position.) If the plates are 30 mm long and located 0.20 m behind a screen that is 0.30 m high, what electric field magnitude is required to deflect an electron to the bottom of the screen if the electron has an initial horizontal velocity of 3.0×10^5 m/s?

Figure WG23.9

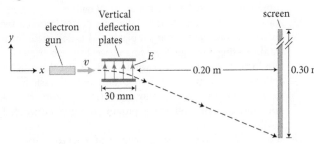

① GETTING STARTED
1. What physical interactions control the electron's trajectory? What simplifications and assumptions can or must you make?
2. What happens to its motion as the electron travels from gun to screen, and why?

② DEVISE PLAN
3. How can you determine the electron's trajectory? Remember that you have done trajectory calculations before with the gravitational force as the dominant one. Is there a similarity with the electric force in this case?
4. Does the electron experience a constant force? Does the answer to this question depend on whether the electron is between the plates or in the region from the plates to the screen? Whether or not the answer depends on the electron's position, remember that the trajectory must be continuous at the boundary between the regions.

③ EXECUTE PLAN

④ EVALUATE RESULT

Questions and Problems

For instructor-assigned homework, go to MasteringPhysics® (MP)

Dots indicate difficulty level of problems: • *= easy,* •• *= intermediate,* ••• *= hard;* CR *= context-rich problem.*

23.1 The field model

1. What is the magnitude of the gravitational field that Earth feels due to the Sun? •
2. Determine the magnitude of Earth's gravitational field for (a) a 70.0-kg person standing at Earth's surface, (b) a 700.0-kg satellite in orbit 150 km above Earth's surface, and (c) the Moon (use 3.844×10^8 m for the center-to-center distance between Earth and the Moon. •
3. Sketch the gravitational field at 15 positions uniformly distributed along the comet orbit in Figure P23.3. ••

Figure P23.3

4. Suppose there is an electric field pointing horizontally toward the east at some location near Earth's surface. Does it make sense to add the gravitational and electric *fields* to determine the behavior of a proton at that location? ••

23.2 Electric field diagrams

5. The units of the gravitational field are those of acceleration. Is that true of the electric field as well? If not, why not? •

6. Two electrons initially repel each other with an electric force of magnitude 2.5×10^{-20} N. What is the magnitude of the electric field at one electron due to the other? •
7. The dwarf planet Pluto and its moon Charon have very similar masses. Suppose the masses are equal, and draw a gravitational field diagram for this system of two source objects. ••
8. Draw two vector field diagrams, one for a particle carrying charge $+q$ and located at the origin of a rectangular coordinate system and one for a particle carrying charge $-2q$ and located at the origin. Describe the principal differences between the two diagrams. ••

23.3 Superposition of electric fields

9. The two Ping-Pong balls in Figure P23.9 carry charges that have the same magnitude but opposite signs. Sketch the vectors that represent the electric fields the balls produce at locations A, B, C, D, and E, which all lie in a common plane that includes the line joining the centers of the balls. Use a ruler to estimate that relative distances between locations. •

Figure P23.9

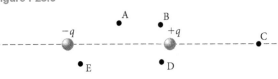

10. Positive charge is distributed uniformly on a plastic rod bent to form a quarter-circular arc (Figure P23.10). What is the direction of the electric field at the center of the circle? •

Figure P23.10

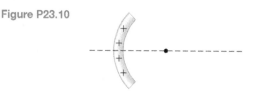

11. Repeat Problem 9 for the case where the positive charge in Figure P23.9 remains $+q$ but the negative charge is changed to $-2q$. ••

12. The two particles in Figure P23.12 carry identical charges. Sketch the vectors that represent the electric fields the particles produce at locations A, B, and C, which all lie in the plane that is midway between the two particles and perpendicular to the line connecting them. ••

Figure P23.12

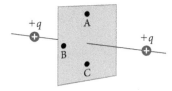

13. Charged beads are placed at the corners of a square in the various configurations shown in Figure P23.13. Each red bead carries a charge $+q$, and the blue bead carries a charge $-q$. Rank the configurations according to the magnitude of the electric field at the center of the square, smallest magnitude first. ••

Figure P23.13

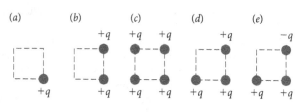

14. The charge on a nonconducting rod increases linearly from end A to end B. The rod is bent in a circle so that ends A and B almost meet very near the top of the circle (Figure P23.14). What is the direction of the electric field at the center of the circle? (Hint: Consider contributions from diametrically opposite segments!) •••

Figure P23.14

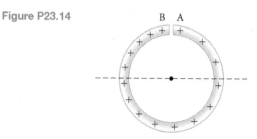

23.4 Electric fields and forces

15. To what extent is the gravitational field uniform inside the room in which you are sitting? •

16. A positively charged test particle is placed midway between two fixed, identical positively charged source particles. (a) Is the test particle in a stable or unstable equilibrium at that location? (b) If the test particle is replaced by a negatively charged test particle, is it in a stable or unstable equilibrium at that location? •

17. A box full of charged plastic balls sits on a table. The electric force exerted on a ball near one upper corner of the box has components 1.2×10^{-3} N directed north, 5.7×10^{-4} N directed east, and 2.2×10^{-4} N directed vertically upward. The charge on this ball is 120 nC. If this ball were replaced with one that has a charge of -50 nC, what would be the force components exerted on the replacement ball? ••

18. An electron traveling horizontally east passes between two horizontal, oppositely charged plates and is deflected downward. Passing through the same space between the plates, in which direction (if any) would each of the following be deflected: (a) a proton traveling horizontally east, (b) an electron traveling horizontally west, (c) a proton traveling horizontally west, and (d) a proton traveling horizontally north? ••

19. A 30.0-mg oil drop carrying a charge of $+3.5 \mu C$ passes undeflected through a region in which there is a uniform, constant electric field. What are the magnitude and direction of the electric field? ••

20. Each dipole in Figure P23.20 is free to rotate about an axis that is perpendicular to the plane of the page (represented by the dot in the center of each dipole). The dipoles are initially held fixed in a horizontal line as shown but are then released and begin rotating. What is their most likely final orientation if there is a mechanism for energy dissipation? ••

Figure P23.20 $+q$ $-q$ $-3q$ $+3q$

$3m$ $3m$ m m

21. Suppose two plates lie in parallel horizontal planes, one plate in the xy plane at $z = 0$ and the other plate in the plane that is parallel to the xy plane at $z = 10$ mm. Between the plates is a constant electric field directed vertically upward (that is, in the positive z direction). A proton and an electron are launched in the positive x direction with the same initial velocity from position $(0, 0, 5.0$ mm$)$. If the proton strikes a plate at $(200$ mm, $0, 10$ mm$)$, where does the electron strike? •••

23.5 Electric field of a charged particle

22. Two uniformly charged pellets A and B are held some distance from each other, and then the charge on A is doubled. Which of the following statements is most correct? (a) The magnitude of the electric force exerted on A is doubled because the electric field at the position of A is doubled. (b) The magnitude of the electric force exerted on A is doubled because the electric field at the position of B is doubled. (c) The magnitude of the electric force exerted on B is doubled because the electric field at the position of B is doubled. •

23. What is the magnitude of the electric field 200 mm away from a particle carrying 3.0 μC of charge? •

24. A small, charged, spherical object at the origin of a Cartesian coordinate system contains 3.30×10^4 more electrons than protons. What are the magnitude and direction of the electric field at the position (2.00 mm, 1.00 mm)? •

25. Two protons A and B are separated by a distance $d = 9.00\ \mu$m. What are the magnitude and direction of the electric field along the line connecting the protons (a) halfway between them and (b) a distance $d/4$ away from A and $3d/4$ away from B? Use the relationship between electric force and electric field. •

26. A positively charged particle initially at rest on the ground accelerates upward to 100 m/s in 2.00 s. If the particle has a charge-to-mass ratio of 0.100 C/kg and the electric field in this region is constant and uniform, what are the magnitude and direction of the electric field? ••

27. A proton is located in the xy plane at (4.00 mm, 3.00 mm) and experiences an electric force exerted by a particle at the origin carrying a positive charge of $6.95\ \mu$C. (a) Determine the magnitude and direction of the electric force exerted on the proton. (b) Using the relationship between electric field and electric force and the result from part a, determine the magnitude and direction of the electric field at (4.00 mm, 3.00 mm) due to the positive charge at the origin. (Assume the proton has been removed.) ••

28. A particle at the origin of a Cartesian coordinate system carries a charge of 3.89×10^{-9} C. What are the magnitude and direction of the electric field at (a) (4.00 mm, 0), (b) (0, 4.00 mm), and (c) (−2.829 mm, 2.829 mm)? ••

29. (a) Plot the value of the radial component of the electric field due to a positively charged pellet as a function of distance from the pellet center. (b) Repeat for a negatively charged pellet. Take each pellet to be a uniformly charged nonconducting sphere having a radius of 18.5 mm and carrying a charge of 1.11 nC. ••

30. An electron initially placed 0.10 m to the right of a small charged sphere moves to the right with an initial acceleration of 4.0×10^7 m/s². What is the magnitude of the charge on the sphere? (Ignore gravity.) ••

31. A small sphere carrying 6.0 nC of charge is placed 100 mm from a small sphere carrying 3.0 nC of charge. Assume the spheres are tiny relative to the 100-mm separation distance. At what position on the line joining the spheres is the electric field magnitude zero? ••

32. Two beads, one carrying charge $+q$ and the other carrying charge $+4q$, are separated by a distance d that is much greater than the radius of each bead. (a) Is there any location along the line between them where the electric field magnitude is zero? If so, what is that location in terms of d? (b) Is there any other position where the electric field magnitude is zero? ••

33. In an inkjet printer, tiny drops of ink of inertia m are given a charge q and then fired toward the paper at speed v. They first pass between two charged plates of length ℓ that create a uniform electric field of magnitude E between them (Figure P23.33). The field direction is perpendicular to the plates and to the initial path of the drops. The electric field deflects each drop from its initial horizontal path and is used to control what is printed on the paper. (a) Derive an expression for how far in the vertical direction a drop is deflected as it passes between the plates. (b) For a drop inertia of 1.5×10^{-10} kg, an electric field strength of 1.2×10^6 N/C, a plate length of 10 mm, and a drop speed of 20 m/s, calculate

the drop charge necessary to result in a deflection of 1.3 mm. (c) Is it acceptable to ignore the effects of gravity in this case? ••

Figure P23.33

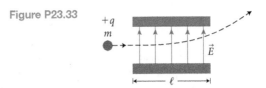

34. (a) What electric field magnitude is needed to balance the gravitational force exerted by Earth on an electron near Earth's surface? (b) Relative to the electron's position, where would you have to place a proton in order to create an equivalent electric force on the electron? ••

35. Consider a rectangle with diagonal length $2a$ in the yz plane with the origin at the center of the rectangle. Four beads, each carrying charge q, are placed on the rectangle perimeter, one bead at each corner. Show that the electric field along the x axis is given by ••

$$E_x = k\left(\frac{4qx}{(x^2+a^2)^{3/2}}\right)\hat{\imath}.$$

36. A particle carrying a charge of 6.0 μC is located at the origin of a rectangular coordinate system, and a particle carrying a charge of 4.0 μC is located at (0, 5.0 m). What are the magnitude and direction of the electric field at the positions (a) (5.0 m, 0), (b) (−5.0 m, 0), and (c) (0, −5.0 m)? ••

37. Five charged particles are equally spaced around a semicircle of radius 100 mm, with one particle at each end of the semicircle and the remaining three spaced equally between the two ends. The semicircle lies in the region $x < 0$ of an xy plane, such that the complete circle is centered on the origin. (a) If each particle carries a charge of 1.00 nC, what is the electric field at the origin? (b) Where could you put a single particle carrying a charge of −5.00 nC to make the electric field magnitude zero at the origin? ••

38. A positively charged particle 1 is at the origin of a Cartesian coordinate system, and there are no other charged objects nearby. You need the electric field magnitude at the position (3.00 nm, 4.00 nm) to be zero, so that no electric force is exerted on any charged object placed at that location. (a) Make a plot of all positions where a single additional charged particle 2 (of arbitrary charge) could be placed to make the electric field magnitude zero at (3.00 nm, 4.00 nm). Explain some of the key points of your graph. (b) Where would you need to place particle 2 if it carried the same charge as particle 1? ••

39. Three particles carrying equal positive charge are located at the corners of an equilateral triangle with side length a. What are the magnitude and direction of the electric field (a) at the center of the triangle, (b) at the midpoint of any side of the triangle, and (c) a distance a above the triangle apex? •••

40. Two nonconducting spheres 1 and 2 carry the same charge, and the magnitude of the electric force exerted by each sphere on the other is 0.10 N when they are 50 mm apart. (a) What is the magnitude of the charge on each sphere, assuming each has a diameter much smaller than 10 mm? (b) What is the magnitude of the electric field 50 mm directly above sphere 1 if sphere 2 is located to the left of sphere 1? (c) Would your answers change if each sphere had a radius of 10 mm? •••

41. A particle carrying a charge of $-5.0\ \mu C$ is located at the origin of a rectangular coordinate system, and a particle carrying a charge of $12.0\ \mu C$ is located at (1.0 m, 0.50 m). Determine the coordinates of the position at which $E = 0$. ●●●

42. In table salt—sodium chloride, NaCl—the Na^+ and Cl^- ions are arranged in a cubic crystal structure. You can observe in this structure a cube made up of eight ions: four Na^+ and four Cl^- in alternating corners. Each Na^+ has a radius of 99 pm, each Cl^- has a radius of 181 pm, and the ions are spaced as though they were solid balls of these sizes, touching their neighbors. (*a*) For a single cube of this arrangement, what are the magnitude and direction of the electric field at one of the Na^+ ions due to the other seven ions in the cube? (*b*) What are the magnitude and direction of the vector sum of the electric forces exerted on this Na^+ ion by the other seven ions? ●●●

23.6 Dipole field

43. A water molecule (Figure P23.43) has a dipole moment of $6.19 \times 10^{-30}\ C \cdot m$. If the O–H bonds were ionic bonds (in reality they are polar covalent bonds), the electrons from the two hydrogen atoms would be completely transferred to the oxygen atom. Using the measured dipole moment and the fact that the centers of positive and negative charge are 0.058 nm apart, can you rule out the hypothesis that the O–H bonds are ionic? ●

Figure P23.43

44. Two plastic bowling balls, 1 and 2, are rubbed with cloth until they each carry a uniformly distributed charge of magnitude 0.10 nC. Ball 1 is negatively charged, and ball 2 is positively charged. If the balls are held apart by a 600-mm stick stuck through the holes so that it runs from the center of one ball to the center of the other, what is the dipole moment of the arrangement? ●

45. As Figure P23.45 shows, the water molecule is bent, and the angle formed by the three atoms is 104.5°. Given that the permanent dipole moment of the molecule is $6.186 \times 10^{-30}\ C \cdot m$, determine the dipole moment of each OH bond. ●●

46. A proton located several proton diameters away from a small charged object carrying charge q is subject to an electric field of magnitude E. As the proton moves a distance d along the x axis away from the object, the electric field magnitude drops to $E/4$. If the charged object had instead been an electric dipole (with a charge of magnitude q on each end) oriented in the z direction, by what factor would the initial electric field magnitude E have dropped as the proton receded by distance d along the x axis? ●●

47. A dipole consisting of a proton and an electron held a distance d apart is aligned along a z axis. A second proton is then placed at the midpoint of the line joining the electron and proton of the dipole. What is the ratio of the electric field magnitude at $(0, 0, 10d)$ to the electric field magnitude at $(0, 0, 20d)$? ●●

48. Equation 23.12,

$$E_y = k\frac{q_p}{y^2}\left[\left(1 - \frac{d}{2y}\right)^{-2} - \left(1 + \frac{d}{2y}\right)^{-2}\right],$$

was derived for the case $y > d/2$. Explain why this equation holds for the case $y < -d/2$. ●●

49. An electric *quadrupole* can be constructed by placing four charged objects at the corners of a square (Figure P23.49). The objects are identical except for the charge they carry: The two objects in one diagonally opposed pair each carry charge $+q$, and the other two objects carry charge $-q$. (Note that there is no charge on the quadrupole overall and that the combination of four charges has no dipole moment.) How does the magnitude of the electric field depend on the distance r from the center of the quadrupole? Take the side length for the square to be d and assume $r \gg d$. ●●

Figure P23.49

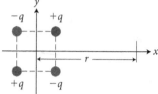

50. A dipole is centered at the origin of a coordinate system, and a small charged sphere is some distance away along the perpendicular bisector of the dipole. The particle carries a uniformly distributed charge of -3.0 nC, and experiences a 200 nN electric force in the positive y direction. (*a*) If the dipole charge is 10 nC and the dipole separation is 20 mm, how far away from the dipole is the sphere? (*b*) How is the dipole moment oriented? ●●

51. Two thin plastic rods, each of length ℓ, are joined end to end. One rod is positively charged with a uniform linear charge density λ, and the other carries a negative charge density $-\lambda$. What is the effective dipole moment of the rod? ●●

52. An electric dipole that has dipole separation d is aligned along the y axis of an xy coordinate system, pointed in the positive y direction. (*a*) Show that for x and y much greater than d, the x and y components of the electric field of the dipole are given by

$$E_x = \frac{3kpxy}{(x^2 + y^2)^{5/2}}; \quad E_y = \frac{kp(2y^2 - x^2)}{(x^2 + y^2)^{5/2}}.$$

(*b*) Show that this general result includes the special results derived in *Principles* Section 23.6. ●●●

23.7 Electric fields of continuous charge distributions

53. You've been given the task of charging a spherical weather balloon made of a conducting material, and you want to put as much charge on it as possible. An experienced colleague advises you that the air surrounding the balloon becomes conducting when the electric field at the balloon surface reaches 100,000 N/C, causing a spark that discharges the balloon. Because the balloon must stay charged, you cannot allow this air breakdown to occur. By measuring the balloon's shadow, you calculate the balloon diameter to be 3.5 m. This gives you enough information to estimate the maximum charge the balloon can have without causing air breakdown. ●

54. A positively charged particle is released from rest along the axis of symmetry of a fixed ring carrying a uniformly distributed negative charge. Describe the motion of the particle. ●

55. A uniformly charged rod lies along the z axis of an xyz coordinate system, from $z = -100$ mm to $z = +100$ mm. The linear charge density on the rod is 100 nC/m. What is the vector expression for the electric field at (40 mm, 30 mm, 0)? •

56. In the uniform charge distribution shown in Figure P23.56, each of the three arcs forms one-fourth of the circumference of a ring. The upper right and lower left arcs each carry a positive charge q, while the upper left arc carries a charge $-q$. Determine the electric field at P, the ring center, in terms of q and R. ••

Figure P23.56

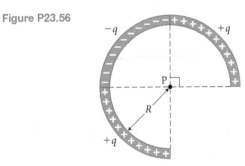

57. The thin glass rod of length ℓ in Figure P23.57 has a linear charge density that starts out as zero at the left end of the rod and increases linearly from left to right. The positive charge on the rod is q_{rod}. (a) What is the electric field along the rod's axis at position P, which lies a distance d from the right end of the rod? (b) What is the approximate expression for the magnitude of the electric field at distances $d \gg \ell$—that is, far enough away to make the rod look small? ••

Figure P23.57

+ + + + ++   P
+ + + + ++ →x
|← ℓ →|← d →|

58. You have two disks, 1 and 2, both of radius $R = 25.0$ mm and both made of the same nonconducting material. Disk 1 carries a uniformly distributed charge $q_1 = 1.50\ \mu C$, and the uniformly distributed charge q_2 on disk 2 is unknown. You place disk 1 at $z_1 = 0$ and disk 2 at $z_2 = +32.0$ mm such that the symmetry axis of each disk coincides with the z axis. Using a small charged pith ball, you locate one position on the z axis where the electric force exerted on the pith ball is zero; this position is $z_{E=0} = +88.0$ mm. What is the charge on disk 2? ••

59. What percentage error in the electric field magnitude do you introduce by approximating the charged disk of *Principles* Figure 23.29 as an infinite charged sheet with the same surface charge density for (a) $z = 0.1R$, (b) $z = 0.5R$, and (c) $z = R$? ••

60. You wish to determine the electric field magnitude along the perpendicular bisector of a 250-mm line along which 30 nC of charge is distributed uniformly. You want to get by with a minimal amount of work, so you need to know when it is sufficient to approximate the line of charge as a charged particle. At what distance along the perpendicular bisector does your error in E reach 5% when you use this approximation? ••

61. For a uniformly charged disk of radius 90 mm, you wish to determine the electric field magnitude along the axis that runs through the disk center and perpendicular to the disk face. You want to get by with a minimal amount of work, so you need to know when you can get by with approximating the disk as an infinite sheet. At what distance along the

perpendicular axis does your error in E reach 10% when you use this approximation? ••

62. Three narrow concentric rings of radii 50 mm, 70 mm, and 90 mm are centered about the origin, with the axis of symmetry of each ring oriented along the y axis. The charge on the inner ring is $1.0\ \mu C$, that on the middle ring is $-2.0\ \mu C$, and that on the outer ring is $1.0\ \mu C$. (a) What is the electric field magnitude at (0, 100 mm, 0)? (b) What quantity of charge must be placed at $(0, -100$ mm, 0) to make the electric field magnitude zero at the position calculated in part a? ••

63. Two large oppositely and uniformly charged parallel plates are separated by 10 mm. An electron is projected halfway between the plates and parallel to them with an initial speed of 4.0×10^6 m/s. The electron hits the top plate 20 mm from where the electron was projected. (a) Which plate is negatively charged, top or bottom? (b) What is the surface charge density on the plates if you know that the densities have the same magnitude? ••

64. A particle of inertia m that carries charge q is held above an infinite sheet on which the surface charge density is σ. The charge on the sheet is of the same type as the charge on the particle. The particle is then released from rest. (a) Describe its motion. (b) What is its acceleration? (c) What is the change in its kinetic energy after it has traveled a distance s? ••

65. A uniformly charged thin rod lies along the x axis from $x = 0$ to $x = +\infty$. (a) Derive an expression for the magnitude E_y of the electric field along the positive y axis, and (b) show that the electric field at positions on this axis makes an angle of 135° with the rod. •••

66. One half of a charged thin ring of radius R carries a charge q_1 uniformly distributed over it, and the other half of the ring carries a charge q_2 uniformly distributed over it. For any position along the axis of symmetry of the ring, derive an expression for (a) the component of the electric field parallel to the axis and (b) the component of the electric field perpendicular to the axis. •••

67. In Figure P23.67, determine the x and y components of the electric field at position P, which is a distance d above one end of a rod of length ℓ carrying uniformly distributed charge q. •••

Figure P23.67

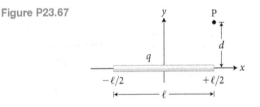

68. A thin rod of length 2ℓ has a linear charge density that is λ_0 at the left end but decreases linearly with distance going from left to right in such a way that the charge on the entire rod is zero. (a) What is the magnitude of the electric field along the rod's axis at a position P that is a distance $d > \ell$ to the right of the center of the rod? (b) Does your expression simplify to a familiar result for the limiting case $d \gg \ell$? (Hint: The dipole moment of the rod has magnitude $p = 2\lambda_0\ell^2/3$.) •••

69. You place 2.2 μC of charge along a long nonconducting rod. The rod extends from $x = 0$ farther than you can see along the positive x axis. The charge distribution has the form of a decreasing exponential: $q(x) = q_0 e^{-x/\ell}$, where $\ell = 28.6$ mm. Calculate the electric field magnitude 20 mm from the near end of the rod, along its long axis. •••

23.8 Dipoles in electric fields

70. The water molecule is a permanent dipole with a dipole moment of 6.186×10^{-30} C·m. If a single water molecule were oriented such that its dipole moment is along a z axis, what torque is caused on it by the electric force due to an 8500-N/C electric field if that field is in the xz plane and directed 42° above the x axis? •

71. A microwave oven, which fills the oven chamber with oscillating electric fields, works well at heating food that has a high water content. However, it does not work well with frozen food or with food that has a high oil content but low water content. Can you think of a reason for this? (Hint: Water molecules in ice are much more rigidly constrained than they are in liquid, and oil molecules are nonpolar.) •

72. The electric force due to a uniform external electric field causes a torque of magnitude 10.0×10^{-9} N·m on an electric dipole oriented at 30° from the direction of the external field. The dipole moment of the dipole is 8.0×10^{-12} C·m. (a) What is the magnitude of the external electric field? (b) If the two particles that make up the dipole are 2.5 mm apart, what is the magnitude of the charge on each particle? •

73. A dipole is to be released in a region where there is a uniform electric field and no dissipative forces. Describe the motion of the dipole if it is released from rest in an orientation (a) parallel to the electric field and (b) almost perpendicular to the electric field. •

74. A small object with dipole moment p is released near its equilibrium orientation in a uniform electric field of magnitude E. The rotational inertia of the dipole is I. (a) What is the effective torsional constant κ of this simple harmonic system? (b) Calculate the angular frequency ω of small oscillations about the equilibrium orientation. ••

75. A dipole that is free to move is placed near a fixed dipole, with the midpoint of the free dipole on the perpendicular bisector of the fixed dipole. The distance from the free dipole to the fixed one is much greater than the dipole separation d of the fixed dipole. Draw a diagram to illustrate the motion of the free dipole if it is placed with its dipole moment (a) in the same direction as the direction of $\vec{p}_{fixed}$, the dipole moment of the fixed dipole, (b) in the direction opposite that of $\vec{p}_{fixed}$, and (c) perpendicular to the direction of $\vec{p}_{fixed}$. ••

76. In a particular region of space, an electric field has a constant direction but its magnitude increases smoothly along that direction. A dipole is placed in this field, its dipole moment is oriented perpendicular to the field, and it is released from rest. If no dissipative forces are present, describe the dipole's motion, paying particular attention to how it differs from what the motion would be if the electric field were uniform. ••

77. A particle carrying 5.0×10^{-7} C of charge is located on the perpendicular bisector of a small dipole, 300 mm from the center of the line joining the two poles of the dipole. The magnitude of the electric force exerted on the particle is 10.0×10^{-6} N. Draw a diagram showing the dipole and indicating the direction of its dipole moment. On this diagram, show (a) the direction of the electric force exerted on the particle and (b) the direction of the electric force exerted on the dipole. (c) Determine the magnitude of the electric force exerted on the dipole. ••

78. There are two possible alignments of a dipole in an external electric field where the dipole is in equilibrium. (a) Draw a field diagram for a uniform electric field and show these two alignments. (b) Are both alignments stable? (Consider what would happen in each case if you gave the dipole a slight twist.) (c) Based on your answer to part b and your experience in mechanics, in which orientation does the dipole have less potential energy? ••

79. In very rare cases, the polarizability of a molecule may be negative. (a) Draw a picture showing the resultant charge distribution when such a molecule is placed in the electric field surrounding a positively charged particle. (b) Describe the motion of the molecule that would result. ••

80. Two identical particles, each carrying charge q, are a distance r apart. A dipole for which the dipole moment magnitude is p and the dipole separation is $d < r$ is placed on the (imaginary) line joining the two particles in such a way that the center of the dipole coincides with the center of the line joining the two particles. Determine the electric force exerted on the dipole. (Hint: You may wish to use a Taylor series expansion to determine the small difference in the electric forces exerted on the two poles of the dipole.) •••

81. An electrically neutral molecule is collinear with (and located between) two charged particles, one carrying a charge of $+3.56$ μC and the other carrying a charge of -1.05 μC. The center of the molecule is 2.57 μm from each particle. If the vector sum of the electric forces exerted on the molecule is 45.0 nN, what is the polarizability of the molecule? •••

Additional Problems

82. Express the SI unit of electric field in terms of joules and other SI base units. •

83. Four particles are located at the corners of a square that is 50 mm on a side. All four particles carry a charge of magnitude 3.0 nC, with positive charge at the lower left corner and negative charge at the other corners. Draw the electric field vectors at the center of the square caused by each of the four source charges, then determine the magnitude and direction of the electric field at the center of the square. •

84. Determine the electric field (magnitude and direction) at the position (8.00 nm, 6.00 nm) caused by a particle located at the origin and carrying a charge of (a) 8.00 μC, (b) -23.0 μC, (c) 10.0 nC. •

85. Each of the two particles in Figure P23.85 carries a charge of magnitude q. Determine a position, if one exists, where the electric field magnitude is zero if the charge (a) is of the same type on the two particles and (b) is positive on one particle and negative on the other. •

Figure P23.85

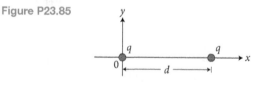

86. An electron is launched into a region of constant electric field, $\vec{E} = 2 \times 10^4$ N/C directed along the positive y axis of a rectangular coordinate system, with an initial velocity of 2.1×10^7 m/s in the positive x direction. How far has the electron traveled in the y direction during the time interval it takes to move 40 mm in the x direction? (Even though the speed at which the electron moves is an appreciable fraction of the speed of light, ignore relativistic effects.) ••

87. An electrically neutral, linear, polar molecule has positive charge equivalent to the charge on one proton centered

0.30 nm from its center of mass and an equal quantity of negative charge centered 0.10 nm from its center of mass (opposite the positive charge). In an electric field of magnitude 100.0 N/C, what are (a) the greatest possible and (b) the smallest possible torque experienced by this molecule? ••

88. You have a pair of objects that interact with each other electrically. The objects initially are separated by a distance r and exert a force of magnitude F^E on each other. If the separation is increased to $2r$, calculate the new force magnitude between the objects if they are (a) charged particles, (b) permanent dipoles with their separation along their dipole axis, (c) permanent dipoles with their separation perpendicular to their dipole axis, (d) a charged particle and a permanent dipole with the dipole pointing directly away from the charged particle, (e) a charged particle and an induced dipole. ••

89. A particle carrying a charge of +32.0 nC is located at (10.0 nm, 95.0 nm), and a particle carrying a charge of +98.0 nC is located at (45.0 nm, 56.0 nm). Calculate the electric force exerted on a charged particle placed at the origin if the charge on that particle is (a) 3.50 μC, (b) 7.22 μC, (c) 95.1 nC, (d) −77.5 nC, (e) 1.00 mC, and (f) 33.2 C. (Hint: Once part a is done, there is a fast way to do this.) ••

90. Figure P23.90 shows four charged particles, each having a charge equal to +3.00 μC, arranged in a square. What are the magnitude and direction of the electric field at P, located midway between the top two particles? ••

Figure P23.90

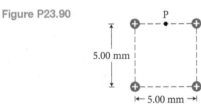

91. A uniformly charged rod extends from $y = -150$ mm to $y = +150$ mm along the y axis of an xy coordinate system. The charge on the rod is 30 nC. (a) With the goal of eventually calculating the electric field magnitude along the rod's perpendicular bisector, approximate the rod as three charged particles, and draw a picture showing the locations of the three particles you will use for the calculation and the magnitude of the charge on each one. (b) What is the electric field magnitude at $x = 200$ mm using this approximation? (c) What is the error in your result in part b? (d) If you were unable to integrate, what could you do to your approximation to make it better? ••

92. A small sphere 1 carrying charge q_1 and having inertia m_1 is constrained to moving inside a narrow vertical tube (Figure P23.92). Fixed at the bottom of the tube is a small sphere 2 carrying charge q_2. (a) Determine the equilibrium height h for sphere 1 (ignore friction). (b) Show that if sphere 1 is displaced from this equilibrium position by a small amount and then released, it moves in simple harmonic motion with angular frequency $\omega = (2g/h)^{1/2}$. •••

Figure P23.92

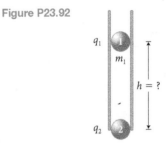

93. Your boss is designing a new data storage system that will have a lot of dipoles very close to one another. They will point in the z direction and be closely spaced in the x and y directions. The data reader will detect E_z as it passes some small distance above the sheet of dipoles. You know that Equation 23.13 is valid only for large distances from the dipole, but it is much easier to apply than the exact result. You prefer the easiest calculation possible, but your boss demands 1.00% accuracy at distances only a few dipole separations from one of the source dipoles. ••• CR

94. You are designing a new guidance mechanism for an inkjet printer. You believe that a circular arc of charge, mounted in the xy plane, is needed in order to deflect the ink droplets most efficiently from their original path along the z axis. You want to use a uniformly charged arc of arc length s that subtends an angle 2θ along a circle of radius R through whose center the ink droplets will pass. The amount of charge that can easily be transferred to the arc is q, which limits the magnitude of the electric field that can be attained at the center of the circle. ••• CR

95. A rod of length πR is composed of three nonconducting segments of equal length. The middle segment is electrically neutral, and each end segment carries a uniformly distributed negative charge $-q$. The rod is bent into a semicircle of radius R. Determine the magnitude of the electric field at the center of the semicircular arc. •••

Answers to Review Questions

1. A field is a set of values, each value associated with a position in space surrounding one or more field sources.
2. It is impossible to deal with the interactions of moving charged particles without the field concept, and it is often easier to deal with fields than with distributions of charge.
3. Ball A is the source of the electric field that acts on B; the electric field created by B does not act on B.
4. A scalar field, such as the temperature at any position in the space of interest, specifies a scalar value (magnitude only) at each position. A vector field, such as the gravitational field, specifies a vector value (magnitude and direction) at each position.
5. A vector field diagram is a map that uses small vector arrows to represent, at selected positions in space, the field created by a field source. Such a diagram is useful in illustrating how the magnitude and direction of the field vary from one location to another in the field.
6. Place the charged test particle at point P and measure the electric force exerted on the particle by the source. Divide this electric force by the charge of the test particle to obtain the electric field of source S at point P.
7. Nothing. The pellet contributes nothing to the electric field created by the sphere. Because nothing has changed with the source of the field (the sphere), the field the pellet experiences doesn't change.
8. The electric field is defined to be in the direction that a positive test particle would experience an electric force, which is opposite the force on the negative test particle in this question. Hence the electric field is directed toward the east.
9. No, because the two electric field contributions must be added as vectors. The magnitude of the electric field at the pushpin can be anywhere from $|E_1 - E_2|$ to $|E_1 + E_2|$.
10. A negatively charged particle placed in a uniform electric field is accelerated in the direction opposite the direction of $\vec{E}$, and so the upward acceleration of the electron tells you that $\vec{E}$ must have a component that is directed vertically downward. (There might also be a component parallel to the initial motion of the electron. This would change the electron's speed but not its direction.) If the electron is accelerated downward, $\vec{E}$ must have a component that is directed vertically upward.
11. See Figure RQA23.11.

Figure RQA23.11

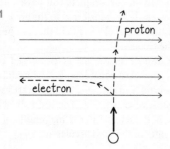

12. No, because the forces exerted on the two charged regions of the dipole are equal in magnitude but opposite in direction, making the vector sum of forces zero.
13. No. The acceleration is not constant (it is centripetal and always changing direction). Therefore the electric force exerted on the electron must be nonconstant, implying the electric field is not uniform.
14. Both. The contribution E_2 makes to the electric field at P would increase, affecting both the x and y components of the electric field (and not in the same proportion).
15. The field magnitude decreases in proportion to the square of the distance between the two objects. To reduce the field by a factor of 100, therefore, you must increase the separation distance by a factor of 10, which means moving it to a position 20 paces from the sphere. Moving the instrument another 18 paces out will do the trick.
16. The magnitude of the electric field due to the sphere is proportional to $1/r^2$, while that due to the dipole is proportional to $1/r^3$. The ratio $E_{\text{dipole}}/E_{\text{sphere}}$ is thus $(qd/r^3)/(q/r^2) = d/r < 1$. That is, the dipole field is weaker at this distance.
17. The dipole moment is a vector pointing from the negative charge in an electric dipole to the positive charge. The magnitude of the dipole moment is $p = qd$, where q is the magnitude of either charge on the dipole and d is the dipole separation.
18. The ratio is 2. The magnitude of the field differs along the axis of the dipole and along the perpendicular bisector of that axis, as given by Equations 23.10 and 23.13. These two, which differ by a factor of 2, are the extreme cases at a given distance R. In the space between these axes the field smoothly varies between these extremes.
19. The radius of the annular ring is $R \sin \theta$, and its width is $R \, d\theta$. Thus the area of the ring is $2\pi(R \sin \theta)R \, d\theta = 2\pi R^2 \sin \theta \, d\theta$. Since the hemispheric half-shell has an area of $2\pi R^2$, the ratio of the ring areas to the shell area is $\sin \theta \, d\theta$. This ratio of the areas also represents the ratio of the infinitesimal charge on the ring dq to the charge on the shell q: $dq/q = \sin \theta \, d\theta$. Thus the infinitesimal charge on the ring is $dq = q \sin \theta \, d\theta$.
20. (a) $1/r^2$, (b) $1/r$, (c) constant.
21. The units are $\text{C}^2 \cdot \text{m/N}$.
22. Because the two forces form an interaction pair, the force magnitude F_{pd}^E must equal the magnitude F_{dp}^E; thus $F_{\text{pd}}^E \propto 1/r^3$. The electric field around the charged particle decreases as the distance squared, not the distance cubed, but the electric force exerted on the dipole decreases more rapidly than the surrounding field does. This is because the electric force exerted on the dipole is the result of a near cancellation of the electric forces exerted on the two ends of the dipole. This cancellation gets more complete as the dipole separation becomes small relative to the distance between the dipole and the particle.
23. Permanent dipoles have separation between their centers of positive and negative charge even in the absence of external electric fields, whereas charge separation for an induced dipole is created only when the object is placed into an external electric field. The charge separation in an induced dipole is proportional to the external field strength E, at least for small values of E.

Answers to Guided Problems

Guided Problem 23.2 At the center, $\vec{E}$ points toward the negatively charged particle and has magnitude $E = 9kq/a^2$. Clever trick: Due to symmetry, adding charge $-q$ to each of the three vertices will not change $\vec{E}$ at the center.

Guided Problem 23.4 In the orientation shown in the figure, the force between the two dipoles is repulsive, with magnitude

$$F = \frac{kq_p}{(a+d)^2} + \frac{kq_p}{(a-d)^2} - \frac{2kq_p}{a^2},$$

which for $d \ll a$ can be approximated as $F \approx 6kq_p d^2/a^4$.

Guided Problem 23.6 If we take the semicircular rod to be the top half of a circle, then $\vec{E}$ at the circle center points downward (for $q > 0$) and has a magnitude

$$E = \frac{kq}{\pi R^2} \int_{\phi=0}^{\pi} \sin \phi \, d\phi = \frac{2kq}{\pi R^2}.$$

Guided Problem 23.8 To accelerate the electrons downward, the electric field between the plates points upward with magnitude

$$E = \frac{mv_i^2 h}{e\ell(\ell + 2d)}$$

$$= \frac{(9.1 \times 10^{-31} \text{ kg})\left(3.0 \times 10^5 \, \dfrac{\text{m}}{\text{s}}\right)^2 (0.30 \text{ m})}{(1.6 \times 10^{-19} \text{ C})(0.030 \text{ m})(0.030 \text{ m} + 2 \times 0.20 \text{ m})}$$

$$= 12 \text{ N/C}.$$

24

PRACTICE
Gauss's Law

PRACTICE

Chapter Summary

Electric field lines and electric flux (Sections 24.1–24.3, 24.6)

Concepts **Electric field lines** let us visualize the electric field around any charge distribution. The lines are drawn so that at any point the electric field $\vec{E}$ is tangent to the lines.

The number of electric field lines that emanate from a positively charged object or terminate on a negatively charged object is proportional to the charge carried by the object.

The **field line density** at a given position in an electric field is the number of field lines per unit area that cross a surface perpendicular to the field lines at that position. At every position in a field line diagram, the magnitude of the electric field is proportional to the field line density at that position.

The electric flux through a closed surface depends only on the amount of charge enclosed by the surface. The flux through a closed surface due to charge carriers outside the surface is always zero.

Quantitative Tools The *area vector* $\vec{A}$ associated with a flat surface area has a magnitude A equal to the surface area and is directed normal to the plane of the area.

The **electric flux** Φ_E ($\text{N} \cdot \text{m}^2/\text{C}$) through a surface due to an electric field $\vec{E}$ is

$$\Phi_E = \begin{cases} \int \vec{E} \cdot d\vec{A} & (24.4) \\ \oint \vec{E} \cdot d\vec{A} & \text{(closed surface),} \quad (24.5) \end{cases}$$

where $d\vec{A}$ is an infinitesimal surface area segment and $\vec{E}$ is the electric field at that location. If the surface is closed, the direction of $d\vec{A}$ is chosen to point outward.

Gauss's law (Sections 24.4, 24.7)

Concepts A **Gaussian surface** is any closed surface used to apply Gauss's law. When using Gauss's law to determine an electric field, we choose a Gaussian surface such that the electric field is the same (and possibly zero) everywhere along as many regions of the surface as possible.

The electric field outside a uniformly charged spherical shell is the same as the electric field due to a particle that carries an equal charge and is located at the shell center. The shell's contribution to the electric field is zero everywhere inside the shell.

Quantitative Tools **Gauss's law:** The electric flux through a Gaussian surface is

$$\Phi_E = \oint \vec{E} \cdot d\vec{A} = \frac{q_{\text{enc}}}{\epsilon_0}, \qquad (24.8)$$

where q_{enc} (the **enclosed charge**) is the sum of all the charge inside the surface, and

$$\epsilon_0 \equiv \frac{1}{4\pi k} = 8.85 \times 10^{-12} \, \text{C}^2/(\text{N} \cdot \text{m}^2) \qquad (24.7)$$

is the **permittivity constant** ($k = 9.0 \times 10^9 \, \text{N} \cdot \text{m}^2/\text{C}^2$, Eq. 22.5).

Calculating electric fields (Sections 24.5, 24.8)

Concepts A Gaussian surface used to determine an electric field should have the same symmetry (spherical, cylindrical, planar) as the symmetry of the charge distribution producing the field. See *Principles* Figure 24.27 and the Procedure box.

A system in which the distribution of charge does not change is in **electrostatic equilibrium.** The electric field inside a conducting object that is in electrostatic equilibrium is zero. Any surplus charge placed on the object arranges itself at the surface of the object, and the electric field at the surface is perpendicular to the surface. A metal reaches electrostatic equilibrium so quickly that this rearrangement is virtually instantaneous.

Quantitative Tools The magnitude of the electric field a distance r from the center of a sphere that has radius $R \geq r$ and contains charge of magnitude q distributed uniformly throughout the sphere volume is

$$E = \frac{1}{4\pi\epsilon_0}\frac{q}{R^3}r = k\frac{q}{R^3}r.$$

The magnitude of the electric field a distance r from an infinite rod having a uniform linear charge density λ is

$$E = \frac{\lambda}{2\pi\epsilon_0 r} = \frac{2k\lambda}{r}.$$

The magnitude of the electric field produced by a nonconducting sheet having a uniform surface charge density σ is

$$E = \frac{\sigma}{2\epsilon_0}.$$

The magnitude of the electric field produced by an infinite conducting plate having a uniform surface charge density σ is

$$E = \frac{\sigma}{\epsilon_0}. \tag{24.17}$$

Review Questions

Answers to these questions can be found at the end of this chapter.

24.1 Electric field lines

1. Describe how to draw an electric field line for a given charge distribution.
2. Explain how to determine the number of field lines to draw around a given charged object.

24.2 Field line density

3. Explain how electric field lines represent both the direction and the magnitude of the electric field at a given location in an electric field.
4. What is the definition of *field line density*?
5. Why do we measure field line density only through a surface that is perpendicular to the field lines?

24.3 Closed surfaces

6. The field line flux through a certain closed surface is zero. Does that mean there are no charged objects inside the closed surface?
7. The enclosed charge for a closed surface is zero. Does that mean there are no electric field lines crossing the surface?
8. Eight electrons are the only charged particles inside an isolated balloon, producing a field line flux through its surface. (*a*) If eight additional electrons are set outside the balloon to form the eight corners of a cube, how does the field line flux through the balloon change? (*b*) How does the flux change if the eight additional electrons are all placed at one location outside the balloon instead of being distributed at the corners of a cube?
9. Given a drawing of the electric field lines surrounding a closed surface, explain how to determine the field line flux through that surface.

24.4 Symmetry and Gaussian surfaces

10. Describe the electric fields inside and outside a uniformly charged spherical shell.
11. Describe the characteristics of planar symmetry.

24.5 Charged conducting objects

12. Under what conditions is the electric field magnitude equal to zero inside a conducting material?
13. Under what conditions is the electric field magnitude nonzero inside the cavity enclosed by a hollow conducting sphere?
14. A hollow conducting object in electrostatic equilibrium carries a surplus electric charge. Without additional information, what must be true about the distribution of this surplus charge?

24.6 Electric flux

15. What is the distinction between *field line flux* and *electric flux*? Why is electric flux the preferred variable for analyzing electric fields?
16. In the formula for electric flux, $\Phi_E = EA \cos \theta$, what does A represent? What does θ represent?
17. When working with irregular surfaces and/or nonuniform electric fields, we obtain the electric flux by integrating a scalar product of the electric field and a small segment of the area of the surface. Why is the scalar product needed?
18. In flux calculations for a closed surface, why is it important to define the area vector as pointing outward, away from the interior of the surface?

24.7 Deriving Gauss's law

19. A spherical surface encloses one electron and one proton. Is the enclosed charge positive, negative, or zero?
20. Would Gauss's law hold if the electric field due to a charged particle had a $1/r$ dependence rather than a $1/r^2$ dependence?

24.8 Applying Gauss's law

21. Inside a ball of volume V and radius R that carries a uniformly distributed charge q, you draw a spherical Gaussian surface that is concentric with the ball and has radius $r < R$. Write an expression for the charge q_{enc} enclosed by the Gaussian surface.
22. A thin spherical metal shell of radius R carries a uniformly distributed charge $+q$. It is surrounded by a concentric thin spherical metal shell of radius $2R$ that carries a uniformly distributed charge $-q$. For which of the following regions enclosed by a concentric spherical Gaussian surface of radius r is the electric field zero: $r < R$, $R < r < 2R$, $r > 2R$?
23. In sketching a Gaussian surface for an infinitely long charged rod when you need to determine the electric field at some distance r from the rod axis, it makes sense to draw a cylinder of radius r for the Gaussian surface, but what value should you use for the length of the cylindrical Gaussian surface? Must this length be infinity just as the rod length is?

Developing a Feel

Make an order-of-magnitude estimate of each of the following quantities. Letters in parentheses refer to hints below. Use them as needed to guide your thinking.

1. The gravitational flux that enters the roof of a typical one-story house due to Earth's gravitational field (E, I, P, L)
2. The electric flux through a horizontal cake pan held 10 m directly above a small object that carries a charge of 100 μC (B, H, M)
3. The surface charge density that results when you place 50 μC of charge on a metal baking sheet (D, J)
4. The surface charge density required to "float" an electron 10^{-2} m above a plastic cutting board (C, G, K, N, A)
5. The surface charge density on the ground that is required to create an upward electric field of magnitude 100 N/C a few meters above the ground (O, F)

Hints

A. What electric field strength is required to create the electric force needed to cancel the gravitational force exerted on the electron?
B. What is the bottom surface area of a cake pan?
C. What forces must cancel in order to float the electron?
D. What is the area of a baking sheet?
E. What is the floor area of a typical one-story house?
F. Does it matter exactly how far above the ground you are?
G. What are the dimensions of a cutting board?
H. What is the magnitude of the electric field at the location of the cake pan?
I. What should you do about the tilt angle θ of the roof surface?
J. How does the charge distribute itself?
K. What does the order-of-magnitude difference between the 10-mm separation distance and the surface area of the board tell you about the board?
L. What are the gravitational quantities that correspond to these electrical quantities?
M. Is the electric field uniform over the cake pan surface?
N. What is the inertia of an electron?

O. Which geometry is more appropriate here: spherical or planar?
P. If this estimate were of electric flux, which quantities would you need?

Key (all values approximate)

A. 6×10^{-11} N/C; B. 0.04 m^2; C. the electric force exerted by the charged board and the gravitational force exerted by Earth; D. 0.2 m^2; E. 150 m^2; F. this value is not needed as long as you approximate Earth's surface as an infinite sheet; G. 0.3 m $\times$ 0.4 m; H. 9000 N/C; I. nothing—the floor area, $A \cos \theta$, includes the roof slope; J. approximately uniformly on both sides of the sheet; K. the board might as well be infinitely large at this small separation distance; L. $\vec{E} \leftrightarrow \vec{g}$, $\vec{A} \leftrightarrow \vec{A}$; M. because the pan is about 0.3 m across, the variation in the angular direction of $\vec{E}$ over the surface is diameter/distance = 0.3 m/10 m = 0.03 rad $\approx 2°$, small enough to consider the field uniform; N. 9×10^{-31} kg; O. planar because Earth's curvature is negligible for such a small separation distance; P. $\vec{E}$, $\vec{A}$

Worked and Guided Problems

Procedure: Calculating the electric field using Gauss's Law

Gauss's law allows you to calculate the electric field for charge distributions that exhibit spherical, cylindrical, or planar symmetry without having to carry out any integrations.

1. Identify the symmetry of the charge distribution. This symmetry determines the general pattern of the electric field and the type of Gaussian surface you should use (see Figure 24.27).
2. Sketch the charge distribution and the electric field by drawing a number of field lines, remembering that the field lines start on positively charged objects and end on negatively charged ones. A two-dimensional drawing should suffice.
3. Draw a Gaussian surface such that the electric field is either parallel or perpendicular (and constant) to each face of the surface. If the charge distribution divides

space into distinct regions, draw a Gaussian surface in each region where you wish to calculate the electric field.
4. For each Gaussian surface determine the charge q_{enc} enclosed by the surface.
5. For each Gaussian surface calculate the electric flux Φ_E through the surface. Express the electric flux in terms of the unknown electric field E.
6. Use Gauss's law (Eq. 24.8) to relate q_{enc} and Φ_E and solve for E.

You can use the same general approach to determine the charge carried by a charge distribution given the electric field of a charge distribution exhibiting one of the three symmetries in Figure 24.27. Follow the same procedure, but in steps 4–6, express q_{enc} in terms of the unknown charge q and solve for q.

These examples involve material from this chapter but are not associated with any particular section. Some examples are worked out in detail; others you should work out by following the guidelines provided.

Worked Problem 24.1 Pair of charged spheres

(a) Draw the electric field line pattern that arises from two very small spheres, each carrying a charge $+q$. (Assume that the radius of each sphere is much smaller than the distance between the spheres.) (b) What is the electric flux through the plane that bisects and is perpendicular to a line segment drawn between the centers of the two spheres? (c) How would the field line pattern change if the charge on each small sphere were $-q$?

❶ GETTING STARTED We have two spheres that carry equal charge, and we must show the field line pattern for the electric field they create in two cases: both spheres positively charged and both negatively charged. We must also determine the electric flux through a plane midway between the spheres. We start with the sketch of Figure WG24.1, showing our given information and the quantities we must determine.

Figure WG24.1

We know the relationship between the type of charge an object carries and the direction of the electric field around the object, and we know how to draw the field lines for a known electric field. We therefore need to figure out the electric field direction at several locations in the space around the spheres and then connect these points to draw the field lines. To determine the electric flux through the bisecting plane, we need to sum over the entire plane the quantity $\vec{E} \cdot d\vec{A}$, which is $E_x dA$ if we take the separation between the

two spheres to be in the x direction. This seems as if it could be a lengthy calculation, but we hold out hope that once we start drawing field lines, we may find that symmetry simplifies the problem. Because we are told that the spheres are much smaller than their separation distance, we will treat each sphere as a particle in drawing field lines.

❷ DEVISE PLAN We obtain the direction of the electric field by determining the direction of the electric force exerted on a positively charged test particle located near the spheres. We could determine this force direction at many locations around the spheres and from these electric force vectors determine the direction of $\vec{E}$ and then draw the field lines. For a complex charge distribution, this is the only way. In this problem, however, we can use the symmetry of our two-sphere system to figure out the field line pattern.

Once we have the field line diagram, we can use Eq. 24.4 to express the electric flux through the specified plane. We can answer part c from our knowledge of the relationship between charge type and field line direction.

❸ EXECUTE PLAN (a) Because the charge on each sphere is positive, the electric field is directed radially outward from each sphere. We know that, no matter where we put it, the test particle is repelled by both spheres. We also know that wherever we place the test particle it is repelled more strongly by the sphere closer to it. In the plane midway between the spheres, the electric forces exerted on the test particle by the two spheres must be of equal magnitude because the spheres are equidistant from the plane. Thus for the test particle placed in the plane between the spheres, the force $\vec{F}_{sp}^E$, which is the vector sum of forces exerted on the test particle by the two spheres, has no x component. Drawing in a few electric force vectors gives the pattern shown in Figure WG24.2. Using the force vectors as a

Figure WG24.2

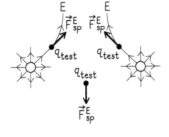

guide and the fact that field lines cannot cross each other, we trace out a dozen or so lines for the electric field due to the two spheres (Figure WG24.3). ✔

(b) Notice in Figure WG24.3 that no electric field lines cross the plane between the two spheres. This tells us that the normal component E_x of the electric field is zero, and thus the electric flux through this plane is zero. ✔

(c) If both spheres were negatively charged, the field line pattern would look the same except the directions of the field lines would be reversed. ✔

Figure WG24.3

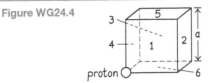

④ **EVALUATE RESULT** We know from *Principles* Section 24.1 that electric field lines between two objects that are oppositely charged run from the positively charged object to the negatively charged one. Thus, we expect that the field lines between two objects that carry the same type of charge should look as if they are pushing the objects apart, just as Figure WG24.3 shows. It makes sense that the electric flux through the bisecting plane is zero because the electric field component perpendicular to the plane is zero by symmetry: The charge distribution is unchanged when reflected about the bisecting plane.

Guided Problem 24.2 Charged square sheet

A square sheet carries a charge $+q$ uniformly distributed over its surface. Make a sketch of the sheet, and draw the electric field lines outside the sheet in the plane that contains the sheet. Based on this sketch, what is the electric flux through a plane perpendicular to the sheet and passing through its center?

① **GETTING STARTED**

1. After drawing your sketch, describe the problem in your own words. What is the problem asking you to determine? Are you asked for a qualitative or a quantitative answer?
2. What do you know about the direction of the electric field near the sheet edges?
3. What should the electric field look like at distances far from the sheet?

② **DEVISE PLAN**

4. Are there any symmetries you can use to simplify the problem?
5. What equation helps you get the electric flux? Can you already guess what the flux is?

③ **EXECUTE PLAN**

6. Draw several field lines connecting the two limiting cases: close to the sheet and far away from it.

④ **EVALUATE RESULT**

7. What can you say about the electric flux through any plane that is perpendicular to the sheet through a symmetry axis of the sheet?

Worked Problem 24.3 Flux through a cube

As you ponder your drink, you notice an ice cube floating in your glass. Because you are studying electric flux, this floating cube leads you to formulate an interesting question: What electric flux is produced though each face of an imaginary cube of side length a, at one corner of which is a single proton?

① **GETTING STARTED** We are given the size of a cube and the fact that one corner is occupied by a proton. We are asked to determine the electric flux through the cube's faces. We draw a sketch containing this information (Figure WG24.4). We treat the proton as a particle with a uniform charge distribution, which means that it creates a spherically symmetrical electric field. This means that the field line density across any face of the cube is nonuniform, with most (but not all) field lines missing the cube entirely.

Figure WG24.4

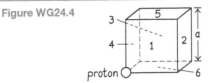

② **DEVISE PLAN** We know the flux is given by Eq. 24.5, and because the electric field is not constant over each face of the cube, the integration may be challenging. However, we can treat each cube face separately and hope to exploit symmetry to simplify the flux calculation. We also know that the electric field due to the single proton is given by Eq. 24.15, with $q = +e$:

$$\vec{E} = \frac{1}{4\pi\epsilon_0} \frac{e}{r^2}\hat{r},$$

where q is the charge on the proton and r is the radial distance from the proton to the point at which $\vec{E}$ is evaluated. Although the electric field magnitude varies over the three faces that have the proton at their common corner (faces 1, 4, and 6 in Figure WG24.4), we know the *directions* of the field at these faces: $\vec{E}$ at face 1 is parallel to face 1, $\vec{E}$ at face 4 is parallel to face 4, and $\vec{E}$ at face 6 is parallel to face 6. Because the electric field is parallel to these three faces, we can say that for each of them $\vec{E} \cdot d\vec{A} = E \cos 90° \, dA = 0$. Moreover, the fluxes through faces 2, 3, and 5 are all the same because each vector area segment $d\vec{A}$ on one of these three faces has a corresponding area segment on the other two faces, all making the same angle with the electric field. Thus, the only thing we need to calculate is the flux through one of the three faces that have nonzero flux. Figure WG24.5, showing face 2, helps us with setting up the integral. With the xyz axes shown in Figure WG24.5, the area

Figure WG24.5

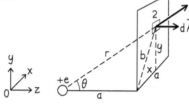

segment $d\vec{A}$ equals $dx\,dy$. For the right triangle that has the proton at one vertex, we have $\cos \theta = a/r$ and $r^2 = a^2 + b^2$, where b is the distance from the area segment $d\vec{A}$ to the corner of face 2 that is nearest the proton: At that corner, $x = y = 0$ and $z = a$. For the right triangle inside face 2, we have $b^2 = x^2 + y^2$. Thus $r = \sqrt{a^2 + (x^2 + y^2)}$. The flux through face 2 is

$$\Phi_E = \int \vec{E} \cdot d\vec{A} = \int E \cos \theta \, dA = \int \frac{1}{4\pi\epsilon_0} \frac{e}{r^2} \cos \theta \, dA$$

$$= \int_0^a \int_0^a \frac{1}{4\pi\epsilon_0} \frac{ea}{\sqrt{(a^2 + x^2 + y^2)^3}} dx \, dy.$$

❸ **EXECUTE PLAN** Referring to integral tables (or using a computer program to do symbolic integration), we determine that integration over x yields

$$\Phi_E = \frac{ea}{4\pi\epsilon_0} \int_0^a \left[\frac{x}{(a^2 + y^2)\sqrt{a^2 + x^2 + y^2}} \right]_0^a dy$$

$$= \frac{ea^2}{4\pi\epsilon_0} \int_0^a \frac{dy}{(a^2 + y^2)\sqrt{2a^2 + y^2}}.$$

If you cannot find this last integral in a reference source, the integration over y is not easy, but a substitution of variables can put the integral in a form found in most integral tables. The substitutions

$$u^2 = a^2 + y^2$$

$$dy = \frac{u}{y} du$$

transform the integral into

$$\Phi_E = \frac{ea^2}{4\pi\epsilon_0} \int_a^{\sqrt{2}a} \frac{(u/y)du}{u^2 \sqrt{u^2 + a^2}}$$

$$= \frac{ea^2}{4\pi\epsilon_0} \int_a^{\sqrt{2}a} \frac{du}{u\sqrt{u^2 + a^2}\sqrt{u^2 - a^2}}$$

$$= \frac{ea^2}{4\pi\epsilon_0} \int_a^{\sqrt{2}a} \frac{du}{u\sqrt{u^4 - a^4}}$$

Checking a table of integrals, we obtain

$$= \frac{ea^2}{4\pi\epsilon_0} \left[\frac{-2}{4a^2} \arcsin \frac{a^2}{u^2} \right]_a^{\sqrt{2}a}$$

$$= -\frac{e}{8\pi\epsilon_0} \left[\arcsin \left(\tfrac{1}{2} \right) - \arcsin(1) \right] = -\frac{e}{8\pi\epsilon_0} \left[\frac{\pi}{6} - \frac{\pi}{2} \right].$$

The electric flux through faces 2, 3, and 5, the three faces that do not contain the proton at one corner, is thus

$$\Phi_E = \frac{e}{24\epsilon_0}. ✔$$

As noted in Devise Plan, the electric flux through the other three faces is zero.

❹ **EVALUATE RESULT** You might say "There must be an easier way!" Sometimes there is; sometimes not. (In this case there *is* a much easier way, shown in Worked Problem 24.5.) Nonetheless, you should not be afraid to tackle integration problems like this. The important thing is to set up the physics properly, as we did in Devise Plan. Then use the math tools you know or can find to obtain an answer.

Although it might seem surprising that the flux through faces 2, 3, and 5 is independent of the cube side length a, this is to be expected when you think of the "rays" of the electric field that radiate from the proton. Doubling the size of the cube would still catch the same number of field lines on these three faces and thus not affect the flux through them.

Guided Problem 24.4 Charged rod, cubed

An infinitely long, positively charged rod whose linear charge density is λ, runs through a cube of side length a. The rod passes through the cube's center and is perpendicular to the top and bottom faces. Use integration to determine the electric flux through each face.

❶ **GETTING STARTED**

1. What information are you given? What quantity are you asked to determine? Make a sketch showing all this information.
2. In what sense is this problem similar to Worked Problem 24.3? In what sense is it different?

3. What physical symmetry can you use to simplify the problem? What does the electric field due to an infinitely long charged wire look like?

❷ **DEVISE PLAN**

4. Is the electric flux through any face zero? Why?
5. Which equations allow you to express the unknown quantities in terms of known ones? What information can help you determine the electric field at a position on, the location of, and the surface normal direction of a face of the cube that has nonzero flux?

6. Begin with the definition of electric flux. Determine the direction of the electric field at any location on each face so that you can integrate over the surface. Rewrite dA in terms of the coordinates of that location (probably x, y, z).

7. The scalar product includes the factor $\cos \theta$. Can you relate this cosine function to the coordinate variables? What about the distance from the rod to area segment dA?

8. Once you have the flux through one face, can you use symmetry or analogy to infer the flux through the other faces?

❸ EXECUTE PLAN

9. Perform the integration over one face that has nonzero flux and extend the result to the other faces.

❹ EVALUATE RESULT

10. As we will work out in detail in Guided Problem 24.6, you can cleverly calculate the answer without using integration, as a check on the brute-force answer. Using symmetry to argue that two faces have zero flux and four faces have equal fluxes, see whether the sum of the fluxes through the nonzero faces equals q_{enc}/ϵ_0, as Gauss's law requires.

Worked Problem 24.5 Revisiting flux through a cube

Use Gauss's law to determine the electric flux through each face of the cube of Worked Problem 24.3.

❶ GETTING STARTED As in Worked Problem 24.3, our given information is that the cube side length is a and the cube has an isolated proton embedded at one corner (Figure WG24.4). Our task here is to use Gauss's law, Eq. 24.8, to solve the problem of how much electric flux passes through each face of the cube. We know how to calculate the electric field surrounding the proton, and we know the locations and orientations of the faces. We also know that a cube possesses symmetries that we can exploit to simplify the problem.

❷ DEVISE PLAN Because the proton is at the corner of the cube, the cube does not enclose it and so cannot be our Gaussian surface. However, we can enclose the proton by attaching seven additional cubes, each of side length a, to our original cube, creating a cube of side length $2a$ and having the proton at its geometric center (Figure WG24.6). This large cube is our Gaussian surface. We can

Figure WG24.6

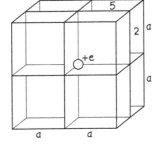

apply Gauss's law to get the electric flux through any face of this surface and then use symmetry to get the flux through any face of our original cube of side length a.

❸ EXECUTE PLAN From Gauss's law, we know that the flux through the large cube enclosing a single proton is e/ϵ_0. Because the proton is at the geometric center, symmetry tells us that the electric flux is the same through all six faces of the large cube. As Figure WG24.6 shows, each face of the large cube is composed of four squares, each of side length a: One face of the large cube contains four faces of our original cube. Thus, if we apply Gauss's law and symmetry, the flux through each of these smaller faces must be

$$\Phi_E = \frac{1}{(6)(4)} \frac{e}{\epsilon_0} = \frac{e}{24\epsilon_0}.$$

This is the same answer we obtained in Worked Problem 24.3 by tedious integration!

This result gives us the flux through sides 2, 3 and 5 of our original cube. The fact that the electric field is parallel to faces 1, 4, and 6 of the original cube tells us that the flux through sides 1, 4, and 6 is still zero. ✔

❹ EVALUATE RESULT Using Gauss's law is much easier than the method we used in Worked Problem 24.3 to do the same task. This law is extremely powerful in cases where symmetry can be exploited. It takes practice and experience to see how to construct Gaussian surfaces, but as this example shows, learning to do so is well worth the effort.

Guided Problem 24.6 Revisiting charged rod cubed

Use Gauss's law to determine the electric flux through each face of the cube of Guided Problem 24.4.

❶ GETTING STARTED

1. Because this problem asks you to determine the same quantity as in Guided Problem 24.4, should you draw the same sketch?

2. In what sense is this problem similar to Worked Problem 24.5? In what sense is it different?

3. What physical symmetry can you use to simplify the problem? What does the electric field due to an infinitely long charged wire look like?

❷ DEVISE PLAN

4. Is the electric flux through any face zero? Why?

5. Which equations allow you to express the unknown quantities in terms of known ones? What information can help you determine these unknown quantities?

6. What should you draw as your Gaussian surface? What is the amount of charge enclosed by this surface?

❸ EXECUTE PLAN

7. Apply Gauss's law, using the symmetry of the system.

❹ EVALUATE RESULT

8. Should your answer agree with your answer in Guided Problem 24.4? Does it?

Worked Problem 24.7 Nonuniformly charged cylinder

A very long, solid nonconducting cylinder of radius R has a volume charge density that is proportional to the radial distance r from the long central axis of the cylinder according to the expression $\rho(r) = \rho_0 r$, where ρ_0 is a constant with units C/m^4. (*a*) For any location near the midpoint of the cylinder's length, obtain an expression for the magnitude of the electric fields inside and outside the cylinder in terms of ρ_0, R, and r. (*b*) Sketch a graph showing the electric field magnitude as a function of the radial distance r from the cylinder's long central axis.

❶ GETTING STARTED We are given an equation showing how volume charge density changes inside a solid cylinder and told that the cylinder is very long. Our tasks are (*a*) to determine expressions for the magnitude of the electric field inside and outside the cylinder, in both cases working near the middle of the cylinder's length, and (*b*) to graph how the electric field changes as we move radially away from the cylinder's long central axis.

The cylinder's symmetry makes this a prime candidate for the application of Gauss's law. Because our task is to determine the magnitude of the electric field midway along the length and we're told that the cylinder is very long, we assume that we can ignore any deviation from cylindrical symmetry of the electric field near the cylinder ends. Thus we can assume that the field in the region we concentrate on is directed radially outward from the long axis of the cylinder.

❷ DEVISE PLAN We'll use Gauss's law to obtain expressions for the electric fields inside and outside the cylinder, making use of cylindrical symmetry. For our task in part *b*, we will take the expressions obtained in part *a*, insert numerical constants where needed, and graph E versus r, making sure that the expressions agree at $r = R$.

❸ EXECUTE PLAN (*a*) Because the symmetry is cylindrical, we use a cylindrical Gaussian surface and show it surrounding a portion of the charge inside the cylinder (Figure WG24.7). As usual, we use r for the Gaussian surface radius and show the surface extending some distance h along the cylinder's length. Because it is radial, the electric field is perpendicular to this Gaussian surface everywhere except on the two end caps of the surface. On the end caps, $d\vec{A}$ is perpendicular to $\vec{E}$ (because the surface is parallel to $\vec{E}$, and $d\vec{A}$ is normal to the surface) and so $\vec{E} \cdot d\vec{A} = E \cos 90° \, dA = 0$. By symmetry, the magnitude of the electric field is the same everywhere on the curved part of the Gaussian surface. Thus, we need to integrate only over the area of the curved part:

$$\Phi_E = \oint \vec{E} \cdot d\vec{A} = \oint E \cos 0° \, dA = E \oint dA = E(2\pi rh).$$

Figure WG24.7

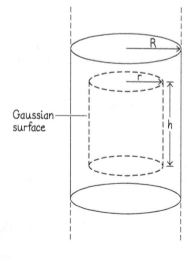

Note that the scalar product leads us to an integral over the scalar area segment dA rather than over the vectorial area segment $d\vec{A}$. Using the vectorial form would yield $\oint d\vec{A} = \vec{0}$! (You should be able to explain why.) Applying Gauss's law, we say

$$\Phi_E = E(2\pi rh) = \frac{q_{enc}}{\epsilon_0}$$

$$E = \frac{q_{enc}}{2\pi rh\epsilon_0}.$$

In determining the charge enclosed by our Gaussian surface, we must remember that the volume charge density $\rho = \rho(r) = \rho_0 r$ varies with the radial distance r from the cylinder's axis. We therefore divide the interior of the Gaussian surface into a series of thin-walled cylindrical shells each of radius r_{shell}, wall thickness dr_{shell}, and wall length h (Figure WG24.8). The infinitesimal amount of charge contained in the wall of each shell is $dq = \rho(r = r_{shell})dV$, where $dV = 2\pi r_{shell}hdr_{shell}$ is the volume of the wall. The charge contained within the Gaussian surface of radius r is thus

$$q_{enc} = \int dq = \int \rho(r_{shell})dV = \int_0^{r_{shell}=r} \rho_0 r_{shell} [2\pi r_{shell}hdr_{shell}]$$

$$= \frac{2\rho_0\pi hr^3}{3}.$$

Figure WG24.8

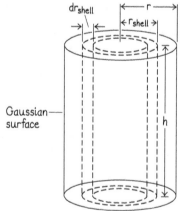

The magnitude of the electric field at radius r inside the solid cylinder ($r < R$) is thus

$$E_{inside} = \frac{2\rho_0\pi hr^3/3}{2\pi rh\epsilon_0} = \frac{\rho_0}{3\epsilon_0}r^2. \checkmark$$

Outside the cylinder, the amount of charge enclosed by the Gaussian surface is independent of the radial distance because the charge distribution ends at the surface of the cylinder. Thus we evaluate the charge enclosed at distance $r = R$, which means $q_{enc} = 2\pi h\rho_0 R^3/3$. This gives an electric field magnitude at radial distance r outside the cylinder ($r > R$) of

$$E_{outside} = \frac{2\rho_0\pi hR^3/3}{2\pi rh\epsilon_0} = \frac{\rho_0 R^3}{3\epsilon_0}\frac{1}{r}. \checkmark$$

(b) Plotting the magnitude E as a function of the radial distance r from the cylinder's central axis yields the graph of Figure WG24.9. The shape of the curve tells us that the field magnitude is proportional to r^2 up to the cylinder's surface ($r = R$) and then is proportional to $1/r$ for $r > R$. ✔

Figure WG24.9

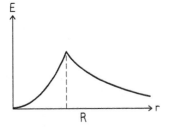

④ **EVALUATE RESULT** It makes sense that the electric field magnitude is an increasing function of r inside the solid cylinder but is a decreasing function of r outside. As we go radially outward from the cylinder's center to its surface, more and more charge is enclosed by the Gaussian surface and so the electric field becomes stronger and stronger until we reach $r = R$. Once outside the solid cylinder, the field magnitude decreases as we get farther away, just as in *Principles* Exercise 24.7 for an infinitely long thin rod. We also check to make sure that our expressions for the electric fields inside the rod and outside the rod agree at the rod's boundary at $r = R$, and gratifyingly we determine that they give the same result for the limiting case of $r \rightarrow R$ from either side; in both cases, $E(r = R) = \rho_0 R^2 / 3\epsilon_0$.

Guided Problem 24.8 Nonuniformly charged sphere

A solid nonconducting sphere of radius R carries a charge q in its interior. The charge is distributed throughout the region $r < R$ nonuniformly, but with spherical symmetry. The volume charge density as a function of the radial distance r from the center of the solid sphere is proportional to $1/r$. Determine the electric fields for positions inside and outside the solid sphere, and then sketch a graph showing the field magnitude as a function of r.

① **GETTING STARTED**

1. List the information you are given, and then describe what you must determine. Make a sketch of the situation.
2. In what sense is this problem similar to Worked Problem 24.7? In what sense is it different?
3. Do you have enough information to work the problem? Are there any assumptions you must make?

② **DEVISE PLAN**

4. What physical symmetry can you use to simplify the problem? What does the electric field look like for a sphere of charge?
5. What is the volume charge density as a function of the radius, in terms of quantities given in the problem statement?
6. What is an appropriate Gaussian surface?
7. What amount of charge is enclosed in this Gaussian surface?

③ **EXECUTE PLAN**

8. Apply Gauss's law, using the symmetry of the system. The volume charge density is not uniform in this case, so determining the enclosed charge involves an integral. Be attentive!

④ **EVALUATE RESULT**

9. Does the way the electric field inside the sphere depends on r make sense? Explain why this behavior of E is reasonable.

Questions and Problems

For instructor-assigned homework, go to MasteringPhysics® (MP)

Dots indicate difficulty level of problems: • = *easy,* •• = *intermediate,* ••• = *hard;* CR = *context-rich problem.*

24.1 Electric field lines

1. Suppose a charged particle is located at the origin. What is the direction of the electric field at the point (0.6, 1.2) if the particle is (*a*) positively charged and (*b*) negatively charged? •

2. Because of the presence of positively charged ions in Earth's atmosphere, on a calm day free electrons (that is, electrons not bound to atoms) just above Earth's surface generally experience a small upward electric force. Sketch the electric field lines near Earth's surface. •

3. Can you draw an electric field line through a location in space where the electric field magnitude is zero? •

4. You and a friend are asked to draw the two-dimensional electric field line pattern for two charged objects located near each other. The charge on the first object is $+2q$ (with q positive), and the charge on the second object is $-q$. You show 32 field lines emanating from the first charge and 16 field lines terminating on the second charge. Your friend shows 24 field lines emanating from the first object and 12 terminating on the second object. Which diagram is correct? •

5. A positively charged test particle is released from rest in a uniform electric field. The only force experienced by the particle is the electric force exerted by the sources of the uniform field. (*a*) Describe the trajectory the particle follows. (*b*) How does the trajectory change, if at all, if the particle is given an initial velocity in the direction of the electric field? (*c*) How does the trajectory change if the particle has an initial velocity that makes an angle $\theta \neq 0$ with the electric field? (*d*) Repeat parts *a–c* for a negatively charged test particle. ••

6. A certain field line diagram illustrates the electric field due to three particles that carry charges 5.0 μC, -3.0 μC, and -2.0 μC. If 20 field lines emanate from the positively charged particle, how many field lines terminate on each of the negatively charged particles? ••

7. Figure P24.7 shows the electric field produced by an electric dipole. How would a positively charged test particle begin to move when released from rest (*a*) at point A, (*b*) at point B, (*c*) at point C, and (*d*) at point D? Assume that no other objects exert forces on the test particle. (*e*) How does your answer to part *a* change if the test particle has an initial velocity that makes some angle $\theta \neq 0$ with the electric field at A? ••

Figure P24.7

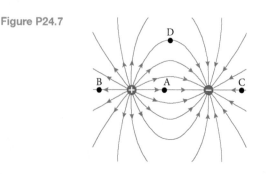

8. Two particles of charge $+q$ are located at opposite ends of one diagonal of a square, and two particles of charge $-q$ are located at opposite ends of the square's other diagonal. Sketch the pattern of electric field lines created, showing eight lines per particle in the plane that contains the square. ••

9. Assume that a test particle is released from rest in an electric field and experiences no forces other than the electric force exerted by the objects that create the electric field. Does an electric field line passing through the particle's initial position represent the particle's trajectory over time? If not, illustrate with an example. ••

10. Draw several field lines surrounding the three charged particles shown in Figure P24.10. ••

Figure P24.10

11. Two classmates sitting next to you have made an electric field diagram. You are looking at it (not during a test) to see if they did it correctly, but part of the diagram is covered by a quarter, as shown in Figure P24.11. If your classmates made the diagram correctly, what can you say about the region covered by the quarter? State all the information you can determine about any charged particles in that region. ••

Figure P24.11

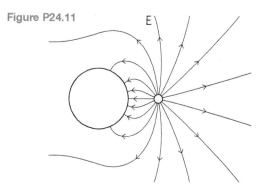

12. Outline an algorithm for a computer program that traces out the electric field lines surrounding a charged object. Assume that functions have already been provided to draw the charged object itself and to draw line segments between pairs of points that your program chooses. •••

13. There are many parallels between gravitational phenomena and electrical phenomena: One can think of a test object with mass in a gravitational field as analogous to a test object with positive charge in an electric field. (*a*) Draw the gravitational field line pattern for the Earth-Moon system, showing arrows on the lines to indicate direction. (*b*) Now consider a system made up of two charged objects. Which type of charge (positive or negative) must each object carry in order to have an electric field line pattern match the gravitational field line pattern that you drew in part *a*? (*c*) Do you see any differences between electrical and gravitational phenomena? •••

24.2 Field line density

14. A small charged ball is suspended at the center of a spherical balloon that is nestled snugly inside a cubical cardboard box. On one side, the balloon touches the wall of the box. (*a*) At this point of contact, is the electric field magnitude on the balloon

surface equal to the electric field magnitude on the box surface? Assume neither object is polarized. (*b*) At this point of contact, is the number of field lines per unit of balloon surface area equal to the number of field lines per unit of box surface area? •

15. Where in Figure P24.15 does the electric field have the greatest magnitude? •

Figure P24.15

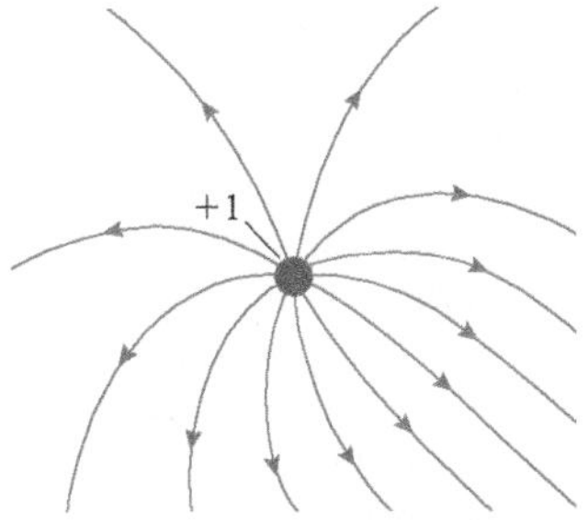

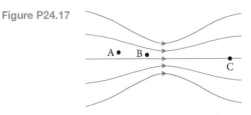

16. Suppose a certain planar surface has 2000 field lines passing through each square meter, normal to the surface. How many field lines pass through each square meter if the surface is tilted by 60°? •

17. Consider the pattern of five field lines shown in Figure P24.17. Rank positions A, B, and C according to the magnitude of their electric fields, from greatest to smallest. •

Figure P24.17

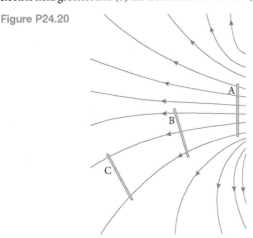

18. Make a geometric argument, based on how the field lines spread out into space, that the magnitude of the electric field surrounding a long, straight, charged wire is proportional to $1/r$, where r is the radial distance from the long axis of the wire. ••

19. Make a geometric argument, based on the pattern of electric field lines, that the magnitude of the electric field surrounding a large, flat, charged metal plate is constant and independent of the distance d from the plate as long as d is small relative to the area of the plate. ••

20. Figure P24.20 shows electric field lines due to a distribution of charge (not shown). The labeled regions of space are all equal in size. In which of the labeled regions, A, B, and C, is (*a*) the electric field greatest and (*b*) the electric field smallest? (*c*) How

Figure P24.20

much greater is the largest labeled electric field than the smallest nonzero labeled electric field? ••

21. Identical charged pellets are released from rest from equidistant starting lines A, B, and C in Figure P24.21, in a region of nonuniform electric field. (*a*) Rank the pellets according to the time interval it takes the pellet on line A to cross line B, the pellet on B to cross C, and the pellet on C to cross D, smallest interval first. (*b*) How does your answer to part *a* change if each pellet is given an identical initial velocity directed upward along lines A, B, and C? ••

Figure P24.21

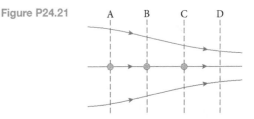

22. You decide to make an electric field line diagram in two dimensions, with 16 lines per coulomb of charge. (*a*) How many lines should you draw surrounding a particle that carries +1.5 C of charge? Should the lines enter or leave that particle? (*b*) Answer the same questions for a particle that carries −0.375 C of charge. (*c*) Could you represent a particle that carries +0.8 C in this diagram? ••

23. Two surfaces are near two different charged objects, and the surfaces are identical in size. Surface A has N field lines passing perpendicularly through it. Surface B has only $N/2$ field lines passing through it, and they pass through at an angle 72° from normal. Is the field line density greater near surface A or surface B, and by how much? •••

24.3 Closed surfaces

24. Imagine a system that consists of only a single positively charged object. Is it possible to have in this system a closed surface that has a negative field line flux through it? (Note: The charged object need not lie inside the surface.) •

25. Closed surface A is a sphere of radius R, closed surface B is a sphere of radius $2R$, and closed surface C is a cube with side length R. At the geometric center of each closed surface is a small ball that is completely enclosed by the surface and carries electrical charge $+q$. Assuming there are no other charged objects inside any of the closed surfaces, rank the surfaces according to the electric field line flux through them, largest first. •

26. Three charged pellets are arranged along a line. Three hypothetical closed surfaces are drawn around this set of three pellets. The three surfaces have identical cylindrical walls but different top caps (Figure P24.26). Rank the closed surfaces from smallest to greatest in terms of the electric field line flux through them. •

Figure P24.26   (*a*)   (*b*)   (*c*)

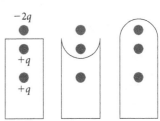

27. In Figure P24.27, assume that a Gaussian surface drawn to surround only sphere 1 would have an electric field line flux of +4. Sketch Gaussian surfaces that contain sphere 1 plus one or more additional spheres and have field line fluxes of (a) +24, (b) −4, and (c) +8. ••

Figure P24.27

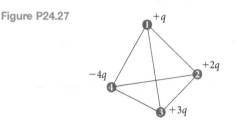

28. In the electric field line diagram for the charge arrangement shown in Figure P24.28, 12 field lines emanate from the object of charge +1 C. What is the field line flux through closed surfaces (a) A, (b) B, (c) C, (d) D, and (e) H? ••

Figure P24.28

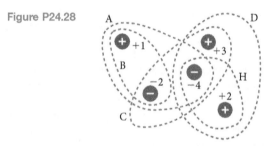

29. In a certain field line diagram, a single electron is drawn that has four field lines terminating on it. If a closed surface in another part of this diagram is shown to have 16 field lines coming out of it, what can be said about the number of charge carriers inside the surface and the type of charge they carry? ••

30. For the dipole in Figure P24.30, can you draw a two-dimensional closed surface through which the field line flux is (a) zero, (b) +16, (c) −16, and (d) +3? ••

Figure P24.30

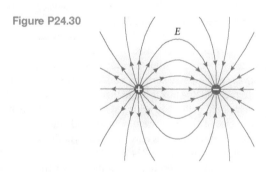

31. Make an argument based on Gauss's law that a charged object cannot be held in stable translational equilibrium by electric fields alone. For a start, assume there is no other charged object in the region of interest even though the external electric field can be due to charged objects outside this region. •••

32. The chapter explains that the charge inside a closed surface is proportional to the flux through that surface. To illustrate why the surface must be closed, draw an example of a charge distribution and a surface for which the flux through the surface would be considerably altered if the surface had any holes (unclosed regions of the surface through which flux is not counted). ••••

24.4 Symmetry and Gaussian surfaces

33. (a) Can you draw a Gaussian surface that offers a simple way to compute the electric field surrounding a charged dipole? (b) If not, does this mean that the relationship between field line flux and enclosed charge and the relationship between field line density and magnitude of the electric field do not apply to charged dipoles? •

34. An isolated system consists of one object carrying charge +q and one object carrying charge −q. Are all the electric field lines for the system contained inside some boundary? •

35. When a charged particle is placed at the center of a spherical Gaussian surface, the field line flux through the surface is +Φ. Suppose that the spherical Gaussian surface is to be replaced by a cubical Gaussian surface composed of six square plates. Square plates are positioned above and below the charged particle to form two sides of the cubical Gaussian surface that is centered on the charged particle, as shown in Figure P24.35. What is the field line flux through each plate? •

Figure P24.35

36. Figure P24.36 shows a cross section through an infinitely long, uniformly charged hollow cylinder. How does the magnitude of the electric field vary with the radial distance r from the cylinder's long central axis (a) inside the hole in the cylinder and (b) outside the cylinder? ••

Figure P24.36   Charged hollow cylinder

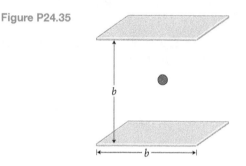

37. Figure P24.37 shows a cylindrical Gaussian surface straddling a charged sheet. Are there any other shapes that would be appropriate for the Gaussian surface in this situation? ••

Figure P24.37

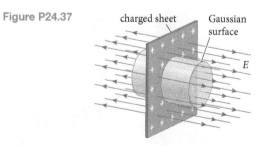

38. Suppose you want to determine the amount of charge on a spherical shell. You start out by surrounding the shell with a cylindrical Gaussian surface. Is it possible to use the flux everywhere on the surface of the cylinder to determine the charge on the spherical shell? Why isn't this recommended in the chapter? ••

39. The magnitude of the electric field a distance R away from a particle carrying charge q is E_0. Now consider this same quantity of charge q distributed uniformly throughout the volume of a nonconducting solid sphere of radius R. What is the electric field magnitude, in terms of E_0, (a) a distance $2R$ from the center of the sphere, (b) at the sphere surface, and (c) a distance $R/4$ from the sphere center? ••

40. You are given a uniformly charged spherical shell that has a radius R and carries a positive charge q. In order to measure the electric field magnitude inside, you drill a small hole that removes 0.01% of the shell's material and insert a probe into the shell. What are the direction and approximate magnitude of the electric field at the shell center? (Hint: The answer is small but not zero.) •••

41. You and your friend are working in a lab and wish to measure the surface charge density on a slab of metal. The slab is very long and very wide, but flat. You begin adding up the field line flux through a cylindrical Gaussian surface that passes through the slab as in Figure P24.37. Your friend begins adding up the field line flux through a cubical Gaussian surface that passes through the slab. Her cube is a little shorter than your cylinder, and it is wider than your cylinder. Will the two of you still obtain the same result for the surface charge density? If so, why? If not, what needs to be changed about your friend's cube? •••

42. You have a hollow spherical shell of radius R that carries a positive charge. The shell is very thin. You make many Gaussian surfaces concentric with the shell to determine the electric field line density at various distances from the center. Qualitatively plot the electric field line density as a function of the distance from the center of the shell. Show regions inside the shell as well as outside. •••

24.5 Charged conducting objects

43. The two-cavity metal object in Figure P24.43 is electrically neutral, but each cavity contains a charged particle as shown. What are (a) the charge on the surface of each cavity and (b) the charge on the outer surface of the object? •

Figure P24.43

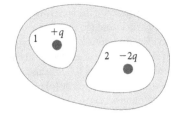

44. Some charged particles are suspended inside a hollow metal object by supports made of a material that is an electrical insulator. The metal object has charge $+q$ distributed over its outer surface and charge $-2q$ distributed over its inner surface.

(a) How much charge is suspended in the cavity? (b) What is the charge on the object? (Hint for part b: What is the electric field a very large distance r from the center of the object?) ••

45. Delicate electronic devices are sometimes enclosed inside metal boxes to protect them from external electric fields. Explain what physical phenomena might cause this protection. ••

46. A *coronal discharge* occurs when the electric field magnitude just above the surface of a conductor exceeds approximately 3×10^6 N/C, a magnitude strong enough to ionize atoms in the air by ripping electrons from them. Coronal discharge is most likely to occur near a sharp tip of a conductor. (This is why solder joints in electronics must not have sharp protrusions and why it's easier to draw a spark from your fingertip than from your knee after scuffing your feet on a carpet.) (a) Make an argument based on the geometry of the field lines emerging from a conducting surface that charge is more likely to concentrate on a convex region of the surface than on a concave region. (b) Sketch a paring knife that has a surplus charge on it, and shade the regions where charge is most likely to concentrate on the surface. ••

47. Two concentric spherical metal shells are insulated from each other and from the surroundings. The inner shell carries a charge $+2q$, and the outer shell carries a charge $-q$. In electrostatic equilibrium, what is the charge on (a) the outer surface of the inner shell, (b) the inner surface of the outer shell, and (c) the outer surface of the outer shell? (d) The shells are then connected to each other by a metal wire. Do parts a–c for the situation obtained after electrostatic equilibrium is reached. ••

48. A small ball carrying a charge $-2q$ is placed at the center of a spherical metal shell that carries a charge $+q$. What are the sign and magnitude of the charge (a) on the inner surface of the shell and (b) on the outer surface of the shell? (c) Do your answers change if the ball is not at the center of the shell? If so, how? ••

49. Figure P24.49 shows a neutral conducting block with four hollow chambers inside. A charge of $-5q$ has collected on the outer surface of the block. Inside three of the chambers are particles that carry charges $+q$, $+q$, and $+2q$. Determine the charge inside the fourth chamber in terms of q. ••

Figure P24.49

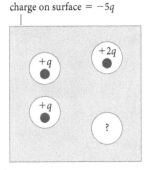

charge on surface $= -5q$

50. A pellet carrying charge $+q$ is centered inside a spherical cavity that has been cut off-center in a solid metal sphere that carries charge $-2q$ (Figure P24.50 on next page). (a) How much charge resides on the inner surface of the cavity? Is this charge distributed uniformly or nonuniformly? (*b*) How much charge resides on the outer surface of the metal sphere? Is this charge distributed uniformly or nonuniformly? •••

Figure P24.50

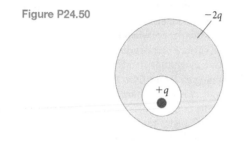

51. A particle carries a charge of $2q$ and is located at the origin. The particle is surrounded by a conducting shell of inner radius R and thickness t. The shell carries a charge of $-3q$. Determine (*a*) the charge on the inner surface of the shell and (*b*) the charge on the outer surface of the shell. (*c*) Make a qualitative plot of the electric field line density as a function of distance from the origin. Be sure to show the field line density in the hollow region, inside the material of the shell, and outside. •••

24.6 Electric flux

52. Imagine a cubical Gaussian surface snugly surrounding a volleyball that is charged uniformly over its surface. The electric flux through one side of the cube is 5.2×10^2 N·m²/C. What is the charge on the volleyball? •

53. A flat sheet that has an area of 3.0 m² is placed in a uniform electric field of magnitude 10 N/C. While keeping the sheet flat, can you orient it so that the electric flux through it is 6 N·m²/C? So that the flux is 60 N·m²/C? •

54. Figure P24.54 shows a cylindrical Gaussian surface enclosing a segment of a long charged wire. Consider using a spherical Gaussian surface to enclose the same segment of the wire. (*a*) Which surface, cylindrical or spherical, has the greater electric flux through it? (*b*) Which surface is more appropriate for calculating the electric flux? Justify your answer. •

Figure P24.54

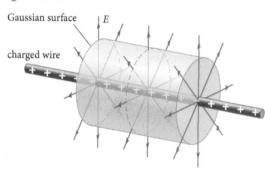

55. A particle carries a charge of 6.0 μC. Calculate the electric flux through a spherical Gaussian surface that is centered on the particle and has a radius of (*a*) 0.04 m and (*b*) 0.08 m. •

56. Use a symmetry argument to determine the electric flux through a Gaussian surface that encloses both charged particles that form an electric dipole. Does the value calculated for the flux depend on the shape of the surface? ••

57. Figure P24.57 shows a charged particle surrounded by three different closed surfaces, (*a*), (*b*), and (*c*). In each case, the charge on the particle and the geometry of the left side (left of the dashed line) of the surface are identical. The closed surfaces have different geometries to the right of the dashed line. In which case is the flux through the right side of the surface the greatest? In which case is it the smallest? ••

Figure P24.57

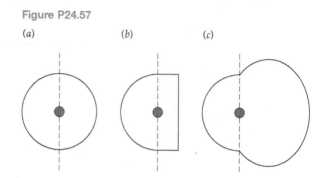

58. A butterfly net hangs from a circular loop of diameter 400 mm. You hold the loop horizontally in a region where the electric field is 150 N/C downward, as shown in Figure P24.58. (*a*) What is the electric flux through the net? (*b*) Does the flux through the net increase or decrease if you rotate the loop so that it lies in a vertical plane? ••

Figure P24.58

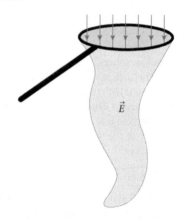

59. A particle that carries an unknown amount of charge is placed at the center of a hollow metal sphere of inner radius R_i and outer radius R_o. The magnitude of the electric field outside the sphere at any radial distance r from the center is $3kq/r^2$ (with $q > 0$), directed toward the center, and the charge on the inner surface of the sphere is $-2q$. What are (*a*) the charge on the particle and (*b*) the charge on the sphere? ••

60. A small conducting ball that carries a charge of 30.0 nC is located at the center of an electrically neutral hollow conducting sphere of inner radius 100 mm and outer radius 150 mm. What is the surface charge density (*a*) on the sphere's inner surface and (*b*) on its outer surface? (*c*) Determine the electric field as a function of r, the radial distance from the center of the sphere. ••

61. A solid conducting sphere 60 mm in radius carries a charge of 5.0 nC. A thick conducting spherical shell of inner radius 100 mm and outer radius 120 mm carries a charge of -4.0 nC and is concentric with the sphere. (*a*) Draw the electric field lines for the situation, marking the location of all charge on your diagram. (*b*) Calculate the surface charge density on the surface of the solid sphere and on the inner and outer surfaces of the thick shell. (c) Determine the electric field as a function of r, the radial distance from the center of the sphere. ●●●

24.7 Deriving Gauss's law

62. Three particles each carrying charge $+q$ are located at the corners of an equilateral triangle of side length a, and the triangle is centered on the origin of a Cartesian coordinate system. What is the electric flux through a spherical Gaussian surface centered at the origin if the radius of the Gaussian surface is (a) $a/4$ and (b) $2a$? ●

63. A particular closed surface has four sides. The electric flux is $+5.0 \text{ N} \cdot \text{m}^2/\text{C}$ through side 1, $+8.0 \text{ N} \cdot \text{m}^2/\text{C}$ through side 2, and $-9.0 \text{ N} \cdot \text{m}^2/\text{C}$ through side 3. (a) If there is no surplus charge enclosed by the surface, what is the flux through side 4? (b) If the flux through side 4 is $-8.0 \text{ N} \cdot \text{m}^2/\text{C}$, how much charge is enclosed by the surface? ●

64. A particular cylindrical Gaussian surface encloses no charge. If 20 electric field lines pass into the cylinder through one of the flat ends of the cylinder and 16 of these lines emerge from the other flat end, what can you conclude about the other 4 electric field lines? ●

65. Consider a rod of length ℓ that carries a uniform charge distribution. Is Gauss's law appropriate for calculating the electric field at a radial distance r from the midpoint of the rod's length (a) when $r \ll \ell$, (b) when $r = \ell$, and (c) when $r \gg \ell$? For each case in which your answer is yes, describe the shape of the most useful Gaussian surface. ●●

66. Any collection of N charged particles can be divided into N collections each containing one of the particles. Use the superposition property of electric fields to show that the electric flux through any Gaussian surface due to a collection of N charged particles is the sum of the fluxes through the same Gaussian surface produced by the N individual particles. ●●

67. A horizontal rectangular sheet of length ℓ and width w is positioned with its center a vertical distance $w/2$ below an infinitely long positively charged rod that has a uniform linear charge density λ. (a) If the sides of length ℓ are parallel to the rod's axis, what is the magnitude of the electric flux through the sheet? (b) If the vertical distance between the sheet center and the rod is reduced to $w/4$, does the flux magnitude increase, decrease, or stay the same? ●●

68. A cubical shell with edges of length a is positioned so that two adjacent sides of one face are coincident with the $+x$ and $+y$ axes of a rectangular coordinate system and the corner formed by these two sides is at the origin. (a) Sketch the electric field vectors in the region of the shell if an electric field of magnitude $E = bx^2$ directed along the $+x$ axis exists in this region. (b) How much charge is contained in the volume of the shell? ●●

69. A cubical Gaussian surface 30 mm on each side is centered on a particle that carries a charge of $+3.0 \ \mu\text{C}$. (a) If you draw a field line diagram with four field lines per microcoulomb, how many lines pass through the Gaussian surface? In which direction are these lines? (b) Ignoring corners and edges, how many field lines pass through each face of the Gaussian surface? (c) What is the electric flux through the Gaussian surface? (d) What is the electric flux through one face? (e) Which of your answers change if the particle is moved 10 mm away from the center of the Gaussian surface? (You don't need to obtain new values for the answers that change, if any.) ●●

70. There is a Gauss's law for gravity analogous to Gauss's law for electricity. (a) If the electric flux through a closed surface is proportional to the enclosed charge, what is the gravitational flux proportional to? (b) Write an equation for Gauss's law for gravity. ●●

71. A dipole that carries charges $\pm q$ is aligned along the y axis of an xyz rectangular coordinate system, with the midpoint of the dipole at the origin. (a) Use Gauss's law to calculate the electric flux through the xz plane, which bisects the dipole and is perpendicular to the dipole moment. (Hint: Calculate the electric flux for each charge separately and apply the principle of superposition.) (b) Calculate the flux through the xz plane by integrating the electric field in Eq. 23.8 over the plane. (You'll need to generalize Eq. 23.8 to any point on the xz plane by making the substitution $x^2 \rightarrow r^2 = (x^2 + z^2)$.) (c) Which of the two techniques lets you obtain the flux through the xz plane more easily? ●●●

24.8 Applying Gauss's law

72. A positively charged hollow sphere of radius $+100$ mm has a uniform surface charge density of $10 \text{ nC}/\text{m}^2$. Determine the electric field (a) 20 mm, (b) 90 mm, and (c) 110 mm from the center of the sphere. ●

73. A positively charged solid sphere of radius 100 mm has a uniform volume charge density of $250 \text{ nC}/\text{m}^3$. Determine the electric field (a) 20 mm, (b) 90 mm, and (c) 110 mm from the center of the sphere. ●

74. A positively charged thin cylindrical shell of length 10 m and radius 50 mm has no end caps and a uniform surface charge density of $9 \times 10^{-9} \text{ C}/\text{m}^2$. (a) What is the charge on the shell? Determine the electric field magnitude far from either end of the shell at (b) $r = 49$ mm and (c) $r = 51$ mm, where r is the radial distance from the long central axis of the shell. ●

75. An infinitely long positively charged cylindrical shell of radius a has a uniform linear charge density λ_a. An infinitely long cylindrical shell of radius $b > a$ is concentric with the first and has a uniform linear charge density λ_b. (a) Determine $\vec{E}$ in all regions. (b) If $\lambda_a = +5.0 \text{ nC}/\text{m}$, which type of charge must the shell of radius b carry and what value must λ_b have in order for the electric field to be zero for radial distances $r > b$? (c) Sketch the electric field lines for this situation. ●●

76. Two parallel vertical sheets of infinite extent carry surplus charge and are 50 mm apart. Determine the magnitude and direction of the electric field in all regions of space (a) when each sheet has a uniform surface charge density $\sigma = +3.0 \text{ nC}/\text{m}^2$ and (b) when $\sigma = +3.0 \text{ nC}/\text{m}^2$ for the left sheet and $\sigma = -3.0 \text{ nC}/\text{m}^2$ for the right sheet. (c) Draw a diagram showing the sheets and the electric field lines for the situations described in parts a and b. ●●

77. A long, thin, positively charged wire runs along the long central axis of a hollow conducting cylinder of length 10 m, inner radius 50 mm, and outer radius 70 mm. The wire has a uniform linear charge density of $+1.5 \ \mu\text{C}/\text{m}$. (a) Ignoring the regions near the two ends, calculate the surface charge density on the cylinder's inner and outer surfaces. Again ignoring the ends, determine the electric field magnitude at (b) $r = 49$ mm, (c) $r = 51$ mm, and (d) $r = 100$ mm, where r is the radial distance from the wire. ●●

78. A positively charged nonconducting hollow sphere of outer radius R and inner radius $R/2$ has a uniform volume charge density ρ. Determine the magnitude and direction of the

electric field as a function of r, the radial distance from the sphere center. ••

79. A positively charged nonconducting sphere of radius a has a uniform volume charge density ρ_0. It is snugly surrounded by a positively charged thick, nonconducting spherical shell of inner radius a and outer radius b. This thick shell has a volume charge density $\rho_0 r/a$ for $a < r \le b$. Determine the electric field in all regions as a function of r, the radial distance from the center of the sphere. ••

80. An infinitely long nonconducting solid cylinder of radius R has a nonuniform but cylindrically symmetrical charge distribution. The volume charge density is given by $\rho(r) = c/r$, where c is a positive constant having units C/m^2 and r is the radial distance from the long central axis of the cylinder. (a) What is the charge in a section of the cylinder of length ℓ? Write an expression for the electric field magnitude for (b) $r < R$ and (c) $r > R$. ••

81. An infinitely long positively charged wire with a uniform linear charge density $+\lambda$ is parallel to the y axis of a Cartesian coordinate system and passes through the x axis at $x = -d$. At the origin, the electric field due to this charged wire has magnitude E_0 and is directed to the right along the positive x axis. A second infinite charged wire, parallel to the first and with a uniform linear charge density, passes through the x axis at $x = +3d$. The vector sum of the electric field at the origin due to the two lines of charge has magnitude $2E_0$. What is the linear charge density of the second charged wire? Obtain all the possible answers. ••

82. Figure P24.82 shows a cross section through a system that consists of an infinitely long charged rod centered in a thick cylindrical shell of inner radius R and outer radius $2R$. The shell is made of a conducting material; the rod is made of a nonconducting material and has a uniform linear charge density. The electric field associated with the system is indicated by the field lines in the diagram. For each finite length ℓ of the system, there is a charge of $-q$ on the shell inner surface. For that same finite length ℓ, determine the charge on (a) the rod and (b) the shell outer surface. (c) In length ℓ, what is the charge on the shell? (d) What is the ratio of the surface charge density on the shell's inner surface to the surface charge density on the outer surface? ••

Figure P24.82

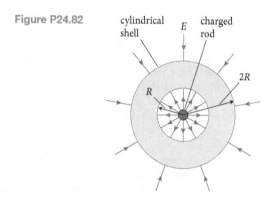

cylindrical shell · E · charged rod · $2R$ · R

83. A positively charged solid nonconducting cylinder of length $\ell = 10$ m and radius $R = 50$ mm has uniform volume charge density $+9.0 \times 10^{-9}$ C/m³. (a) What is the charge inside the cylinder? Avoiding the regions near the ends, determine the electric field magnitude at (b) $r = 40$ mm and (c) $r = 60$ mm, where r is the radial distance from the long central axis of the cylinder. ••

84. Three nonconducting infinite sheets are parallel to the yz plane of an xyz coordinate system. Each sheet has a uniform surface charge density. Sheet 1, negatively charged with surface charge density $-\sigma$, passes through the x axis at $x = 1.0$ m. Sheet 2 has an unknown surface charge density and passes through the x axis at $x = 2.0$ m. Sheet 3, negatively charged with surface charge density -3σ, and passes through the x axis at $x = 4.0$ m. The electric field due to the sheets is zero at $x = 1.5$ m. (a) What is the surface charge density on sheet 2? If the electric field at $x = 0$ is $\vec{E}_0$, what is the electric field at (b) $x = -2.0$ m (c) $x = 3.0$ m, and (d) $x = 6.0$ m? ••

85. A particle that carries positive charge $+q$ is located at the center of one or more concentric, thick or thin spherical shells. The shells are either made of a conducting material but are electrically neutral or made of a nonconducting material and have uniform surface charge densities. Figure P24.85 is the graph of the electric flux passing through spherical Gaussian surfaces centered on the particle, as a function of radial distance r from the particle. (a) What is the minimum number of spherical shells required to produce the graph? (b) Describe each shell completely, specifying its charge, its inner and outer radii, and whether it is made of a conducting or nonconducting material. ••

Figure P24.85

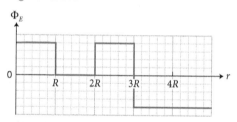

86. Can the graph in Figure P24.87 be produced by a system that consists of only charged particles? If not, explain why not. If so, describe the system that contains the minimum number of charged particles. ••

87. At what radius along the perpendicular bisector of a wire of length 0.25 m carrying 30 nC of charge does the assumption of cylindrical symmetry in applying Gauss's law give you an answer whose error exceeds 5%? ••

88. An infinitely long positively charged wire that carries a uniform linear charge density λ passes through the origin of an xy coordinate system and lies on the y axis. At the position $x = d$ on the x axis, the electric field created by this wire has magnitude E and is directed to the right along the positive x axis. A charged particle is then placed on the x axis at $x = 2d$. At $x = d$ on the x axis, the electric field created by this particle has magnitude $2E$ and is directed to the left along the x axis. (a) At what positions on the x axis is the vector sum of the electric fields zero? (b) What is the magnitude of the electric field produced by the wire at the locations you identified in part a? ••

89. The origin of an x axis is placed at the center of a nonconducting solid sphere of radius R that carries a charge $+q_{sphere}$ distributed uniformly throughout its volume. A particle that carries an unknown charge q_{part} is located on the x axis at $x = +2R$. The magnitude of the electric field due to the sphere-particle combination is zero at $x = +R/4$ on the x axis. (a) What is q_{part} in terms of q_{sphere}? (b) At what other locations on the x axis is the electric field zero? •••

90. A particle that carries charge $+4q$ is located at the origin of an x axis, and a uniformly charged nonconducting solid sphere of radius R and carrying charge $+q$ is centered at $x = +6R$ on the x axis. (*a*) At what locations on the x axis is the electric field zero? (*b*) If the nonconducting sphere is replaced by a conducting sphere of the same radius and carrying the same charge, would the answers to part *a* change? •••

91. The nonuniform volume charge density inside a positively charged solid nonconducting sphere of radius R is $\rho(r) = \rho_0 r / R$, where r is the radial distance from the sphere center. (*a*) Calculate the electric field as a function of r for $r < R$ and $r > R$. Repeat for volume charge densities of (*b*) $\rho(r) = \rho_0(1 - \frac{1}{2}R/r)$ and (*c*) $\rho(r) = \rho_0(1 - R/r)$. •••

92. A positively charged nonconducting solid sphere of radius R has a nonuniform volume charge density given by ρ_0 for $r \le R/2$ and given by $2\rho_0(1 - r/R)$ for $R/2 \le r \le R$, where r is the radial distance from the sphere center. (*a*) Determine the charge q on the sphere in terms of ρ_0 and R. (*b*) Determine $\vec{E}$ in terms of ρ_0, r, and R. (*c*) Show that the electric field is continuous at the boundaries. •••

Additional problems

93. Can an electric field line have a kink in it? •

94. Three particles each carrying charge $+q$ are located at the corners of an equilateral triangle whose side length is a. The triangle is centered on the origin of a Cartesian coordinate system. (*a*) Draw the electric field line diagram for this configuration of charge. What is the electric flux through a Gaussian surface that contains (*b*) one of the particles and (*c*) two of the particles? •

95. A particle of charge q and mass m is placed above an infinite charged sheet for which the surface charge density is σ. The sheet carries the same type of charge as the particle. What is the acceleration of the particle as a function of its distance d above the sheet? •

96. Infinite positively charged sheet 1 has uniform surface charge density $\sigma_1 = +4.0$ nC/m^2 and is located in the yz plane of a Cartesian coordinate system. Infinite negatively charged sheet 2 is parallel to sheet 1 and has uniform surface charge density $\sigma_2 = -8.0$ nC/m^2. Sheet 2 is 4 m to the right of sheet 1 along the $+x$ axis. (*a*) Determine the magnitude and direction of the electric field in all regions of space. (*b*) Draw a diagram showing the locations of the two sheets, labeling the regions and drawing the field lines for each region. ••

97. A conducting, thick spherical shell of inner radius 100 mm and outer radius 120 mm has a particle carrying a 3.0-nC charge placed at its center. (*a*) Draw the electric field line diagram for the situation, marking the location of all charge on your diagram. (*b*) Calculate the surface charge density at the inner and outer shell surfaces. (*c*) Determine the electric field as a function of r, the radial distance from the center of the shell. (*d*) Draw an electric field line diagram for the situation when the particle is displaced by 30 mm from the shell's center. ••

98. A system is composed of two infinitely long concentric cylinders, an outer cylinder O and an inner cylinder I. Each is either conducting or nonconducting, and both have a uniform surface or volume charge density. Cylinder O is a shell, and cylinder I is either solid or a shell. The graph in Figure P24.98 shows the magnitude of the electric field as a function of the radial distance r from the long central axis of the concentric cylinders. At all values of r, the electric field either is zero or has a nonzero magnitude and is directed away from the long central axis. (*a*) Deduce whether the cylinders are conducting or nonconducting, and give the relevant radii R (inner and outer radii for O; either one radius or two for I depending on whether it is solid or a shell) in terms of the general radius R shown in the graph. (*b*) What is the ratio of the charge on cylinder I to the charge on cylinder O? ••

Figure P24.98

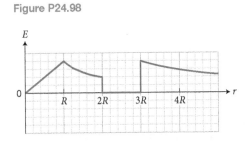

99. Near Earth's surface, the electric field has a magnitude of 150 N/C and points downward. Treating Earth's surface as a conducting sphere, calculate the surface charge density necessary to produce this electric field. ••

100. An electron initially 3.00 m from a nonconducting infinite sheet of uniformly distributed charge is fired toward the sheet. The electron has an initial speed of 400 m/s and travels along a line perpendicular to the sheet. When the electron has traveled 2.00 m, its velocity is instantaneously zero, and it then reverses its direction. (*a*) What is the surface charge density on the sheet? (*b*) Given the same initial velocity, from what distance should the electron be fired if it is to just reach the sheet? ••

101. Figure P24.101 shows four charge distributions in an xyz coordinate system. A is a charged particle at the origin, B is a charged conducting solid sphere of radius R centered at the origin, C is a uniformly charged nonconducting solid sphere of radius R centered at the origin, and D is a nonconducting infinite sheet of uniformly distributed charge in the yz plane, shown in cross section. In each case the electric field at $x = R$ is the same. Rank the magnitudes of the electric fields for the four cases, largest first, at (*a*) $x = 2R$ and (*b*) $x = R/2$. ••

Figure P24.101

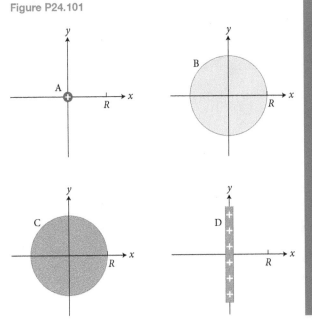

102. A positively charged nonconducting infinite sheet that has a uniform surface charge density σ lies in an xy plane. As shown in Figure P24.102, a circular region of radius R has been cut out of the sheet. (a) What is the electric field magnitude at the center of the circle? (b) Use superposition to calculate the electric field, both magnitude and direction, at a distance $z = 4R$ above the center of the circle. ••

Figure P24.102

103. A nonconducting positively charged slab 1 of thickness $2a$ has a nonuniform but symmetrical volume charge density $\rho_0 x/a$. The sheet is centered, at $x = 0$, on the yz plane of a Cartesian coordinate system. (a) Determine the magnitude and direction of the electric field in all regions of space as a function of x, the distance from the yz plane. (b) A nonconducting charged slab 2, of thickness $2t$, is placed parallel to sheet 1 such that sheet 2 intersects the x axis at $x = d$. Sheet 2 is positively charged and has a uniform volume charge density ρ_0. Determine the electric field in all regions of space as a function of x. •••

104. A quantity of positive charge is distributed throughout the volume of a long nonconducting rod, which lies on the z axis and is centered at $z = 0$. The rod's radius R is much smaller than its length ℓ. For positions $r \ll \ell$ and $|z| \ll \ell$, calculate the electric fields inside and outside the rod as a function of the radial distance r from the rod's long central axis if the volume charge density is (a) ρ_0 and (b) $\rho_0(1 - 2r/R)$. •••

105. You are a crewmember on a space station orbiting Earth. To investigate some physics you remember from college, you drill a small hole all the way through a large solid nonconducting sphere of radius R that has a negative charge q_s evenly distributed

throughout its volume, making sure the hole goes through the sphere's center. You then go outside the station with the sphere and release a small pellet carrying positive charge $+q_p$ at one entrance of the hole. You are gratified to observe that the pellet oscillates with the frequency you calculated beforehand based on Gauss's law and your knowledge of simple harmonic motion. ••• CR

106. You need to create a uniform electric field in a small region of space, and all you have to work with is one large styrofoam ball that carries a uniform volume charge distribution ρ. You cut the ball into two sections and scoop a hemispherical hole out of each section so that putting the sections back together results in a spherical cavity *off-center* inside the ball. You know that the cavity can be described as a region composed of equal amounts of uniformly distributed positive and negative charge carriers, giving it a charge of zero. You suspect the principle of superposition might be useful. ••• CR

107. Electrical power lines are often not insulated, and the magnitude of the electric field of the surrounding air is about 3×10^6 N/C. At greater electric field magnitudes, the air dissociates into charged particles, causing a breakdown and a big spark. You've been given a long sample of wire to test in the lab under electrostatic conditions, and you measure its diameter to be 16.6 mm. You have lots of equipment to produce a uniform linear charge density on the wire sample, and you figure you'd better build in a safety factor of 3 to account for humid days and so forth. ••• CR

108. An infinitely large positively charged nonconducting sheet 1 has uniform surface charge density $\sigma_1 = +130.0$ nC/m^2 and is located in the xz plane of a Cartesian coordinate system. An infinitely large positively charged nonconducting sheet 2 has uniform surface charge density $\sigma_2 = +90.0$ nC/m^2 and intersects the xz plane at the z axis, making an angle of 30° with sheet 1. (a) Draw a diagram showing the end view of the sheets in the xy plane. (b) Determine the expression for the electric field in the region between the sheets for positive values of x and y. Calculate the value of the electric field at (3 m, 1 m, 0). •••

Answers to Review Questions

1. Imagine placing a positively charged test particle near any charged object in the distribution—call it object 1—and then imagine dragging the test particle a short distance in the direction of the electric force exerted by object 1 on the particle. Draw a directed line segment along the drag path, with the arrowhead of the segment pointing in the direction of the test particle's motion. This directed line segment is the first portion of the field line. Examine the surroundings of the test particle in its new position and then imagine dragging it a short distance in the direction of the vector sum of the electric forces it now experiences due to the charge distribution. Extend the line segment along this drag path, again showing an arrowhead pointing in the direction of the test particle's motion. Repeat until you reach a charged object in the distribution (or until you reach the edge of the area you are using for your field drawing).

2. The number is arbitrary, subject to the constraint that, in a given field line diagram, the number of lines that begin or terminate on any charged object contributing to the electric field is proportional to the magnitude of the charge on that object.

3. The direction of the electric field vector at any point is tangent to the field line at that point. The density of the electric field lines in any region represents the magnitude of the electric field in that region.

4. Field line density is the number of lines per unit area that cross a surface that is perpendicular to the electric field.

5. If the surface were parallel to the electric field, no field lines would cross the surface. At an intermediate angle θ from the perpendicular, a fraction $\cos \theta < 1$ as many field lines would cross the surface. To define field line density unambiguously, we choose the surface to be perpendicular to the field lines.

6. Not necessarily. That the flux through the surface is zero tells you only that the enclosed charge (the algebraic sum of the charges on all charged objects inside the surface) is zero. There may be several charged objects inside, whose charges sum to zero. A closed surface surrounding the one proton and one electron that make up a hydrogen atom is one example.

7. Not necessarily. If any electric field lines cross the surface, then there must be one outgoing field line for every incoming field line, so that the field line flux through the surface is zero. One example is a closed surface surrounding an electric dipole. Another example is a charged particle outside a closed surface whose enclosed charge is zero.

8. (a) Because the amount of charge enclosed by the balloon does not change, the field line flux through its surface does not change. (b) Again the field line flux does not change because the enclosed charge does not change. (However, in either case the field line *pattern* changes when the electrons are placed outside the balloon.)

9. Count the number of field lines that penetrate the surface going outward as $+1$ for each penetration; count the number of field lines that penetrate the surface going inward as -1 for each penetration. Do not count field lines that do not penetrate the surface. The algebraic sum of the inward and outward values is the field line flux.

10. The electric field in the space enclosed by a uniformly charged spherical shell is zero. The electric field at points outside a uniformly charged spherical shell is the same as the electric field due to a particle carrying an equal charge located at the center of the shell.

11. Planar symmetry is the symmetry of an infinite sheet. The appearance of the sheet remains unchanged if it is rotated by any amount about an axis perpendicular to the sheet, or translated by any amount along either of the two axes perpendicular to this perpendicular axis.

12. The electric field is zero under conditions of electrostatic equilibrium (any condition where the distribution of the charged particles in the conductor does not vary with time) because the vector sum of the electric forces exerted on a test particle within the conducting material is zero.

13. If there are no charged particles inside the cavity, then the electric field is zero inside the cavity, no matter what the charge distribution is outside the sphere. The electric field inside the cavity can be nonzero when there are charged particles inside the cavity. In either case, the electric field is zero within the conducting material of the sphere itself.

14. The surplus charge must be distributed on the surfaces of the conducting object. The surplus charge resides on the outer surface of the conducting material in the absence of other charged objects, and possibly also on the inner surface surrounding the cavity if there is a charged object in the cavity.

15. The two are proportional to each other. The field line flux has an arbitrary value, depending on how many lines are drawn to represent a certain amount of charge. The electric flux is uniquely defined by Eq. 24.4.

16. A represents the area of a flat surface through which we wish to measure the electric flux. θ represents the angle between the electric field and the surface normal. So $\cos \theta = \pm 1$ if the surface is perpendicular to the electric field (that is, if the surface normal vector is parallel or antiparallel to the electric field).

17. For each small segment of the area of the surface, we need to compute the contribution $\Phi_E = EA \cos \theta$. If we simply multiplied the magnitudes of $\vec{E}$ and $\vec{A}$ without using the scalar product, we would miss the factor $\cos \theta$. The scalar product correctly incorporates the magnitude of $\vec{E}$, the magnitude of $\vec{A}$, and the cosine of the angle between $\vec{E}$ and the surface normal.

18. If we had defined the area vector as pointing inward, we would have obtained the wrong sign for Φ_E. Just as the field line density for a closed surface enclosing a positively charged particle is defined to be positive, we want the electric flux to be positive through a closed surface enclosing a positively charged particle.

19. The enclosed charge is zero because we must compute the algebraic sum of the charges on the individual particles enclosed by the spherical surface.

20. No. Checkpoint 24.20 makes a similar point. Gauss's law is a direct consequence of the $1/r^2$ dependence of the electric field due to a charged particle. Any deviation from this behavior renders Gauss's law invalid.

21. Because the charge distribution is uniform, the ratio of the charge enclosed by the Gaussian surface to the charge enclosed by the ball is the same as the ratio of the volumes of the two spheres. Therefore $q_{enc}/q = V_{enc}/V = (4\pi r^3/3)/(4\pi R^3/3)$, or $q_{enc} = q(r/R)^3$.

22. The electric field is zero anywhere the algebraic sum of the charge inside the Gaussian surface is zero. This happens for $r < R$ and $r > 2R$.

23. It doesn't matter how long you make the cylindrical Gaussian surface because this length cancels as you do the calculation coming out of Eq. 24.8. (Such a cancellation is a feature of many types of physics problems. You have to define a variable to completely specify the calculation, but if that variable is not important for the physics—and the details of an imaginary surface certainly should not be important—that variable should cancel somewhere during your calculation. If it does not, you've probably made a mistake somewhere.)

Answers to Guided Problems

Guided Problem 24.2 The electric flux is zero because the charge distribution is symmetrical under reflection through this plane.

Guided Problem 24.4 The electric flux through the top and bottom faces is zero. The electric flux through each of the other four faces is $\lambda a/4\epsilon_0$.

Guided Problem 24.6 The electric flux through the top and bottom faces is zero. The electric flux through each of the other four faces is $\lambda a/4\epsilon_0$.

Guided Problem 24.8 For $r \leq R$, $E = q/(4\pi R^2 \epsilon_0)$. For $r \geq R$, $E = q/(4\pi r^2 \epsilon_0)$.

Figure WGA24.8

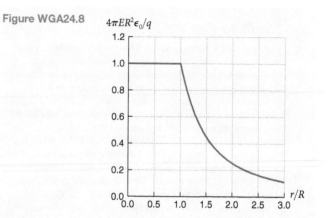

25

PRACTICE

Work and Energy in Electrostatics

PRACTICE

Chapter Summary

Energy and work (Sections 25.1, 25.2, 25.4)

Concepts **Electric potential energy** is the potential energy associated with the relative positions of charged objects.

The **electrostatic work** done by an electric field on a charged particle as the particle moves from one position to another is independent of the path taken and depends on only the particle's initial and final positions.

The constant electric field created by stationary charged objects is sometimes called an *electrostatic field*.

Quantitative Tools If two particles carrying charges q_1 and q_2 are separated by a distance r_{12}, their **electric potential energy** U^E is

$$U^E = \frac{q_1 q_2}{4\pi\epsilon_0} \frac{1}{r_{12}}, \tag{25.8}$$

where U^E is taken as zero at infinite separation. The electric potential energy of a system of charged particles is the sum of the potential energies of all possible particle pairs. For three particles, the energy is

$$U^E = \frac{q_1 q_2}{4\pi\epsilon_0} \frac{1}{r_{12}} + \frac{q_1 q_3}{4\pi\epsilon_0} \frac{1}{r_{13}} + \frac{q_2 q_3}{4\pi\epsilon_0} \frac{1}{r_{23}}. \tag{25.14}$$

Electrostatic potential (Sections 25.2, 25.3, 25.5)

Concepts The **potential difference** between points A and B in an electrostatic field is equal to the negative of the electrostatic work per unit charge done by the field on a charged particle as it moves from A to B.

An **equipotential surface** is a surface over which the electrostatic potential is constant. The electric field lines associated with a stationary charge distribution are always perpendicular to the equipotential surfaces for the charge distribution. The electrostatic work done on a charged particle moving along an equipotential surface is zero.

An electrostatic field is directed from points of higher potential to points of lower potential. The electric force pushes positively charged particles toward regions of lower potential, whereas it pushes negatively charged particles toward regions of higher potential.

Quantitative Tools If we set the zero of potential at infinity, the potential $V(r)$ at a distance r from a particle carrying a charge q is

$$V(r) = \frac{1}{4\pi\epsilon_0} \frac{q}{r}. \tag{25.21}$$

Potential is measured in **volts**:

$$1\text{ V} \equiv 1\text{ J/C}. \tag{25.16}$$

If we set the zero of potential at infinity, the potential at a point P due to a group of n charged particles of charge q_n at distances r_{nP} from point P is

$$V_P = \frac{1}{4\pi\epsilon_0} \sum_n \frac{q_n}{r_{nP}}. \tag{25.30}$$

The work W_q done on a charged particle q by an electric field $\vec{E}$ as the particle moves from point A to point B is

$$W_q(A \rightarrow B) = q\int_A^B \vec{E} \cdot d\vec{\ell}. \tag{25.24}$$

The potential difference V_{AB} between points A and B due to an electrostatic field $\vec{E}$ is

$$V_{AB} \equiv \frac{-W_q(A \rightarrow B)}{q} = -\int_A^B \vec{E} \cdot d\vec{\ell}. \tag{25.25}$$

For any electrostatic field,

$$\oint \vec{E} \cdot d\vec{\ell} = 0. \tag{25.32}$$

Continuous charge distributions (Section 25.6)

Quantitative Tools At any point P, the potential due to an extended charged object is

$$V_P = \frac{1}{4\pi\epsilon_0} \int \frac{dq_s}{r_{sP}}, \tag{25.34}$$

where r_{sP} is the distance from the infinitesimal charge element dq_s to P and the integral is taken over the object. (See the Procedure box "Calculating the electrostatic potential of continuous charge distributions.")

If a thin rod of length ℓ carries a uniformly distributed charge q, the potential due to the rod at any point P on a line that runs perpendicular to the rod and passes through either end is

$$V_P = \frac{1}{4\pi\epsilon_0} \frac{q}{\ell} \ln\left(\frac{\ell + \sqrt{\ell^2 + d^2}}{d}\right),$$

where d is the distance from P to the rod.

If a thin disk of radius R carries a uniform surface charge density σ, the potential due to the disk at any point P on a line that runs perpendicular to the plane of the disk and passes through the disk center is

$$V_P = \frac{\sigma}{2\epsilon_0}(\sqrt{z^2 + R^2} - |z|),$$

where z is the distance from P to the disk.

Calculating the electrostatic field from the potential (Section 25.7)

Quantitative Tools If we know the potential due to a charge distribution, we can use the equation

$$\vec{E} = -\frac{\partial V}{\partial x}\hat{\imath} - \frac{\partial V}{\partial y}\hat{\jmath} - \frac{\partial V}{\partial z}\hat{k} \tag{25.40}$$

to calculate the value of the electrostatic field due to the distribution at any point P(x, y, z).

We can also calculate individual components of the electric field from the potential. For example, $E_x = -\partial V/\partial x$ and $E_r = -\partial V/\partial r$.

Review Questions

Answers to these questions can be found at the end of this chapter.

25.1 Electric potential energy

1. What is electric potential energy?
2. In what way is electric potential energy more complicated than gravitational potential energy?
3. How does the electric potential energy of a dipole placed near a stationary charged object depend on the orientation of the dipole relative to the charged object?

25.2 Electrostatic work

4. What is electrostatic work?
5. When a charged particle moves in an electrostatic field, on which aspects of its path does the electrostatic work done on the particle depend? Which aspects of the path have no bearing on the amount of electrostatic work done on the particle?
6. What is electrostatic potential difference?
7. What is the distinction between the potential difference in an electric field and the potential at any point in the field?

25.3 Equipotentials

8. What are equipotential lines? Equipotential surfaces? Equipotential volumes?
9. How are equipotential lines and surfaces spatially related to electric field lines?
10. In an electric field, how does the electrostatic potential vary along a given field line?
11. What characteristic of a charged particle determines whether it tends to move from a region of higher electrostatic potential to a region of lower electrostatic potential or from a region of lower potential to one of higher potential?

25.4 Calculating work and energy in electrostatics

12. What is the mathematical expression for the electrostatic work done on a charged particle in moving the particle from one location to another in the electrostatic field created by a second charged particle?
13. What is the relationship between the electrostatic work done on a charged particle in moving it around in an electric field and the path of the motion?

14. What is the mathematical relationship between the electrostatic work done on a charged particle in moving it from point A to point B and the electrostatic potential difference between points A and B?
15. How can the electric potential energy of a system made up of two charged particles be defined when only differences in potential energy are physically meaningful?
16. What is the electric potential energy for any system of charged particles?

25.5 Potential difference

17. What is the SI unit of potential difference?
18. For (*a*) a system of charged particles and (*b*) an electric circuit, what is the common reference position used to allow us to assign a unique value of electrostatic potential to each position in the system?
19. What is the expression for determining the electrostatic potential at any given position in a system of charged particles when the potential at infinity is assigned a value of zero?
20. Is it possible to extract energy from an electrostatic field by going around a closed path?

25.6 Electrostatic potentials of continuous charge distributions

21. How can the expression for the electrostatic potential of an object that carries a continuous distribution of charge be obtained from the expression for the electrostatic potential of a system of charged particles?
22. Is there any advantage to computing the electrostatic potential of a distribution of charge rather than the electric field due to the distribution?

25.7 Obtaining the electric field from the potential

23. Can the field line pattern for the electrostatic field created by a charged object be determined from a map of the equipotentials?
24. What is the relationship between the electrostatic field and the electrostatic potential?

Developing a Feel

Make an order-of-magnitude estimate of each of the following quantities. Letters in parentheses refer to hints below. Use them as needed to guide your thinking.

1. The electrostatic work done while assembling one proton and one electron to form a hydrogen atom (F, X, A)
2. The minimum work done by an external agent to bring two protons together to form a helium nucleus (F, M, A)
3. The potential difference needed to give 10^{-12} J of kinetic energy to a proton that is initially at rest (Q, A)
4. The electrostatic potential at a point that is 30 mm from one end of a charged glass rod and lies on the line that runs through that end perpendicular to the rod's long axis (C, R, W)
5. The surface charge density on a utility-hole cover charged with a car battery (D, V, I, N, S)

6. The potential difference between floor and ceiling needed to "float" a proton in your room (Z, K, AA, U, P)
7. The potential difference required to stop an electron whose initial speed is 1×10^6 m/s (H, Q, A)
8. The initial speed, expressed as a multiple of the speed of light c, of an alpha particle (which is a helium atom stripped of its two electrons) that approaches to within 9×10^{-15} m of the center of a gold nucleus (BB, B, G, L, Q)
9. The minimum work needed to assemble eight protons, one at each of the eight corners of a 5-mm cube (E, J, O, T, Y)

Hints

A. What is the magnitude of charge on any proton or electron?
B. What is the electrostatic potential at the particle's initial position? At its final position?
C. What is the length of the charge distribution on a typical glass rod used in the laboratory?
D. How can this be done physically, and what type of charged object results?
E. How much work is required to place the first proton at the lower left front corner?
F. What is the initial separation between the two particles?
G. What is the charge of a gold nucleus?
H. What is $K_{initial}$?
I. What equipotential surface is at a potential of 12 V?
J. How much work is required to place the second proton at the lower left rear corner?
K. Which of the two surfaces, floor or ceiling, must be positively charged?
L. What is the particle's final speed?
M. What is their final separation?
N. What is a typical radius of a utility-hole cover?
O. How much work is required to place the third proton at the lower right rear corner?
P. What is the distance from floor to ceiling?
Q. How are ΔV and ΔK related for the particle?
R. What is a reasonable guess for how much charge the rubbed rod can carry?
S. How does this situation relate to the charged disk in *Principles* Example 25.7?
T. Do you see a trend in the number of terms?
U. What value of E is required in order to have the electric force balance this gravitational force?
V. What is the potential difference between the terminals of a car battery?

W. Where is the potential equal to zero?
X. What is their final separation?
Y. How many terms must be combined to get the minimum work required to place all eight protons?
Z. What forces must balance to float the proton?
AA. What is the magnitude of the gravitational force exerted?
BB. What is the initial separation distance?

Key (all values approximate)

A. elementary charge, $e = 1.6 \times 10^{-19}$ C; **B.** zero at initial position, $V = (1/4\pi\epsilon_0)(q/r)$ at final position; **C.** 0.2 m; **D.** place cover on nonconducting stand, attach positive battery terminal to cover, and negative battery terminal to ground, producing a charged disk; **E.** none, because there is no potential difference to move through; **F.** essentially infinite; **G.** 79 protons, thus $+79e$; **H.** 5×10^{-19} J; **I.** the surface of the cover; **J.** $W = q\Delta V = (1/4\pi\epsilon_0)(q^2/r)$, where r is cube edge length and q is proton charge; **K.** the floor; **L.** zero; **M.** nuclear separation distance, 2×10^{-15} m; **N.** 0.3 m; **O.** $q\Delta V = (1/4\pi\epsilon_0)(q^2/r) + (1/4\pi\epsilon_0)(q^2/\sqrt{2}r)$; **P.** 3 m; **Q.** assuming only electrostatic work, $q\Delta V + \Delta K = 0$; **R.** 1×10^1 μC; **S.** both upper and lower surfaces of the cover are charged, so there are two thin disks to superpose; **T.** each proton added requires one term for each proton already in place; **U.** $E = mg/q \approx 1 \times 10^{-7}$ V/m; **V.** 12 V; **W.** infinitely far from the rod; **X.** the atom's radius, 5×10^{-11} m; **Y.** 28, counting each pair of protons once: 12 edge terms, 12 face diagonals, and 4 body diagonals; **Z.** gravitational force exerted by Earth on proton and electric forces exerted by charged floor and ceiling on it; **AA.** 2×10^{-26} N; **BB.** infinite

Worked and Guided Problems

Procedure: Calculating the potential difference between two points in an electric field

The potential difference between two points in an electric field is given by Eq. 25.25. The following steps will help you evaluate the integral:

1. Begin by making a sketch of the electric field, indicating the points corresponding to the two points between which you wish to determine the potential difference.
2. To facilitate evaluating the scalar product $\vec{E} \cdot d\vec{\ell}$, choose a path between the two points so that $\vec{E}$ is either parallel or perpendicular to the path. If necessary, break the path into segments. If $\vec{E}$ has a constant value along the path (or a segment of the path), you can pull it out of the integral; the remaining integral is then equal to the length of the corresponding path (or the segment of the path).

3. Remember that to determine V_{AB} ("the potential difference between points A and B"), your path begins at A and ends at B. The vector $d\vec{\ell}$ therefore is tangent to the path, in the direction that leads from A to B (see also Appendix B).

At this point you can substitute the expression for the electric field and carry out the integral. Once you are done, you may want to verify the algebraic sign of the result you obtained: *negative* when a positively charged particle moves along the path in the direction of the electric field, and *positive* when it moves in the opposite direction.

Procedure: Calculating the electrostatic potential of continuous charge distributions

To calculate the electrostatic potential of a continuous charge distribution (relative to zero potential at infinity), you need to evaluate the integral in Eq. 25.34. The following steps will help you work out the integral:

1. Begin by making a sketch of the charge distribution. Mentally divide the distribution into infinitesimally small segments carrying a charge dq_s. Indicate one such segment in your drawing.
2. Choose a coordinate system that allows you to express the position of dq_s in the charge distribution in terms of a minimum number of coordinates (x, y, z, r, or θ). These coordinates are the integration variables. For example, use a radial coordinate system for a charge

distribution with radial symmetry. Never place the representative segment dq_s at the origin.
3. Indicate the point at which you wish to determine the potential. Express the factor $1/r_{sP}$, where r_{sP} is the distance between dq_s and the point of interest, in terms of the integration variable(s).
4. Determine whether the charge distribution is one dimensional (a straight or curved wire), two dimensional (a flat or curved surface), or three dimensional (any bulk object). Express dq_s in terms of the corresponding charge density of the object and the integration variable(s).

At this point you can substitute your expressions for dq_s and $1/r_{sP}$ into Eq. 25.34 and work out the integral.

These examples involve material from this chapter but are not associated with any particular section. Some examples are worked out in detail; others you should work out by following the guidelines provided.

Worked Problem 25.1 Relocating a charged particle

Consider a group of charged toner particles and how one of them can be moved around in the group. Four charged particles form a square with side length $a = 6.9\ \mu$m. Particles 1, 3, and 4 carry charge $+q = 3.9 \times 10^{-15}$ C, and particle 2 carries charge $-2q$. Particles 2 and 4 are diagonally opposite each other. How much work must be done by an external agent on particle 4 to pull it out of its corner, slide it around outside the perimeter of the square past particles 3, 2, and 1, and then place it stationary at the center of the square?

❶ GETTING STARTED We begin with a sketch of the arrangement and what we want to do with particle 4 (Figure WG25.1). We are not given much information about the external agent that causes particle 4 to move, but we do know that the change in the particle's kinetic energy is zero because it starts out with zero kinetic energy and has zero kinetic energy again after it is placed at the center of the square. Thus the work done by the external agent, the quantity

Figure WG25.1

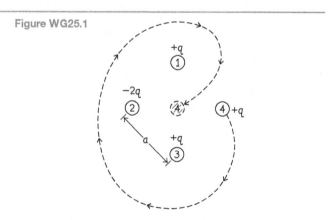

we must calculate, is the negative of the electrostatic work done by the other three particles as particle 4 is moved.

②ᴅᴇᴠɪsᴇ ᴘʟᴀɴ Because the change in kinetic energy for particle 4 is zero, we can use

$$W_{\text{on } 4} = W_{\text{by agent}} + W_{\text{by 1,2,3}} = \Delta K = 0.$$

Because electrostatic interactions are nondissipative, we know that the work done by particles 1, 2, and 3 on particle 4 equals the negative of the change in electric potential energy of the system. Thus we can use

$$W_{\text{by agent}} = - W_{\text{by 1,2,3}} = -(-q_4\Delta V) = q_4\Delta V. \qquad (1)$$

For particle 4 at any given location, the electrostatic potential at that location due to particles 1, 2, and 3 is given by

$$V = \frac{1}{4\pi\epsilon_0}\sum_{j=1}^{3}\frac{q_j}{r_j}, \qquad (2)$$

where r_j is the separation distance between particle 4 and particle j (where $j = 1, 2, 3$).

We need to determine the difference between the electrostatic potential at the initial and final positions of particle 4. We can calculate this difference in potential in two ways: use Eq. 2 with either the final or initial separation distances to calculate the potentials at those positions and then substitute the values obtained into Eq. 1, or substitute Eq. 2 into Eq. 1 and sum the potential differences due to each particle separately. We choose the latter method because it allows us to consolidate common factors easily.

③ᴇxᴇᴄᴜᴛᴇ ᴘʟᴀɴ The work done by the external agent on particle 4 is

$$W_{\text{by agent}} = q_4\left[V_f - V_i \right] = q_4\frac{1}{4\pi\epsilon_0}\left[\sum_{j=1}^{3}\frac{q_j}{r_{j,f}} - \sum_{j=1}^{3}\frac{q_j}{r_{j,i}}\right]$$

$$= \frac{q_4}{4\pi\epsilon_0}\left\{\sum_{j=1}^{3}q_j\left[\frac{1}{r_{j,f}} - \frac{1}{r_{j,i}}\right]\right\} = \frac{q_4}{4\pi\epsilon_0}\left\{ q_1\left[\frac{1}{\frac{1}{2}a\sqrt{2}} - \frac{1}{a}\right]\right.$$

$$\left. + q_2\left[\frac{1}{\frac{1}{2}a\sqrt{2}} - \frac{1}{a\sqrt{2}}\right] + q_3\left[\frac{1}{\frac{1}{2}a\sqrt{2}} - \frac{1}{a}\right]\right\}.$$

Removing the subscripts on q to simplify, with $q_4 = q_1 = q_2 = q$ and $q_2 = -2q$, we have

$$W_{\text{by agent}} = \frac{q}{4\pi\epsilon_0}\left[q\left(\frac{1}{\frac{1}{2}a\sqrt{2}} - \frac{1}{a}\right) + (-2q)\left(\frac{1}{\frac{1}{2}a\sqrt{2}} - \frac{1}{a\sqrt{2}}\right)\right.$$

$$\left. + q\left(\frac{1}{\frac{1}{2}a\sqrt{2}} - \frac{1}{a}\right)\right] = \frac{2q^2}{4\pi\epsilon_0 a}\left(\frac{1}{\sqrt{2}} - 1\right)$$

$$= \frac{2(3.9 \times 10^{-15}\,\text{C})^2}{4\pi(8.85 \times 10^{-12}\,\text{C}^2/\text{N}\cdot\text{m}^2)(6.9 \times 10^{-6}\,\text{m})}\left[\frac{1}{\sqrt{2}} - 1\right]$$

$$= -1.2 \times 10^{-14}\,\text{J}. ✔$$

④ᴇᴠᴀʟᴜᴀᴛᴇ ʀᴇsᴜʟᴛ As a check on this result, let's try the alternative approach of calculating the potential V_f at particle 4's final position, due to particles 1, 2, and 3; then calculating V_i at particle 4's initial position, due to particles 1, 2, and 3; and directly using $W_{\text{by agent}} = q_4\left[V_f - V_i \right]$. Taking the potential at infinity to be zero, we obtain

$$V_f = \frac{1}{4\pi\epsilon_0}\left(\frac{q}{a/\sqrt{2}} + \frac{q}{a/\sqrt{2}} + \frac{(-2q)}{a/\sqrt{2}}\right) = 0,$$

and we get

$$V_i = \frac{1}{4\pi\epsilon_0}\left(\frac{q}{a} + \frac{q}{a} + \frac{(-2q)}{a\sqrt{2}}\right) = \frac{q}{4\pi\epsilon_0 a}(2 - \sqrt{2}).$$

So

$$q_4\left[V_f - V_i \right] = 0 - \frac{q^2}{4\pi\epsilon_0 a}(2 - \sqrt{2}) = -1.2 \times 10^{-14}\,\text{J},$$

just as we found above. It makes sense that $V_f = 0$ because particle 4's final position is equidistant from three charged particles whose charges sum to zero. And it makes sense that $V_i > 0$ because particle 4's initial position is closer to the two positively charged particles than to the negatively charged particle. The electrostatic work done on particle 4 as it moves from $V_i > 0$ to $V_f = 0$ (negative potential difference) is positive. Because particle 4's kinetic energy does not change, this positive electrostatic work is balanced by negative work done by the external agent. So it makes sense that our answer is negative.

Guided Problem 25.2 Forming and straightening a charged triangle

You have three charged particles that are initially very far apart from one another, and you must bring them together to form an equilateral triangle of side length ℓ. Particles A and B each carry a charge $-q$, and particle C carries a charge $4q$. How much work must you do to form the triangle? How much work must you do to rearrange the particles so that they are in a straight line with particle C in the center and a distance ℓ between adjacent particles?

❶ ɢᴇᴛᴛɪɴɢ sᴛᴀʀᴛᴇᴅ

1. Sketch the triangle and the line, and describe the problem in your own words. What two values are you asked to determine?

❷ ᴅᴇᴠɪsᴇ ᴘʟᴀɴ

2. How can you relate the work you need to do in forming the triangle to the electric potential energy of the configuration?

3. What kind of drawing should you make to show the process of forming the triangle? What kind to show the straightening process?

4. How many terms are in the potential-energy sum for each configuration? What are those terms?

❸ ᴇxᴇᴄᴜᴛᴇ ᴘʟᴀɴ

5. By comparing the initial and final potential differences, compute the work done in forming the triangle. Repeat for the work done in forming the straight line.

6. Is there a shortcut for evaluating the amount of work needed to form the straight line?

❹ ᴇᴠᴀʟᴜᴀᴛᴇ ʀᴇsᴜʟᴛ

7. Which configuration do you expect to have a greater potential energy?

Worked Problem 25.3 Nonuniformly charged rubber ball

A solid rubber ball of radius R carries a charge q_{ball}, with the volume charge density increasing linearly from zero at the center to the ball's surface. What is the difference in potential between a position B on the ball's surface and any position D located a distance $d < R$ from the ball's center?

1 GETTING STARTED As usual we begin with a sketch of the situation (Figure WG25.2). Note that the problem statement does not specify that positions B and D must be on the same radial line. We could just as easily have shown D on, say, the radius that runs from the center to the 12 o'clock position at the ball's surface. Because of symmetry, the electrostatic potential is the same at each point on a spherical shell concentric with the ball, however, and so we arbitrarily show B and D on the same radial line.

Figure WG25.2

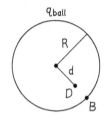

q_{ball}

The difference in potential between B and D is a line integral of the electric field from the initial position at B, where radial distance $r = R$, to the final position at D, where $r = d$. Thus we must determine $\vec{E}$. We know from symmetry that the electric field is directed radially, and we also know that the field magnitude is affected by the charge distribution, so we must determine a way to calculate that magnitude as a function of the charge distribution.

2 DEVISE PLAN The difference in potential between B and D is given by Eq. 25.25, $V_{BD} = -\int_B^D \vec{E} \cdot d\vec{\ell}$. We know from Chapter 24 that we can determine the electric field at any radial distance r from the center by using the symmetry of the problem and Gauss's law (Eq. 24.8), $\Phi_E = \oint \vec{E} \cdot d\vec{A} = q_{enc}/\epsilon_0$, where q_{enc} in our case is the quantity of charge enclosed within a sphere that is concentric with the ball and has a radius $r = d$. We can get q_{enc} by noting that the volume charge density increases linearly from zero with distance x from the center, $\rho(x) = \rho_0 x$, where ρ_0 is a constant of dimension C/m^4, and using

$$q_{enc}(r) = \int \rho \, dV,$$

where dV is the volume of a thin spherical shell concentric with the ball. The value of ρ_0 can be determined by noting that q_{ball} is the charge carried by the ball—that is, $q_{ball} = q_{enc}(R)$.

3 EXECUTE PLAN The charge enclosed by a solid sphere of arbitrary radius r is the sum of the contributions from a series of spherical shells each of radius x and thickness dx:

$$q_{enc}(r) = \int \rho \, dV = \int_0^r (\rho_0 x)(4\pi x^2 dx) = \pi \rho_0 r^4.$$

From this, we can express ρ_0 in terms of q_{ball}:

$$q_{enc}(R) = \pi \rho_0 R^4 = q_{ball}$$

$$\rho_0 = \frac{q_{ball}}{\pi R^4}.$$

Now we use Gauss's law (Eq. 24.8). Because the ball's symmetry requires that the electric field be radially directed, we have at any radial distance r from the ball's center

$$\oint \vec{E}(r) \cdot d\vec{A} = E(r)A(r) = \frac{q_{enc}(r)}{\epsilon_0}$$

$$E(r)(4\pi r^2) = \frac{\pi \rho_0 r^4}{\epsilon_0} = \frac{q_{ball} r^4}{\epsilon_0 R^4}$$

$$E(r) = \frac{q_{ball}}{4\pi \epsilon_0 R^4} r^2.$$

The difference in potential between point B on the ball's surface ($r = R$) and point D a distance $r = d$ from the ball's center is then

$$V_d - V_R = -\int_R^d \vec{E}(r) \cdot d\vec{r} = -\int_R^d E(r) dr$$

$$= -\int_R^d \frac{q_{ball}}{4\pi \epsilon_0 R^4} r^2 dr = -\frac{q_{ball}}{4\pi \epsilon_0 R^4} \left[\frac{1}{3} r^3 \right]_R^d$$

$$= \frac{q_{ball}}{12\pi \epsilon_0 R^4} (R^3 - d^3). ✔$$

4 EVALUATE RESULT If q_{ball} is positive, the electric field is directed radially outward. This means that as we move from B to D, we are moving in the direction opposite the direction of the electric field, thereby increasing the electrostatic potential. Consequently, the potential difference should be positive, which is what our answer says. The opposite is true if q_{ball} is negative, which is also consistent with our equation. Our equation says that the potential difference is a linear function of q_{ball}, and we expect $V_d - V_R$ to be greater if the ball carries more charge. We note that if we locate D such that $d = R$, the potential difference is zero, as it must be.

Guided Problem 25.4 Charged plastic sphere

A quantity q_{sphere} of charge is uniformly distributed throughout a solid plastic sphere of radius R. What is the potential difference between the center and a point A located a distance r from the center when $r < R$ and when $r > R$?

① GETTING STARTED
1. Sketch the sphere.
2. What information is given, and what variable or variables are you asked to determine?

② DEVISE PLAN
3. How do you determine the potential difference between any two positions inside the sphere? What quantities do you need to know in order to determine this difference?

4. How do you determine the charge enclosed within a spherical shell of any radius?
5. How do you relate the potential at any position outside the plastic sphere to the potential at any position inside by matching expressions at a boundary of these two regions?

③ EXECUTE PLAN

④ EVALUATE RESULT
6. Does your expression give the correct result for the potential at a location very far from the sphere center?

Worked Problem 25.5 Line of charge

A plastic rod of length ℓ is rubbed with fur to uniformly distribute a quantity q_{rod} of surplus charge. It is then placed on a nonconducting stand, and the stand is positioned so that the rod lies along the x axis of an xy coordinate system and the rod's center is at the origin. Determine the electrostatic potential at any point P located at an arbitrary position (x_P, y_P) outside the rod.

① GETTING STARTED This problem is similar to *Principles* Example 25.6, which determines the electrostatic potential for points along a line that runs through one end of a rod and is perpendicular to the rod's long axis. However, we're now asked to determine the potential at *any* location in the space surrounding the rod. We need to calculate the electrostatic potential that a charge distribution creates at a point P, and for this we need Eq. 25.34:

$$V = \int \frac{1}{4\pi\epsilon_0} \frac{dq}{r},$$

where r is the distance from P to an infinitesimal charge element dq in the charge distribution. We draw a diagram that shows the necessary information (Figure WG25.3).

Figure WG25.3

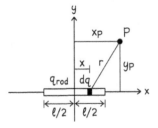

② DEVISE PLAN We need to determine the contribution to the potential from each infinitesimal charge element dq of the rod because the distance from P to the rod is different for each element. Then we integrate all the contributions to get the potential due to all the charge distributed in the rod. We need to determine appropriate values for r and dq for each position x along the rod. The amount of charge in an infinitesimal rod length dx is $dq = \lambda dx$, where $\lambda = q_{rod}/\ell$ is the linear charge density. We then integrate from one end of the rod to the other to add up the contribution of each dq to the potential.

③ EXECUTE PLAN The charge on the element dq is

$$dq = \frac{q_{rod}}{\ell}dx$$

and the distance from the element to P is

$$r = \sqrt{(x_P - x)^2 + y_P^2}.$$

Substituting gives us our expression for the potential at P:

$$V = \frac{1}{4\pi\epsilon_0} \frac{q_{rod}}{\ell} \int_{-\ell/2}^{\ell/2} \frac{dx}{\sqrt{(x_P - x)^2 + y_P^2}}.$$

By making a simple substitution, we can put the integral in a form we can look up:

$$u = x_P - x$$
$$du = -dx$$
$$V = \frac{1}{4\pi\epsilon_0} \frac{q_{rod}}{\ell} \int_{x_P+\ell/2}^{x_P-\ell/2} \frac{-du}{\sqrt{u^2 + y_P^2}}.$$

Note how the limits of integration have changed to match the change of variable to u. This integral is identical to the integral in Example 25.6:

$$V = \frac{1}{4\pi\epsilon_0} \frac{q_{rod}}{\ell} \left[-\ln\left(u + \sqrt{u^2 + y_P^2}\right) \right]_{x_P+\ell/2}^{x_P-\ell/2}$$

$$= \frac{1}{4\pi\epsilon_0} \frac{q_{rod}}{\ell} \left[\ln\left(x_P + \ell/2 + \sqrt{(x_P + \ell/2)^2 + y_P^2}\right) \right.$$

$$\left. -\ln\left(x_P - \ell/2 + \sqrt{(x_P - \ell/2)^2 + y_P^2}\right) \right]$$

$$= \frac{1}{4\pi\epsilon_0} \frac{q_{rod}}{\ell} \ln\left(\frac{x_P + \ell/2 + \sqrt{(x_P + \ell/2)^2 + y_P^2}}{x_P - \ell/2 + \sqrt{(x_P - \ell/2)^2 + y_P^2}}\right). \checkmark \quad (1)$$

We now use this equation to plot the potential due to the rod everywhere in the xy plane. A contour plot of the potential for a rod 2.0 m long is shown in Figure WG25.4 on the next page.

Figure WG25.4

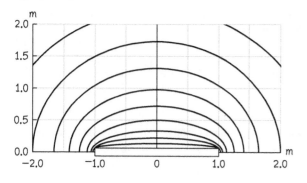

④ **EVALUATE RESULT** If P is located on a line parallel to the y axis above or below the end of the rod, then $x_P = \ell/2$. You should check

Eq. 1 for V in this special case of $x_P = \ell/2$ to confirm that we get the same expression as in Example 25.6:

$$V = \frac{q}{4\pi\epsilon_0\ell} \ln\left(\frac{\ell + \sqrt{\ell^2 + d^2}}{d}\right),$$

with the modification that our y_P corresponds to d in the *Principles* equation. Equation 1 is a complicated expression, but with it we can calculate the potential anywhere in the xy plane outside the rod. If P is very far from the rod, the rod viewed from P looks like a particle, and the potential at P calculated with Eq. 1 should be that due to a particle carrying charge q_{rod}: zero. If we let either x_P, y_P, or both become infinite in Eq. 1, the argument of the natural logarithm is unity, and $\ln(1) = 0$, yielding the expected potential of zero.

Guided Problem 25.6 Charged ring

A thin, flat ring made of a nonconducting material has inner radius R_{in} and outer radius R_{out}. Its surface charge density $\sigma(a)$ decreases with distance a from the center as $\sigma(a) = \sigma_0/a$, where σ_0 is a constant with units C/m. Determine the electrostatic potential at any location along the axis that passes through the ring's center and is perpendicular to the plane of the ring.

① **GETTING STARTED**

1. Draw a sketch of the system.
2. What makes locations on this axis special for determining electrostatic potential?

② **DEVISE PLAN**

3. What expression can you use to determine the contributions from all the charge elements dq on the ring?
4. What symmetry of the ring can you exploit to establish a group of charge elements that are all at the same distance from the desired location?

5. What mathematical quantities can you use to specify this group of charge elements?
6. What is the distance between this group of charge elements and the location you are interested in?
7. What variable(s) do you integrate to account for all the charge elements on the ring, and what are the appropriate limits of integration?

③ **EXECUTE PLAN**

8. Where can you obtain an analytic expression for the value of the resulting integral?

④ **EVALUATE RESULT**

9. Does the expression you obtained for electrostatic potential behave properly at large distances from the ring?

Worked Problem 25.7 Electric field around a charged rod

The electric field surrounding a charged object that lacks sufficient symmetry to use Gauss's law can be determined either from Coulomb's law (as we saw in Chapter 23) or from the electrostatic potential as given by Eq. 25.40. Use the latter method to determine, for any location in space, the component of the electric field perpendicular to the rod in Worked Problem 25.5.

① **GETTING STARTED** We are given, from Worked Problem 25.5, the orientation of a charged rod of length ℓ and charge q_{rod} in an xy coordinate system and are asked to use Eq. 25.40 to obtain an expression, valid at any location in the space surrounding the rod, for the perpendicular component of the electric field due to the rod. From Figure WG25.3 we see that the y component of the electric field is the one perpendicular to the rod.

② **DEVISE PLAN** We need to calculate $E_y = -\partial V/\partial y$. We have to take the partial derivative of the potential with respect to y while holding all other variables constant; in other words, we treat the position x as a constant. At any arbitrary location (x, y) the electrostatic potential is given by

$$V(x, y) = \frac{1}{4\pi\epsilon_0}\frac{q_{rod}}{\ell} \ln\left(\frac{x + \ell/2 + \sqrt{(x + \ell/2)^2 + y^2}}{x - \ell/2 + \sqrt{(x - \ell/2)^2 + y^2}}\right).$$

Taking the derivative of the logarithm's argument appears daunting, but we can simplify things by using the identity $\ln(a/b) = \ln a - \ln b$.

3 EXECUTE PLAN

$$E_y = -\frac{\partial V}{\partial y} = \frac{1}{4\pi\epsilon_0}\frac{q_{rod}}{\ell}\frac{\partial}{\partial y}\left\{\ln\left[x - \ell/2 + ((x - \ell/2)^2 + y^2)^{1/2}\right]\right.$$

$$\left. -\ln\left[x + \ell/2 + ((x + \ell/2)^2 + y^2)^{1/2}\right]\right\}$$

$$= \frac{1}{4\pi\epsilon_0}\frac{q_{rod}}{\ell}\left\{\left[\frac{\frac{1}{2}((x - \ell/2)^2 + y^2)^{-1/2}2y}{x - \ell/2 + ((x - \ell/2)^2 + y^2)^{1/2}}\right]\right.$$

$$\left. -\left[\frac{\frac{1}{2}((x + \ell/2)^2 + y^2)^{-1/2}2y}{x + \ell/2 + ((x + \ell/2)^2 + y^2)^{1/2}}\right]\right\}$$

$$= \frac{1}{4\pi\epsilon_0}\frac{q_{rod}}{\ell}y\left\{\left[\frac{((x - \ell/2)^2 + y^2)^{-1/2}}{x - \ell/2 + ((x - \ell/2)^2 + y^2)^{1/2}}\right]\right.$$

$$\left. -\left[\frac{((x + \ell/2)^2 + y^2)^{-1/2}}{x + \ell/2 + ((x + \ell/2)^2 + y^2)^{1/2}}\right]\right\}.\ ✔$$

This algebra is complicated but very useful because it is much easier to get the electric field component via the known potential than from superposition of electric fields as was done in Chapter 23. The expression for the x component of $\vec{E}$ is even more complicated than this expression for E_y, but the procedure for obtaining it is the same. You should try it.

4 EVALUATE RESULT We can check to see that our expression for E_y is not unreasonable by looking at a few limiting cases. If the location we're interested in is along the x axis, E_y should be zero by symmetry. We see that setting $y = 0$ gives $E_y(x, 0) = 0$ as expected. If the location is along the perpendicular bisector of the rod ($x = 0$), the expression we get for $E_y(0, y)$ should match the expression obtained in *Principles* Example 23.4 once we note that our rod is along the x axis whereas the rod in Example 23.4 is along the y axis:

$$E_y(0, y) = \frac{1}{4\pi\epsilon_0}\frac{q_{rod}}{\ell}y\left\{\left[\frac{((\ell/2)^2 + y^2)^{-1/2}}{((\ell/2)^2 + y^2)^{1/2} - \ell/2}\right]\right.$$

$$\left. -\left[\frac{((\ell/2)^2 + y^2)^{-1/2}}{((\ell/2)^2 + y^2)^{1/2} + \ell/2}\right]\right\}$$

$$= \frac{1}{4\pi\epsilon_0}\frac{q_{rod}}{\ell}y\left\{\frac{\ell((\ell/2)^2 + y^2)^{-1/2}}{y^2}\right\}$$

$$= \frac{1}{4\pi\epsilon_0}\frac{q_{rod}}{y((\ell/2)^2 + y^2)^{1/2}} = k\frac{q_{rod}}{y(\frac{1}{4}\ell^2 + y^2)^{1/2}}.$$

This indeed matches the result of *Principles* Example 23.4. (Remember that from Eq. 24.7 defining the permittivity constant ϵ_0, we know $k = 1/4\pi\epsilon_0$.)

Guided Problem 25.8 Electric field due to a charged disk

A thin disk of radius R has a uniform surface charge density σ. Use Eq. 25.40 to obtain an expression for the electric field along the axis that runs through the disk center and is perpendicular to the plane of the disk. Orient the disk in the xy plane of an xyz coordinate system, with the disk center at the origin, so that the axis you work with is the z axis.

1 GETTING STARTED

1. What are your knowns in this problem? What must you determine? Obtain the expression for the potential for this system from the Chapter Summary above.

2 DEVISE PLAN

2. What is the expression for the potential $V(z)$ along the z axis ($x = y = 0$)?
3. What is the relationship between an electric field and the electrostatic potential at any location in the field?

4. Which component or components of the electric field are zero by symmetry?
5. Which quantities should you hold constant when you take the appropriate partial derivative?

3 EXECUTE PLAN

4 EVALUATE RESULT

6. Is the result obtained the same as that derived in *Principles* Example 23.6? That result expressed E_z in terms of ϵ_0 and R:

$$E_z = \frac{1}{2\epsilon_0}\sigma z\left(\frac{1}{\sqrt{z^2}} - \frac{1}{\sqrt{z^2 + R^2}}\right).$$

Questions and Problems

Dots indicate difficulty level of problems: • = *easy,* •• = *intermediate,*
••• = *hard;* CR = *context-rich problem.*

25.1 Electric potential energy

1. What orientation of an electric dipole in a uniform electric field has the greatest electric potential energy? What orientation has the least? (Let the system comprise both the electric dipole and the sources of the uniform electric field.) •

2. Identical positively charged objects A, B, and C are launched with the same initial speed from the same position above a negatively charged sheet that produces a uniform electric field. The directions of the initial velocities are shown in Figure P25.2. Assuming the objects do not interact with one another, rank them in order of their speeds at the instant they reach the sheet, greatest speed first. •

Figure P25.2

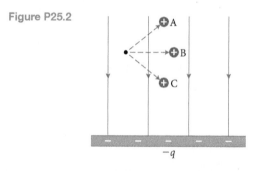

3. You release three balls simultaneously from the same height above the floor. The balls all carry the same quantity of surplus positive charge, but they have different masses: 1 kg, 2 kg, and 3 kg. In addition to the gravitational field due to Earth, there is a uniform electric field directed downward. Assume that the balls are far enough apart that they have negligible influence on one another and that air resistance can be ignored. (*a*) Which ball has the greatest speed when it reaches the floor? (*b*) If all three were negatively charged, which ball would reach the floor first? ••

4. A proton, a deuteron (a hydrogen nucleus containing one proton and one neutron), and an alpha particle (a helium nucleus consisting of two protons and two neutrons) initially at rest are all accelerated through the same distance in the uniform electric field created by a very large charged plate. Compare their final (*a*) kinetic energies, (*b*) momentum magnitudes, (*c*) speeds, and (*d*) time intervals needed to cover the distance. (*e*) How do the changes in electric potential energy compare? ••

5. A proton, a deuteron (a hydrogen nucleus containing one proton and one neutron), and an alpha particle (a helium nucleus consisting of two protons and two neutrons) initially at rest are all accelerated for the same time interval in the uniform electric field created by a very large charged plate. Compare their final (*a*) kinetic energies, (*b*) momentum magnitudes, (*c*) speeds, and (*d*) distances traveled. (*e*) How do the changes in electric potential energy compare? ••

6. Consider an isolated system of two identical electric dipoles as in Figure P25.6. For which orientation is the electric potential energy smaller? ••

Figure P25.6   (*a*)   (*b*)

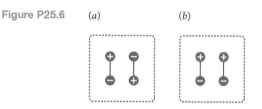

7. A dipole carrying charges $+q$ and $-q$ separated by a distance d is rotated 180° in a uniform electric field (Figure P25.7). What is the change in electric potential energy associated with this rotation? (Consider a system comprising both the dipole and the sources of the electric field.) ••

Figure P25.7

(*a*)   (*b*)

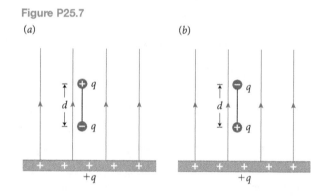

25.2 Electrostatic work

8. In an electrostatic field, path 1 between points A and B is twice as long as path 2. If the electrostatic work done on a negatively charged particle that moves from A to B along path 1 is W_1, how much work is done on this particle if it later goes from A to B along path 2? •

9. The electrostatic work done on a particle carrying charge q as the particle travels from point A to point B in an electric field is W. How much electrostatic work is done on a particle carrying charge $-2q$ that travels from B to A in the field? •

10. Electrostatic work W is done on a charged particle as it travels 10 mm along a straight path from point A to point B in an electric field. If you return the particle to point A and then exert a force on it to move it from A to B along a curved path that is 20 mm long, how much electrostatic work is done on the particle relative to the work W done along the straight path? •

11. Points A and B are on the same electric field line. If the potential difference between A and B is positive, is the field directed from A to B or from B to A? •

12. In three separate experiments, an object is moved from point A to point B in the uniform electric field of a large charged plate (Figure P25.12). The object is at rest in both the initial and final positions. Object 1 carries charge $+q$ and has mass m; object 2 carries charge $+q$ and has mass $2m$; object 3 carries charge $-q$ and has mass m. Rank the objects in order of

the changes their displacements produce in the electric potential energy of the object-plus-plate system, greatest change first. ••

Figure P25.12

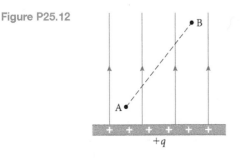

$+q$

13. Electrostatic work W is done on a charged particle as the particle travels from point A to point B in an electric field. You then apply a force to move the particle back to A, increasing its kinetic energy by an amount equal to $2W$. How much work did you do? ••

14. Points A, B, and C form the vertices of a triangle in a nonuniform electrostatic field. The electrostatic work done on a particle of charge q as the particle travels from A to B is W_{AB}, and that done on the particle as it travels from A to C is $W_{AC} = -W_{AB}/2$. How much electrostatic work is done on the particle as it travels from B to C? ••

15. In the presence of an electrostatic field, you find that you must do positive work on an electron to move it from point A to point B without changing its kinetic energy. (*a*) Considering just the electron as our system, has the system's electric potential energy increased, decreased, or remained the same? (*b*) What if your system consists of both the electron and the charged particles that are the source of the electrostatic field? (*c*) Is the electrostatic potential difference between A and B positive, negative, or zero? ••

16. In the presence of an electrostatic field, you find that you must do positive work on a proton to move it from point A to point B without changing its kinetic energy. (*a*) Considering just the proton as your system, have you increased, decreased, or left unchanged its electric potential energy? (*b*) What if your system consists of both the proton and the charged particles that are the source of the electrostatic field? (*c*) Is the potential difference between A and B positive, negative, or zero? ••

17. An electron moves from point A to point B under the influence of an electrostatic field in which the potential difference between A and B is negative. (*a*) If your system includes both the electron and the particles generating the electrostatic field, does the system's electric potential energy increase, decrease, or remain the same? (*b*) Does the electron's kinetic energy increase, decrease, or remain the same? (*c*) How would the answers in parts *a* and *b* change if your system included only the electron? ••

18. A proton moves from point A to point B under the influence of an electrostatic field in which the potential difference between A and B is negative. (*a*) If your system includes both the proton and the particles generating the electrostatic field, does the system's electric potential energy increase, decrease, or remain the same? (*b*) Does the proton's kinetic energy increase, decrease, or remain the same? (*c*) How would the answers in parts *a* and *b* change if your system included only the proton? ••

19. Four objects are moved in various ways in the electrostatic field of Figure P25.19. Rank the following motions in order of the amount of electrostatic work done on the object, smallest amount first: (*a*) an object carrying charge $+q$ is moved from A to B, (*b*) an object carrying charge $+q$ is moved from A to C, (*c*) an object carrying charge $+q$ is moved from B to C, (*d*) an object carrying charge $-q$ is moved from A to B. ••

Figure P25.19

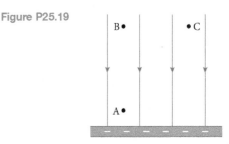

20. Points A, B, C, and D are at the corners of a square area in an electric field, with B adjacent to A and C diagonally across from A. The potential difference between A and C is the negative of that between A and B and twice that between B and D. In terms of the potential difference between A and B, what is the potential difference (*a*) between B and C, (*b*) between C and D, and (*c*) between A and D? •••

25.3 Equipotentials

21. Can an equipotential line ever cross itself? •

22. Can you draw an equipotential surface through a position where the electric field vanishes? •

23. Describe the equipotential surfaces associated with an infinitely long charged wire that has a uniform linear charge density. •

24. Sketch some equipotential lines for the electric field line pattern of a electric dipole. ••

25. Sketch some electric field lines and equipotential lines associated with two identical charged particles spaced horizontally. ••

26. Some equipotential lines surrounding a negatively charged object are shown in Figure P25.26, where the potential difference between any two adjacent lines is the same. (*a*) In which region is the electric field magnitude greatest? (*b*) What is the direction of the electric field in that region? (*c*) Which equipotential line has the greatest potential? ••

Figure P25.26

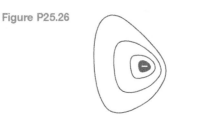

27. You determine that it takes no electrostatic work to move a charged object from point A to point B along a particular path. (*a*) Can you conclude that A and B are on the same equipotential surface? (*b*) Can you say that the path is part of an equipotential surface that includes A and B? Justify your answers. ••

28. Figure P25.28 shows that the spacing between equipotential surfaces surrounding a charged particle increases with radial distance r away from the particle. (a) How would the potential have to depend on r in order to make the spacing between equipotential surfaces uniform? (b) How would the electric field depend on r in that case? ••

Figure P25.28

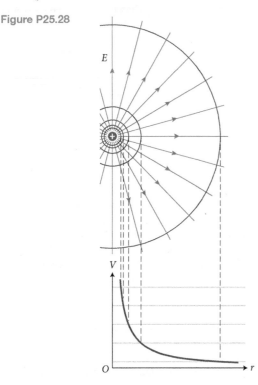

25.4 Calculating work and energy in electrostatics

29. Particle A carrying a charge of 3.0 nC is at the origin of a Cartesian coordinate system. (a) What is the electrostatic potential (relative to zero potential at infinity) at a position $r = 4.0$ m from the origin? (b) With particle A held in place at the origin, how much work must be done by an outside agent to bring particle B, also carrying a 3.0-nC charge, from infinity to $r = 4.0$ m? (c) Particle B is returned to infinity, and particle A is moved to $r = 4.0$ m and held there. How much work must be done by an outside agent to bring particle B from infinity to the origin? •

30. A particle carrying a charge of 6.0 nC is released from rest in a uniform electric field of magnitude 2.0×10^3 N/C. What are (a) the electrostatic work done on the particle after it has moved 4.0 m and (b) the particle's kinetic energy at that instant? •

31. Particles A, B, C, and D in Figure P25.31 each carry a charge of magnitude 3.0 nC. Calculate the electric potential energy for the charge distribution in this 3.0-m square (a) if all the

Figure P25.31

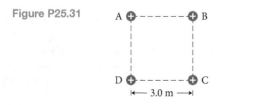

charges are positive; (b) if B, C, and D are positive and A is negative; (c) if B and C are positive and A and D are negative; and (d) if A and C are positive and B and D are negative. ••

32. Particles A and B, each carrying a charge of 2.0 nC, are at the base corners of an equilateral triangle 2.0 m on a side. (a) What is the potential (relative to zero at infinity) at the apex of the triangle? (b) How much work is required to bring a positively charged particle carrying a charge of 5.0 nC from infinity to the apex if A and B are held fixed? (c) Answer parts a and b for the case where particle B is replaced by a particle carrying a charge of -3.0 nC. (d) Calculate the electric potential energy for each of the two triangular charge distributions. ••

33. Six particles, each carrying a charge of 3.0 nC, are equally spaced along the equator of a sphere that has a radius of 0.60 m and has its center at the origin of a rectangular coordinate system. What is the electrostatic potential (relative to zero at infinity) (a) at the sphere center and (b) at either pole of the sphere? ••

34. An electron and a proton are held on an x axis, with the electron at $x = +1.000$ m and the proton at $x = -1.000$ m. (a) How much work is required to bring an additional electron from infinity to the origin? (b) If, instead of the second electron coming in from infinity, it is initially at $x = +20.00$ m on the axis and is given an initial velocity of 500.0 m/s toward the origin, does it reach the origin? If so, what is its speed at the instant it reaches the origin? If not, how close to the origin does it come? ••

35. Four objects, each carrying a charge of magnitude q, are placed at the corners of a square measuring d on each side. Two of the objects are positively charged, and two are negatively charged, with like-charged objects placed at opposite corners of the square. (a) Is the electric potential energy associated with this charge distribution positive, negative, or zero? (b) Confirm your answer to part a by calculating the electric potential energy. ••

25.5 Potential difference

36. Show that the units of electric field, newtons per coulomb, are equivalent to the units volts per meter. •

37. Four possible paths for a positively charged object traveling from a 2-V equipotential to a 3-V equipotential are shown in Figure P25.37. Rank the paths in order of the electrostatic work done on the object along each path, greatest value first. •

Figure P25.37

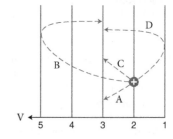

38. An infinite sheet carries a surface charge density of 3.5 nC/m². How far apart are the equipotential surfaces whose potentials differ by 100 V? •

39. Four particles, each carrying a charge of magnitude 3.0 nC, are at the corners of a square that has a side length of 3.0 m. For zero potential set at infinity, calculate the potential at the

center of the square (*a*) if all particles are positively charged, (*b*) if three particles are positively charged and one is negatively charged, and (*c*) if two particles are positively charged and two are negatively charged. ••

40. A particle carrying charge +9.00 nC is at the origin of a rectangular coordinate system. Taking the electrostatic potential to be zero at infinity, locate the equipotential surfaces at 20.0-V intervals from 20.0 V to 100 V, and sketch them to scale. Are these surfaces equally spaced? ••

41. A particle carrying charge +*q* is located on the *x* axis at *x* = +*d*. A particle carrying charge −3*q* is located on the *x* axis at *x* = −7*d*. (*a*) With zero potential at infinity, at what locations on the *x* axis is the electrostatic potential zero? (*b*) At what locations on the *y* axis is the potential zero? (*c*) Answer the questions of parts *a* and *b* for the case where the object at *x* = −7*d* carries charge +3*q*. ••

42. In a rectangular coordinate system, a positively charged infinite sheet on which the surface charge density is +2.5 μC/m^2 lies in the *yz* plane that intersects the *x* axis at *x* = 0.10 m. What are (*a*) $\vec{E}$ for *x* > 0.10 m and (*b*) the potential difference *V*(0.20 m) − *V*(0.50 m)? (*c*) A +1.5-nC charged particle is initially at *x* = 0.50 m. How much work must an external agent do to move this particle to *x* = 0.20 m? (*d*) Taking the potential to be zero at the sheet, draw three equipotential surfaces at 20-V intervals on each side of the plane, labeling each surface with its potential value. ••

43. In a rectangular coordinate system, an infinite sheet having a positive surface charge density lies in the *yz* plane that intersects the *x* axis at *x* = 0.50 m. Points A and B are on the *x* axis at *x* = 2.0 m and *x* = 7.0 m, respectively. (*a*) Is the potential difference *V*$_B$ − *V*$_A$ positive or negative? If the magnitude of the potential difference is 15.0 V, what are (*b*) $\vec{E}$ in this region and (*c*) the numerical value of +σ? ••

44. Figure P25.44 shows three configurations of charged particles. All the particles are the same distance from the origin. Rank the configurations in terms of (*a*) the electrostatic potentials at the origin, greatest first, and (*b*) the electric potential energies of the three-particle system, greatest first. ••

Figure P25.44

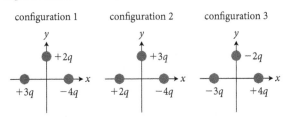

45. Two parallel conducting plates are 0.10 m apart and carry equal and opposite charges. They are large enough relative to the 0.10-m separation distance that we can assume the electric field between them is uniform. The potential difference between them is 500 V. An electron is released from rest at the negative plate. (*a*) Draw the electric field between the plates, indicating the sign of the charge on each plate and which plate is at the higher electrostatic potential. (*b*) What is the magnitude of the electric field between the plates? (*c*) What is the change in the potential energy of the system comprising the plates and the electron when the electron moves from the negative plate to the positive plate? (*d*) How much work is

done by the electric field on the electron as it makes this trip? (*e*) What is the electron's kinetic energy when it reaches the positive plate? ••

46. Two parallel conducting plates carry equal and opposite charges. The plates are large relative to their separation distance, so we can assume the electric field between them is uniform. The potential difference between them is 0.25 V, and the magnitude of the electric field between them is 50 V/m. (*a*) What is the surface charge density on the plates? (*b*) What is the separation distance? (*c*) How much work is done by the electric field on an electron as it moves from the negative plate to the positive plate? ••

47. Particle 1 carrying charge +*q*$_1$ is placed on the *x* axis at *x* = −*d*. Particle 2 carrying some unknown charge *q*$_2$ is placed somewhere on the *x* axis. The potential energy associated with the charges is +*q*$_1^2$/(2$\pi\epsilon_0 d$), and the electrostatic potential due to the charges is +*q*$_1$/($\pi\epsilon_0 d$) at the origin and zero at an infinite distance. (*a*) What is the sign of the charge on particle 2? (*b*) What is the magnitude of the charge on particle 2, and where on the *x* axis was particle 2 placed? Determine all possible answers. ••

48. Two charged particles are placed near the origin of an *xyz* coordinate system. Particle 1 carries charge +*q* and is on the *x* axis at *x* = +*d*. Particle 2 carries an unknown charge and is at an unknown location. The magnitude of the electric field at the origin is *q*/(2$\pi\epsilon_0 d^2$), and the electrostatic potential at the origin, relative to *V* = 0 at infinity, is +3*q*/(4$\pi\epsilon_0 d$). (*a*) If particle 2 is on the *x* axis, what are its charge and location? (*b*) If particle 2 is on the *y* axis, what are its charge and location? Determine all possible solutions. •••

25.6 Electrostatic potentials of continuous charge distributions

49. A thin disk of radius *R* = 62.5 mm has uniform surface charge density σ = 7.5 nC/m^2. Calculate the potential on the axis that runs through the disk center and is perpendicular to the disk face at distances (*a*) 5.0 mm, (*b*) 30 mm, and (*c*) 62.5 mm from the disk. •

50. Charge *q* = +10 nC is uniformly distributed on a spherical shell that has a radius of 120 mm. (*a*) What are the magnitude and direction of the electric field just outside and just inside the shell? (*b*) What is the electrostatic potential just outside and just inside the shell, relative to zero at infinity? (*c*) What are the electrostatic potential and electric field magnitude at the shell's center? •

51. A very long positively charged wire on which the linear charge density λ is 150 nC/m lies on the *z* axis of a rectangular coordinate system. Calculate the electrostatic potential (*a*) 2.0 m, (*b*) 4.0 m, and (*c*) 12 m from the wire, assuming that *V* = 0 at 2.5 m. ••

52. A particle carrying charge +*q* is placed at the center of a thick-walled conducting shell that has inner radius *R* and outer radius 2*R* and carries charge −4*q*. A thin-walled conducting shell of radius 3*R* carries charge +4*q* and is concentric with the thick-walled shell. Defining *V* = 0 at infinity, calculate all distances from the particle at which the electrostatic potential is zero. ••

53. Four uniformly charged nonconducting rods, each of length ℓ and carrying charge +*q*, are arranged in a square of side length ℓ. At the center of the square, what are (*a*) the magnitude of the electric field and (*b*) the electrostatic potential? ••

54. Figure P25.54 shows three charge distributions. In A, a particle carrying a charge $+q$ is located a distance R from the origin. In B, $+q$ charge is spread uniformly over a semicircle of radius R centered at the origin. In C, $+q$ charge is spread uniformly over a circle of radius R centered at the origin. Rank these distributions in terms of (a) the electric field magnitude at the origin, smallest first, and (b) the electrostatic potential at the origin, smallest first. (c) Using infinity as the location where the electrostatic potential is zero, write an expression for the electrostatic potential at the origin in distribution B. ••

Figure P25.54

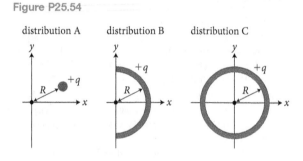

distribution A   distribution B   distribution C

55. A particle carrying charge $q_p = +10$ nC is located at $y_p = 0.030$ m on the y axis of an xy coordinate system. A nonconducting rod of length $\ell = 0.10$ m carrying charge $q_r = -10$ nC lies on the x axis, extending from $x = 0$ to $x = 0.10$ m. Write an expression for the electrostatic potential for any position along the y axis. ••

56. A disk of radius R has positive charge uniformly distributed over an inner circular region of radius a and negative charge uniformly distributed over the outer annular (ring-shaped) region (Figure P25.56). The surface charge density on the inner region is $+\sigma$, and that on the annular region is $-\sigma$. The electrostatic potential at P, located on the central perpendicular axis a distance $z = R$ from the disk center, is zero. What is a in terms of R? •••

Figure P25.56

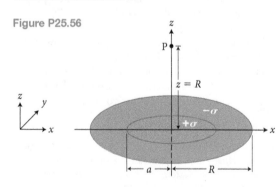

57. The surface charge density on a nonconducting disk of radius R varies with the radius as $\sigma(r) = cr$, where c is a positive constant ($c > 0$). Derive an expression for the electrostatic potential as a function of position x along an x axis that runs through the disk center and is perpendicular to the disk face, with the disk center at $x = 0$ on this axis. •••

58. A very long, solid, positively charged cylinder has a radius R and is made of a nonconducting material. The nonuniform volume charge density is given by $\rho = +ar$, where r is the radial distance away from the long central axis of the cylinder. Calculate the difference in electrostatic potential between a location on the axis and a location on the outer surface of the cylinder. •••

25.7 Obtaining the electric field from the potential

59. The electrostatic potential in some region of space is given by $V(x) = A + Bx$, where V is in volts, x is in meters, and A and B are positive constants. Determine the magnitude of the electric field in this region. In what direction is the field? •

60. The electrostatic potential in a particular xy coordinate system is given by $V(x, y) = 3xy - 5y^2$. Obtain the expression for the electric field. •

61. A particle carrying $+3.00$ nC of positive charge is at the origin of an xy coordinate system. Take $V(\infty)$ to be zero for these calculations. (a) Calculate the potential V on the x axis at $x = 3.0000$ m and at $x = 3.0100$ m. (b) Does the potential increase or decrease as x increases? Compute $\Delta V/\Delta x$ for distances along the x axis, where ΔV is the difference in potential between $x = 3.0000$ m and $x = 3.0100$ m, and $\Delta x = 0.0100$ m. (c) Calculate the electric field magnitude at $x = 3.0000$ m, and compare this magnitude with value calculated for $\Delta V/\Delta x$ in part b. (d) Calculate the electrostatic potential at the position $x = 3.0000$ m, $y = 0.0100$ m, and compare your result with the potential at $x = 3.0000$ m calculated in part a. Discuss the significance of this result. ••

62. Two particles, each carrying positive charge q, are on the y axis, one at $y = +a$ and the other at $y = -a$. (a) Calculate the potential for any point on the x axis. (b) Use your result in part a to determine the electric field at any point on the x axis. ••

63. Figure P25.63 shows a two-dimensional slice through a set of equipotential surfaces. (a) At which of the locations marked A, B, C, and D is the magnitude of the electric field greatest? (b) Is the magnitude of the electric field greater at B or at F? (c) Sketch some electric field lines to support your arguments. ••

Figure P25.63

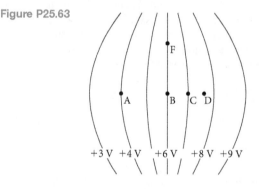

+3 V +4 V   +6 V   +8 V +9 V

64. A particle carrying 3.00 nC of positive charge is at the origin of a rectangular coordinate system, and a particle carrying 3.00 nC of negative charge is on the x axis at $x = 6.00$ m. (a) Calculate the potential on the x axis at $x = 3.00$ m, relative to zero potential at infinity. (b) Calculate the electric field on the x axis at $x = 3.00$ m. (c) Calculate the potential on the x axis at $x = 3.01$ m. (d) Compute $\Delta V/\Delta x$ for ΔV between $x = 3.00$ m and $x = 3.01$ m, and $\Delta x = 0.01$ m, and compare your result with your result in part b. ••

65. A ring of radius a carrying a uniformly distributed charge q is located in the yz plane of a rectangular coordinate system, with the center of the ring at the origin. (a) Sketch a graph of the electrostatic potential $V(x)$ as a function of distance along the x axis. (b) At what position is $V(x)$ a maximum? (c) What is E_x at this position? •••

66. Consider a spherically symmetrical distribution of charged particles. The magnitude of charge for the distribution is q, and the radius of the distribution is R. The electrostatic potential varies with radial distance r away from the center of the distribution. For $r > 2R$, $V(r) = -q/(4\pi\epsilon_0 r)$; for $R < r < 2R$, $V(r) = -q/(8\pi\epsilon_0 R)$; and for $r < R$, $V(r) = -3q/(4\pi\epsilon_0 r) + 5q/(8\pi\epsilon_0 R)$. (a) What is the electric field in these three regions? Use $V(\infty) = 0$ in your calculations. (b) Describe a set of objects that could produce an electrostatic potential that behaves in this way. ●●●

Additional problems

67. An electron travels from point A to point B in an electrostatic field and gains kinetic energy. (a) Is the electrostatic work done on the electron positive, negative, or zero? (b) Is the potential at A higher than, lower than, or the same as the potential at B? ●

68. A proton travels from point A to point B in an electrostatic field and gains kinetic energy. (a) Is the electrostatic work done on the proton positive, negative, or zero? (b) Is the potential at A higher than, lower than, or the same as the potential at B? ●

69. Calculate E_x for each potential: (a) $V(x) = a + bx$, $a = 4000$ V, $b = 6000$ V/m. (b) $V(x) = ax + b/x$, $a = 1500$ V/m, $b = 2000$ V·m. (c) $V(x) = ax - bx^2$, $a = 2000$ V/m, $b = 3000$ V/m^2. (d) $V(x) = -2000$ V (independent of x). ●

70. Consider an isolated, uniformly charged spherical shell of radius R carrying positive charge q. Point A is on the shell, point B is a distance $2R$ from the center, point C is a distance $R/2$ from the center, and point D is at the center. Is the potential difference positive or negative (a) between A and B, (b) between A and C, (c) between A and D? ●●

71. You are sketching equipotentials for a positively charged particle, having defined $V = 0$ at infinity. If you draw the 5.0-V equipotential as a circle with a radius of 50 mm, what is the radius of (a) the 10-V equipotential and (b) the 2.0-V equipotential? ●●

72. A uniformly charged rod of length ℓ and charge $+q$ lies on the x axis of a Cartesian coordinate system, extending from the origin to $x = -\ell$. What is the electric potential due to this rod at a position on the positive x axis that is a distance d from the origin? ●●

73. A solid sphere of radius R is concentric with a conducting spherical shell that carries charge $+q_{shell}$ and has an inner radius of $2R$ and outer radius of $3R$. If the electrostatic potential at the common center of the sphere and shell is the same as the potential at infinity, what is the charge q_{sphere} on the solid sphere (a) if the sphere is conducting and (b) if the sphere is nonconducting and has a uniform charge distribution throughout it? ●●●

74. You really like your new job at the atomic physics lab. Your boss casually mentions that the electron in a helium ion (He$^+$) emits energy in the form of radiation as it jumps from an orbit that has a radius of 0.42 nm to an orbit that has a radius of 0.24 nm. Sensing a chance to make a good impression, you wonder if any more information is needed in order to figure out the energy carried off by the emitted radiation. ●●● CR

75. You have always wondered exactly how strong is the interaction called the *strong nuclear interaction*, and you suspect that an element like uranium could make a good test case. You begin to wonder if the electric potential energy discussed in this chapter might provide a path to an answer. As you search for a starting point, you return to *Principles* Example 25.4, which examines the energy associated with holding the hydrogen atom together. But there is only one proton in the hydrogen nucleus, whereas a uranium nucleus has 92 protons, separated from one another by about 2×10^{-15} m. Clearly something must be able to hold all those protons so close to one another. ●●● CR

76. Two charged objects 1 and 2 are held a distance r apart. Object 1 has mass m and charge $+2q$, and object 2 has mass $2m$ and charge $+q$. The objects are released from rest. Assume that the only force exerted on either object is the electric force exerted by the other object. (a) When the objects are in motion, what is the ratio of their kinetic energies K_2/K_1? When the objects are a distance $4r$ apart, what is the speed of (b) object 1 and (c) object 2? When the objects are very far apart, what is the speed of (d) object 1 and (e) object 2? ●●●

Answers to Review Questions

1. Electric potential energy is the potential energy associated with the relative positions of objects that carry electrical charge.
2. The gravitational interaction can be only attractive, but the electric interaction can be either attractive or repulsive, depending on whether the charged objects carry charge of the same type (interaction is repulsive) or charge of opposite types (interaction is attractive). For oppositely charged objects, electric potential energy (like gravitational potential energy) decreases with decreasing separation, but for charged objects of the same sign, electric potential energy increases with decreasing separation.
3. The electric potential energy of the dipole is at its minimum when the dipole is oriented in the direction of the electric field created by the charged object and increases as the angle between the dipole orientation and the field direction increases.
4. Electrostatic work is the work done by an electrostatic field on a charged particle or charged object.
5. The amount of electrostatic work done on the particle depends on the two endpoints of the path. The work done is not affected by either path length or path shape.
6. The electrostatic potential difference between any two points A and B in an electrostatic field is the negative of the electrostatic work per unit charge done on a charged particle moved along any path from A to B.
7. Potential difference is a quantity related to *two locations* in an electric field and is numerically equivalent to the electrostatic work per unit charge done on a charged particle moved from one location to the other. Potential is a quantity that is related to any *one location* in an electric field; a value for potential can be assigned to any location in the field once we choose a reference location at which the potential in the field is zero.
8. Equipotential lines and surfaces are any lines and surfaces in an electric field along which the electrostatic potential is the same everywhere. An equipotential volume is the interior of a conducting object in electrostatic equilibrium, because the electric field magnitude in that interior is zero, making the whole interior an equipotential volume.
9. Equipotential lines and surfaces in an electric field are always perpendicular to the field lines.
10. The potential decreases as you move along the field line in the direction of the field.
11. The type of charge the particle carries. The electric force exerted on a positively charged particle is in the direction of the electric field, which means the force tends to move the particle in the direction from higher to lower electrostatic potential. The electric force exerted on a negatively charged particle is in the opposite direction and so tends to move the particle from a region of lower potential to a region of higher potential.
12. The expression, derived from a line integral of the electric force over the path of the particle's motion, is given by Eq 25.5.
13. There is no relationship. The amount of electrostatic work done is independent of the path; it depends on only the initial and final positions of the particle.
14. The electrostatic work per unit charge done on a charged particle as it moves from A to B is the negative of the potential difference between point A and point B.
15. We define the system's electric potential energy by choosing some reference configuration of the particles in which the electric potential energy is defined to be zero. Usually, the best choice for this zero-potential-energy configuration is infinite separation between the particles (which corresponds to zero electric force between them). The potential energy of the system when the separation distance is some finite value is then the difference between U^E at that separation distance and $U^E(=0)$ at infinity.
16. For a system of charged particles, the electric potential energy is the sum of the potential energies for each pair of particles, as given in Eq. 25.14 for a system of three particles.
17. The volt, which equals one joule per coulomb.
18. (*a*) The reference position at which electrostatic potential is defined to be zero is either infinity (which means infinite separation between particles) or (*b*) in dealing with electric circuits the ground.
19. Equation 25.30, $V_P = (1/4\pi\epsilon_0)\sum_n q_n/r_{nP}$, where r_{nP} is the distance between the particle whose charge is q_n and the position P at which the electrostatic potential is being measured.
20. No, because the work done by an electrostatic field is path-independent, which means the work done by the field is zero for a closed path because the beginning and end of the path are at the same location.
21. Treat each infinitesimal element of charge as a particle and integrate over the object, obtaining Eq. 25.34, $V = (1/4\pi\epsilon_0)\int (dq/r)$, where r is the distance between the infinitesimal element that carries charge dq and the position at which the potential is being measured.
22. Yes, because electrostatic potential is a scalar (which is easier to calculate than an electric field, which is a vector) and potential and field represent two different ways of expressing equivalent information.
23. Yes, because we know that the field lines are perpendicular to the equipotentials and that the direction of the field is the same as the direction of decreasing potential. The field magnitude correlates with the density of the equipotentials: The more closely spaced the equipotentials, the greater the field magnitude.
24. The component of the electrostatic field in any of the Cartesian directions x, y, z is equal to the negative of the derivative of the electrostatic potential with respect to distance in that direction (Eq. 25.40).

Answers to Guided Problems

Guided Problem 25.2 To form the triangle: $W_1 = U_i^E = -\dfrac{7q^2}{4\pi\epsilon_0\ell}$. To rearrange:

$$W_2 = U_f^E - U_i^E = -\frac{q^2}{8\pi\epsilon_0\ell}.$$

Guided Problem 25.4 The potential difference from the center of the sphere to radius r is $V_{0r} = -\dfrac{q_{sphere}r^2}{8\pi\epsilon_0 R^3}$ for $r < R$ and
$V_{0r} = \dfrac{q_{sphere}}{8\pi\epsilon_0}\left(\dfrac{2}{r} - \dfrac{3}{R}\right)$ for $r > R$.

Guided Problem 25.6 With the ring centered at the origin of the z axis,
$$V(z) = \frac{\sigma_0}{2\epsilon_0}\ln\left(\frac{R_{out} + \sqrt{R_{out}^2 + z^2}}{R_{in} + \sqrt{R_{in}^2 + z^2}}\right).$$

Guided Problem 25.8 $E_z = \dfrac{1}{2\epsilon_0}\sigma z\left(\dfrac{1}{\sqrt{z^2}} - \dfrac{1}{\sqrt{z^2 + R^2}}\right)$

26

PRACTICE

Charge Separation and Storage

PRACTICE

Chapter Summary

Capacitors (Sections 26.1, 26.2, 26.5)

Concepts A **charge-separating device** (such as a battery) has some mechanism that moves charge carriers *against* an electric field. The work done in this process increases the system's electric potential energy.

A **capacitor** consists of a pair of conducting objects separated by a nonconducting material or vacuum. The objects store electric potential energy once charge has been transferred from one to the other.

A *parallel-plate capacitor* consists of two parallel conducting plates of surface area A separated by a gap of width d. The electric field is uniform between the plates.

A *coaxial capacitor* consists of two coaxial conducting cylinders of radii R_1 and $R_2 > R_1$ and length $\ell \gg R_2$.

A spherical capacitor consists of two concentric conducting spherical shells of radii R_1 and $R_2 > R_1$.

Quantitative Tools The conducting objects in a capacitor carry charges of equal magnitude q but opposite sign. The charge separation produces a potential difference of magnitude V_{cap} between the objects. The **capacitance** C of this arrangement is

$$C \equiv \frac{q}{V_{cap}}. \tag{26.1}$$

Capacitance is measured in **farads** F, where

$$1\ F \equiv 1\ C/V.$$

The capacitance of a *parallel-plate capacitor* is

$$C = \frac{\epsilon_0 A}{d}.$$

The capacitance of a *coaxial capacitor* is

$$C = \frac{2\pi\epsilon_0 \ell}{\ln(R_2/R_1)}.$$

The capacitance of a spherical capacitor is

$$C = 4\pi\epsilon_0 \frac{R_1 R_2}{R_2 - R_1}.$$

Electric field energy and emf (Sections 26.4, 26.6)

Concepts The **energy density** of an electric field is the energy per unit volume stored in the field.

The **emf** of any charge-separating device is the work per unit charge done by nonelectrostatic interactions in separating positive and negative charge carriers.

Quantitative Tools The electric potential energy U^E stored in a capacitor is

$$U^E = \tfrac{1}{2}\frac{q^2}{C} = \tfrac{1}{2}CV_{cap}^2 = \tfrac{1}{2}qV_{cap}. \tag{26.4}$$

In air or vacuum, the **energy density** u_E of an electric field is

$$u_E = \tfrac{1}{2}\epsilon_0 E^2. \tag{26.6}$$

The **emf** $\mathcal{E}$ of a charge-separating device is

$$\mathcal{E} \equiv \frac{W_{nonelectrostatic}}{q}. \tag{26.7}$$

Dielectrics (Sections 26.3, 26.7, 26.8)

Concepts A **dielectric** is a polarizable nonconducting material. A *polar* dielectric is made up of molecules that have a permanent dipole moment, whereas a *nonpolar* dielectric consists of molecules that do not have a dipole moment in the absence of an electric field.

Quantitative Tools The **dielectric constant** κ of a material between capacitor plates is

$$\kappa \equiv \frac{V_0}{V_d}, \tag{26.9}$$

where V_0 is the potential difference across the capacitor without the dielectric and V_d is the potential with the dielectric in place.

A dielectric inserted between the plates of a capacitor becomes polarized by the electric field of the capacitor. This polarization gives the two faces of the dielectric thin layers of charge of equal magnitude but opposite sign. This charge is **bound** because the charge carriers are not free to move. The charge on the capacitor plates is **free** because the charge carriers are free to move.

If a capacitor has capacitance C_0 without a dielectric, its capacitance with a dielectric is

$$C_d = \kappa C_0. \tag{26.11}$$

If q_{free} is the **free charge** on a capacitor, then the **bound charge** q_{bound} is

$$q_{\text{bound}} = \frac{\kappa - 1}{\kappa} q_{\text{free}}. \tag{26.18}$$

Gauss's law in matter is

$$\oint \kappa \vec{E} \cdot d\vec{A} = \frac{q_{\text{free, enc}}}{\epsilon_0}, \tag{26.25}$$

where $q_{\text{free, enc}}$ is the free charge enclosed by the Gaussian surface.

Review Questions

Answers to these questions can be found at the end of this chapter.

26.1 Charge separation

1. What is the difference between the potential difference in a system and the system's electric potential energy?
2. When two charged objects that make up a system are separated by some distance, on what quantities does the system's electric potential energy depend?
3. In a system of charged objects separated from one another, where in space should one say that the system's electric potential energy is stored?
4. What does a Van de Graaff generator produce?

26.2 Capacitors

5. What is a capacitor?
6. Describe a parallel-plate capacitor. What geometric approximation is usually made in treating parallel-plate capacitors, and what simplification for its electrical properties results?
7. How is the amount of charge on each plate of a parallel-plate capacitor related to the potential difference between the plates?
8. For a given potential difference between the plates of a parallel-plate capacitor, how does the quantity of charge on each plate vary with plate area and separation distance?
9. In practice, what limits the quantity of charge that can be stored on the plates of a parallel-plate capacitor?

26.3 Dielectrics

10. Distinguish between the two general types of dielectrics, including a description of how each type behaves in an external electric field.
11. From a macroscopic point of view, what happens to a dielectric material when it is placed in an external uniform electric field?
12. What is the distinction between bound charge and free charge?
13. Why is the electric field magnitude in a parallel-plate capacitor with no dielectric between the plates greater than the electric field magnitude when a dielectric is inserted between the plates?
14. Does the electric field created in a polarized dielectric store less, the same, or more energy than an electric field of equal magnitude in a vacuum? Why?

26.4 Voltaic cells and batteries

15. What is a battery, and what does it do?
16. What is emf?

26.5 Capacitance

17. How is the capacitance of a capacitor defined?
18. On what properties of a capacitor does capacitance depend?
19. What is the unit of capacitance? Is its size appropriate to most practical applications in electronic devices?

26.6 Electric field energy and emf

20. How does the electric potential energy stored in a capacitor depend on the quantity of charge on each conductor?
21. How does the electric potential energy stored in a capacitor depend on the potential difference between the conductors?
22. What is energy density, and what is the algebraic relationship between the energy density of an electric field and the field magnitude?
23. How is the potential difference between the negative and positive terminals of the charge-separating device related to the emf in an ideal device and in a real-world device?

26.7 Dielectric constant

24. What is the definition of dielectric constant for a dielectric material?
25. Why is the dielectric constant of liquid water greater than that of other common materials used in capacitors, like paper or mica?
26. For a parallel-plate capacitor with a dielectric material filling the space between its plates, how is the bound charge on either dielectric surface related to the free charge on the surface of the adjacent conducting plate?
27. Why does the energy stored in an isolated charged capacitor decrease as a dielectric is inserted into the capacitor?

26.8 Gauss's law in dielectrics

28. When Gauss's law is used to calculate the electric field in a dielectric, the charge enclosed by any Gaussian surface we choose is $q_{\text{free, enc}} - q_{\text{bound, enc}}$. How can we use the law for a dielectric when we know nothing about $q_{\text{bound, enc}}$?
29. What is Gauss's law in a dielectric material, and what is its relationship to the form of Gauss's law we worked with in Chapter 24?

PRACTICE

Developing a Feel

Make an order-of-magnitude estimate of each of the following quantities. Letters in parentheses refer to hints below. Use them as needed to guide your thinking.

1. The maximum potential difference between two metal baking sheets separated by 100 mm of air (A, D)
2. The maximum quantity of charge that can be placed on a metal-coated basketball in air (A, J, S, Q)
3. The potential difference that causes a lightning strike (A, O)
4. The dimensions of the plates in a square, 1-F parallel-plate capacitor with air between the plates (T, U, F, K, P)
5. The capacitance of a raindrop in dry air (B, G)
6. The plate area of a 50-fF capacitor on a computer memory chip (C, N)
7. The maximum energy density achievable in an electric field in air (A, V)
8. The maximum amount of electrical energy that can be stored in an electric field that fills your physics laboratory (A, H)
9. The capacitance of the coaxial cable that connects the cable box sitting atop your television to the cable outlet in the wall (E, I, M, R)
10. The capacitance of a metal-coated softball (G, L)

Hints

A. What is the electric field at the breakdown threshold of air?
B. What is the radius of a raindrop?
C. What is between the plates?
D. How does the magnitude of the electric field between two parallel plates E relate to the magnitude of the potential difference V between them?
E. What is the length of the cable?
F. For a given capacitance, what is the relationship between plate area and plate separation distance?
G. What is the radius of the "other" sphere serving as a conductor in this "capacitor"?
H. What is the laboratory volume?
I. What are the radii of the conductors?
J. Where is the magnitude of potential greatest?
K. What is a reasonable value for the smallest gap that can be maintained between two large metal plates?
L. What is the radius of a softball?
M. What shape can you assume for the cable?
N. What is the gap width?
O. What is the length of a lightning bolt?
P. What plate area is needed in order to have 1-F capacitance when the plate separation distance is 2 mm?
Q. What is the radius of a basketball?
R. What is a reasonable dielectric constant value for the cable?
S. If you model the ball as a conducting sphere, how do you determine its capacitance?

T. Is 1 F considered a common capacitance value or an extremely high value?
U. What does having such a large capacitance suggest about plate size?
V. What is the relationship between the energy density of an electric field and the field magnitude?

Key (all values approximate)

A. 3×10^6 V/m; B. 0.004 m; C. some dielectric material, probably silicon dioxide (κ approximately 5); D. $V = Ed$; E. 3 m; F. as separation distance increases, plate area must increase proportionally to maintain constant capacitance, which means you want a small gap; G. infinite; H. 4×10^2 m³; I. $R_{inner} = 5 \times 10^{-4}$ m, $R_{outer} = 3 \times 10^{-3}$ m; J. near the ball surface; K. 2 mm; L. 50 mm; M. ignore any bends and loops, assuming all radii of curvature are much greater than R_{outer}, so that you can treat the cable as a cylinder; N. 1×10^{-8} m; O. 2×10^3 m; P. 2×10^8 m²; Q. 0.1 m; R. with plastic insulation, κ is approximately 2; S. imagine the ball being concentric with a sphere of infinitely large radius so that you form a capacitor in which the ball surface is one conductor, the surface of the infinite sphere is the other conductor, and the gap is filled with air; T. extremely high; U. plates must be quite large; V. the energy density is proportional to the square of the field magnitude, with $\epsilon_0/2$ as the proportionality constant.

Worked and Guided Problems

Procedure: Calculating the capacitance of a pair of conductors

To calculate the capacitance of a pair of conductors:

1. Let the conductors carry opposite charges of magnitude q.
2. Use Gauss's law, Coulomb's law, or direct integration to determine the electric field along a path leading from the negatively charged conductor to the positively charged conductor.

3. Calculate the electrostatic work W done on a test particle carrying a charge q_t along this path (Eq. 25.24) and determine the potential difference across the capacitor from Eq. 25.15,

$$V_{\text{cap}} = -W_{q_t}(-\rightarrow+)/q_t.$$

4. Use Eq. 26.1, $C \equiv q/V_{\text{cap}}$, to determine C.

These examples involve material from this chapter but are not associated with any particular section.
Some examples are worked out in detail; others you should work out by following the guidelines provided.

Worked Problem 26.1 Roll-up capacitor

In a roll-up parallel-plate capacitor (Figure WG26.1), the plates are thin sheets of metal foil with a Mylar dielectric between them. Suppose that the foil and Mylar sheets are each 0.0500 mm thick and the capacitor is 20.00 mm tall and has a radius of 6.00 mm. Estimate the charge stored in the capacitor when there is a 25-V potential difference across the capacitor leads.

Figure WG26.1

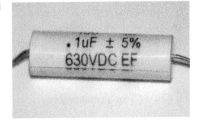

❶ GETTING STARTED We must first visualize how this capacitor is constructed. As usual, we begin with a sketch, in this case a sketch of the components—two foil sheets separated by a Mylar sheet—before the capacitor is rolled up (Figure WG26.2). We label the thickness of each sheet t. We assume that the Mylar completely fills the space between the foil sheets, so that the plate separation distance is equal to the Mylar thickness. Now we roll it up. However, there's a trick here: If we roll up the three-sheet sandwich of foil-Mylar-foil, the bottom foil touches the top foil, connecting the two plates and effectively nullifying the capacitor. To avoid this, the unrolled capacitor we start with has to be a four-sheet sandwich configured foil-Mylar-foil-Mylar (Figure WG26.3). The thickness

of this sandwich is $4t$, where $t = 0.0500$ mm is the thickness of each sheet, and the radius of the rolled-up capacitor is $R = 6.00$ mm.

Figure WG26.3

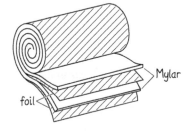

❷ DEVISE PLAN The radius R of the capacitor is related to the sheet thickness t and to the number of sheets in the length R. Because we are given values for the capacitor height and radius, as well as the thickness of each sheet, we should be able to unroll the sandwich and compute the capacitance of the equivalent parallel-plate capacitor. The problem asks how much charge can be stored in this capacitor when the potential difference across it is 25 V. Because capacitance is defined as the quantity of charge that can be stored for a given potential difference, calculating the capacitance should allow us to determine the quantity of stored charge.

If we unroll the capacitor, we have two foil sheets (the parallel plates) separated by a Mylar sheet of the same size. (The second Mylar sheet shown in Figure WG26.3 lies outside the capacitor and hence is irrelevant to the capacitance.) From Eq. 26.11 and the result of *Principles* Example 26.2, $C = \epsilon_0 A/d$, we know that the capacitance of parallel plates with a dielectric between them is

$$C = \frac{\kappa \epsilon_0 A}{d}.$$

In this expression, d is the separation distance between the plates, and in our problem that distance is the thickness $t = 0.0500$ mm of the Mylar sheet. After we look up the dielectric constant of Mylar ($\kappa = 3.3$), what we need to do is estimate the area $A = \ell w$ of each foil sheet. When the capacitor is unrolled, the height of the capacitor is one dimension of either foil sheet—let's say the width, so that $w = 20.00$ mm. We know how long the foil and Mylar sheets are

Figure WG26.2

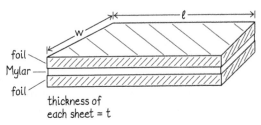

(the ℓ in $A = \ell w$), and their combined thickness determines the radius $R = 6.00$ mm of the rolled-up capacitor. So we can infer the length of the foil sheets from what we know about their thickness, the Mylar thickness, and the radius of the rolled-up capacitor.

❸ EXECUTE PLAN One way to estimate the length of the un-rolled foil sheets is to assume the capacitor is rolled as tightly as possible and then use the volume of the rolled-up capacitor. When you imagine starting with the four-sheet sandwich (foil-Mylar-foil-Mylar) and rolling it up, the width $w = 20.00$ mm in Figure WG26.2 becomes the height of the capacitor. The other dimension of the four sheets, ℓ, is related to the capacitor radius ($R = 6.00$ mm). When the capacitor is fully rolled up, the volume of the unrolled parallel-plate sandwich ($w \times \ell \times 4t$) must match the volume of the cylindrical capacitor ($\pi R^2 w$). Thus we have

$$V = \pi R^2 w = w\ell(4t)$$

$$\ell = \frac{\pi R^2}{4t}.$$

Another way to estimate the sheet length ℓ is to note that it requires many turns to roll up the capacitor. Each turn is a spiral ring of thickness $4t$, but because there are many turns, we can model the capacitor as if the spirals were circles. That means the capacitor is composed of a set of nested cylindrical shells, each of thickness $4t$ but with different radii, ranging from $r = 2t$ for the inner shell to $r = R - 2t$ for the outer shell. Then $R/4t$ gives the number of four-sheet shells across the capacitor radius. If we add up the circumferences of these shells, we have our ℓ. The average circumference of the shells in the roll is then $2\pi R/2$, so the length ℓ becomes

$$\ell = (\text{number of four-sheet shells}) \times (\text{average circumference})$$

$$= \left(\frac{R}{4t}\right)\left(\frac{2\pi R}{2}\right) = \frac{\pi R^2}{4t}.$$

It is reassuring that both methods give the same estimate for sheet length ℓ.

Now we obtain our expression for the capacitance of this Mylar-filled capacitor, noting that the separation distance d between "plates" is the thickness t of the Mylar between the two foil sheets:

$$C = \frac{\kappa\epsilon_0 A}{d} = \frac{\kappa\epsilon_0 \ell w}{t} = \frac{\kappa\epsilon_0\left(\dfrac{\pi R^2}{4t}\right)w}{t} = \frac{\kappa\epsilon_0 \pi R^2 w}{4t^2}. \quad (1)$$

Finally, the quantity of charge that can be stored with a 25-V potential difference across the capacitor is

$$q = CV = \frac{\kappa\epsilon_0 \pi R^2 wV}{4t^2}$$

$$= \frac{3.3(8.85 \times 10^{-12}\,\text{F/m})\pi(6.00 \times 10^{-3}\,\text{m})^2(20.0 \times 10^{-3}\,\text{m})(25\,\text{V})}{4(5.00 \times 10^{-5}\,\text{m})^2}$$

$$= 1.7 \times 10^{-7}\,\text{C}. \checkmark$$

❹ EVALUATE RESULT Our algebraic result shows that a larger capacitor (greater R or w) means that more charge can be stored for a given value of V, which makes sense. It also says that if the sheets are packed more tightly (smaller t), the quantity of charge that can be stored also increases because more foil is packed in the same volume. (However, you then need to worry about electrical breakdown of the Mylar film.) Equation 1 yields a capacitance of 6.6×10^{-9} F. Although you probably haven't developed a feel yet for capacitors, a capacitance in the nanofarad range is not unreasonable for a capacitor of this size and construction. Typical capacitors in most electric circuits have capacitances ranging from a few picofarads to several hundred microfarads. Because we know that $q = CV$ and we are given $V = 25$ V, a charge in the hundred-nanocoulomb (10^{-7} C) range makes sense for this capacitor.

Guided Problem 26.2 Home-made capacitor

Estimate the greatest capacitance you might achieve at home by rolling layers of aluminum foil and waxed paper around a number 2 pencil.

❶ GETTING STARTED
1. Are the results of Worked Problem 26.1 applicable?

❷ DEVISE PLAN
2. What is the length of an unused number 2 pencil?
3. What is the greatest length of foil or waxed paper you can (a) easily obtain and (b) handle without aid while creating the roll?
4. How are these lengths related to the capacitance?

❸ EXECUTE PLAN
5. What is a reasonable value for the dielectric constant of waxed paper?

❹ EVALUATE RESULT
6. Is your numerical value reasonable?
7. Try it and see if you are able to construct such a capacitor.

Worked Problem 26.3 Capacitance of television cable

Estimate the capacitance of a length L of the "RG-6" coaxial cable used for cable television. This type of cable consists of an inner wire of 0.50-mm radius and a concentric outer conductor of 6.8-mm diameter, with the space between the two conductors filled with polyethylene (dielectric constant $\kappa = 2.3$).

❶ GETTING STARTED We are asked to estimate the capacitance of a given length of television cable. We know that the geometry closely resembles that of *Principles* Example 26.3, except that we need to include the dielectric material between the two conductors. Because doubling the length of the cable doubles the surface area of each conductor while keeping the separation unchanged, we expect the capacitance to be proportional to L. We know that putting charge $+q$ on the inner wire and charge $-q$ on the outer conductor results in an electric field pointing radially outward from the inner wire, and hence a potential difference between the two conductors. Because the space between the two conductors is filled with a dielectric material, we need to account for the effect of the dielectric material on the electric field in the region between the two conductors.

❷ **DEVISE PLAN** We will follow the Procedure box on page 471 to calculate the capacitance. For the path over which electrostatic work is done, we choose the straight path that goes radially inward from the inner surface of the outer conductor (radius 3.4 mm) to the outer surface of the inner conductor (radius 0.50 mm). To compute the electric field, we will use Gauss's law in matter, Eq. 26.25.

❸ **EXECUTE PLAN** Let $R_1 = 0.50$ mm be the radius of the inner conductor, and let $R_2 = 3.4$ mm be the radius of the outer conductor. The electric field in the region $R_1 < r < R_2$ is given by Gauss's law in matter: $\oint \kappa \vec{E} \cdot d\vec{A} = q_{\text{free, enc}}/\epsilon_0$. We choose a cylindrical Gaussian surface of radius r and length L, concentric with the two conductors. The electric field points radially outward, so $\vec{E} \cdot d\vec{A} = 0$ on the two flat ends of the cylinder. On the curved surface of the cylinder (area $A = 2\pi rL$), the electric field is constant due to cylindrical symmetry, so the Gauss's-law integral simplifies to $\kappa EA = q/\epsilon_0$, where the charge $+q$ on the inner conductor is the free charge enclosed by the Gaussian surface. The electric field for $R_1 < r < R_2$ points radially outward and has magnitude

$$E = \frac{q}{\kappa A \epsilon_0} = \frac{q}{\kappa 2\pi rL\epsilon_0}.$$

The potential difference between the capacitor's two conductors is then (using Eq. 26.25)

$$V_{21} = -\int_{R_2}^{R_1} \vec{E} \cdot d\vec{\ell} = -\int_{R_2}^{R_1} E\, dr = -\frac{q}{2\pi\kappa\epsilon_0 L}\int_{R_2}^{R_1} \frac{dr}{r}$$

$$= -\frac{q}{2\pi\kappa\epsilon_0 L}\Big[\ln(r)\Big]_{R_2}^{R_1} = -\frac{q}{2\pi\kappa\epsilon_0 L}\ln\left(\frac{R_1}{R_2}\right)$$

$$= \frac{q}{2\pi\kappa\epsilon_0 L}\ln\left(\frac{R_2}{R_1}\right).$$

Then using $q = CV$, we obtain

$$C = \frac{q}{V_{21}} = \frac{2\pi\kappa\epsilon_0 L}{\ln(R_2/R_1)}.$$

Putting in numbers, we calculate the capacitance per unit length to be

$$\frac{C}{L} = \frac{2\pi\kappa\epsilon_0}{\ln(R_2/R_1)} = \frac{(6.283)(2.3)(8.85 \times 10^{-12}\,\text{F/m})}{\ln(3.4/0.50)}$$

$$= 6.7 \times 10^{-11}\,\text{F/m} = 67\,\text{pF/m}. ✔$$

❹ **EVALUATE RESULT** *Principles* Example 26.3 found the capacitance of a coaxial cable (with air or vacuum between the inner and outer conductors) to be $C = (2\pi\epsilon_0 L)/\ln(R_2/R_1)$. Our expression is greater by a factor $\kappa = 2.3$. This makes sense, as we have seen in other examples that filling the space between a capacitor's two conductors with a nonconductor having dielectric constant κ increases the capacitance by a factor κ. We can also check online that the numerical value 67 pF/m agrees with tabulated values for the capacitance per unit length of commercial RG-6 television cable.

Guided Problem 26.4 Laptop power

The rechargeable batteries needed in laptop computers are both heavy and expensive. Moreover, the lifetime of many rechargeable batteries is relatively short—perhaps at best a few thousand charge-discharge cycles. Because of this, capacitors have been considered as one possible option to store the required energy. Capacitors are quickly charged, and because no chemical reaction is involved, they have a much longer lifetime than do batteries. Let us say your ultra-low-power laptop requires a potential difference of 8 V to run, and you'd like it to run for a minimum of 4 h using an average power of 1 W. Assume it is possible to "tap" a constant 8 V from a capacitor that has a potential difference greater than or equal to 8 V, but whose potential difference cannot exceed 48 V. (*a*) In order to use this capacitor in your laptop, what would its capacitance have to be? (*b*) If this were a parallel-plate capacitor, how large would the plate area have to be if the plates were separated by a Mylar layer 0.05 mm thick? Does this type of capacitor seem a feasible alternative to today's rechargeable batteries?

❶ **GETTING STARTED**
1. How much energy must be available for use?
2. Can the capacitor be fully discharged at the end of 4 h, or must it still be partially charged?

❷ **DEVISE PLAN**
3. Express the required capacitance in terms of initial and final potential differences and the required energy that must be supplied by the capacitor.
4. How does capacitance depend on surface area, separation distance, and dielectric constant in a parallel-plate capacitor?

❸ **EXECUTE PLAN**

❹ **EVALUATE RESULT**
5. Work out numbers for the energy removed from the capacitor and for the energy needed to run the computer for 4 h. Do they agree?
6. Is the plate area feasible for a capacitor that must fit inside a laptop computer?
7. Modern dielectric materials and construction techniques (see, for example, Problem 79 in this chapter) allow capacitors on the order of 1 F to fit into a volume of 10^{-5} m³. Would knowing this change your answer about feasibility?

PRACTICE

Worked Problem 26.5 Earth-sized capacitor

What is the capacitance of Earth when you model it as a conducting sphere?

❶ GETTING STARTED It is hard to think of Earth as being part of an electronic device, in this case a gigantic capacitor, but let's accept that premise for the sake of argument. We know the definition of capacitance: the amount of charge that can be stored per unit of potential difference between the two conductors of a capacitor. If Earth is one conductor in our capacitor, what can act as the other conductor? That the potential of a spherical object is typically measured by defining infinitely far away as the position of zero potential gives us the clue we need: We should consider the other conductor to be an infinitely large spherical shell that is concentric with Earth.

❷ DEVISE PLAN We know from Eq. 26.1 that capacitance is given by $C = q/V_{cap}$, but in this problem q is the charge on Earth's surface, a quantity we do not know. To use Eq. 26.1, however, we also need to know the potential V_{cap} at Earth's surface. We found in *Principles* Section 25.5 that the potential at some radial distance r from a charged particle is given by Eq. 25.21, $V(r) = q/4\pi\epsilon_0 r$. When we use this expression for V in Eq. 26.1, the two q factors

cancel, and so our not knowing a value for q is not an obstacle here.

❸ EXECUTE PLAN In this problem, r in Eq. 25.21 is Earth's radius R_E. Substituting the expression for V given by Eq. 25.21 into Eq. 26.1 therefore yields

$$C_E = \frac{q}{(q/4\pi\epsilon_0 R_E)} = 4\pi\epsilon_0 R_E$$

$$= 4\pi(8.85 \times 10^{-12} \, \text{C}^2/\text{N} \cdot \text{m}^2)(6.4 \times 10^6 \, \text{m}) = 0.71 \, \text{mF.} \checkmark$$

❹ EVALUATE RESULT We see from the algebraic expression that the capacitance of Earth would increase if it had a larger radius. This increase is to be expected because the charge carriers on the surface would then be farther apart, and thus more charge could be stored on the surface. It is also gratifying to note that this is exactly the result we obtained in *Principles* Example 26.4 for a spherical capacitor, $C = 4\pi\epsilon_0 R_1 R_2/(R_2 - R_1)$, when we make the outer sphere's radius infinite.

Guided Problem 26.6: Tin can capacitor

A certain capacitor consists of a solid cylindrical core surrounded by a metal shell. The shell is capped at both ends with metal covers, forming a connected metal surface with the shell but not the rod. The shell has radius R_{shell} and length L. The core is separated from the shell by a distance d and has length $L - 2d$. Assume that $d \ll R_{shell}$ and also that $d \ll L$. What is the capacitance of this capacitor?

❶ GETTING STARTED

1. Start by drawing a sketch of the capacitor, labeling all the given variables and indicating the quantity you must determine.
2. How is this capacitor similar to a coaxial capacitor? How does it differ from a coaxial capacitor?
3. Are the metal covers on the ends at the same potential as the metal shell?

4. What are the appropriate surface areas of the conductors?
5. Is the distance between core and shell (including covers) constant over all but a negligible portion of the capacitor?

❷ DEVISE PLAN

6. What is the expression for capacitance in a coaxial capacitor?
7. What distances correspond to the two radii in this expression?
8. How can you account for the effects of the end caps on the capacitance?

❸ EXECUTE PLAN

❹ EVALUATE RESULT

9. Pick some numerical values and compare this capacitance with that of a roll-up capacitor of similar dimensions from Worked Problem 26.1. What do you conclude?

Worked Problem 26.7 Variable capacitance

A variable capacitor can be constructed by inserting a slab of dielectric material partway between a pair of parallel plates. One such capacitor has plates of length ℓ and area A, where the plates are separated by a distance d. If the dielectric constant of the inserted material is κ, what is the capacitance as a function of how far into the space between the plates the dielectric is inserted?

❶ GETTING STARTED Figure WG26.4 shows our given information. Aligning the x axis along the plate length allows us to use x to represent the inserted length. Our drawing shows that this capacitor has two regions: region 1 with plate length $\ell - x$ and air between the plates and region 2 with plate length x and the dielectric between the plates. Because of the presence of the dielectric, we know that the electric field magnitude is not the same in the two regions. We probably need to use the general definition of capacitance, $C = q/V$, and figure out, for a given potential difference V,

what surface charge is required on the plates above and below each of these two regions.

Figure WG26.4

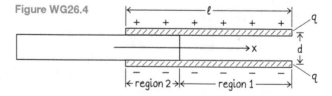

❷ DEVISE PLAN Because there are two regions in this capacitor, we have to be careful when we use our capacitance equation. We want to know how much free charge $q_{cap,free}$ the capacitor can store for a given potential difference across the plates. We know that the potential is the same everywhere on each plate, and so the potential difference V_{cap} is the same everywhere across the plates. Because this potential difference is related to the electric field in each region by $V_{cap} = Ed$ and because d is constant, we conclude that the electric field must be the same in both regions. Because a dielectric decreases the electric field by a factor κ for a fixed density of free charge on the plates, the free-charge density must be greater by a factor κ in region 2 (dielectric-filled region) than in region 1 (air-filled region). The free charge q_{1free} or q_{q2free} on the plates in each region is the free-charge density (charge per unit area) in that region multiplied by the corresponding surface area. The charge $q_{cap,free}$ stored by the capacitor is the sum of q_{1free} and q_{2free}. Then taking the ratio of $q_{cap,free}$ and V_{cap} will give us the capacitance for this variable capacitor.

❸ EXECUTE PLAN Because the plate area is A, the plate width is $w = A/\ell$. The plate area for region 1 is $A_1 = (\ell - x)w$, and the plate area for region 2 is $A_2 = xw$. There is no dielectric in region 1, and so in this region Eq. 26.12 tells us that the electric field is

$$E_1 = \frac{V_{cap}}{d} = E_{1free} = \frac{\sigma_{1free}}{\epsilon_0} = \frac{q_{1free}}{\epsilon_0 A_1},$$

which leads us to

$$q_{1free} = \frac{V_{cap}}{d}\epsilon_0 A_1. \qquad (1)$$

From Eq. 26.14, the field in region 2 is

$$E_2 = \frac{V_{cap}}{d} = E_{2free} - E_{2bound} = \frac{\sigma_{2free} - \sigma_{2bound}}{\epsilon_0}$$

$$= \frac{q_{2free} - q_{2bound}}{\epsilon_0 A_2}.$$

But from Eq. 26.17 ($q_{free} - q_{bound} = q_{free}/\kappa$), we see that this last equation can be rewritten in the form

$$\frac{V_{cap}}{d} = \frac{q_{2free}}{\kappa\epsilon_0 A_2}.$$

The free charge on the plates is therefore

$$q_{cap,free} = q_{1free} + q_{2free} = \frac{V_{cap}}{d}\epsilon_0 A_1 + \frac{V_{cap}}{d}\kappa\epsilon_0 A_2$$

$$= \frac{V_{cap}}{d}\epsilon_0[(\ell - x)w + \kappa xw],$$

which means that the capacitance of our variable capacitor is given by

$$C(x) = \frac{q_{cap,free}}{V_{cap}} = \frac{\epsilon_0 w}{d}[(\ell - x) + \kappa x]$$

$$= \frac{\epsilon_0 w}{d}[\ell + (\kappa - 1)x] = \frac{\epsilon_0 A}{d}\left[1 + (\kappa - 1)\frac{x}{\ell}\right]. ✔$$

❹ EVALUATE RESULT We know that dielectrics are used in capacitors to increase capacitance. Therefore $C(x)$ should increase as we insert more of the dielectric into the space between the plates (increase x). This is just what our result says because $\kappa - 1 > 0$ (remember, κ is always greater than unity). We should also check the limits $x = 0$ and $x = \ell$. With $x = 0$ (no dielectric), our equation reduces to the result from *Principles* Example 26.2 for a dielectric-free parallel-plate capacitor: $C_0 = \epsilon_0 A/d$. When the capacitor is entirely filled with dielectric, $x = \ell$ and our equation becomes

$$C(\ell) = \frac{\epsilon_0 A}{d}\left[1 + (\kappa - 1)\frac{\ell}{\ell}\right] = \frac{\epsilon_0 A}{d}[1 + \kappa - 1]$$

$$= \kappa\frac{\epsilon_0 A}{d} = \kappa C_0,$$

which agrees with Eq. 26.11 giving the capacitance of a capacitor entirely filled with a dielectric.

Guided Problem 26.8 Vacuum Capacitors

Devices used in high-power radio-frequency applications require capacitors that can store large quantities of charge without electrical breakdown. Dielectric materials may be undesirable in these applications because of the materials' finite breakdown thresholds. Instead, high storage capacity is achieved with *vacuum capacitors*, which consist of conducting plates separated by a fairly large distance and sealed inside an evacuated canister so that there is vacuum between the plates rather than air. One problem with these capacitors is that the vacuum is not perfect (that is, some air molecules are present); another problem is that a sufficiently large electric field can ionize the metal plates, ripping off electrons from the plates and leading to electrical breakdown. Suppose the largest electric field that can be supported by a vacuum capacitor is 10 times greater than the breakdown threshold of air. What is the maximum potential difference that can be applied to a 1.0-nF parallel-plate vacuum capacitor with a plate separation of 1.0 mm? What is the maximum charge that can be stored without discharging?

❶ GETTING STARTED
1. How are potential difference and electric field related for a parallel-plate capacitor?
2. Where can you find the value for the maximum electric field in air and then for this capacitor?

❷ DEVISE PLAN
3. How are stored charge and potential difference related for a capacitor?
4. What dielectric constant should be used for a vacuum capacitor?

❸ EXECUTE PLAN

❹ EVALUATE RESULT
5. Is the maximum potential difference quite large compared with potentials encountered in commonplace low-power devices?
6. Is the maximum stored charge fairly large?

Questions and Problems

For instructor-assigned homework, go to MasteringPhysics® (MP)

Dots indicate difficulty level of problems: • = easy, •• = intermediate, ••• = hard; CR = context-rich problem.

26.1 Charge separation

1. When two objects are charged by a charge-separating process or device, how are their charges related? •

2. Positive work is done on a system containing positively and negatively charged particles. All work goes into changing the electric potential energy of the system. What can be said about the electric field between positively and negatively charged particles? What can be said about the electric field everywhere else? ••

3. You are designing a Van de Graaff generator, and you want it to hold as many electrons as possible. Should you make the radius of the sphere very large or very small? ••

4. Draw energy diagrams for the processes of separating charge carriers by (a) rubbing, (b) increasing the separation distance between a positively charged object and a negatively charged object, and (c) increasing the separation distance between two positively charged objects. ••

5. A plastic rod is rubbed with wool, producing a distribution of positive and negative surplus charge that is concentrated in two locations on the rod and two on the wool. This distribution can be approximated as two pairs of small balls of charge as shown in Figure P26.5. The distance d is 30.0 mm, and the magnitude of the charge on each ball is 2.00 μC. If 34.0 J of work went into thermal energy as the rod and wool heated up, how much work was done on the system? ••

Figure P26.5

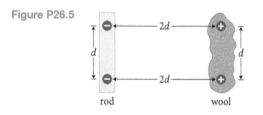

rod   wool

6. A piece of wool is used to charge two plastic spheres. When the spheres are held 200 mm apart, they repel each other with 7.00 N of force. If the wool ends up with a surplus positive charge of 23.5 μC, what is the charge on each of the two spheres? ••

7. Two 0.0450-kg spheres are identical (including the charge they carry) and are initially pinned in place 200 mm apart. You unpin them and push on each sphere with a force of 0.15 N. After their separation increases to 400 mm, each sphere has a speed of 500 mm/s. What is the charge on each sphere? Is there more than one possible answer? ••

8. A fellow scientist heard that a Van de Graaff generator built 70 years ago could collect 5.0 C of charge on its dome, which had a radius of 1.1 m, and has challenged you to do the same. The belt you plan to use is 100 mm wide and 10.0 m long (5.0 m to go up to the dome, and 5.0 m to come back down). Charging the belt gives it a surface charge density of 45 μC/m². How much force must your motor be able to exert

on the belt in order to accomplish your goal? If you had more freedom in the design, what changes would you make to make the charging process easier on your motor, and why? Would your changes alter only the force required for your motor, or would they also affect the energy required for charging? State any assumptions you make, and state whether or not they are physically reasonable. •••

26.2 Capacitors

9. The plates of a capacitor are charged using a battery, and they produce an electric field across the separation distance d between them. The two plates are now to be pushed together to a separation of $d/2$. The pushing together can be done either with the battery connected or with it disconnected. Which way would result in the greater electric field magnitude, and by what factor? •

10. Two parallel-plate capacitors have the same plate area. Capacitor 1 has a plate separation twice that of capacitor 2, and the quantity of charge you place on capacitor 1 is twice the quantity you place on capacitor 2. How do the potential differences across each of the two capacitors compare to each other? •

11. Two parallel-plate capacitors have the same plate area. Capacitor 1 has a plate separation twice that of capacitor 2, and the potential difference you impose across the plates of capacitor 1 is twice the potential difference you impose across capacitor 2. How do the quantities of charge stored on the two capacitors compare to each other? •

12. Suppose a capacitor is fully charged by a battery and then disconnected from the battery. The positive plate has a charge $+q$ and the negative plate has a charge $-q$. The plate area is doubled, and the plate separation is reduced to half its initial separation. What is the new charge on the negative plate? ••

13. Explain why there must always be some nonzero electric field outside the plates of a parallel-plate capacitor (Figure P26.13a), which means that the idealization shown in Figure P26.13b, with all the field lines confined to the region between the plates, can never be exact. (Hint: Consider the potential difference between the plates for paths outside the edges.) ••

Figure P26.13

(a)   (b)

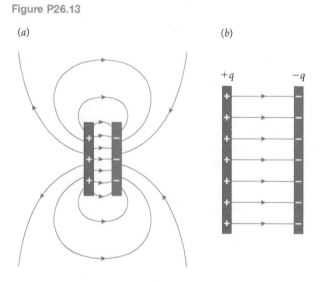

14. Figure P26.14 is a graph of the electric field between two capacitor plates as a function of distance from the left plate. The distance between the plates is d, the direction of the field is to the right, and a battery is connected to the plates. (*a*) Which plate carries a positive charge? (*b*) How many slabs of material have been inserted between the plates? (*c*) What can you say about the slab(s) inserted? (*d*) Make a graph of the electric field between the plates when the slabs between the plates are removed and the battery remains connected. ••

Figure P26.14

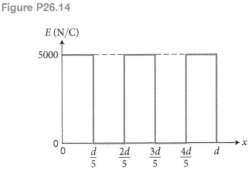

15. When two parallel plates separated by a distance d are connected to a battery that maintains a potential difference of magnitude V between the plates, a charge of magnitude q accumulates on each plate. If the plate separation is increased to $2d$ and the battery is replaced with one that has potential difference $2V$ between the terminals, what is the new charge on each plate? ••

16. Suppose two capacitor plates have an area of 0.0100 m² and are initially separated by 1.00 mm. Each plate holds 3.30 μC of charge. How much energy is required to increase the plate separation to 2.00 mm? ••

17. A certain capacitor is fully charged by a battery, such that the positive plate holds a charge $+q$ and the negative plate holds a charge $-q$. The plates of the capacitor are then pulled apart to twice their initial separation. Determine the new charge on the positive plate if (*a*) the battery is kept attached to the capacitor as the separation is increased, and (*b*) the battery is disconnected before the plate separation is increased. ••

18. You need to insert a metal slab between the two plates of a parallel-plate capacitor. The plates are a distance d apart, and a battery maintains a constant potential difference V_{batt} between them. In order to avoid dielectric breakdown, the electric field in any region cannot exceed $4V_{batt}/d$. (*a*) What is the maximum thickness of the metal slab that can be used without causing dielectric breakdown? (*b*) If this maximum thickness is used, does the insertion of the metal slab affect the amount of charge stored on the capacitor? •••

26.3 Dielectrics

19. Either a dielectric or a conductor could be inserted between the plates of a capacitor. (*a*) State at least two similarities between the effects of inserting a dielectric and inserting a conductor. (*b*) State at least two differences between the effects of inserting a dielectric and inserting a conductor. •

20. A fully charged capacitor initially has an air gap and is disconnected from the battery. A dielectric material is inserted between the plates. What happens to (*a*) the free charge at the surface of the capacitor plates and (*b*) the total charge (free and bound) at the surface of the capacitor plates? •

21. Two parallel-plate capacitors have the same dimensions, but the space between the plates is filled with air in capacitor 1 and with plastic in capacitor 2. The magnitude of the charge on the plates is the same in both capacitors. Compare (*a*) the magnitudes of the electric fields E_1 and E_2 between the plates, (*b*) the potential differences V_1 and V_2 between the plates, and (*c*) the energies stored in the capacitors. ••

22. Two parallel-plate capacitors have the same dimensions, but the space between the plates is filled with air in capacitor 1 and with plastic in capacitor 2. The potential difference between the plates is the same in both capacitors. Compare (*a*) the magnitudes of the electric fields E_1 and E_2 between the plates, (*b*) the magnitudes of the charges on the plates q_1 and q_2, and (*c*) the energies stored in the capacitors. ••

23. A capacitor connected to a battery initially holds a charge of $+q$ on its positive plate and $-q$ on its negative plate. The electric field between the plates is initially $\vec{E}$. A dielectric material is then inserted that polarizes in such a way as to produce an electric field of $-0.30\vec{E}$ (where the $-$ sign indicates that this field opposes the initial field $\vec{E}$). Determine the new charge stored on the positive plate. ••

24. A parallel-plate capacitor with air between the plates and plate separation distance d is connected to a battery that maintains a potential difference V_{batt} between the plates. Sketch a graph of V as a function of x when x is defined as position between the plates, running from $x = 0$ at the surface of the positively charged plate to $x = d$ at the surface of the other plate. Plot the points $x = 0$, $x = d/4$, $x = d/2$, $x = 3d/4$, and $x = d$. A slab that is made of a dielectric material and has a thickness of $d/2$ is inserted between the plates such that the midpoint of the slab thickness is at the position $d/2$ in the space between the plates. Sketch a graph of $V(x)$ for the capacitor now. Comment on how your graph is affected by the magnitude of the bound charge induced on the surface of the dielectric slab. ••

25. A capacitor initially has a charge of magnitude q on each plate. When a dielectric is inserted between the plates, the bound surface charge on the two dielectric surfaces facing the plates has a magnitude $q/3$. What is the ratio of the electric field magnitude in the empty capacitor to the electric field magnitude in the capacitor with the dielectric (*a*) if the battery stays connected to the plates and (*b*) if the battery is removed before the dielectric is inserted? ••

26. A capacitor has a plate area of 0.0045 m² and a charge of magnitude q on each plate. The space between plates has been filled with a dielectric that has a bound surface charge of magnitude $3q/4$ on either side. When the dielectric material is removed, the electrical breakdown of air is observed between the plates. What is the smallest possible value of q? ••

27. The night before an exam, your study partner asks what you can do to a parallel-plate capacitor to avoid the problem of the electrical breakdown of air. You answer that a nonconducting dielectric material can be inserted. Your friend is confused as to why other things wouldn't work. Why wouldn't it help, for example, to add a conducting slab? Why isn't increasing plate separation also a valid answer? After all, moving charge carriers very far apart must decrease their effect on the air between them. Why do these alternatives not work? •••

26.4 Voltaic cells and batteries

28. The term *emf* is an acronym for *electromotive force*. Why is this a misnomer? •

29. As a battery is used to charge a capacitor, does the overall charge inside the battery get smaller, greater, or stay the same? •

30. What limits the lifetime of a battery? •

31. The reactions in a lead-acid battery are

Positive terminal: $PbO_2 + HSO_4^- + 3H^+ + 2e^-$
$$\rightarrow PbSO_4 + 2H_2O$$

Negative terminal: $HSO_4^- + Pb \rightarrow PbSO_4 + H^+ + 2e^-$

If a certain battery supplies 1.0×10^8 electrons per second to the negative terminal and the battery contains 3.00 moles of electrolytic solution (which means the solution contains 3.00 moles of HSO_4^-), what fraction of the solution undergoes a chemical reaction each second? ••

32. One electrode in an alkaline battery is zinc, and the other is manganese dioxide. (*a*) Fill in the blank for the chemical reaction at the zinc electrode: $Zn + 2OH^- \rightarrow ZnO + \underline{\quad} + 2e^-$. (*b*) Fill in the blank for the reaction at the manganese electrode: $2MnO_2 + H_2O + \underline{\quad} \rightarrow Mn_2O_3 + 2OH^-$. (*c*) Which electrode is positive and which is negative? ••

33. Suppose that the metal electrodes in a battery are shaped like large parallel plates and are 1.00 mm apart, so that they are essentially a parallel-plate capacitor. If the battery supplies a potential difference of 4.5 V between the electrodes, what is the surface charge density on the electrodes (before anything has been connected to the battery)? ••

26.5 Capacitance

34. A parallel-plate capacitor initially has capacitance C. The distance between the plates is then doubled, with a 9.0-V battery connected. The battery is then disconnected, and the plate area is doubled. Finally, a 20-V battery is connected across the plates. What is the new capacitance? •

35. A capacitor consisting of two concentric spheres and one consisting of two coaxial cylinders both have an inner radius of 10.0 mm and an outer radius of 30.0 mm. If the two capacitors have the same capacitance, what is the length of the cylinders? •

36. A parallel-plate capacitor initially has capacitance C. What is the capacitance after each of the following single changes is made: (*a*) plate separation distance doubled, (*b*) dielectric material inserted, (*c*) potential difference across plates doubled, (*d*) plate area halved, (*e*) applied emf increased until plate charge doubles. •

37. A coaxial capacitor consisting of an inner wire and an outer cylindrical shell has a length of 80.0 mm and an outer diameter of 10.0 mm. When connected to an 18.0-V battery, this capacitor can hold 1.1 nC of charge on the wire. What is the wire radius? ••

38. Consider a parallel-plate capacitor with charge $+q$ on the top plate and $-q$ on the other, and a plate area that is large relative to the separation distance. Contrast this with a spherical capacitor consisting of two concentric spherical shells, one smaller than the other, with a charge of $+q$ uniformly distributed on the outer shell and a charge of $-q$ uniformly distributed on the inner shell. (*a*) Do the positive and negative charges distribution contribute equally to the electric field inside each capacitor? If not, what fraction of the field comes from the negative distribution? (*b*) What is the electric field magnitude outside each capacitor? ••

39. One way to double the capacitance of a parallel-plate capacitor is to reduce the plate separation distance by a factor of 2. Doubling the capacitance of a spherical capacitor is a bit more complex, though. (*a*) If you had a spherical capacitor consisting of two concentric spherical shells of radii R_{inner} and $R_{outer} > R_{inner}$, you could double the capacitance by changing the radius of the outer shell from R_{outer} to some value d. What is d in terms of R_{inner} and R_{outer}? (*b*) You could also double the capacitance by changing the radius of the inner shell from R_{inner} to some value d. What is d in terms of R_{inner} and R_{outer}? (*c*) Repeat parts *a* and *b* for a capacitor consisting of two long concentric cylindrical shells of radii R_{inner} and $R_{outer} > R_{inner}$. ••

40. A spherical capacitor consists of two concentric conducting spherical shells of radii R and $2R$. (*a*) How long would a coaxial cylindrical capacitor made of two concentric cylindrical conductors of radii R and $2R$ have to be in order to have the same capacitance as the spherical capacitor? (*b*) What plate separation distance would be required for a parallel-plate capacitor made of two circular conductors each of radius R in order to have the same capacitance as the spherical capacitor? ••

41. Two small, irregularly shaped conducting objects, one carrying charge $+q$ and one carrying charge $-q$, are placed on an x axis at $x = -4.0$ m and $x = +4.0$ m, respectively. Between the objects, the electric field on the x axis is given by $E(x) = aq(x^2 + b)$, where a and b are constants. (*a*) What are the units of a and b? (*b*) What is the capacitance of this configuration? •••

42. The expression for the capacitance of a parallel-plate capacitor that has plates of area A separated by a distance d is given in *Principles* Example 26.2. (*a*) Show that the expression for a spherical capacitor, given in *Principles* Example 26.4, reduces to the expression for a parallel-plate capacitor in the limit that R_1 approaches R_2, with $d = R_2 - R_1$. (*b*) Show that the expression for a cylindrical capacitor, given in Example 26.3, reduces to the expression for a parallel-plate capacitor in the limit that R_1 approaches R_2, with $d = R_2 - R_1$. (Hint: You might find the Taylor series expansion of $\ln(1 + x)$ useful.) •••

26.6 Electric field energy and emf

43. A parallel-plate capacitor with air between its plates carries a charge of 6.60 μC when a 9.00-V battery is connected to it. How much energy is stored in the capacitor? •

44. Suppose a certain battery has an internal emf of 9.00 V but the potential difference across its terminals is only 85.0% of that value. If that battery is connected to a 56.0-μF capacitor, how much energy is stored when the capacitor is fully charged? •

45. A parallel-plate capacitor connected to a battery maintaining a potential difference V across the capacitor initially stores electric potential energy U_i^E. If the plate area is doubled and the battery is replaced with one that maintains a potential difference of $2V$ across the capacitor, how much electric potential energy is stored now? •

46. Two parallel-plate capacitors 1 and 2 are identical except that capacitor 1 has charge $+q$ on one plate and $-q$ on the other, and capacitor 2 has charge $+2q$ on one plate and $-2q$ on the other. Compare the two capacitors based on their (a) capacitance, (b) potential difference between the plates, (c) electric field magnitude between the plates, and (d) energy stored. ••

47. Three parallel-plate capacitors are separately connected to identical batteries. Capacitor 1 has a plate area A and a plate separation d. Capacitor 2 has a plate area $2A$ and a plate separation d. Capacitor 3 has a plate area A and a plate separation $2d$. Rank the three capacitors, largest first, based on (a) capacitance, (b) charge stored, (c) electric field magnitude between the plates, (d) energy stored, and (e) energy density. ••

48. Three parallel-plate capacitors each store the same amount of charge. Capacitor 1 has a plate area A and a plate separation d. Capacitor 2 has a plate area $2A$ and a plate separation d. Capacitor 3 has a plate area A and a plate separation $2d$. Rank the three capacitors, largest first, based on their (a) capacitance, (b) potential difference between the plates, (c) electric field magnitude between the plates, (d) energy stored, and (e) energy density. ••

49. (a) A spherical capacitor consists of two concentric conducting spheres of radii R and $2R$. If the two spheres carry charges of $+q$ and $-q$, what is the average energy density inside the capacitor in terms of R and q? (b) A cylindrical capacitor of length ℓ consists of two coaxial conducting cylinders of radii R and $2R$. If the two cylinders carry charges of $+q$ and $-q$, what is the average energy density inside the capacitor? ••

50. A parallel-plate capacitor has plates of area A. The plates are initially separated by a distance d, but this distance can be varied. If the capacitor is connected to a battery, what should the plate separation be if you want to quadruple (a) the capacitance, (b) the charge stored, (c) the energy stored, and (d) the energy density? ••

51. A parallel-plate capacitor has plates of area A. The plates are initially separated by a distance d, but this distance can be varied. If the capacitor is charged by a battery and the battery is then removed so that the capacitor is isolated, what should the plate separation be if you want to quadruple (a) the capacitance, (b) the charge stored, (c) the energy stored, and (d) the energy density? ••

52. A parallel-plate capacitor has an initial charge q and a plate separation distance d. How much work must you do, in terms of q, d, and plate area A, to increase the separation distance to $3d$ if (a) the capacitor is isolated and (b) the capacitor is connected to a battery? (c) The work you do is positive in both cases. Explain why in one situation the electric potential energy increases and in the other it decreases. •••

26.7 Dielectric constant

53. (a) Does it make sense to talk about a dielectric constant for a conductor? If so, what value does the constant have? (b) What is the breakdown threshold for a conductor? •

54. The potential difference across the plates of a parallel-plate capacitor is gradually increased. (a) What happens when the breakdown threshold is exceeded? (b) If you want to increase the potential difference before breakdown occurs, what capacitor variables might you change? •

55. (a) Make a list of ways to increase the capacitance of a parallel-plate capacitor. (b) Does *Increase quantity of charge stored* or *Decrease potential difference* belong on the list? •

56. When you remove a dielectric slab from between the plates of a charged isolated capacitor, what happens to the energy stored in the capacitor? Why does this happen to the stored energy? ••

57. Two parallel-plate capacitors are identical except that capacitor 1 has vacuum between the plates and capacitor 2 has a dielectric slab of dielectric constant κ filling the space between the plates. The capacitors are connected to identical batteries. Compare the two based on (a) capacitance, (b) charge stored, (c) energy stored, (d) electric field magnitude, and (e) energy density. ••

58. Two parallel-plate capacitors are identical except that capacitor 1 has vacuum between the plates and capacitor 2 has a dielectric slab of dielectric constant κ filling the space between the plates. Each capacitor is isolated (that is, not connected to a battery), and they store equal quantities of charge. Compare the two based on (a) capacitance, (b) potential difference between the plates, (c) energy stored, (d) electric field magnitude between the plates, and (e) energy density. ••

59. When a dielectric slab completely fills the space between the plates of a parallel-plate capacitor, the magnitude of the bound charge is one-fourth the magnitude of the free charge. (a) What is the dielectric constant of the material of which the slab is made? (b) If the slab does not fill the space between the plates, but instead has a width equal to half the distance between the plates, does the magnitude of the bound charge change? If so, how? ••

60. If you want to maintain a potential difference of 6000 V between the plates of a parallel-plate capacitor, what is the minimum value of the plate separation if the space between the plates is completely filled by (a) a slab of mica and (b) a slab of barium titanate? (c) What is the ratio of the maximum charges that could be put on a plate of the capacitor in part b to the capacitor in part a. ••

61. A parallel-plate capacitor with a plate area of 50 mm^2 and air between the plates can hold 5.5 pC of charge per volt of potential difference across its plates. When a barium titanate dielectric slab completely fills the space between the plates and the capacitor is connected to a 9.0-V battery, what is the electric field magnitude inside the capacitor? ••

62. You are working on charge-storage devices for a research center. Your goal is to store as much charge on a given device as possible. The facilities allow you to generate almost any potential difference V you need, but you are restricted to using a single parallel-plate capacitor. The area and separation distance of the plates are fixed, and the dielectric materials available to you are paper ($\kappa = 3.0$, $E_{max} = 4.0 \times 10^7$ V/m), Mylar ($\kappa = 3.3$, $E_{max} = 4.3 \times 10^8$ V/m), quartz ($\kappa = 4.3$, $E_{max} = 8 \times 10^6$ V/m), and mica ($\kappa = 5$, $E_{max} = 2 \times 10^8$ V/m). What properties of these materials must you consider in choosing the best dielectric for your needs? Rank the materials in order of their ability to meet your needs, first choice first. ••

63. A spherical capacitor has an inner radius of 8.00 mm and an outer radius of 8.50 mm. With air between the spheres, the capacitor is connected to a battery and allowed to charge fully. With the battery still connected, oil is poured in, filling the volume between the spheres. As the oil is added, the battery does an additional 8.90 nJ of work on the capacitor. What is the potential difference supplied by the battery? •••

64. A dielectric slab completely fills the space between the plates of a parallel-plate capacitor. The magnitude of the bound charge on each side of the slab is 75% of the magnitude of the free charge on each plate. The capacitance is $480\epsilon_0\ell$, where ℓ is a constant with dimensions of length, and the maximum charge that can be stored on the capacitor is $240\ell^2\epsilon_0 E_{max}$, where E_{max} is the breakdown threshold. What are (a) the dielectric constant for the slab, (b) the plate separation distance in terms of ℓ, and (c) the plate area in terms of ℓ? •••

26.8 Gauss's law in dielectrics

65. Two very long wires each carry a linear charge density λ. They initially repel each other with a force F. If the wires are immersed in distilled water, with what force do they repel each other? •

66. A solid conducting sphere of radius R and carrying charge $+q$ is embedded in an electrically neutral nonconducting spherical shell of inner radius R and outer radius $2R$. The material of which the shell is made has a dielectric constant of 3.0. (a) Relative to a potential of zero at infinity, what is the potential at the center of the conducting sphere? (b) If the dielectric constant of the shell is increased, what happens to the potential at the center of the sphere? ••

67. A solid conducting sphere of radius R is embedded in an electrically neutral nonconducting spherical shell that has inner radius R, has outer radius $2R$, and is made of a material having dielectric constant κ. Inside the shell the electric field magnitude is $E = 3Q/(4\pi\epsilon_0 r^2)$ and, relative to a potential of zero at infinity, the potential at the surface of the sphere is $+15Q/(16\pi\epsilon_0 R)$, where Q is a constant with dimensions of electrical charge. What are (a) the charge on the sphere and (b) the dielectric constant of the shell? ••

68. A conducting sphere has a radius of 2.25 m and carries a positive surplus charge of 35.0 mC. A protective layer of barium titanate is applied to the surface of the sphere to make it safe for laboratory workers nearby. Safety considerations dictate that the potential difference between the surface of the conductor and the outside of the nonconductive layer must be 20,000 V (though this is by no means safe under all conditions). How thick must the protective layer be? •••

Additional problems

69. (a) Explain how treating the electric field lines between two oppositely charged objects as elastic bands can help you to understand what happens to the electric potential energy of the system when you increase the separation distance between the objects. (b) Can you think of any limitations to this elastic-band analogy for analyzing field lines? •

70. Why would two objects made of nonconducting material make a poorer capacitor than two objects of the same shape made of material that is an electrical conductor? •

71. Two parallel-plate capacitors have the same plate separation. The plate area of capacitor 1 is twice that of capacitor 2. (a) How do the potential differences across the two capacitors compare if the quantity of charge you place on capacitor 1 is twice the quantity you place on capacitor 2? (b) How do the charge magnitudes on either plate of the two capacitors compare if the potential difference between the plates of capacitor 1 is twice that between the plates of capacitor 2? •

72. During a lightning strike, on the order of 10 C of charge is typically transferred to the ground over a potential difference of 3×10^8 V. (a) What is the capacitance of the cloud-ground system? (b) How much energy is stored in the system just before the strike? (c) As a check on the order of magnitude of your answer for part b, convert the energy released in the lightning strike into liters of gasoline (gasoline has a stored chemical energy of 36 MJ/liter). ••

73. Given that charge separation increases the electric potential energy of a system, what can you conclude about the criteria for keeping a system of positively and negatively charged particles in static equilibrium, in the presence of electrostatic interactions only? ••

74. A parallel-plate capacitor in which the plates are extendable is connected to a battery and charged until there is a charge $+q$ on one plate and a charge $-q$ on the other plate. (a) With the battery still connected, the area of each plate is doubled by sliding the extension out. How much charge is on each plate now? (b) In which case, before the plate area is expanded or after, is more force required to keep the plates apart? Use the elastic-band model described in Problem 69 to explain your answer. ••

75. A parallel-plate capacitor carries a charge $+q$ on one plate and a charge $-q$ on the other plate. The plates have an area A. How much force, in terms of q and A, does one plate exert on the other? ••

76. A 30.5-μF parallel-plate capacitor initially has air between its plates and is connected to a 24.0-V battery. The capacitor is then submerged in distilled water. What is the charge on the plates (a) if the capacitor is submerged with the battery connected and (b) if the battery is removed before submersion? ••

77. Your firm uses a large parallel-plate capacitor to store energy, and you measure the electric field strength between the plates to determine the amount of energy stored. During a test run with a new renewable energy source, you realize that the electric field magnitudes being produced are too small to be accurately detected by your equipment. The capacitor plates are fixed in place, and you cannot yet control the energy source to give you a greater potential difference. All you have to work with are four large flat slabs of metal, one $d/2$ thick, one $d/3$ thick, one $d/4$ thick, and one $d/5$ thick, where d is the fixed plate separation distance. You realize that it is necessary to increase E by at least an order of magnitude, but it takes you a while to figure out what to do. ••• CR

78. You are working for a car-battery manufacturer, and your boss complains that to be more competitive, the company needs to produce batteries that will last longer while minimizing the amount of metal or metal oxide used. She is not concerned about the amount of electrolyte used, but the battery must be powerful enough to supply a great deal of energy quickly when needed. You begin to think about what the shape of the electrodes might have to do with battery life and power, starting with what seem to be the extremes: electrodes shaped like sheets similar to parallel plates and rod-shaped electrodes that extend down into the electrolyte solution. ••• CR

79. In the endless endeavor to make electronic devices as small as possible, you have been hired to make a capacitor that has the greatest capacitance possible in a cubic volume of (10 mm) × (10 mm) × (10 mm). You are allowed to use any capacitor geometry you wish, as well as any combination of geometries. For simplicity, assume a dielectric constant of 1000 (as better materials are found, you can multiply the capacitance appropriately). You begin thinking about the minimum thickness of the conductors and dielectrics, and the scale of about 0.5 μm seems reasonable. There is the question of how to fill the volume while maintaining exactly two conducting surfaces. ••• CR

Answers to Review Questions

1. Potential difference is a measure of the work per unit charge done by the electric field in moving a charged test particle (not part of the system) from one location in the system to another. The system's electric potential energy is determined by the configuration of the charged particles that make up the system.

2. The potential energy depends on the amount of charge on the objects and on their separation distance.

3. Electric potential energy is stored in the system's electric field, in any region of space where that field exists.

4. A Van de Graaff generator produces a very large separation of charge between Earth's surface ("ground") and a metal sphere attached to a nonconducting support, and hence a very large potential difference.

5. A capacitor is a pair of conducting objects separated by a nonconducting material or vacuum. Any such pair of objects stores electric potential energy when charge has been transferred from one object to the other.

6. A parallel-plate capacitor is an arrangement of two parallel conducting plates that have the same area A and are separated by a distance d. When d is small relative to the lateral dimensions of the plates, the electric field is approximately localized and uniform between the charged plates and zero outside them.

7. The magnitude of the charge on each plate is proportional to the potential difference between the plates. For a parallel-plate capacitor, this is because the potential difference equals the product of the electric field strength and the plate separation distance, and the field strength is proportional to the surface charge density on either plate.

8. The quantity of charge on a plate varies directly with plate surface area and inversely with separation distance.

9. Electrical breakdown occurs when the charge on the plates is great enough to produce an electric field sufficient to ionize the air (or other material) between the plates.

10. A dielectric is a nonconducting material. *Polar* dielectrics are made up of molecules that have a permanent dipole moment, whereas *nonpolar* dielectrics consist of molecules that do not have a dipole moment in the absence of an electric field. When either type is placed in an external electric field, the centers of positive and negative charge in the molecules are displaced, producing an induced dipole moment. Molecules in polar dielectrics can also align themselves with the external electric field.

11. In a uniform external field, no surplus charge is induced on any volume that lies entirely inside the material, but uncompensated induced charge densities appear on the surfaces.

12. Bound charge is the surplus of charge in polarized matter due to charge carriers that are bound to atoms and cannot move freely within the bulk of the material. Free charge is the surplus of charge due to charge carriers that can move freely within the bulk of a material.

13. The direction of the electric field $\vec{E}_{cap}$ due to the plates is from the positive plate to the negative plate, but the direction of the electric field $\vec{E}_{dielec}$ due to the polarized dielectric between the plates is in the opposite direction: from the positive induced surface charge near the negative plate to the negative induced surface charge near the positive plate. The vector sum of $\vec{E}_{cap}$ and $\vec{E}_{dielec}$ gives a field magnitude for the dielectric-filled capacitor that is smaller than the magnitude of the capacitor without the dielectric.

14. The field in the dielectric stores more energy than the vacuum field. Work must be done by an external electric field on the dielectric in order to separate the positive and negative charge carriers, and this work done increases the electric potential energy stored in the dielectric's electric field, so that the amount of energy stored is greater than in a field of equal magnitude that exists in a vacuum.

15. A battery is an assembly of one or more voltaic cells that separates charge carriers by converting energy released in chemical reactions into electric potential energy.

16. Emf is the work done per unit charge by nonelectrostatic interactions in a charge-separating device (such as a battery) in order to separate positive and negative charge carriers in the device.

17. The capacitance is the ratio of the magnitude of the charge on either conductor that forms the capacitor and the magnitude of the potential difference between the conductors.

18. In the absence of a dielectric, capacitance depends on only the size and geometric properties of a capacitor—that is, on the shape of the conductors making up the capacitor and on the separation of the conductors. The capacitance also depends on the properties of the dielectric material inserted between the conductors.

19. The unit of capacitance is the farad, which is 1 C/V. Because 1 C is an enormous quantity of charge relative to the quantity of charge on conductors in electronic devices, capacitances in the range of microfarads to picofarads are more commonly used.

20. The electric potential energy is proportional to the square of the charge on each conductor: $U^E = q^2/2C$ (Eq. 26.4).

21. The electric potential energy is proportional to the square of the potential difference: $U^E = CV_{cap}^2/2$ (Eq. 26.4).

22. Energy density is the electric potential energy stored in an electric field per unit volume of the field: $u_E = U^E/\text{field volume}$. The energy density for a given field is proportional to the field magnitude squared, as given (for air or vacuum) by Eq. 26.6: $u_E = \frac{1}{2}\epsilon_0 E^2$.

23. In an ideal charge-separating device, none of the energy associated with the work done by nonelectrostatic interactions is dissipated, and the potential difference between the terminals is equal to the emf. In a nonideal device, some energy is dissipated inside the device and thus not available to be turned into electrostatic work; now the potential difference between the device's terminals is smaller than the emf. (See the discussion in the *Principles* paragraphs that surround Equation 26.8.)

24. The dielectric constant for the material is the potential difference between a capacitor's conductors without any of the dielectric material between the conductors divided by the potential difference between the conductors with the dielectric material completely filling the space between them.

25. The constant for water is greater because water molecules are polar and can align themselves with the electric field, whereas the molecules in paper and mica are nonpolar. The induced polarization in liquid water is therefore much greater than that in paper or mica.

26. The sign of the bound charge on the dielectric surface is opposite the sign of the free charge on the plate, and the quantity of bound charge is smaller than the quantity of free charge. The relationship is given by Eq. 26.18: $q_{bound} = (\kappa - 1)(q_{free})/\kappa$.

27. The stored energy must decrease because as the dielectric comes near the capacitor, the capacitor does positive work on it, pulling it into the space between the conductors.

28. We use Gauss's law for determining the electric field inside a dielectric by substituting $q_{free}[(\kappa - 1)/\kappa]$ (Eq. 26.18) for q_{bound}. This substitution gives us an expression that does not contain q_{bound}. The result is that Gauss's law may be applied using only the free charge enclosed by the Gaussian surface and the electric field inside the dielectric material, Eq. 26.25.

29. Gauss's law in a dielectric material is $\oint \kappa \vec{E} \cdot d\vec{A} = q_{\text{free, enc}}/\epsilon_0$ (Eq. 26.25), where κ is the dielectric constant for the dielectric material and $q_{\text{free, enc}}$ is that portion of the free charge that is enclosed by the chosen Gaussian surface. When no dielectric is present, $\kappa = 1$ and this expression reduces to the Chapter 24 form of Gauss's law, $\oint \vec{E} \cdot d\vec{A} = q_{\text{enc}}/\epsilon_0$ (Eq. 24.8).

Answers to Guided Problems

Guided Problem 26.2 $C = \dfrac{\epsilon_0 \kappa \ell w}{d} = 0.3\ \mu\text{F}$.

Guided Problem 26.4 (a) $C = \dfrac{2P\Delta t}{V_i^2 - V_f^2} = 13\ \text{F}$;

(b) $A = \dfrac{Cd}{\epsilon_0 \kappa} = 2.2 \times 10^7\ \text{m}^2 = (4.7\ \text{km})^2$.

Guided Problem 26.6 $C = \dfrac{\epsilon_0 A}{d} = \dfrac{2\pi \epsilon_0 R_{\text{shell}}}{d}(L + R_{\text{shell}})$.

Guided Problem 26.8 $V_{\max} = E_{\max} d = 30\ \text{kV}$; $Q_{\max} = CV_{\max} = 30\ \mu\text{C}$.

27

PRACTICE
Magnetic Interactions

PRACTICE

Chapter Summary

Magnetic field (Sections 27.1, 27.2)

Concepts Every **magnet** has two *magnetic poles*. The pole attracted to Earth's North Pole is called a *north pole;* the magnet's opposite pole is called a *south pole.*

Like magnetic poles repel each other, and opposite magnetic poles attract each other. Earth's North Pole is a magnetic south pole because it attracts the north pole of a compass needle.

Magnetic materials are attracted to both types of magnetic poles. The presence of a magnet induces **magnetic polarization** in magnetic materials.

A magnet is surrounded by a **magnetic field.** This field exerts a force on the poles of other magnets and is represented by **magnetic field lines.** At any position, the direction of the magnetic field is tangent to the magnetic field line passing through that position. Magnetic field lines form loops that exit a magnet at its north pole and reenter the magnet at its south pole. Near (but outside of) a magnet, magnetic field lines point away from north poles and toward south poles. At any location, the magnitude of the magnetic field is proportional to the field line density at that location.

Currents and magnetic fields (Sections 27.3, 27.5)

Concepts A flow of charged particles, called a **current,** causes a magnetic field.

The *direction of current* through a conductor is the direction in which positive charge carriers would flow, which is from high potential to low potential.

Right-hand current rule: If you point the thumb of your right hand in the direction of the current, the fingers curl in the direction of the magnetic field produced by that current.

Right-hand rule for vector product $I\vec{\ell} \times \vec{B}$

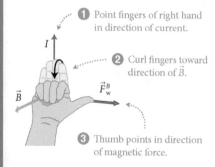

1 Point fingers of right hand in direction of current.

2 Curl fingers toward direction of $\vec{B}$.

3 Thumb points in direction of magnetic force.

Quantitative Tools If a particle carrying charge dq passes a given section of a conductor in a time interval dt, the current I through that section is

$$I \equiv \frac{dq}{dt}. \tag{27.2}$$

We measure current in **amperes** (A), where

$$1\,\text{C} \equiv 1\,\text{A} \cdot \text{s}. \tag{27.3}$$

If a straight wire of length ℓ carrying a current I perpendicular to a uniform magnetic field $\vec{B}$ experiences a force $\vec{F}^B_{w,\,max}$, the magnitude of the magnetic field is

$$B \equiv \frac{F^B_{w,max}}{|I|\ell}. \tag{27.5}$$

The SI unit of the magnetic field is the **tesla** (T), where

$$1\,\text{T} \equiv 1\,\text{N}/(\text{A} \cdot \text{m}) = 1\,\text{kg}/(\text{s}^2 \cdot \text{A}). \tag{27.6}$$

The **magnetic force** $\vec{F}^B_w$ exerted on a straight wire in a uniform magnetic field is

$$\vec{F}^B_w = I\vec{\ell} \times \vec{B}, \tag{27.8}$$

where the direction of $\vec{\ell}$ is the direction of the current through the wire. The direction of $\vec{F}^B_w$ is obtained by curling the fingers of the right hand from the direction of the current to $\vec{B}$.

Table 27.1 **Right-hand rules in magnetism**

	Thumb points in direction of	Fingers curl
Current rule	Current	Along magnetic field
Force rule	Magnetic force	From current to magnetic field

It is sometimes helpful to write out Eq. 27.8 component by component:

$$F_{wx}^{B} = I\ell_y B_z - I\ell_z B_y$$
$$F_{wy}^{B} = I\ell_z B_x - I\ell_x B_z$$
$$F_{wz}^{B} = I\ell_x B_y - I\ell_y B_x.$$

Magnetic flux (Section 27.6)

Concepts The **magnetic flux** through a surface is a measure of the number of magnetic field lines crossing the surface. The magnetic flux through any closed surface is zero because magnetic field lines always form closed loops.

Quantitative Tools The **magnetic flux** Φ_B through a surface is

$$\Phi_B \equiv \int \vec{B} \cdot d\vec{A}, \qquad (27.10)$$

where the integral is taken over the surface.

Magnetic flux is measured in **webers** (Wb), where

$$1 \text{ Wb} \equiv 1 \text{ T} \cdot \text{m}^2 = 1 \text{ m}^2 \cdot \text{kg}/(\text{s}^2 \cdot \text{A}).$$

For any closed surface, **Gauss's law for magnetism** is

$$\Phi_B = \oint \vec{B} \cdot d\vec{A} = 0. \qquad (27.11)$$

Forces exerted on moving particles (Section 27.7)

Quantitative Tools If a charged particle of charge q moves with velocity $\vec{v}$ in the presence of an electric field and a magnetic field, the **electromagnetic force** $\vec{F}_p^{EB}$ exerted on the particle by the fields is

$$\vec{F}_p^{EB} = q(\vec{E} + \vec{v} \times \vec{B}). \qquad (27.20)$$

It is sometimes helpful to write out Eq. 27.20 component by component:

$$F_{px}^{EB} = q(E_x + v_y B_z - v_z B_y) \quad F_{py}^{EB} = q(E_y + v_z B_x - v_x B_z) \quad F_{pz}^{EB} = q(E_z + v_x B_y - v_y B_x).$$

A charged particle of charge q and mass m moving at speed v perpendicular to a uniform magnetic field $\vec{B}$ follows a circular path of radius R given by

$$R = \frac{mv}{|q|B}. \qquad (27.23)$$

The time interval T for one revolution is

$$T = \frac{2\pi m}{|q|B}, \qquad (27.24)$$

and the angular frequency ω is

$$\omega = \frac{|q|B}{m}. \qquad (27.25)$$

PRACTICE

Magnetism and electricity unified (Sections 27.4, 27.8)

Concepts The interaction observed between charge carriers depends on their motion relative to the observer: The interaction can be purely electric, purely magnetic, or a combination of the two. Magnetic and electric interactions are two aspects of one *electromagnetic* interaction, with magnetism being a relativistic correction to the electric interaction.

Review Questions

Answers to these questions can be found at the end of this chapter.

27.1 Magnetism

1. What is a magnet? What is a magnetic material?
2. What are magnetic poles? How are the two types of magnetic poles defined?
3. How do magnetic poles interact with each other?
4. What is an elementary magnet? How does a model based on elementary magnets explain magnetization?

27.2 Magnetic fields

5. How is the concept of a magnetic field used to describe the action of a magnet?
6. What information about a magnetic field is conveyed by its magnetic field line pattern?
7. How does the magnetic field line flux through a closed surface depend on the number and strength of the elementary magnets enclosed by the surface?

27.3 Charge flow and magnetism

8. This section describes another source of magnetic fields besides a magnet. What is this source, and how is it defined?
9. Describe the magnetic field produced near a straight current-carrying wire.
10. In what direction would electrons need to flow in order to produce the same magnetic field as an equal flow of positive ions moving from left to right?
11. When electrons flow upward through a wire, how do we describe the direction of the corresponding current?
12. If you are looking at the face of a clock and see a current toward you from the center of the clock, do the magnetic field lines encircle the current in a clockwise or counterclockwise sense?
13. When a current-carrying wire is aligned perpendicular to a bar magnet, what is the relationship between the direction of the magnetic force exerted by the magnet on the wire and the direction of the magnetic field due to the magnet (call this the *external* magnetic field to distinguish it from the magnetic field due to the current in the wire)? What is the relationship between the direction of the magnetic force exerted by the magnet on the wire and the current direction?

27.4 Magnetism and relativity

14. Why should we expect any observed magnetic interaction to depend on the reference frame of the observer?
15. If the magnetic force exerted by a current-carrying wire is merely a relativistic correction to the internal electric forces in the wire, why is the magnetic force exerted by the wire so readily observable?

16. To an observer at rest relative to a current-carrying wire, how does the linear charge density of the fixed ions in the wire compare with the linear charge density of the moving electrons? How do these charge densities compare according to an observer moving along with the electrons?

27.5 Current and magnetism

17. For a current-carrying wire placed in an external magnetic field, for what orientation is the magnitude of the magnetic force exerted by the external field on the wire a maximum? For what orientation is it a minimum?
18. On what factors does the magnitude of the magnetic force exerted by an external magnetic field on a current-carrying wire depend?
19. A current through a wire is in the positive x direction in the presence of an external magnetic field that points in the positive y direction. In what direction does the magnetic force on the wire point?

27.6 Magnetic flux

20. For a flat surface located in a uniform magnetic field, how is the magnetic flux through the surface defined?
21. What is Gauss's law for magnetism, and what does it imply about magnetic sources?
22. How does the magnetic flux through one surface bounded by a loop compare with the magnetic flux through a different surface bounded by the same loop?

27.7 Moving particles in electric and magnetic fields

23. The magnetic force exerted by an external magnetic field on a current-carrying wire is a combination of what?
24. If a charged particle is moving in a magnetic field, what is the direction of the magnetic force exerted by the field on the particle?

27.8 Magnetism and electricity unified

25. Why does an observer moving along with electrons in a current-carrying wire measure the linear charge density of the fixed positive ions in the wire as being greater than the linear charge density of the electrons?
26. In the Earth reference frame, a positively charged particle moves parallel to a current-carrying wire. What is the difference between how an observer moving along with electrons in the wire interprets the force exerted by the wire on the particle and how an observer in the Earth reference frame interprets that force?

Developing a Feel

Make an order-of-magnitude estimate of each of the following quantities. Letters in parentheses refer to hints below. Use them as needed to guide your thinking.

1. The current needed in a long straight wire to produce, 1 m away from the wire, a magnetic field magnitude equal to the magnitude of the magnetic field due to Earth (C, Q)
2. The magnitude of the flux of Earth's magnetic field through the top of your desk (C, K, F)
3. The magnitude and direction of the magnetic force exerted by Earth on an electron moving west along Earth's equator at 10^5 m/s (C, L, G)
4. The magnitude of the magnetic field contributed by a single elementary magnet in a small iron bar magnet (A, I, M, U)
5. The magnitude of a uniform magnetic field required to keep a proton moving in the field at 10^6 m/s in a circular orbit having the same radius as a basketball (L, P, T)

6. The magnitude of a uniform magnetic field needed to keep an electron moving in the field in a circular orbit if the electron is to complete 1 revolution each microsecond (D, H, L)
7. The minimum current needed to "float" a piece of 18-gauge copper wire in a horizontal magnetic field of magnitude 0.5 T (V, R, N, J, B)
8. The maximum acceleration of a copper rod that is 100 mm long has a radius of 5 mm and carries a current of 100 A in a uniform magnetic field of magnitude 1 T (O, J, S, E)

Hints

A. What is the magnitude of the magnetic field due to a small bar magnet?
B. What is the mass of a length ℓ of this wire?
C. What is the magnitude of the magnetic field near Earth's surface?
D. What is the mass of an electron?
E. What maximum magnetic force is available?
F. What is the area of an average desktop?
G. In what direction does Earth's magnetic field point along the equator?
H. How is the period related to the magnetic field strength?
I. What is the volume of a small bar magnet?
J. What is the mass density of copper?
K. What is the angle between the direction of Earth's magnetic field and the horizontal?
L. What is the magnitude of the charge carried by this particle?
M. What is the mass density of iron?
N. What is the volume of a length ℓ of this wire?
O. What is the volume of the rod?
P. What is the radius of a basketball?

Q. How are magnetic field magnitude B and current I related for a long straight wire?
R. What is the diameter of 18-gauge wire?
S. What is the mass of the rod?
T. What is the mass of a proton?
U. What is the mass of an iron atom?
V. What forces must balance to float the wire?

Key (all values approximate)

A. 0.01 T, from *Principles* Table 27.1;   B. $(7 \times 10^{-3} \, \text{kg/m})\ell$;
C. 5×10^{-5} T;   D. 9×10^{-31} kg;   E. $I\ell B \sim 10$ N;   F. 2 m²;
G. horizontal and north;   H. $T = 2\pi m/qB$;   I. 1×10^{-5} m³;
J. 9×10^3 kg/m³;   K. this varies in the continental United States from 50° to 75°, so say 60°;   L. elementary charge, $e = 1.6 \times 10^{-19}$ C;
M. 8×10^3 kg/m³;   N. $\pi r^2 \ell \approx (8 \times 10^{-7} \text{ m}^2)\ell$;   O. 8×10^{-6} m³;
P. 0.1 m;   Q. $B = 2kI/c_0^2$;   R. 1×10^{-3} m;   S. 0.07 kg;
T. 1.7×10^{-27} kg;   U. 9×10^{-26} kg;   V. gravitational and magnetic.

Worked and Guided Problems

These examples involve material from this chapter but are not associated with any particular section.
Some examples are worked out in detail; others you should work out by following the guidelines provided.

Worked Problem 27.1. Rail gun

A *rail gun* is a device used to accelerate projectiles without the use of explosives. Figure WG27.1 shows an overhead view of one such gun. A crossbar slides on two identical rails that are 100 mm apart. Charge carriers flow along one rail, into the crossbar, and then along the other rail. A uniform external magnetic field pointing up out of the page accelerates the crossbar. (*a*) In which direction is the crossbar accelerated? (*b*) What is the coefficient of kinetic friction μ_k between rails and crossbar if the current is 10 A, the magnetic field magnitude is 0.12 T, and the crossbar has a mass of 2.0 kg and moves at constant speed once it has been accelerated?

Figure WG27.1

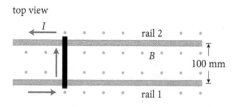

top view

① **GETTING STARTED** A current-carrying wire—or, in this case, a current-carrying crossbar—is subject to a force exerted by the external magnetic field. The force due to this field accelerates the crossbar, and our first task is to determine whether this acceleration is to the left or to the right in Figure WG27.1. (We know the acceleration cannot be up out of the page or down into the page because the magnetic force must be perpendicular to the magnetic field, which points out of the page.) Because the crossbar slides on the rails, we know it must experience a frictional force that opposes the magnetic force. We're given the magnitude and direction of the uniform magnetic field, the separation distance for the rails, values for the current and the crossbar mass, and the fact that the final crossbar speed is constant. We use this information for our second task: calculating the coefficient of kinetic friction.

② **DEVISE PLAN** For part *a*, the direction of the magnetic force $\vec{F}_c^B$ exerted by the external field on the crossbar determines in which direction the crossbar is accelerated. We can determine the direction of this force from the right-hand force rule, $\vec{F}^B = I\vec{\ell} \times \vec{B}$. For part *b*, as for all problems involving forces, we begin with a free-body diagram, this one for the crossbar viewed from the side, end-on (Figure WG27.2).

Figure WG27.2

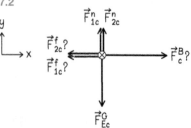

We don't yet know the direction of the magnetic force $\vec{F}_c^B$ exerted on the crossbar, and so we arbitrarily draw that force arrow to the right and add a question mark to remind us that its direction may have to be changed. Because the direction of the frictional forces opposes the magnetic force, we show $\vec{F}_{1c}^f$ and $\vec{F}_{2c}^f$ to the left, but also add question marks. We also show the downward gravitational force and two upward normal forces, one exerted by each rail.

We can use Eq. 27.8, $\vec{F}_c^B = I\vec{\ell} \times \vec{B}$, in its scalar form, $F_c^B = |I|\ell B \sin \theta$ (Eq. 27.7), to get the magnetic force in terms of our given numerical values. Each frictional force exerted by a rail on the crossbar is related to the upward normal force exerted by each rail on the crossbar by Eq. 10.55: $F_{2c}^f = \mu_k F_{2c}^n$ and $F_{1c}^f = \mu_k F_{1c}^n$, where μ_k is the coefficient of kinetic friction.

③ **EXECUTE PLAN** (*a*) Applying the right-hand force rule, we position our right hand above the crossbar in Figure WG27.1, with fingers pointing up in the direction of the current and the palm toward us so that the fingers can curl toward our face, in the direction of the external magnetic field. The thumb points to the right, telling us this is the direction of $\vec{F}_c^B$. We guessed correctly! ✔

The magnetic force accelerates the crossbar to the right. The two frictional forces $\vec{F}_{2c}^f$ and $\vec{F}_{1c}^f$ therefore must be leftward. Because these frictional forces and the magnetic force oppose each other, they can cancel and allow the crossbar to move at constant velocity.

(*b*) Let us work with the *x* and *y* components of the forces, using the coordinate axes shown in Figure WG27.2. In the *x* direction, $a_x = 0$, so the vector sum of the forces exerted on the crossbar becomes

$$\Sigma F_x = ma_x$$
$$F_c^B - (F_{2c}^f + F_{1c}^f) = 0. \tag{1}$$

Because the rails are identical and the crossbar is placed symmetrically, $F_{2c}^f = F_{1c}^f$ and $F_{2c}^n = F_{1c}^n$, which means we can simplify our notation to F_{rc}^f for the frictional force exerted by *each* rail on the crossbar and F_{rc}^n for the normal force exerted by *each* rail on the crossbar. When we make these changes in notation and substitute $I\ell B \sin \theta$ for F_c^B, Eq. 1 becomes

$$I\ell B \sin \theta - 2F_{rc}^f = I\ell B \sin \theta - 2\mu_k F_{rc}^n = 0.$$

Because the magnetic field and the current through the crossbar run at right angles to each other, $\theta = 90°$, $\sin 90° = 1$, and we have

$$I\ell B - 2\mu_k F_{rc}^n = 0. \tag{2}$$

In the *y* direction, we have for the identical rails $F_{2c}^n = F_{1c}^n = F_{rc}^n$. Newton's second law in this direction gives us

$$\Sigma F_y = ma_y = 0$$
$$2F_{rc}^n - F_{Ec}^G = 0$$
$$F_{rc}^n = mg/2. \tag{3}$$

Combining Eqs. 2 and 3 and rearranging, we obtain

$$\mu_k = \frac{I\ell B}{mg} = \frac{(10 \text{ A})(0.100 \text{ m})(0.12 \text{ T})}{(2.0 \text{ kg})(9.8 \text{ m/s}^2)} = 6.1 \times 10^{-3}. \checkmark$$

4 EVALUATE RESULT That the crossbar is accelerated to the right makes sense because the magnetic force on the crossbar points to the right, as we found by applying the right-hand force rule to Figure WG27.1. Our μ_k value seems like a very small coefficient of friction, but that's exactly what you want in a rail gun because its purpose is to move objects. The idea is that at currents much greater than the 10 A we have here (1000 A, say), you can accelerate the crossbar to very high speeds.

Guided Problem 27.2 Magnetic scale

Figure WG27.3 shows a sensitive device for measuring an object's mass. The object hangs by a string from a horizontal rod through which an electric current is directed from left to right. The rod is free to slide up and down a pair of vertical columns with negligible friction, but the rod's orientation remains fixed. The entire unit is placed in an external magnetic field, and the current in the circuit is adjusted until the rod and object are motionless. Once this equilibrium has been attained, the object's mass is calculated from the magnitude of the magnetic force required to balance the gravitational force on the object.

In which direction must the external magnetic field point—into or out of the page in Figure WG27.3—in order for the scale to work? What current is required to balance the rod if the combined mass of the object and the rod is 0.157 kg and the magnetic field has magnitude 0.150 T?

Figure WG27.3

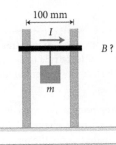

1 GETTING STARTED
1. Describe the problem in your own words. What information are you given, and what quantities must you determine using the given information?
2. Draw a free-body diagram—but of the rod, the object, or something else?
3. Which concepts and principles concerning magnetism apply here?

2 DEVISE PLAN
4. What is your plan for determining the magnetic field direction?
5. For a given current value, which equations allow you to express the unknown current in terms of known quantities?
6. What is the angle between the electric current in the rod and the magnetic field?

3 EXECUTE PLAN
7. Determine the field direction.
8. Work through the algebra and solve for the desired unknown quantity; then substitute known values to get a numerical answer.

4 EVALUATE RESULT
9. Does your direction for the magnetic field make sense?
10. Is your value for the current large or small? Compare it to maximum household current by noting the capacity of the circuit breakers or fuses in your home.

Worked Problem 27.3 Torque on a Wire

A straight current-carrying wire is oriented at an angle of 37.00° to a uniform external magnetic field of magnitude 0.0110 T (Figure WG27.4). The current in the wire is 10.0 A, and the portion within the field has length $\ell = 790$ mm. (a) What is the direction of the magnetic force exerted by the external field on the wire? (b) If the bottom end of the wire is fixed but the rest of the wire is free to move, what is the torque about the fixed end of the wire? In which direction does the torque cause the wire to rotate?

Figure WG27.4

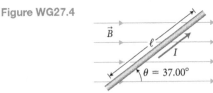

1 GETTING STARTED We must determine three things about a current-carrying wire placed in an external magnetic field: the direction of the force exerted by the magnetic field on the wire, the torque this force causes about one end of the wire, and the direction in which the wire tends to rotate because of this torque. For part *a*, we can determine the magnetic force direction from the right-hand force rule. For part *b*, we can use the principles we learned in Chapter 12 to determine the magnitude and direction of the torque due to the magnetic force on the wire.

2 DEVISE PLAN The force $\vec{F}_w^B$ exerted by the external field on the wire is given by Eqs. 27.8 and 27.7:

$$\vec{F}_w^B = I\vec{\ell} \times \vec{B} \quad \text{or} \quad F_w^B = I\ell B \sin \theta. \tag{1}$$

Each small wire segment of length $d\ell$ experiences the same magnitude and direction of force $d\vec{F} = Id\vec{\ell} \times \vec{B}$, so the force computed in Eq. 1 is uniformly exerted along the length of the wire. Thus, when calculating the torque, we can place the point of application of the force at the wire's midpoint—just as we take the point of application of the force of gravity to be at an object's center of mass. The torque is given by Eq. 12.1, $\tau = rF\sin \theta$, where θ is the angle between the vector $\vec{r}$ (that locates the point of application of the force relative to the rotation axis) and the line of action of the force.

❸ EXECUTE PLAN (*a*) Applying the right-hand force rule, we align our right hand along the current direction in Figure WG27.4 in such a way that we can curl the fingers toward the field lines representing $\vec{B}$. When we do this, our thumb points into the page, which is the direction of $\vec{F}^B_w$. ✔

(*b*) In working with the torque in this problem, we have to be careful about notation because θ in Eq. 1 is not the same as θ in Eq. 12.1 for the torque. To keep things straight, we keep θ as the angle between the magnetic field direction and the current direction, and we change Eq. 12.1 to $\tau = rF\sin\phi$, so that ϕ is the angle between $\vec{F}^B_w$ (into the page) and the vector $\vec{r}$ pointing from the rotation axis (the wire's fixed end) to the point of application of $\vec{F}^B_w$ (Figure WG27.5). Using these angle symbols, Eq. 12.1 gives us

$$\tau = rF\sin\phi = r(I\ell B\sin\theta)\sin\phi$$

$$= \frac{\ell}{2}(I\ell B\sin\theta)(\sin 90°) = \tfrac{1}{2}I\ell^2 B\sin\theta$$

$$= \tfrac{1}{2}(10.0\ \text{A})(0.790\ \text{m})^2(0.0110\ \text{T})(\sin 37.00°)$$

$$= 0.0207\ \text{N}\cdot\text{m}. ✔$$

Figure WG27.5

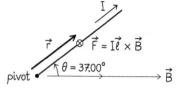

Because $\vec{F}^B_w$ is into the page and the wire initially lies in the plane of the page, the free end of wire tends to rotate into the page. ✔

❹ EVALUATE RESULT Our expression above for the torque is proportional to B. This makes sense, given that a greater magnetic field results in a proportionally greater force, and thus a proportionally greater torque. The torque is zero when θ is 0 or 180°, which makes sense because there is no magnetic force on a wire that runs parallel to the magnetic field: The magnetic force (and thus the torque) is greatest when the wire is perpendicular to the field. It also makes sense that the torque is proportional to ℓ^2: one factor of ℓ for the magnetic force ($\vec{F}^B = I\vec{\ell}\times\vec{B}$) and a factor of $\ell/2$ for the lever arm in the definition of torque. We also note that newton-meters are the correct units for torque.

Guided Problem 27.4 Torque on a Current Loop

A square loop of wire carrying a 1.7-A current is oriented so that the plane of the loop is parallel to a uniform external magnetic field as shown in Figure WG27.6. Each straight segment of the loop is 10 mm long, and the magnetic field magnitude is 0.23 T. Name all of the forces exerted on the loop. Compute the vector sum of these forces. Does the loop experience a torque? If it does, determine the direction of rotation and the torque magnitude. If the loop does not experience a torque, explain why not.

❶ GETTING STARTED

1. State the problem in your own words. How do the magnetic field and current affect the loop?

Figure WG27.6

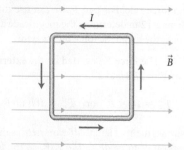

2. Because forces are involved, draw a free-body diagram. Apply the right-hand force rule to determine the direction of the force on each straight segment of the loop.

❷ DEVISE PLAN

3. Examine your free-body diagram to determine whether the loop experiences a torque. Use the right-hand rule for torque direction either to determine the torque direction or to conclude that there is no torque.

4. Decide which algebraic expression you can use to calculate the vector sum of the forces and, if appropriate, the torque magnitude.

❸ EXECUTE PLAN

5. Substitute numbers to get numerical answers.

❹ EVALUATE RESULT

6. Are your force and torque magnitudes reasonable? How do your calculated values compare with the values that you expected?

7. Is the torque direction what you expect?

Worked Problem 27.5. Bad picture?

Televisions manufactured during the 20th century work by shooting electrons at a screen to create the image that you see. The key component of these televisions is a *cathode ray tube* (CRT) that sprays a stream of electrons onto the screen (Figure WG27.7). The electrons are emitted from an *electron gun* located at the back of the CRT and then steered to various parts of the screen by means of variable magnetic fields. But any other magnetic field could also deflect these electrons. (*a*) Estimate the maximum deflection, due to Earth's magnetic field, of an electron aimed at the center of the screen 300 mm away from the electron gun emitting electrons that travel at 3.0×10^7 m/s. Assume that Earth's magnetic field is directed northward, is oriented at an angle of 45° below the horizontal, and has a magnitude of 3.0×10^{-5} T. (*b*) How much, and in which direction, is the image on the screen shifted by Earth's magnetic field when the screen faces east? (*c*) What if the screen faces north?

Figure WG27.7

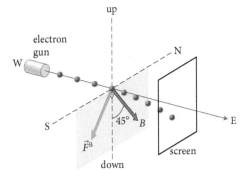

① GETTING STARTED
We are told that the electron beam in a television CRT might be deflected by Earth's magnetic field, and we are asked to determine the greatest possible deflection as each electron travels 300 mm through the field. We must then determine the magnitude and direction of this deflection for two possible orientations of the CRT.

② DEVISE PLAN
The force exerted by a magnetic field on a charged particle—an electron in this case—moving through the field is given by Eq. 27.19, $\vec{F}^B = q\vec{v} \times \vec{B}$. This force is always perpendicular to the direction in which the particle moves, so as each electron is deflected, the direction of the magnetic force exerted on it changes. To simplify the problem, we will assume that the electron isn't deflected very much. We can then make the approximation that the force direction is constant and points perpendicular to the electron's initial direction. Then we can use Newton's second law and kinematics with constant acceleration to determine the electron's deflection, as we would do for projectile motion under constant gravitational acceleration. (We will check at the end whether the small-deflection approximation is justified.) First, however, we need to determine the orientation of the television that gives maximum deflection.

We assume that we can ignore the effect of gravity. Because the spatial directions in this problem are somewhat complicated, we will first write out $\vec{F}^B = q\vec{v} \times \vec{B}$ in vector components, then use the right-hand force rule as a check of our results.

③ EXECUTE PLAN
(*a*) We will define Cartesian coordinates such that $\hat{\imath}$ points east, $\hat{\jmath}$ points north, and $\hat{k}$ points up. We can check with the right-hand rule for vector products that $\hat{\imath} \times \hat{\jmath} = \hat{k}$, as the math requires. Then we can write Earth's magnetic field as $\vec{B} = (\hat{\jmath} \cos 45° - \hat{k} \sin 45°)B_0$, which points north and 45° below the horizontal plane, with magnitude $B_0 = 3.0 \times 10^{-5}$ T. The electron beam travels in the same direction as the television screen faces. Defining θ_C to be the compass direction (0° for north, 90° for east) in which the electrons travel, we can write the electron velocity as

$\vec{v} = (\hat{\jmath} \cos \theta_C + \hat{\imath} \sin \theta_C)v_0$, with magnitude $v_0 = 3.0 \times 10^7$ m/s. Now we write out the components of $\vec{F}^B = q\vec{v} \times \vec{B}$:

$$F_x^B = q(v_y B_z - v_z B_y) = (-ev_0 B_0)(-\cos \theta_C \sin 45°)$$

$$F_y^B = q(v_z B_x - v_x B_z) = (-ev_0 B_0)(\sin \theta_C \sin 45°)$$

$$F_z^B = q(v_x B_y - v_y B_x) = (-ev_0 B_0)(\sin \theta_C \cos 45°)$$

$$F^B = \left(\frac{ev_0 B_0}{\sqrt{2}}\right)\sqrt{1 + \sin^2 \theta_C},$$

where, in writing the magnitude F^B, we used $\cos 45° = \sin 45° = 1/\sqrt{2}$. We can see from the expression for F^B that the electrons experience a nonzero magnetic force, whichever compass direction the CRT screen faces, but that the magnitude varies with the compass direction.

To calculate how far each electron is deflected, we first compute the time interval $\Delta t = \ell/v_0$ required for the electron to travel, at speed v_0, the length $\ell = 300$ mm from the electron gun to the screen. Then we compute the deflection d due to the magnetic force $\vec{F}^B$, where we are approximating $\vec{F}^B$ to be constant and perpendicular to the length of the CRT. From Newton's second law, the electron's acceleration is $\vec{a} = \vec{F}^B/m_e$, where $m_e = 9.11 \times 10^{-31}$ kg is the electron's mass. For constant $\vec{F}^B$, the acceleration is constant and is perpendicular to the initial velocity, so we can write the deflection d due to $\vec{F}^B$ as

$$d = \tfrac{1}{2}a\Delta t^2 = \tfrac{1}{2}\left(\frac{F^B}{m_e}\right)\Delta t^2 = \tfrac{1}{2}\left(\frac{F^B}{m_e}\right)\left(\frac{\ell}{v_0}\right)^2 = \frac{F^B \ell^2}{2m_e v_0^2}$$

$$d = \frac{ev_0 B_0 \ell^2}{2\sqrt{2}m_e v_0^2}\sqrt{1 + \sin^2 \theta_C} = \frac{eB_0 \ell^2}{2\sqrt{2}m_e v_0}\sqrt{1 + \sin^2 \theta_C}.$$

The maximum deflection occurs for $\sin \theta_C = \pm 1$, which occurs when $\theta_C = 90°$ (screen faces east) or $\theta_C = 270°$ (screen faces west). Substituting $\sin \theta_C = \pm 1$ and then canceling the $\sqrt{2}$ in numerator and denominator, we obtain the maximum deflection:

$$d_{max} = \frac{eB_0 \ell^2}{2m_e v_0} = \frac{(1.6 \times 10^{-19}\,\text{C})(3.0 \times 10^{-5}\,\text{T})(0.300\,\text{m})^2}{(2)(9.11 \times 10^{-31}\,\text{kg})(3.0 \times 10^7\,\text{m/s})}$$

$$= 7.9\,\text{mm.} ✔$$

(*b*) If the screen faces east, then $\theta_C = 90°$, so $\sin \theta_C = 1$, $\cos \theta_C = 0$, and the magnitude of the deflection is 7.9 mm. The deflection is in the direction of $\vec{F}^B$, which has components $F_x^B = 0$, $F_y^B < 0$, and $F_z^B = F_y^B$. So the deflection points diagonally downward, 45° below south. From the perspective of the viewer, who is facing west, the image is shifted diagonally down and to the left, with a magnitude of 7.9 mm. ✔

(*c*) If the screen faces north, then $\theta_C = 0$, so $\sin \theta_C = 0$, $\cos \theta_C = 1$, and the magnitude of the deflection is 5.6 mm. Now $\vec{F}^B$ has components $F_x^B > 0$, $F_y^B = 0$, and $F_z^B = 0$. So the deflection points due east. From the perspective of the viewer, who is facing south, the image is shifted 5.6 mm to the left. ✔

④ EVALUATE RESULT
That seems like a pretty big deflection, one big enough to notice by turning the television to different positions. In fact, turning the screen right or left, you can actually see

PRACTICE

the picture shift by a few mm. We can check our approximation that the direction of $\vec{F}^B$ is constant by evaluating the maximum angle $\alpha = \tan^{-1}(at/v_0) = 3.0°$ (for $\sin \theta_C = \pm 1$) between the electron's initial and final velocities: 3° is a pretty small angle, justifying the approximation. You should calculate the effect of gravity on the electron to check our assumption that it was all right to ignore the gravitational force.

We can use the right-hand force rule to check the directions of the deflections in parts *b* and *c*. For the east-facing screen, the electric current is traveling west and the viewer is facing west. From the viewer's perspective, Earth's magnetic field points diagonally down and to the right, so the right-hand force rule gives a magnetic force that is diagonally down and to the left, in agreement with our calculation. For the north-facing screen, the current travels south. Earth's magnetic field points downward and toward the south-facing viewer, so the right-hand force rule gives a magnetic force that is directly to the left, again in agreement with our result.

Guided Problem 27.6 Fusion energy

Nuclear fusion, the process that powers the Sun, can be made to occur in a laboratory by superheating a gas of electrons and protons (called a plasma) to temperatures exceeding 10^6 K. When their energy is high enough, the protons combine to create helium nuclei, and energy is liberated as the protons fuse. These hot, charged particles are trapped by a "containment vessel" formed by a strong magnetic field. Alcator C-mod at the Massachusetts Institute of Technology can achieve magnetic fields greater than 8 T. Assume that the C-mod's containment vessel has a circular cross section and that the magnetic field is uniform and has a constant magnitude of 8.0 T. What is the minimum radius of the vessel so that both electrons and protons are trapped? What is the period of the orbit in which the particles travel? Assume that the average speed of the particles is about 2.0×10^7 m/s.

❶ GETTING STARTED

1. Describe the problem in your own words. What two variables must you determine?
2. What type of motion is implied by "containment"?
3. Which particle, proton or electron, is harder to contain?

❷ DEVISE PLAN

4. What simplification results from seeking the minimum vessel radius?
5. How is the radius related to the given information?
6. What expressions must you use to determine the orbit period?

❸ EXECUTE PLAN

7. Work through the algebra and solve for the desired unknown quantities, and then substitute values you know to get numerical answers.

❹ EVALUATE RESULT

8. Is your value for the vessel radius unreasonable? That is, would such a device fit in a reasonably sized laboratory room?
9. Check that a particle moving in a circular orbit at your calculated radius and period would have the speed given in the problem statement.
10. How should the ratio of the two calculated radii relate to the ratio of the proton and electron masses? Does your answer check out?

Worked Problem 27.7. Going with the flow

A proton moves parallel to a current-carrying wire, at a distance 10 mm from the long axis of the wire, with the proton's velocity equal to the average velocity of the electrons in the wire. The interaction between the wire and the proton is observed from two reference frames: Observer E is at rest in the Earth reference frame, while observer M is moving relative to the Earth reference frame. To observer E, the wire is at rest, carries a 5.0-A current, has an ion charge density $\lambda_{E,ions} = +1.60 \times 10^3$ C/m, and has an electron charge density $-\lambda_{E,ions}$, making the wire electrically neutral. (*a*) What must M's velocity be, relative to the Earth reference frame, such that M observes only an electric force (and no magnetic force) between the wire and the proton? (*b*) What magnitude does observer M measure for this electric force? (*c*) What acceleration does this force give the proton?

❶ GETTING STARTED We are told that a proton moving along with the electrons in a current-carrying wire is examined by two observers: E in the Earth reference frame and M in a reference frame moving relative to E. We are also told that M sees the proton-wire interaction as purely electric and from this information must determine her speed relative to E. We must also calculate what M measures for the magnitude of the electric force exerted by the wire on the proton and the resulting acceleration of the proton.

❷ DEVISE PLAN For part *a*, the only way that M can see the wire-proton interaction as purely electric is if the proton is at rest relative to M. Therefore her speed must be the same as that of the proton (and thus of the electrons), which is related to the current and the linear charge density through Eq. 27.36, $I = \lambda_{proper}v$, where $\lambda_{proper} = \lambda_{E,ions}$ is what E measures for the linear charge density of the ions in the wire.

We can then use the calculated value of v to obtain the magnitude of the electric force needed in part *b*. This electric force is given by Eq. 27.32, $\vec{F}^E_{Mwp} = q\vec{E}_M$, with the electric field magnitude measured by M given by Eq. 27.31:

$$E_M = \frac{2k\lambda_{proper}}{r}\gamma\frac{v^2}{c_0^2},$$

where $\gamma = 1/\sqrt{1 - (v/c_0)^2}$

For part *c*, once we have F^E_{Mwp}, we can obtain the proton's acceleration by dividing the magnitude of this force by the proton mass.

❸ EXECUTE PLAN (*a*) The speed of the electrons measured by E is, from Eq. 27.36,

$$v = \frac{I}{\lambda_{proper}} = \frac{5.0 \text{ A}}{1.60 \times 10^3 \text{ C/m}} = 0.0031 \text{ m/s.} ✔$$

This then must be the speed at which M moves relative to the Earth reference frame.

(*b*) Using the expression for E_M given by Eq. 27.31, we get for the electrostatic force measured by M

$$F^E_{Mwp} = qE_M = q\frac{2k\lambda_{proper}}{r}\gamma\frac{v^2}{c^2}.$$

Here q is the charge on the proton, which is the elementary charge e, and the electron linear charge density is λ_{proper} as we saw in part a, so we have

$$F^E_{Mwp} = (1.6 \times 10^{-19}\,\mathrm{C}) \frac{2(9.0 \times 10^9\,\mathrm{N \cdot m^2/C^2})(1.60 \times 10^3\,\mathrm{C/m})}{0.010\,\mathrm{m}}$$

$$\times\,(1.09 \times 10^{-22}) = 5.0 \times 10^{-26}\,\mathrm{N}. \checkmark$$

(c) A force of this magnitude gives the proton an acceleration that has a magnitude of

$$a = \frac{F^E_{Mwp}}{m_p} = \frac{5.0 \times 10^{-26}\,\mathrm{N}}{1.67 \times 10^{-27}\,\mathrm{kg}} = 30\,\mathrm{m/s^2}. \checkmark$$

④ EVALUATE RESULT Notice that the speed of the electrons, 0.003 m/s, is very small. The density of electrons in the wire is so great that even a very small average speed can create a current of several amperes. The force we calculated is extremely small, as we expect because of the tiny magnitude of the elementary charge e, but the acceleration of the proton is not so small because of its very small mass: The proton's acceleration is greater than that of a freely falling particle in Earth's gravitational field.

Guided Problem 27.8. Half speed

Suppose that in the situation described in Worked Problem 27.7 the proton is moving at only half the speed of the electrons. If you are an observer at rest relative to the wire, what magnitude do you measure for the electric force exerted by the wire on the proton? Would you observe a magnetic force exerted on the proton? If so, what is the magnitude of this force?

① GETTING STARTED

1. What portions of Worked Problem 27.7 can you use in this problem?
2. Which equations can help you determine the two types of interaction?

② DEVISE PLAN

3. Which equations can help you calculate the electric and magnetic fields in this relativistic situation?
4. What important simplification should you make?

③ EXECUTE PLAN

5. Work out the needed quantities algebraically and then substitute numbers to get a numerical answer.

④ EVALUATE RESULT

6. How does the magnitude of the electric force exerted on the proton compare to that found in Worked Problem 27.7? Is this sensible?

Questions and Problems

Dots indicate difficulty level of problems: • = easy, •• = intermediate, ••• = hard; CR = context-rich problem.

27.1 Magnetism

1. Which way does the north pole of a compass needle point in the Southern Hemisphere? •
2. Which type of magnetic pole is located near Earth's geographic South Pole? •
3. How are the elementary magnets aligned in the magnet in Figure P27.3? •

Figure P27.3

4. Can a magnet have more than two magnetic poles, one north and one south? ••
5. You are given three bars of metal. Two of them are magnets, and the third is made of a magnetic material but is not magnetized. Describe how, using only the three bars, you could determine which of them is not a magnet. ••
6. You are given two metal rods. One is a magnet, and the other is made of magnetic material but does not have the elementary magnets aligned. Using no other objects, how can you determine which is the magnet? ••
7. Sketch and describe the magnetic poles of a spherical piece of uniformly magnetized material. •••

27.2 Magnetic fields

8. Which field line patterns in Figure P27.8 can represent a magnetic field? •

Figure P27.8

(a)   (b)   (c)   (d)

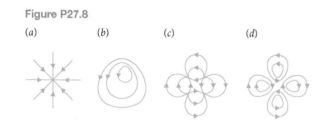

9. A bar magnet is enclosed by a spherical surface. (a) What is the flux through the entire surface? (b) If the magnetic flux through the hemisphere closest to the magnet's north pole is positive, what is the flux through the hemisphere closest to the magnet's south pole positive, negative, or zero? (c) The magnet is now moved so that its north half is outside the surface. What is the flux through the entire surface now (d) The portion of the magnet outside the surface is sawed off. What is the flux through the surface now? •
10. Is the field line pattern created by a magnetic dipole the same as the field line pattern created by an electric dipole? Draw both field line patterns. ••

11. Describe what happens to a bar magnet placed in the nonuniform external magnetic field shown in Figure P27.11. ••

Figure P27.11

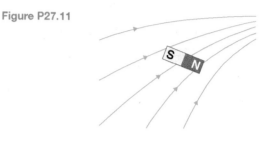

12. Describe what happens to a bar magnet placed in the nonuniform external magnetic field shown in Figure P27.12. ••

Figure P27.12

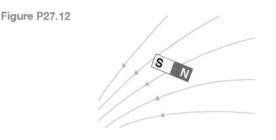

13. Is there a field line pattern that could everywhere represent either the magnetic field due to a magnet or the electric field due to a system of fixed charged particles? ••
14. Estimate the magnitude of the magnetic field at location 2 in Figure P27.14 if the magnetic field magnitude at location 1 is 0.27 T. Note that real magnetic field lines spread out in three dimensions. The spreading is shown in only two dimensions here, but you must imagine that the spreading also occurs into and out of the page. ••

Figure P27.14

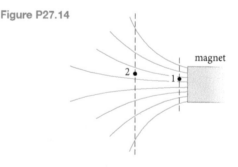

15. Rank the magnet pairs in Figure P27.15 in order of the amount of torque on magnet 2, smallest torque first. Assume all the magnets are equal in strength and the spacing between magnets is comparable in all pairs. •••

Figure P27.15

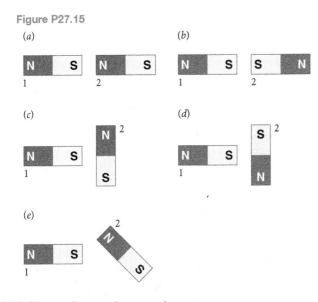

(a)

N S
1
N S
2

(b)

N S
1
S N
2

(c)

N S
1

N 2
S

(d)

N S
1

S 2
N

(e)

N S
1

N 2
S

27.3 Charge flow and magnetism

16. The long, straight current-carrying wire of Figure P27.16 lies in the plane of the page, and the magnetic field it produces at position P points out of the page. (a) In what direction does the magnetic field point at position S? (b) What is the current direction in the wire? •

Figure P27.16

P •

S •

17. Figure P27.17 shows a long, straight current-carrying wire running perpendicular to the plane of the page. The current produces a magnetic field that points to the right at position P. (a) In what direction does the magnetic field point at position S? (b) What is the current direction in the wire? •

Figure P27.17

P •

wire ⊙

S •

18. Figure P27.18 shows three particles passing near the north end of a bar magnet. Particle 1 is an electron, and particles 2 and 3 are protons. All three particles move at the same speed. (a) Determine the direction of the magnetic force exerted on each particle as it passes over the magnet. (b) What is the direction of the force (if any) exerted by each particle on the magnet? •

Figure P27.18

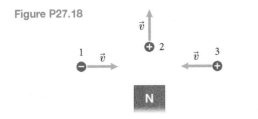

19. Figure P27.19 shows a conducting rod suspended from a spring in a region where a uniform magnetic field points

horizontally out of the page. The rod can be supplied with current by two thin wires connecting its ends to the terminals of a battery (not shown). (a) Does the tension in the spring depend on whether or not the wires are connected to the battery? (b) Does the tension depend on which wire is connected to which battery terminal? If so, which wire should be connected to the positive terminal in order to increase the tension in the spring? ••

Figure P27.19

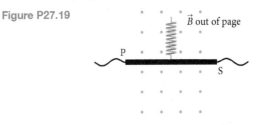

20. A wire is coiled in the shape of a helical spring with closely spaced turns. (a) When current is passed through it, does the coil tend to lengthen, shorten, or stay the same length? (b) Does your answer depend on the current direction? ••

21. The square loop of wire in Figure P27.21 carries a current, and an external magnetic field is directed out of the page everywhere. If the magnetic force exerted on side 1 is to the right, determine (a) the direction of the current in the loop and (b) the directions of the magnetic forces exerted on sides 2, 3, and 4. ••

Figure P27.21

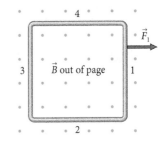

22. The two metal rods in Figure P27.22 are perpendicular to each other. Describe the magnetic force each rod exerts on the other, and then describe the torque caused by each force. •••

Figure P27.22

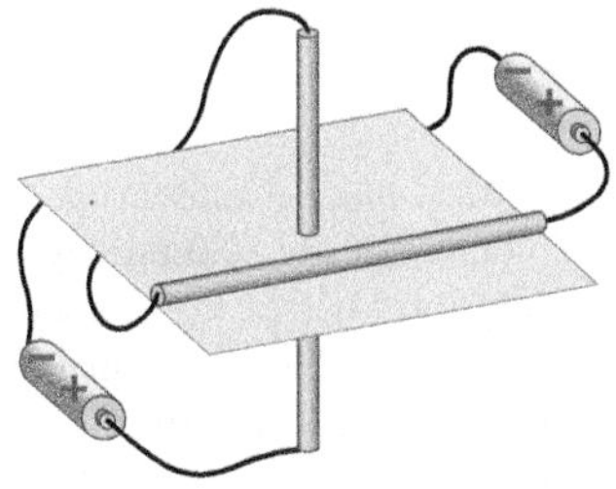

27.4 Magnetism and relativity

23. If two charged particles M and S are at rest relative to each other, there is no magnetic force between them. Suppose instead that particle M is moving relative to particle S while S is at rest in the Earth reference frame. Is a magnetic force exerted on S? •

24. A positively charged particle is at rest on the positive z axis in reference frame S. Reference frame S′ is moving along the positive x axis of S, reference frame S″ is moving along the negative x axis, and reference frame S‴ is moving along the y axis,

all with speed v relative to S. The axes of all the reference frames are oriented the same way, and their origins coincide at instant $t = 0$, when observers in each reference frame make measurements. In which reference frames do observers measure an electric field? •

25. Write expressions for the magnitudes and directions of the electric fields measured in Problem 24. ••

26. Compare the magnitudes and directions of the magnetic fields measured in Problem 24. ••

27.5 Current and magnetism

27. A wire 0.70 m long carries a current of 1.4 A. The wire is at an angle of 53° to a uniform external magnetic field. If the force exerted by the field on the wire is 0.20 N, what is the magnitude of the magnetic field? •

28. In Figure P27.28, an external magnetic field is directed upward throughout a region that contains four current-carrying wires having the lengths and currents shown. Rank the wires according to the magnitude of the magnetic force exerted on them by the external field, smallest force first. Ignore any interactions between the wires. •

Figure P27.28

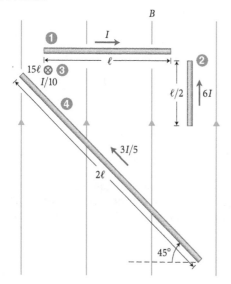

29. Two vertical parallel rails made of material that is an electrical conductor are 80.0 mm apart (Figure P27.29). A wire 80.0 mm long is free to slide along the rails, and the rails allow a current to be maintained through the wire as it slides. An external magnetic field of magnitude 0.250 T is directed into the page in Figure P27.29. If the mass of the wire is

4.00 g, what is the current in the wire if the wire doesn't fall under gravity? ••

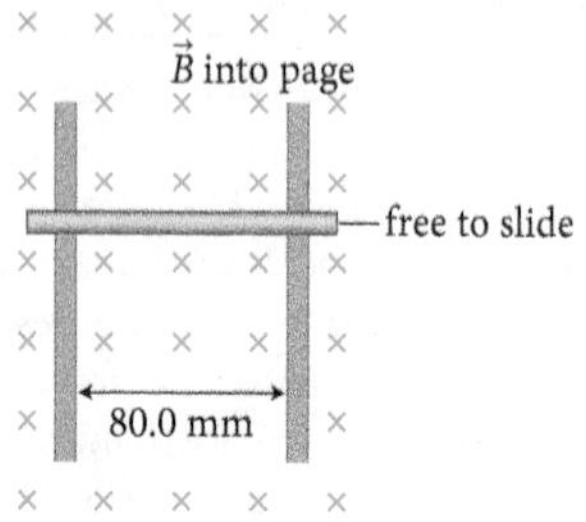

30. A current-carrying wire is bent into a circular loop of radius R and lies in an xy plane. A uniform external magnetic field in the $+z$ direction exists throughout the plane of the loop. What is the magnetic force exerted by the external field on the loop? ••

31. Draw an xyz coordinate system with the x axis pointing horizontally to the right, the y axis pointing up the page, and the z axis pointing out of the page. Show a current-carrying wire lying on the x axis, and a 2.5-A current through the wire directed in the positive x direction. (a) If the charge carriers are only electrons, how many of them pass through a cross-sectional area of the wire each second? (b) In which direction are the electrons moving? (c) If this wire is in a 0.20-T external magnetic field directed into the page, what is the force magnitude per unit length exerted by the external field on the wire? (d) On your diagram, show the direction of the magnetic field and the direction of the force exerted by the external field on the wire. ••

32. A wire 70.0 mm long is bent in a right angle such that the wire starts at the origin and goes in a straight line to $x = 30.0$ mm, $y = 0$, and then in another straight line from $x = 30.0$ mm, $y = 0$ to $x = 30.0$ mm, $y = 40.0$ mm. The wire is in an external uniform 0.500-T magnetic field in the $+z$ direction, and the current through the wire is 4.10 A, directed from the origin into the wire. (a) Determine the magnitude and direction of the magnetic force exerted by the external field on the wire. (b) This wire is removed and replaced by one that is 50.0 mm long and runs directly from the origin to the location $x = 30.0$ mm, $y = 40.0$ mm. If the current through this wire is also 4.10 A, what are the magnitude and direction of the magnetic force exerted by the external field on the wire? ••

33. Figure P27.33 on the next page shows the arrangement we looked at in *Principles* Example 27.2: a metal bar 0.20 m long suspended from two springs, each having a spring constant $k = 0.10$ N/m. Initially there is no current through the bar, and it is suspended at rest below the ceiling. With a current of 0.45 A, the bar rises a distance $d = 1.5$ mm. Suppose that the current is turned off, the bar drops down to its original position, and we attach a 5.0-mg piece of plastic to the center of the bar. Now how much current must there be through the bar to make it rise a distance $d = 1.5$ mm? ••

Figure P27.29

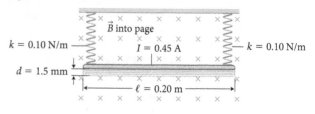

$\vec{B}$ into page

free to slide

80.0 mm

Figure P27.33

$k = 0.10$ N/m

$\vec{B}$ into page

$I = 0.45$ A

$k = 0.10$ N/m

$d = 1.5$ mm

$\ell = 0.20$ m

34. Two horizontal parallel conducting rods are connected such that a conducting crossbar free to slide along them has a constant current I running through it (Figure P27.34). The rods are separated by a distance ℓ and are in an external uniform magnetic field of magnitude B directed out of the page. The crossbar has a length ℓ and mass m. (a) In which direction

does the crossbar move? (*b*) If there is a coefficient of static friction μ_s between rods and crossbar, what is the minimum current I_0 necessary for the crossbar to move? ••

Figure P27.34

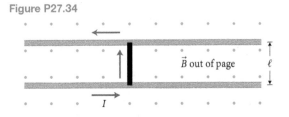

35. The top left portion of Figure P27.35 shows a current-carrying wire shaped into a rectangular loop that is very flexible. The loop is mounted on a base (not shown) that allows it to spin in any direction, and in this way any forces that cause the loop to move, spin, or distort can be detected. If the current direction through the loop is counterclockwise as indicated, what magnetic field direction(s) could cause the shape and orientation changes shown in parts (*a*)–(*e*) of Figure P27.35? If no magnetic field is necessary to make a shown change, write "none." If there is no way a magnetic field could cause a shown change, write "not possible." ••

Figure P27.35

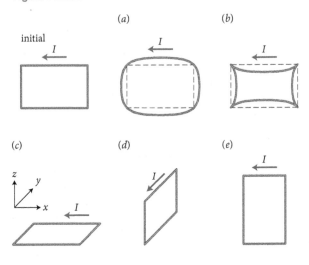

36. An arbitrary-shaped tangle of wire is connected such that it carries a current I_0 from position $\vec{r}_1$ to position $\vec{r}_2$ in a region where there is an external uniform magnetic field $\vec{B}_0$. Show that the magnetic force exerted by the external field on the wire is given by $\vec{F}_w^B = I_0(\vec{r}_2 - \vec{r}_1) \times \vec{B}_0$. •••

37. A 1.00-m metal bar that has a mass of 0.900 kg is initially pinned in place on an incline 65.0° above the horizontal (Figure P27.37). There is a 0.850-T magnetic field directed upward in the region around the bar, and metal contacts along the incline allow a current through the bar. If the co-efficient of static friction between bar and contacts is 0.200, (*a*) what are the minimum magnitude and the direction of the current that must pass through the bar to keep it from moving once it is released? (*b*) Is there a maximum current that can be used in that same direction that will also hold the bar in place? •••

Figure P27.37

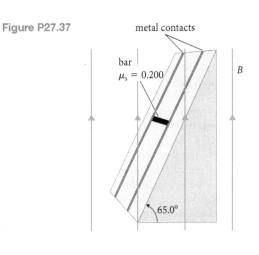

27.6 Magnetic flux

38. Figure P27.38 shows a bar magnet placed at four positions on and near a spherical shell. Rank the positions according to the amount of magnetic flux through the shell, smallest flux first. •

Figure P27.38

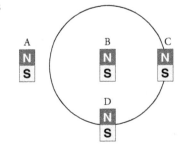

39. Figure P27.39 on the next page shows five objects, all placed in the same uniform, upward-directed external magnetic field. Rank the objects according to the amount of magnetic flux through them, smallest flux first. •

Figure P27.39

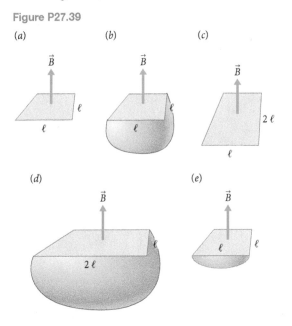

40. A square loop of side length 100 mm is placed on a wooden table in a uniform magnetic field of magnitude 0.25 T. The greatest magnetic flux through the loop is measured when the loop is flat on the table. What is the flux through the loop when it is tilted such that the plane of the loop makes a 60° angle with the table? Draw a diagram indicating all necessary vectors. ●●

41. A circular loop of radius 100 mm is placed in a magnetic field of magnitude 0.030 T. If the magnetic flux through the loop is 3.00×10^{-4} T · m², what is the angle between the plane of the loop and the field? ●●

42. A square loop of wire has a perimeter of 4.00 m and is oriented such that two of its parallel sides form a 25.0° angle with the horizontal. A uniform horizontal magnetic field of magnitude 0.100 T passes though the loop. (a) Calculate the magnetic flux through the loop. (b) Another loop lies in the same plane but has an irregular shape, resembling a starfish. Its area equals that of the square loop. Calculate the flux through this loop. ●●

43. The loop of Figure P27.43 is partially in a region where there is a 2.0-T magnetic field pointing out of the page and partially in a region where there is a 1.0-T magnetic field pointing into the page. Calculate the magnetic flux through the loop. ●●

Figure P27.43

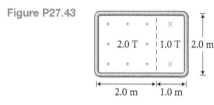

44. A hemispherical bowl of radius R is placed in a uniform magnetic field that has magnitude B_0 and is in the positive z direction. The open top of the bowl is in the xy plane. Obtain an expression for the magnetic flux through the hemispherical surface of the bowl. ●●

27.7 Moving particles in electric and magnetic fields

45. A proton moves at 6.67×10^5 m/s undeflected in the $+x$ direction through a velocity selector, a device containing crossed electric and magnetic fields. You measure the electric field to be 2.0×10^5 N/C in the positive z direction. (a) What are the magnitude and direction of the magnetic field $\vec{B}$? (b) If the proton's speed doubles, in which direction is it deflected? ●

46. Figure P27.46 shows the semicircular path through which charged particles travel in the magnetic field of a mass

Figure P27.46

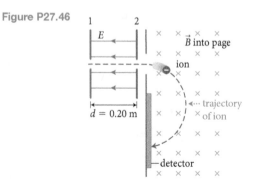

spectrometer. If the particles are oxygen ions carrying a charge of $-2e$ and the magnetic field magnitude is 0.20 T, how long does it take each ion to travel the semicircular path through the magnetic field? The mass of an O^{2-} ion is 2.6×10^{-26} kg. ●

47. An alpha particle ($m = 6.64 \times 10^{-27}$ kg), which has twice the charge and approximately four times the mass of a proton, is moving in a circle of radius 0.75 m perpendicular to a uniform magnetic field of magnitude 0.75 T. Calculate the alpha particle's (a) angular frequency and period of motion, (b) speed, and (c) kinetic energy. ●●

48. A proton moves in a circular orbit 150 mm in radius that is perpendicular to a uniform 0.25-T magnetic field. Determine the proton's (a) angular frequency and period of motion, (b) speed, and (c) kinetic energy. ●●

49. An electron that has a kinetic energy of 7.5×10^{-17} J moves in a circular orbit perpendicular to a uniform magnetic field of magnitude 0.35 T. For this electron, determine (a) the radius of its orbit, (b) its angular frequency and period of motion, and (c) its speed. ●●

50. A deuteron is a charged particle that has the same charge as a proton but approximately twice the mass. An alpha particle has twice the charge and approximately four times the mass of a proton. For this problem, assume the mass ratios are exactly 2 and 4. If a proton, a deuteron, and an alpha particle move in a uniform magnetic field in circles having the same radii, compare their (a) speeds, (b) kinetic energies, and (c) angular momentum magnitudes. ●●

51. The isotopes magnesium-24 (mass 3.983×10^{-26} kg) and magnesium-26 (mass 4.315×10^{-26} kg) are to be separated using a mass spectrometer in which the magnetic field magnitude is 0.577 T. The ions used are the ones that have lost one electron each, $^{24}Mg^+$ and $^{26}Mg^+$. What is the minimum value of the potential difference through which these ions must be accelerated if the separation distance between them on the detector screen must be 2.60 mm? (Assume the mass ratio is 26/24.) ●●

52. A particle that has mass m and charge q enters a uniform magnetic field that has magnitude B and is directed along the x axis. The initial velocity of the particle is in the xy plane. (a) Describe the particle's path as it travels through the magnetic field. (b) If the particle enters the magnetic field at $t = 0$, what is its angular displacement at $t = 2\pi m/qB$? ●●

53. A horizontal metal strip 1.0 mm thick and 20 mm wide carries a 20-A current along its length, and both the length and the width are perpendicular to a uniform magnetic field of magnitude 2.0 T that is directed vertically up. The potential difference across the strip width is 4.27 μV. (a) If the side of the strip width that is to your left as you look in the direction of the current is at the higher potential, what is the sign of the mobile charge carriers? What are (b) the speed and (c) the number density of the charge carriers? ●●

54. The cross section of a copper strip is 1.0 mm thick and 20 mm wide. There is a 10-A current through this cross section, with the charge carriers traveling down the length of the strip. The strip is placed in a uniform magnetic field that has a magnitude of 2.0 T and is directed perpendicular to both the length and the width of the strip. If the number density of free electrons in copper is 8.47×10^{19} mm⁻³, calculate (a) the speed of the electrons in the strip and (b) the potential difference across the strip width. ●●

55. A proton is accelerated through a potential difference of 120 V, as shown in Figure P27.55, and fired into a chamber. There is no electric field in the chamber, but there is a 0.15-T magnetic field in the positive z direction. The proton enters the chamber at a 25° angle above the horizontal, and this entry location is the origin of the xyz coordinate system. Determine the coordinates of the location at which the proton will later strike this same wall from the inside. ••

Figure P27.55

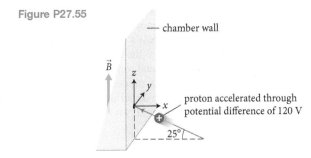

56. A beam of protons enters the network of five chambers shown in Figure P27.56 with an initial speed of 300 m/s and moves through the network along the path indicated by the dashed black line. In each chamber, the electric field is as specified, and the radius of curvature R is 0.40 m wherever it is shown. For each chamber, calculate the component of the magnetic field perpendicular to the path of the protons. •••

Figure P27.56

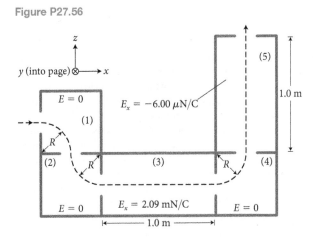

57. Electrons are made to flow through the copper strip of Figure P27.57. The strip's cross section is 1.00 mm high and 30.5 mm wide, and the strip is placed in a 2.00-T magnetic field that is directed out of the page. If the number of electrons per unit volume in the copper is $8.46 \times 10^{28} \text{ m}^{-3}$ and the current in the strip is 12 A, calculate the potential difference across the width of the strip when conditions have been allowed to equilibrate. •••

Figure P27.57

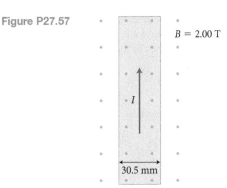

$B = 2.00$ T

I

30.5 mm

27.8 Magnetism and electricity unified

58. On average, the number density of free electrons in copper is $8.46 \times 10^{19} \text{ mm}^{-3}$. (a) Calculate what the linear charge density λ for a copper wire 1.00 mm in radius would be if this quantity of electrons were missing. (b) Assume this copper wire is electrically neutral in the Earth reference frame, in which it is at rest and carrying a current. Calculate the linear charge density λ' of the copper wire in a reference frame moving along with the electrons if the electrons are moving at 4.70×10^{-4} m/s. ••

59. A square loop of wire 1.00 m on a side is at rest and has a linear charge density of zero in the Earth reference frame. The loop lies in the xy plane of an xyz coordinate system, and there is a clockwise electric current through the loop as seen by a person looking down the positive z axis to the xy plane. The electrons move at speed v, and an observer M, moving at this same speed v, approaches the loop along the y axis (moving in the positive y direction). In which side(s) of the loop $(+x, +y, -x, -y)$ does M see the linear charge density as being due (a) to surplus positive charge carriers and (b) to surplus negative charge carriers? ••

60. Suppose electrons move through a copper wire at speed v. Call the linear charge densities in the Earth reference frame λ_{Ep} for the fixed positive ions in the wire and λ_{En} for the (negative) electrons. Observer E in the Earth reference frame (which is also the reference frame of the positive ions) measures the wire to be electrically neutral. Observer M is moving along with the electrons (in the same direction as the electrons and at speed v). Calculate the linear charge density of the wire as measured by M in terms of λ_{En} if the speed is (a) 3.0×10^5 m/s and (b) 3.0 mm/s (an achievable speed for electrons in copper wire). ••

61. A long wire that is at rest in the Earth reference frame initially carries no current. Observer E in this reference frame measures linear charge densities of $\lambda_{\text{En}} = 45.00 \ \mu\text{C/m}$ for the (negative) electrons in the wire and $\lambda_{\text{Ep}} = 60.00 \ \mu\text{C/m}$ for the positive ions. A current is created as electrons are made to move through the wire at speed v, and observer M moves along with the electrons at their speed v. What value must v have in order for M to measure an electric field of magnitude $E = 3.00 \times 10^7$ N/C at a distance 0.0100 m above the wire? •••

Additional problems

62. In Figure P27.62, an external magnetic field is directed out of the page, and six wires are placed, one at a time, in this field. Each wire carries a current in the direction indicated; if there is no indicated direction, the current is zero. Determine the direction of the magnetic force exerted by the magnetic field on each wire. •

Figure P27.62

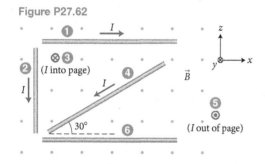

63. Three charged particles initially have identical masses, charges, and speeds and are traveling perpendicular to the same magnetic field. Because they are all in the same magnetic field and have identical masses and charges, all particles have the same initial cyclotron frequency and revolve with the same period T. The speed of particle 1 is doubled; particle 2 enters a region in which the magnetic field has been reduced by a factor of 2; and particle 3 collides with and sticks to a neutral particle of the same mass, causing a change in speed. Determine the new period of each particle in terms of the initial period T. •

64. At the equator, the direction of Earth's magnetic field is horizontal and to the north, and the magnitude is 3.5×10^{-5} T. (a) What is the magnetic flux through a circular loop of radius 0.10 m, lying flat on the ground at the equator? The loop is now balanced on its edge and the axis that runs perpendicular to the plane of the loop is pointed in different directions. What is the magnetic flux through the loop when this axis is pointed (b) northwest, (c) due north, and (d) west? •

65. When a wire 1.0 m long carries a 20-A current in the $+x$ direction in a uniform external magnetic field, the magnetic force exerted by the field on the wire is given by $F_x^B = 0, F_y^B = 3.0$ N, $F_z^B = 2.0$ N. When the wire is rotated until the charge carriers travel in the $+y$ direction, the magnetic force exerted by the field on the wire is given by $F_x^B = -3.0$ N, $F_y^B = 0, F_z^B = -2.0$ N. What are the magnitude and direction of the magnetic field? ••

66. Blood contains both positive and negative ions. In a certain patient being tested, the speed of these ions in a large artery is measured at 0.60 m/s. The patient is placed in a uniform magnetic field of magnitude 0.20 T. If a potential difference of 1.0×10^{-3} V is measured across the diameter of the artery, what is that diameter? ••

67. Electrons enter a region of perpendicular electric and magnetic fields (similar to *Principles* Example 27.5). The region occupied by the fields is 40.0 mm long in the x direction, where x is taken to be the original direction of motion. After passing through this region, the electrons then travel an additional 300 mm in the x direction before hitting a phosphorescent screen that lights up where the electrons strike it. The electrons pass undeflected through the region of perpendicular fields when $E = 2.0 \times 10^3$ N/C and $B = 1.2 \times 10^{-5}$ T. (a) Determine the speed of the undeflected electrons. (b) If the magnetic field is turned off but the electric field is left on, by what distance have the electrons been deflected when they reach the phosphorescent screen? ••

68. A particle of mass m and charge q moves in a circle of radius r in a uniform magnetic field of magnitude B. Show that (a) the particle's momentum is given by Bqr and (b) its kinetic energy is given by $B^2q^2r^2/2m$. ••

69. You are designing magnetic motors. A colleague insists that like magnetic poles attract—north poles attract north poles and south poles attract south poles. You feel the need to remove this idea from his head. You possess three unlabeled bar magnets. Surely that will be enough . . . ••• CR

70. Figure P27.70 shows a 1.0-m, 0.350-kg horizontal metal rod attached to two ropes, each of which makes an angle of 30° with the horizontal. Each rope then drapes over a pulley and is attached to a vertical rod of mass m. Assume the pulleys have negligible mass. There is a 0.25-T magnetic field in the region of the rod, parallel to the xy plane, oriented 45° from the long axis of the horizontal rod. When the horizontal rod is made to carry a current I, suddenly the rod moves upward until the ropes holding it make an angle of 5.0° with the horizontal. What was the value of I? •••

Figure P27.70

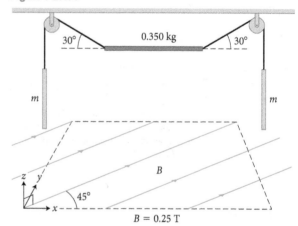

71. A wire bent into a semicircle of radius R lies in a plane that is perpendicular to a uniform external magnetic field $\vec{B}$. If the wire carries a current I, what are the magnitude and direction of the magnetic force exerted by the external field on the wire? •••

72. You are working with the square wire loop shown in Figure P27.72. The loop lies in a magnetic field, is connected to a battery, and is attached to an axis that runs through its center and is parallel to the plane of the loop. Initially the loop is held in place, but once it is released, it immediately rotates 180° about this axis. You know that magnetic fields can induce a torque on a current-carrying wire, but you are surprised by the rotation of exactly 180°. In an attempt to explain why this happened, you determine the direction of the current in the loop and the direction of the magnetic field in the region of the loop. You begin to wonder if multiple answers might be possible and if there is any way to keep the loop rotating in the same direction. ••• CR

Figure P27.72

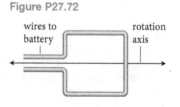

Answers to Review Questions

1. A magnet is an object that attracts objects made of iron, nickel, cobalt, or certain alloys, including most types of steel. A magnetic material is one that is attracted to a magnet.

2. Magnetic poles are the places on a magnet where a magnetic material is attracted most strongly. In a magnet that is free to align in any direction, the pole that settles toward geographic north is defined to be the magnet's north pole, and the opposite pole is the south pole.

3. Two like magnetic poles repel each other; two magnetic poles of opposite types attract each other.

4. An elementary magnet is the tiny magnetic dipole corresponding to a single atom of magnetic material such as iron, nickel, or cobalt, or to an elementary particle such as an electron or proton. In the elementary-magnet model for magnetism, a large number of the elementary magnets in a magnetic material have their north poles aligned in one direction and their south poles aligned in the opposite direction. This alignment of elementary N and S poles creates the overall N and S poles of the magnet.

5. A magnet is surrounded by a magnetic field, which exerts a force on the poles of another magnet.

6. Magnetic field lines tell us the direction and relative magnitude of the magnetic field. The field lines point in the direction of the magnetic field, and the density of field lines is proportional to the magnetic field's magnitude. For the field created by a magnet, magnetic field lines on the outside of the magnet point from the magnet's north pole to its south pole; within the magnet, magnetic field lines point from the magnet's south pole to its north pole.

7. It doesn't; the magnetic field line flux through a closed surface is always zero, because magnetic field lines always form closed loops.

8. The magnetic field source described is moving charge carriers, which constitute a *current*, defined as the flow of charge carriers.

9. The magnetic field lines are circles, centered on the wire and in planes perpendicular to it.

10. The electrons would need to flow from right to left, because a flow of positive charge in one direction produces the same magnetic field as an equal flow of negative charge in the opposite direction.

11. Because electrons are negatively charged particles, the current direction is downward.

12. Counterclockwise, as shown using the right-hand current rule. If you point the thumb of your right hand in the direction of the current (that is, toward yourself), the fingers curl counterclockwise, indicating the direction of the magnetic field produced by that current.

13. The direction of the force exerted by the magnet on the wire is perpendicular to the direction of the external magnetic field and also perpendicular to the current direction, as determined by the right-hand force rule. When the outstretched fingers of your right hand align with the current such that they can curl toward the direction of the external magnetic field, the thumb points in the direction of the force exerted by the external field on the wire.

14. We expect this because electric currents, which both cause and interact with magnetic fields, depend on velocity, and velocity is always relative to an observer's reference frame.

15. The huge internal electric forces between the charged constituents in the wire balance to zero because there are equal amounts of positive and negative charge carriers. Because the electric forces are so huge, however, even a small relativistic correction to them is measurable, so the magnetic force is observable.

16. The observer at rest relative to the wire sees equal charge densities for the ions and the electrons, and so the wire appears electrically neutral to this observer. The observer moving with the electrons sees a greater linear charge density for the ions than for the electrons, and thus to this observer the wire is not electrically neutral.

17. The magnetic force is a maximum when the wire is perpendicular to the external field and a minimum (zero) when the wire and external field are either parallel or antiparallel.

18. It depends on the magnitude of the external magnetic field, the absolute value of the current, the length of wire in the field, and the sine of the angle between the directions of the current and the field: $F_w^B = |I|\ell B \sin\theta$ (Eq. 27.7).

19. From the right-hand force rule and Eq. 28.8, the force exerted by the field on the wire points in the positive z direction: $\hat{\imath} \times \hat{\jmath} = \hat{k}$.

20. The magnetic flux through the surface is the scalar product of the magnetic field vector and the area vector for the surface.

21. The magnetic flux through any closed surface is zero. This implies that there are no isolated magnetic monopoles (analogous to isolated charged particles).

22. The flux is the same through *all* surfaces bounded by a given loop, except for a plus or minus sign determined by the chosen direction of the normal area vector.

23. The magnetic force exerted on the wire is the vector sum of the magnetic forces exerted by the field on the moving charged particles that make up the current in the wire. The force exerted on each particle is $\vec{F}_p^B = q\vec{v} \times \vec{B}$ (Eq. 27.19).

24. The force is directed perpendicular to the magnetic field direction and perpendicular to the particle's velocity, in accordance with the right-hand force rule.

25. The ions are moving relative to the observer, so she sees the distance between ions decrease because of the length contraction due to special relativity. Decreased distance between ions means increased linear charge density for them.

26. The observer in the Earth reference frame interprets the force as a purely magnetic interaction between the particle and the current, as the wire carries no surplus charge when observed from the Earth reference frame. The observer moving along with the electrons interprets the force as a combination of electric and magnetic interactions: The electric interaction arises because the wire appears positively charged to the observer who moves along with the electrons; the magnetic interaction is now due to the motion of the positive ions as seen from the reference frame of the electrons. For the special case in which the velocity of the positively charged particle equals the velocity of the electrons, the interaction observed from the moving reference frame is purely electric.

PRACTICE

Answers to Guided Problems

Guided Problem 27.2 $\vec{B}$ points into the page; $I = \dfrac{mg}{\ell B} = 103$ A.

Guided Problem 27.4 There is no force on the top or bottom side of the square. The force on the right side is into the plane of the figure, and the force on the left side is out of the plane of the figure, as shown in Figure WGA27.2. The vector sum of these two forces

Figure WGA27.2

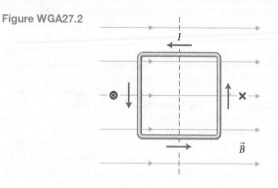

is zero. The torque tends to rotate the loop about the dashed line in the figure. The right side moves into the plane of the figure, while the left side moves out. The magnitude of the torque is
$\tau = 2(\ell/2)(I\ell B) = 3.9 \times 10^{-5}$ N·m.

Guided Problem 27.6

For protons, $R = \dfrac{m_p v}{eB} = 0.026$ m, $T = \dfrac{2\pi m_p}{eB} = 8.2$ ns. For electrons, $R = \dfrac{m_e v}{eB} = 14$ μm and $T = \dfrac{2\pi m_e}{eB} = 4.5$ ps. So the minimum vessel radius is 26 mm.

Guided Problem 27.8 In the Earth reference frame (at rest with respect to the wire), I measure no electric force exerted by the wire on the proton: $F_{Ewp}^{E} = 0$. But I do measure a magnetic force:

$$F_{Ewp}^{B} = |q| v_p \dfrac{2kI}{rc_0^2} = 2.5 \times 10^{-26} \text{ N}.$$

28

Magnetic Fields of Charged Particles in Motion

Chapter Summary

Current loops (Sections 28.1–28.3)

Concepts A magnetic field is produced by magnets, by current-carrying wires, and by moving charged particles.

The magnetic field pattern produced by a wire carrying a current and bent into a circular **current loop** is similar to the field pattern of a magnetic dipole.

A spinning charged particle has a magnetic field identical to that of an infinitesimally small magnetic dipole.

The **magnetic dipole moment** $\vec{\mu}$ is a vector that specifies the orientation and magnitude of a magnetic dipole. The direction of $\vec{\mu}$ is the same as the direction of the magnetic field at the dipole center. For a bar magnet, the direction of $\vec{\mu}$ is from south pole to north pole. For a current loop, the direction of $\vec{\mu}$ is the direction in which your thumb points when you curl the fingers of your right hand in the direction of the current.

A current loop placed in a magnetic field tends to rotate such that the direction of $\vec{\mu}$ aligns with the direction of the magnetic field.

Ampère's law (Sections 28.4, 28.5)

Concepts **Ampère's law** states that the line integral of the magnetic field along a closed path, called an **Ampèrian path**, is proportional to the current encircled by the path. See the Procedure box before the Worked and Guided Problems for how to apply Ampère's law.

Quantitative Tools If a constant current I_{enc} is encircled by an **Ampèrian path**, then by **Ampère's law**, the line integral of the magnetic field around the path is

$$\oint \vec{B} \cdot d\vec{\ell} = \mu_0 I_{enc}, \tag{28.1}$$

where $d\vec{\ell}$ is an infinitesimal segment of length of the Ampèrian path and μ_0, called the **permeability constant,** has the value

$$\mu_0 = 4\pi \times 10^{-7} \text{ T} \cdot \text{m/A}.$$

If a long, straight wire carries a current I, the magnitude of the magnetic field it produces at a distance d from the wire is

$$B = \frac{\mu_0 I}{2\pi d}.$$

The magnitude of the magnetic field produced by a large sheet carrying a uniformly distributed current is

$$B = \tfrac{1}{2}\mu_0 K,$$

where K is the current magnitude per unit width of the sheet.

Solenoids and toroids (Section 28.6)

Concepts A **solenoid** is a long, tightly wound helical coil of wire. The diameter of the coil is much smaller than its length. Outside an infinitely long solenoid, the magnetic field approaches zero; inside the solenoid, the magnetic field is directed parallel to the solenoid length.

A **toroid** is a solenoid bent into a circle. The entire magnetic field is contained within the windings of the toroid, and the magnetic field lines form circles around the center of the toroid.

Quantitative Tools If an infinitely long **solenoid** that has n windings per unit length carries a current I, the magnetic field the solenoid produces in its interior has magnitude

$$B = \mu_0 nI. \tag{28.6}$$

If a **toroid** that has N windings carries a current I, the magnetic field the toroid produces inside the windings at a distance r from the toroid center has magnitude

$$B = \mu_0 \frac{NI}{2\pi r}. \tag{28.9}$$

Biot-Savart law (Section 28.7)

Quantitative Tools **Biot-Savart law:** If a small segment of wire $d\vec{\ell}$ carries a constant current I, the magnetic field produced by the segment at a point P a distance r_{sP} from the segment is

$$d\vec{B}_s = \frac{\mu_0}{4\pi} \frac{I d\vec{\ell} \times \hat{r}_{sP}}{r_{sP}^2}, \tag{28.12}$$

where $d\vec{\ell}$ points in the current direction and $\hat{r}_{sP}$ points from the segment to P. The magnetic field is

$$\vec{B} = \int_{\text{current path}} d\vec{B}_s. \tag{28.10}$$

A circular arc of radius R spanning an angle ϕ and carrying a current I produces a magnetic field at the center of the circle of magnitude

$$B = \frac{\mu_0 I \phi}{4\pi R}.$$

Magnetic field of a moving charged particle (Section 28.8)

Quantitative Tools A particle that has charge q and velocity $\vec{v}$ produces at a point P a magnetic field

$$\vec{B} = \frac{\mu_0}{4\pi} \frac{q\vec{v} \times \hat{r}_{pP}}{r_{pP}^2} \tag{28.21}$$

where $\hat{r}_{pP}$ points from the particle to P and r_{pP} is the distance from the particle to P.
If charged particles 1 and 2 carrying charges q_1 and q_2 are a distance r_{12} apart and have velocities $\vec{v}_1$ and $\vec{v}_2$, the electromagnetic force exerted by particle 1 on particle 2 is

$$\vec{F}_{12}^{EB} = \frac{1}{4\pi\epsilon_0} \frac{q_1 q_2}{r_{12}^2} \left[\hat{r}_{12} + \frac{\vec{v}_2 \times (\vec{v}_1 \times \hat{r}_{12})}{c_0^2} \right], \tag{28.26}$$

where $\hat{r}_{12}$ points from particle 1 to particle 2 and

$$c_0 = \frac{1}{\sqrt{\mu_0 \epsilon_0}}$$

is the speed of light. Equations 28.21 and 28.26 are valid only if $v \ll c_0$.

Review Questions

Answers to these questions can be found at the end of this chapter.

28.1 Source of the magnetic field

1. What is the fundamental source of magnetic fields?
2. Are all magnetic forces central?
3. Is it possible to have a magnetic field without any magnetic poles?

28.2 Current loops and spin magnetism

4. What do the patterns of magnetic field lines from a current loop and from a bar magnet have in common?
5. What does the magnetic field surrounding a spinning charged particle look like?

28.3 Magnetic dipole moment and torque

6. What is the direction of the magnetic dipole moment vector used to specify the orientation of a magnetic dipole?
7. Describe the three right-hand rules used in studying magnetism.
8. Describe the magnetic interaction experienced by a current loop placed in a uniform external magnetic field.
9. What does the commutator do in an electric motor?

28.4 Ampèrian paths

10. Magnetic flux through any closed surface is zero, but electric flux need not be. How can this difference be accounted for in terms of the properties of electrostatic field lines and magnetic field lines?
11. How does the value of the line integral of the electrostatic field along a closed path encircling a charge distribution compare with the value of the line integral of the magnetic field along a closed path encircling a current-carrying wire?
12. State Ampère's law.
13. How can you determine whether a current encircled by an Ampèrian path makes a positive or negative contribution to the line integral of the magnetic field around the path?

28.5 Ampère's law

14. The proportionality constant in Ampère's law shows the relationship between what two variables associated with a current-carrying wire?
15. What kind of symmetry is displayed by a long straight wire carrying a steady current? How does this symmetry determine what you choose for the Ampèrian path when using Ampère's law to calculate the magnitude of this magnetic field?

16. How does the magnitude of the magnetic field around a long, straight current-carrying wire of radius R depend on radial distance $r > R$ from the long axis of the wire? Assuming that the current is steady and uniformly distributed within the wire, how does the field magnitude depend on the radial distance $r < R$ from the wire axis? From the point of view of Ampère's law, why is this?
17. Describe the magnetic field produced by a large flat sheet of uniformly distributed current for which the current per unit width is K. What are the magnitude and direction of the field above and below the sheet?

28.6 Solenoids and toroids

18. What is a solenoid? Describe the magnitude and direction of the magnetic field produced by a long solenoid carrying a steady current.
19. What is a toroid? Describe the magnitude and direction of the magnetic field produced by a toroid carrying a steady current.
20. Does the magnetic field inside a very long solenoid differ from that inside a toroid if the two devices carry the same current in the same number of turns? If so, how?

28.7 Magnetic fields due to currents

21. Compare and contrast the expression for the infinitesimal magnetic field at some location P near a small segment of current-carrying wire given by the Biot-Savart law (Eq. 28.12) and the expression for the electrostatic field at some location P near a source charged particle, which we obtained from Coulomb's law in Section 23.7, $d\vec{E}_s(P) = k(dq_s \hat{r}_{sP}/r_{sP}^2)$ (Eq. 23.14).
22. What steps can we follow to calculate the magnetic force between two parallel straight wires of length ℓ, carrying constant currents I_1 and I_2 and separated by a distance d?
23. Comment on the range of applicability of the Biot-Savart law relative to the range of applicability of Ampère's law.

28.8 Magnetic field of a moving charged particle

24. What is the origin of each of the two vector products in Eq. 28.26, the expression for the electromagnetic force between two moving charged particles 1 and 2?
25. What is the numerical value of the product of the proportionality constants μ_0 and ϵ_0? How does it relate to the speed of light c_0?
26. Does the force between two moving charged particles obey Newton's third law?

Developing a Feel

Make an order-of-magnitude estimate of each of the following quantities. Letters in parentheses refer to hints below. Use them as needed to guide your thinking.

1. The maximum magnetic field magnitude you are exposed to due to current in the electrical wiring in your house (E, K, P)
2. The straight-wire current needed to reverse the deflection of a compass needle sitting on your laboratory table (H, A, O, W)
3. The maximum magnetic field strength 10 m from a typical lightning bolt (G, R)
4. The maximum magnitude of the magnetic field you can produce in a solenoid sitting on your laboratory table when the core contains only air (D, N, Q, U)
5. The maximum magnetic force per meter between the antiparallel currents in your household wiring (P, E)
6. The electric current around the equator needed to produce Earth's magnetic field at the North Pole (B, I, M, S)
7. The magnitude of the magnetic field at the center of a Bohr-model hydrogen atom caused by the electron orbiting the nucleus (C, J, T)
8. The magnitude of the magnetic field at the North Pole that might be attributed to Earth's rotation, assuming a uniformly charged surface (F, L, I, V)

Hints

A. What is the horizontal component of Earth's magnetic field in your neighborhood?
B. What is the magnetic field magnitude at the North Pole?
C. What is the orbit radius?
D. What are the crucial variables to maximize?
E. What is the current configuration?
F. What is the magnitude of the electric field near Earth's surface?
G. How should you model the current?
H. How should the wire be oriented?
I. What is the radius of Earth?
J. What is the electron's speed?
K. How close do you come to the wiring?
L. What surface charge density could create this electric field magnitude?
M. What is the straight-line distance from a point on the equator to the North Pole?
N. What maximum current is reasonable?
O. What magnetic field strength is needed?
P. What is the maximum likely current in each conductor?
Q. What is a typical wire diameter used to carry currents of this magnitude in household or building wiring?
R. What is the peak current?
S. How can you compute the vector sum of the magnetic field magnitudes due to a large number of tiny segments of the current loop?
T. What magnitude of charge does the electron carry, and what is its inertia?

U. What is the maximum number of turns n per meter of solenoid?
V. How should you model the current?
W. How close to the wire can you place the compass?

Key (all values approximate)

A. 2×10^{-5} T; B. 7×10^{-5} T; C. 5×10^{-11} m; D. because $B = \mu_0 nI$, both I and n (number of windings per unit length) should be maximized; E. paired conductors separated by 10^{-2} m (two copper wires inside a nonconducting sheath) and carrying equal-magnitude currents in opposite directions; F. 100 V/m; G. approximately a vertical line; H. the compass detects horizontal magnetic fields, so orient the wire vertically; I. 6×10^6 m; J. electrical attraction provides centripetal force, so 2×10^6 m/s; K. 0.1 m if you stand near a wall; L. from Coulomb's law, 10^{-9} C/m^2; M. 9×10^3 km; N. laboratory tables are powered with 20 A, 120 V circuits, so the available current will be on the order of 20 A; O. enough to more than cancel Earth's magnetic field, say 4×10^{-5} T; P. 20 A for large appliances; Q. About 2 mm wire diameter; R. 10^5 A; S. by using the Biot-Savart law; T. $e = 1.6 \times 10^{-19}$ C, $m_e = 9.11 \times 10^{-31}$ kg; U. with 2-mm wire diameter, 500 turns per meter (or some small multiple of 500 turns per meter, if the wire is wound in more than one layer) are possible; V. as a stack of horizontal current loops of different radii (careful: current depends on radius); W. 0.02 m.

Worked and Guided Problems

Procedure: Calculating the magnetic field using Ampère's law

For magnetic fields with straight or circular field lines, Ampère's law allows you to calculate the magnitude of the magnetic field without having to carry out any integrations.

1. Sketch the current distribution and the magnetic field by drawing one or more field lines using the right-hand current rule. A two-dimensional drawing should suffice.
2. If the field lines form circles, the Ampèrian path should be a circle. If the field lines are straight, the path should be rectangular.
3. Position the Ampèrian path in your drawing such that the magnetic field is either perpendicular or tangent to the path and constant in magnitude. Choose the direction of the Ampèrian path so that, where it runs parallel to the magnetic field lines, it points in the same direction as the field. If the current distribution divides space into distinct regions, draw an Ampèrian path in each region where you wish to calculate the magnetic field.

4. Use the right-hand current rule to determine the direction of the magnetic field of each current encircled by the path. If this magnetic field and the Ampèrian path have the same direction, the contribution of the current to I_{enc} is positive. If they have opposite directions, the contribution is negative.
5. For each Ampèrian path, calculate the line integral of the magnetic field along the path. Express your result in terms of the unknown magnitude of the magnetic field B along the Ampèrian path.
6. Use Ampère's law (Eq. 28.1) to relate I_{enc} and the line integral of the magnetic field and solve for B. (If your calculation yields a negative value for B, then the magnetic field points in the opposite direction you assumed in step 1.)

You can use the same general approach to determine the current given the magnetic field of a current distribution. Follow the same procedure, but in steps 4–6, express I_{enc} in terms of the unknown current I and solve for I.

These examples involve material from this chapter but are not associated with any particular section. Some examples are worked out in detail; others you should work out by following the guidelines provided.

Worked Problem 28.1 Electrical wiring

A hobbyist has decided to install several new electrical accessories in her houseboat. To power these devices, she lays two wires along the ceiling of her boat as indicated in Figure WG28.1. (The plane of the drawing corresponds to the boat ceiling.) The wires are designed to carry the currents indicated in the figure, but she worries that the magnetic field near the wires might be strong enough to disrupt the operation of the compass that is already mounted to the ceiling. To reassure her that there will be no such problems, determine the magnitude and direction of the magnetic field at the position $x = 0$, $y = 4.0$ m, where the compass is located.

Figure WG28.1

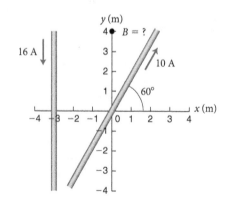

❶ GETTING STARTED Currents generate magnetic fields. Here two current-carrying wires contribute to a magnetic field at the position

indicated. We are asked to determine the magnitude and direction of this magnetic field.

❷ DEVISE PLAN We know from *Principles* Example 28.3 that the magnitude of the magnetic field generated at a radial distance r from a long, straight current-carrying wire is $B = \mu_0 I / 2\pi r$. Because the magnetic field is a vector, we need to determine the vector sum of the individual fields created by the two wires. We also know that near a current-carrying wire, magnetic field lines form concentric circles around the wire. We can use this information and the right-hand current rule to determine the field direction.

❸ EXECUTE PLAN Let's call the 10-A current I_1 and the corresponding magnetic field $\vec{B}_1$, and let's call the 16-A current I_2 and its magnetic field $\vec{B}_2$. Using the right-hand current rule, we point our right thumb in the direction of I_1 and notice that $\vec{B}_1$ points out of the plane of the page (i.e., points in the $+\hat{k}$ direction) at the position $x = 0$, $y = 4.0$ m, which we'll call position P. Similarly, by pointing our right thumb along I_2, we see that $\vec{B}_2$ also points out of the plane of the page at position P. The distance r_1 from the first wire to P, measured along a path perpendicular to the wire, is $r_1 = y \cos(60°) = 2.0$ m. The distance from the second wire to P is $r_2 = 3.0$ m. So the two wires' contributions to the magnetic field at point P are $\vec{B}_1 = +(\mu_0 I_1 / 2\pi r_1)\hat{k}$ and $\vec{B}_2 = +(\mu_0 I_2 / 2\pi r_2)\hat{k}$. The combined field $\vec{B}$ at point P is then

$$\vec{B} = \frac{\mu_0}{2\pi}\left(\frac{I_1}{r_1} + \frac{I_2}{r_2}\right)\hat{k} = \frac{4\pi \times 10^{-7}\,\text{T} \cdot \text{m/A}}{2\pi}\left(\frac{10\,\text{A}}{2.0\,\text{m}} + \frac{16\,\text{A}}{3.0\,\text{m}}\right)\hat{k}$$

$$= +(2.1 \times 10^{-6}\,\text{T})\hat{k}. ✔$$

④ **EVALUATE RESULT** A magnitude of 2.1×10^{-6} T for the magnetic field associated with these two currents is reassuring because it is about 20 times smaller in magnitude than Earth's magnetic field, and thus unlikely to affect the compass reading. It is also reassuring that the magnetic field points up toward the sky, while the compass is designed to measure the horizontal component of Earth's magnetic field. Finally, a value smaller than Earth's magnetic field makes sense for a current of several amperes at a distance of several meters, because I know from experience that a compass is affected by everyday electrical wiring only when it is held very close to a wire.

Guided Problem 28.2 Bell wire

A student runs a long wire along one wall of her room, curves the wire at the corner, and continues to run it to a bell on the adjacent wall. The wire at the corner forms a circular arc of radius 10 mm (Figure WG28.2). What are the magnitude and direction of the magnetic field at position P if the current in the wire is 540 mA?

Figure WG28.2

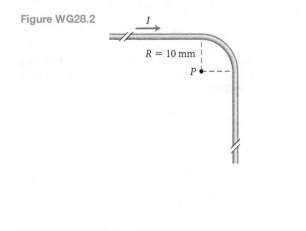

① **GETTING STARTED**
1. Describe the problem in your own words.
2. What concept(s) apply to this situation?
3. What assumptions must you make?

② **DEVISE PLAN**
4. Can you break the problem into parts?
5. Which equations will help you get the magnetic field for the various parts?
6. Can the equations specific to a slightly different situation be modified for this situation?
7. Magnetic field is a vector. How can you determine the vector direction?

③ **EXECUTE PLAN**
8. Solve for the desired unknown quantity. Substitute values you know to get a numerical answer. Be sure to determine the vector direction and include it in your answer.

④ **EVALUATE RESULT**
9. Does your answer behave as you expect it to as you change the radius of curvature?

Worked Problem 28.3 Galvanometer

A galvanometer is an old-fashioned device used to measure current. The simple model shown in Figure WG28.3 consists of a coil of wire, a vertical spring, a permanent magnet, and an indicator needle. A rigid rod (not shown) that runs perpendicular to the page is attached to the coil, and the coil is free to rotate about this rod axis. (The rod is also wired to allow the current to enter and leave the coil.) One end of the spring is attached to the coil, and the other end of the spring is attached to a fixed support. With no current through the device, the coil is horizontal, the spring is relaxed, and the needle points straight up. When there is a current in the coil, a torque is induced on the coil, causing it to rotate about the rigid rod, and the spring becomes either stretched or compressed. This rotation of the coil causes the needle to swing right or left, indicating the magnitude and sign of the current on a numerical scale (not shown in Figure WG28.3). As long as the angle ϕ through which the needle deflects from the vertical is not too large, the spring is stretched or compressed only vertically. (a) Viewed from above, what is the current direction with the coil rotated to the position shown? (b) Derive an algebraic expression for ϕ as a function of the current in the coil. (c) Calculate the current required to deflect the needle to an angle of 5.7°.

Figure WG28.3

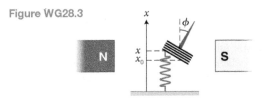

The coil has a square cross section, with sides of length ℓ. The coil has $N = 100$ turns, the magnet produces a uniform magnetic field of magnitude 0.010 T, and the spring constant is 2.0 N/m.

① **GETTING STARTED** We are given data for a galvanometer and asked to determine (a) the direction of the current in the coil, (b) an expression for the needle-deflection angle as a function of the current, and (c) the value of the current when that angle is 5.7°. We know that the magnet produces a magnetic field that is directed from the north pole to the south pole—that is, left to right in Figure WG28.3. We also know that a current loop experiences a torque when placed in an external magnetic field, and we know how to compute the magnitude of such a torque.

② **DEVISE PLAN** To deduce the current direction, we can use the right-hand force rule to determine the direction of the magnetic force on each side of the coil.

To derive an expression for ϕ as a function of I, we recall that Newton's second law applied to rotational motion tells us that the rotational acceleration of an object is proportional to the sum of the torques it experiences. We have two torques in this system: one due to the spring force and one due to the magnetic force between the external magnetic field and the current in the coil. These two torques balance to give the needle zero rotational acceleration once it reaches the position on the numerical scale corresponding to the amount of current in the coil. We can compute these torques because we know that the torque an object experiences when a force is exerted on it is $\vec{\tau} = \vec{r} \times \vec{F}$ (Eq. 12.38). The spring is stretched in the view shown in Figure WG28.3, and so the spring force is exerted downward on the left side of the coil. We know from Hooke's law

PRACTICE

(Eq. 8.20) that its magnitude is $F^c = |-k(x - x_0)|$, where k is the spring constant.

Each of the four sides of the coil experiences a magnetic force. Regardless of what the current direction is, the side of the coil facing us in Figure WG28.3 and its parallel side (behind the page) must feel forces that are perpendicular to the page and pointing in opposite directions. These forces not only cancel but also create zero torque on the coil because they are directed along the axis of rotation. Thus the only magnetic torques on the coil are those caused by the forces exerted on the two sides of the coil that face the two poles of the magnet. Because Figure WG28.3 shows the needle rotated to the right through angle ϕ, we know that the force direction is upward on the coil side facing the north pole and downward on the coil side facing the south pole. The magnitude of the force exerted on any straight wire segment in the coil can be found from Eq. 28.13,

$$F^B = |I\vec{\ell} \times \vec{B}| = \ell IB;$$

where ℓ is the length of each coil side. Note that the angle in this vector product is always 90° as the coil rotates, but the angle in the vector product for the torque, $\vec{\tau} = \vec{r} \times \vec{F}$, depends on ϕ. We just need to put these pieces together to get ϕ as a function of I and then a value for I when $\phi = 5.7°$.

❸ EXECUTE PLAN (a) The force exerted by the stretched spring is downward, and so to keep the left side of the coil tilted upward as shown, the magnetic force exerted on this side must be upward. By the same reasoning, the right side of the coil must experience a downward magnetic force. Thus we know two of the three variables covered by the right-hand force rule—magnetic force direction and magnetic field direction—and so let's use this rule to determine the current direction. The current is either clockwise or counterclockwise as viewed from above. In the left side of the coil, a clockwise current means that, in order to make the fingers of our right hand able to sweep from I direction to $\vec{B}$ direction, we must position the hand with the fingers touching the coil's left side and pointing into the page with the palm facing to the right. Our thumb, which indicates the direction of the magnetic force on this side of the coil, points downward, but we know that this force is directed upward. Thus the current is not clockwise; it must be counterclockwise. ✔

To confirm that the current is counterclockwise as viewed from above, we apply the right-hand force rule to the right side of the coil. A counterclockwise current in this side means that when we point our fingers at this side in such a way that we can sweep them from I direction to $\vec{B}$ direction, the thumb points down for the direction of $\vec{F}^B$. Knowing that this is indeed the direction of $\vec{F}^B$ here, we have confirmed that the current in the coil is counterclockwise. ✔

(b) Because the needle does not accelerate once there is a steady current through the coil, the magnitude τ^B of the combined torques due to the two magnetic forces must be equal to the magnitude τ^c of the torque due to the spring force. Because these two torques must be of equal magnitude in order to balance each other, we have $\tau^B = \tau^c$:

$$\tau^B_\vartheta + \tau^c_\vartheta = \tau^B + (-\tau^c) = 0$$

$$\tau^B = \tau^c.$$

The coil is composed of a stack of N turns, and each turn consists of four segments. We know that only the segments facing the north and south magnetic poles contribute to the torque, so we must consider the magnetic force on these two segments of each turn. The torque due to the magnetic force exerted on each segment is the vector product of the force due to the magnetic field and the radius vector $\vec{r}$ pointing from the axis of rotation (the central axis of the coil) to the segment. The magnitude of this vector product is $rF^B \sin\theta = rF^B \cos\phi$, where $\theta = \frac{\pi}{2} - \phi$ is the angle between $\vec{r}$ and $\vec{F}$. Because there are N turns in the coil, there are N wire segments on each side of the coil. Because there are two sides experiencing the magnetic force that creates the torque, the torque on the coil due to the magnetic field is

$$\tau^B = 2|\vec{r} \times \vec{F}^B|$$

$$= 2\left[\tfrac{1}{2}\ell(\ell NIB)\sin\left(\tfrac{\pi}{2} - \phi\right)\right]$$

$$= \ell^2 NIB \cos\phi,$$

where I is the current through each segment and thus the current through the coil. The torque caused by the spring force can be approximated, for small angles, by

$$\tau^c = |\vec{r} \times \vec{F}^c|$$

$$= \tfrac{1}{2}\ell\,|k(x - x_0)|\sin\left(\tfrac{\pi}{2} - \phi\right)$$

$$= \tfrac{1}{2}\ell\,|k(\tfrac{1}{2}\ell\sin\phi)|\cos\phi$$

$$\approx \tfrac{1}{4}k\ell^2 \sin\phi\cos\phi.$$

The substitution we just used, $\Delta x = \tfrac{1}{2}\ell\sin\phi$, is an approximation because we have assumed that the spring stretches only vertically, whereas in reality it is also pulled slightly to the right. Nevertheless, our approximation should be fine for small angles of rotation. Setting the two torques' magnitudes equal to each other, we get for the current

$$I = \frac{k}{4NB}\sin\phi.$$

For small angles, $\sin\phi \approx \phi$ (in radians), which means that the angle of deflection is approximately linear with the current:

$$I = \frac{k}{4NB}\phi, \quad \text{or} \quad \phi = \frac{4NBI}{k}. ✔$$

(c) For $\phi = 5.7°$, we get

$$I = \frac{2.0\ \text{N/m}}{4(100)(0.010\ \text{T})}(5.7°)\left(\frac{1\ \text{rad}}{57.3°}\right) = 50\ \text{mA}. ✔$$

❹ EVALUATE RESULT In the equation we derived for I, notice how the needle-deflection angle does not depend on the size of the coil; it depends only on the number of turns N and on the strength of the magnetic field. Can you figure out why the coil size doesn't play a role? Hint: Look at how the two opposing torques—one from the spring and one from the magnetic force due to the current—depend on the dimensions of the coil.

Make sure you fully understand each vector product used in the solution and where each angle comes from. The torques caused by magnetic forces can be fairly complex because of all the angles involved.

The magnitude of the current is neither excessively large nor small. Galvanometers often have a switch to allow you to measure different ranges of current while keeping the needle-deflection angle small. Moreover, a real galvanometer has a construction somewhat different from the version shown in Figure WG28.3. A spiral spring is typically used, and the magnets are designed so that the magnetic field direction is mostly radial. What would this accomplish?

This problem is a good example of how to solve a seemingly complex problem by putting several smaller pieces together. You may need to reach back to Chapter 8 to review how springs work and to Chapter 12 to review torque.

Guided Problem 28.4 Force on a rectangular current loop

A circuit board has a rectangular loop of wire next to a long straight wire located a distance $x = 0.300$ mm away from the loop (Figure WG28.4), with a 39-mA current through each element. What is the magnetic force exerted by the wire on the loop? The rectangle dimensions are $\ell = 5.7$ mm and $w = 0.90$ mm.

Figure WG28.4

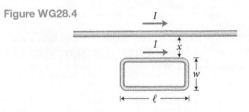

① GETTING STARTED

1. Can you break the problem into parts?
2. What simplification can you make immediately just by looking at the problem?
3. What assumptions do you need to make?

② DEVISE PLAN

4. Along each side of the rectangle, in what direction does the magnetic field generated by the wire point? In what direction does the magnetic force exerted on that side point?

5. Are there any two sides of the rectangle whose magnetic forces cancel one another?
6. What is an expression for the magnetic force between two parallel current-carrying wires?

③ EXECUTE PLAN

7. Apply the right-hand current rule to determine the direction of the magnetic field, and the right-hand force rule to obtain the directions of the forces.
8. Obtain an algebraic expression for the vector sum of the forces exerted on the loop. Then substitute numbers to get a numerical answer.

④ EVALUATE RESULT

9. Is your value for the magnitude of the magnetic force exerted on the loop unreasonable? Do you expect this force magnitude to be large or small?
10. How does the force depend on the dimensions of the loop? If ℓ and w become so large that only one side of the rectangle is near the wire, does the force per unit length reduce to a familiar expression? Does your algebraic expression also make sense if w becomes so small that the two long sides of the rectangle lie on top of one another, with equal but oppositely directed currents?

Worked Problem 28.5 Wire with nonuniform current

A long, straight wire that has a cross-sectional radius R carries a current I, but this current is not uniformly distributed over the circular cross section of the wire. Instead, the number density of charge carriers n depends linearly on the radial distance r from the wire's central axis: $n(r) = n_R r/R$, where n_R is the number density of charge carriers at the wire surface; these charge carriers all move at the same velocity v. (a) Derive an expression for the magnetic field magnitude B as a function of r for $r < R$ and for $r > R$. (b) Plot B as a function of r.

① GETTING STARTED
We are asked to derive expressions for the magnetic field magnitude inside and outside a current-carrying wire when the current is distributed nonuniformly across the wire cross section (rather than just outside an infinitesimally thin wire, as we did in the *Principles* discussion). We know that the magnetic field due to current in a wire has field lines that form closed loops around the wire. Ampère's law will be useful, but the nonuniform current requires a careful computation of the enclosed current for each value of r, the radial distance away from the wire center. This means we must break the wire cross section into a large number of small elements, with each element small enough to have a uniform current through it, and then integrate to obtain the current enclosed at any value of r. We can then draw a graph showing B as a function of r.

② DEVISE PLAN
Because of the cylindrical symmetry, we use Ampère's law:

$$\oint \vec{B} \cdot d\vec{\ell} = \mu_0 I_{enc}$$

for a tiny segment $d\vec{\ell}$ along some chosen Ampèrian path. The current enclosed inside any Ampèrian path we choose must be computed with an integral, but how can we set that up? From Chapter 27, we know that the current in a wire is related to the number density of charge carriers by Eq. 27.16, $I = nAqv$. Because we are dealing with an electric current, the charge q is the magnitude of the elementary charge e carried by an electron, and we are told that v does not depend on the distance r from the wire center. However, n is a function of r, so we cannot simply multiply the number density by the volume of the wire. We must imagine breaking the wire into small volume elements, but what kind? Because nothing varies with length along the wire, we can allow our elements to have any length. That is good because length along the wire is absorbed into the speed v of the charge carriers.

The cross-sectional area factor in our volume is another matter: Because n depends on r, we must break the cross-sectional area A of the wire into tiny portions, with n approximately constant over each portion. This suggests that we use very thin rings so that all portions of the cross section of a ring have the same value of r. The cross-sectional area dA of such a ring (Figure WG28.5) of radius r and thickness dr is its circumference times its thickness: $dA = 2\pi r\, dr$. This can be seen by imagining the ring being sliced through the thickness dr and unrolled to produce a rectangle of length $2\pi r$ and height dr.

Putting all this together in applying Eq. 27.16, with the substitutions $n = n(r)$, $A = 2\pi r\, dr$, and $q = e$, we get for the current dI through any infinitesimally thin cylindrical shell of radius r:

$$dI = n(r)ev2\pi r\, dr.$$

At any radial distance r from the wire center, the current enclosed by a circular Ampèrian path can be found by integrating this expression from the wire center out to r. We should have no trouble applying Ampère's law in this case of a nonuniform current distribution, as long as we can do the integrals.

Figure WG28.5

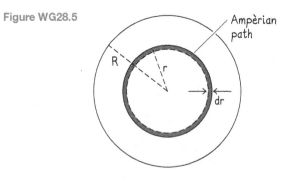

3 EXECUTE PLAN (a) We draw a circular Ampèrian path at a radius r inside the wire (Figure WG28.5). $\vec{B}$ and $d\vec{\ell}$ are parallel all along the Ampèrian path, so $\vec{B} \cdot d\vec{\ell} = Bd\ell \cos 0 = Bd\ell$. Because the current depends only on the distance r from the wire center, the symmetry is not disturbed for any given path radius. Thus the magnitude of the magnetic field at all points along this circular Ampèrian path has the same value, and we can bring it outside the integral:

$$B \oint d\ell = \mu_0 I_{enc}$$

$$2\pi rB = \mu_0 I_{enc}. \qquad (1)$$

We must now compute the current enclosed by integrating over a large number of infinitesimally thin cylindrical shells, each of radius r and thickness dr and carrying current dI:

$$I_{enc}(r) = \int dI = \int_0^r 2\pi evn(r)r\, dr$$

$$= 2\pi ev \int_0^r n_R \frac{r}{R}r\, dr = \frac{2\pi evn_R}{R}\int_0^r r^2\, dr$$

$$= \frac{2\pi evn_R}{R}\frac{r^3}{3}, \qquad (2)$$

where R is the wire radius.

We could next substitute this expression for I_{enc} into Ampère's law, but there is a great simplification to be made. We do not know values for n_R and v, but we do know that the current in the wire is I. Perhaps we can eliminate some unknowns by computing the integral all the way to the wire surface (where $r = R$), which must give us an expression that represents the wire current I:

$$I = \frac{2\pi evn_R}{R}\int_0^R r^2\, dr = \frac{2\pi evn_R}{R}\frac{R^3}{3}.$$

This allows us to simplify Eq. 2 for the current enclosed at any Ampèrian path radius r to

$$I_{enc}(r) = I\frac{r^3}{R^3}.$$

Substituting this value for I_{enc} in Eq. 1 shows us that inside a wire of radius R, the magnetic field as a function of the radial distance r from the wire center is given by

$$2\pi rB = \mu_0 I(r/R)^3$$

$$B = \frac{\mu_0 I}{2\pi}\frac{r^2}{R^3}.$$

Outside the wire, $r > R$, the enclosed current is just I at any path radius r, and so the expression for the magnetic field magnitude at any radial distance r from the wire center is the same as that for a thin wire:

$$B = \frac{\mu_0 I}{2\pi r}. ✔$$

(b) Figure WG28.6 is a graph of the magnetic field magnitude B as a function of the radial distance r from the wire center. ✔

Figure WG28.6

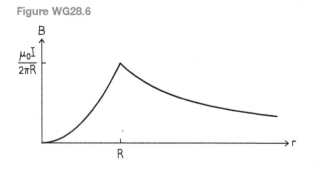

4 EVALUATE RESULT The problem statement tells us that n increases linearly with the radial distance r from the wire center. This nonuniform current distribution means that as we move radially away from the wire center, more and more current is enclosed by our Ampèrian path. Thus, the magnetic field magnitude increases quadratically until we reach the wire surface. Outside the wire, the current enclosed is always I, as it is for a wire carrying a uniformly distributed current, and so the magnetic field magnitude drops off as $1/r$. In this region our result agrees with what we found for an infinitesimally thin wire (see *Principles* Example 28.3)

Guided Problem 28.6 Magnetic field in a coaxial cable

A coaxial cable consists of two concentric elements, an inner conducting wire and an outer conducting shell, typically separated by some dielectric material. One reason for using this type of cable is that when there is a current in it, the magnetic field due to the current is "trapped" inside the cable. Show that this is true by deriving one expression for the magnetic field magnitude in the region between the inner wire and the outer shell, and another expression for the magnetic field outside of the outer shell. Assume a uniform current and model that current as having one direction in the inner wire and the opposite direction in the outer shell. You can treat the outer shell as if its thickness were infinitesimal.

❶ GETTING STARTED

1. How is this problem similar to Worked Problem 28.5?
2. What approach seems best to attack this problem?

❷ DEVISE PLAN

3. Assign symbols for each radius you need. How many different radii must you use to establish the results you need?

4. What portions of Worked Problem 28.5 are relevant?

❸ EXECUTE PLAN

5. Apply Ampère's law as many times as needed.
6. Sketch a graph of the magnetic field magnitude as a function of distance from the center of the inner wire to check the behavior inside and outside the cable.

❹ EVALUATE RESULT

7. What is the radial dependence of the magnetic field in each region? Are your results unreasonable?
8. Do your results match what the problem statement says about the magnetic field being trapped inside the cable? If not, you probably made an error somewhere. Go back and check your work.

Worked Problem 28.7 Equivalence

A charged particle moves parallel to a long, straight current-carrying wire. The particle is a perpendicular distance a away from the wire, and the direction of the particle's velocity is the same as the direction of the current in the wire. Show that F^B_{wp}, the magnitude of the magnetic force exerted by the wire on the particle, is equal to F^B_{pw}, the magnitude of the magnetic force exerted by the particle on the wire, and that these two forces are in opposite directions.

❶ GETTING STARTED We are told that a charged particle moves alongside a current-carrying wire, that the perpendicular distance between the particle and the wire is a, and that the particle's direction of motion is the same as the current direction. Our task is to show that the magnetic force exerted by the wire on the particle, which moves in the magnetic field created by the current in the wire, is equal in magnitude to the force exerted by the particle on the wire and that these two forces point in opposite directions. That the two forces should be equal and opposite—that is, $\vec{F}^B_{wp} = -\vec{F}^B_{pw}$—is not true in general for magnetic interactions, as discussed in *Principles* Section 28.8, but we are told that it should be true in this special case.

Let's spell out the concepts that will help us to solve this problem. We know that a long, straight current-carrying wire generates a magnetic field whose field lines encircle the wire, and we know that a charged particle moving through this magnetic field will experience a magnetic force that is perpendicular both to the field and to the particle's velocity. Similarly, we know that a moving charged particle generates a magnetic field and that a current-carrying wire will experience a force due to this magnetic field.

❷ DEVISE PLAN As we've drawn in Figure WG28.7, we let the current I in the wire run in the $+x$ direction, along the x axis. We let the position P of the charged particle be on the y axis at $x = 0$, $y = a$, $z = 0$. We call the particle's charge q, and we let the particle's velocity $\vec{v}$ point in the x direction: $\vec{v} = v\hat{\imath}$.

To evaluate the magnetic field $\vec{B}_w$ due to the wire at position P, we can use Ampère's law, Eq. 28.1, as applied in *Principles* Example 28.3, where we found the magnitude of the magnetic field at a distance d from a long, straight wire to be

$$B = \frac{\mu_0 I}{2\pi d}. \tag{1}$$

Figure WG28.7

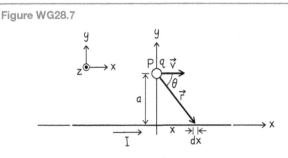

To compute the force $\vec{F}^B_{wp}$ exerted on a charged particle moving in the field of the wire, we can use Eq. 27.19:

$$\vec{F}^B_P = q\vec{v} \times \vec{B}. \tag{2}$$

To evaluate at any position $(x, 0, 0)$ along the wire the magnetic field $\vec{B}_p$ due to the moving particle, we can use the expression for the magnetic field of a moving charged particle, Eq. 28.21, with the vector $\vec{r}$ indicated in Figure WG28.7 pointing from the moving charged particle (the source of the magnetic field) to the segment dx along the wire at $(x, 0, 0)$. Finally, to compute the force $\vec{F}^B_{pw}$ exerted on the wire, we can break the wire up into infinitesimal segments $d\vec{\ell} = dx\hat{\imath}$ along the x axis and calculate each segment's infinitesimal contribution $d\vec{F}^B_w$ to the force using Eq. 27.8:

$$d\vec{F}^B = I\,d\vec{\ell} \times \vec{B}. \tag{3}$$

We can then integrate Eq. 3 over the entire length of the wire to obtain $\vec{F}^B_{pw}$.

Finally, we can use the right-hand current rule and the right-hand force rule to check that the directions make sense for the magnetic fields and forces that we calculate.

❸ EXECUTE PLAN Substituting the distance a into Eq. 1 yields the magnitude $B_w = \mu_0 I/2\pi a$ at the point P where the charged particle is located. Using the right-hand current rule, we point our right thumb along the positive x axis and our fingers point out of the page at P. Because $\hat{\imath} \times \hat{\jmath} = \hat{k}$ is a vector identity, the z axis in Figure WG28.7 must point out of the page. Thus the magnetic field at point P due to the wire is

$$\vec{B}_w = \frac{\mu_0 I}{2\pi a}\hat{k}. \tag{4}$$

We obtain the magnetic force $\vec{F}^B_{wp}$ exerted on the charged particle by substituting $\vec{B}_w$ from Eq. 4 into Eq. 2:

$$\vec{F}^B_{wp} = q\vec{v} \times \left(\frac{\mu_0 I}{2\pi a}\hat{k} \right) = (qv\hat{\imath}) \times \left(\frac{\mu_0 I}{2\pi a}\hat{k} \right) = \frac{\mu_0 Iqv}{2\pi a}(-\hat{\jmath}),$$

where we used the vector identity $\hat{\imath} \times \hat{k} = -\hat{\jmath}$ to see that the force points downward, in the $-y$ direction, for $q > 0$. We can check this direction using the right-hand force rule: If $q > 0$, then the vector $q\vec{v}$ points to the right, while $\vec{B}_w$ points out of the page. Pointing the fingers of our outstretched right hand to the right and then curling them out of the page leaves our thumb pointing downward, confirming that the force on the particle points down toward the wire (along $-\hat{\jmath}$) if $q > 0$.

We evaluate the magnetic field $\vec{B}_p$ at position $(x, 0, 0)$ along the wire due to the moving charged particle by substituting the vector $\vec{r} = x\hat{\imath} - a\hat{\jmath}$ into Eq. 28.21:

$$\vec{B}_p = \frac{\mu_0}{4\pi}\frac{q\vec{v} \times \hat{r}}{r^2} = \frac{\mu_0}{4\pi}\frac{(qv\hat{\imath}) \times \left(\dfrac{x\hat{\imath} - a\hat{\jmath}}{\sqrt{x^2 + a^2}} \right)}{(\sqrt{x^2 + a^2})^2}.$$

Remember that $\vec{r}$ points from the moving charged particle, at location $(0, a, 0)$, to the point $(x, 0, 0)$ at which $\vec{B}_p$ is evaluated. The length of this vector is $r = \sqrt{x^2 + a^2}$, and the unit vector pointing along $\vec{r}$ is

$$\hat{r} = \frac{\vec{r}}{r} = \frac{x\hat{\imath} - a\hat{\jmath}}{\sqrt{x^2 + a^2}}.$$

Collecting the square roots into the denominator and simplifying, we get

$$\vec{B}_p = \frac{\mu_0 qv}{4\pi}\frac{\hat{\imath} \times (x\hat{\imath} - a\hat{\jmath})}{(x^2 + a^2)^{3/2}} = \frac{\mu_0 qva}{4\pi(x^2 + a^2)^{3/2}}(-\hat{k}),$$

where in the last step we used $\hat{\imath} \times (x\hat{\imath} - a\hat{\jmath}) = (\hat{\imath} \times x\hat{\imath}) - (\hat{\imath} \times a\hat{\jmath}) = -a\hat{k}$, because $\hat{\imath} \times \hat{\imath} = \vec{0}$ and $\hat{\imath} \times \hat{\jmath} = \hat{k}$. This magnetic field points in the $-z$ direction, which is into the plane of the page. We can check this direction by noting that a positively charged particle (assuming $q > 0$) moving to the right constitutes an electric current directed to the right. So we can point our right thumb along the charged particle's velocity vector, with our fingers wrapping around the particle, and notice that along the x axis (where the current-carrying wire is) our fingers are directed into the page, confirming the direction $-\hat{k}$.

Now we can substitute $\vec{B}_p$ into Eq. 3 to calculate the magnetic force $d\vec{F}^B_{pw}$ exerted on segment dx of the current-carrying wire. We also note that the current is in the $+x$ direction and substitute $Id\vec{\ell} = Idx\hat{\imath}$ to get

$$d\vec{F}^B_{pw} = Id\vec{\ell} \times \vec{B}_p = [Idx\hat{\imath}] \times \left[\frac{\mu_0 qva}{4\pi(x^2 + a^2)^{3/2}}(-\hat{k}) \right]$$

$$= \frac{\mu_0 Iqva\, dx}{4\pi(x^2 + a^2)^{3/2}}\hat{\jmath},$$

where we used the vector identity $\hat{\imath} \times \hat{k} = -\hat{\jmath}$ to determine that the force points upward ($+\hat{\jmath}$) toward the charged particle, if $q > 0$. We can use the right-hand force rule to check that the force (for $q > 0$) points upward by pointing the outstretched fingers of our right hand to the right, along the current, and curling our fingers into the page, along $\vec{B}_p$; when we do this, our thumb points upward. Next we integrate $d\vec{F}^B_{pw}$ along the length of the wire to calculate the force $\vec{F}^B_{pw}$ exerted on the wire:

$$\vec{F}^B_{pw} = \frac{\mu_0 Iqv}{4\pi}\hat{\jmath}\left(\int_{x=-\infty}^{\infty} \frac{a\, dx}{(x^2 + a^2)^{3/2}} \right) = \frac{\mu_0 Iqv}{4\pi}\hat{\jmath}\left(\frac{2}{a} \right) = \frac{\mu_0 Iqv}{2\pi a}\hat{\jmath}.$$

We found that the integral in parentheses equals $2/a$ by looking it up on-line, but it turns out that by integrating over the angle θ shown in Figure WG28.7 instead of the coordinate x, we obtain an integral that is much easier to solve. Because we can see from the figure that $a/x = \tan\theta$, we can write $x = a/\tan\theta$ and differentiate to get $dx = -(a\, d\theta/\sin^2\theta)$. Then, because $a/\sqrt{x^2 + a^2} = a/r = \sin\theta$, we can write

$$\frac{a\, dx}{r^3} = -\frac{\sin\theta\, d\theta}{a}.$$

Now we can change the integration variable from x to θ and get

$$\int_{x=-\infty}^{\infty} \frac{a\, dx}{(x^2 + a^2)^{3/2}} = \int_{\theta=\pi}^{0} \left(-\frac{\sin\theta\, d\theta}{a} \right) = \frac{1}{a}\int_{\theta=0}^{\pi} \sin\theta\, d\theta = \frac{2}{a}.$$

Looking at the expressions we obtained above for $\vec{F}^B_{wp}$ and $\vec{F}^B_{pw}$, we can see that $\vec{F}^B_{pw} = -\vec{F}^B_{wp}$, as we were told in the problem statement to expect. ✔

❹ **EVALUATE RESULT** The force magnitude depends linearly on the current and on the speed and charge of the moving particle, as we expect. That Newton's third law applies here is reassuring, though we know that this is not necessarily to be expected in magnetic interactions. It makes sense that the particle and the wire are attracted toward one another for $q > 0$ and are repelled from one another for $q < 0$, because we can view the motion of the charged particle as an electric current, and we know that the magnetic force between two parallel currents is attractive, while the magnetic force between two antiparallel currents is repulsive.

Guided Problem 28.8 Tubular current

A very long, hollow cylindrical conductor of inner radius R_{in} and outer radius R_{out} carries current I distributed uniformly throughout its cross-sectional area (Figure WG28.8). Derive an expression for the magnitude of the magnetic field due to this current as a function of the radial distance r from the central axis in all regions: (a) $0 \leq r \leq R_{in}$, (b) $R_{in} \leq r \leq R_{out}$, (c) $r > R_{out}$.

Figure WG28.8

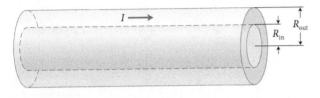

① GETTING STARTED

1. What is the symmetry of the current distribution?
2. What general law provides the easiest method to compute the magnetic field in each region?

② DEVISE PLAN

3. How many different applications of your chosen general law will be required to determine the magnetic field in each region?
4. In which region(s) will it be necessary to perform a calculation to determine the current encircled?

③ EXECUTE PLAN

5. In region b, what fraction of the current is encircled by a circle of radius r?

④ EVALUATE RESULT

6. How does your answer behave as r varies over the full range in each region? Does the result from one region match the result from the adjacent region at the boundary?

Questions and Problems

For instructor-assigned homework, go to MasteringPhysics® (MP)

Dots indicate difficulty level of problems: • = *easy,* •• = *intermediate,* ••• = *hard;* CR = *context-rich problem.*

28.1 Source of the magnetic field

1. A negatively charged particle sits midway between the two magnets in Figure P28.1, at rest relative to the magnets. If the magnet on the left is twice as strong as the magnet on the right, what is the direction of the magnetic force exerted on the particle? •

Figure P28.1

2. Two parallel wires each carry a current I in the positive x direction. What is the direction of the magnetic field at any point that lies midway between the wires and in the plane defined by them? •
3. Consider a square loop of wire that carries a clockwise current when viewed from above. What is the direction of the magnetic field at the center of the square loop due to (a) the left side, (b) the top side, (c) the right side, and (d) the bottom side? •
4. A negatively charged particle is at rest in a region where a uniform magnetic field points in the positive x direction and a uniform electric field points in the positive y direction. What is the direction of the vector sum of the forces exerted on the particle? ••
5. Suppose two electrons move on parallel, closely spaced paths in the $+z$ direction, each with velocity $\vec{v}$ in the Earth reference frame. Discuss all forces exerted on the electrons. ••
6. Two protons are fired toward each other on closely spaced paths, one moving in the $+z$ direction and one in the $-z$ direction. As they pass close to each other, is the magnetic force between them attractive, repulsive, or neither? ••

7. The two insulated, current-carrying wires in Figure P28.7 cross at right angles, and each carries a current I. The locations labeled 1–4 are all in the plane defined by the wires, with each location a perpendicular distance d from both wires. At how many of these four locations is the magnetic field (a) directed out of the page, (b) directed into the page, and (c) equal to zero? ••

Figure P28.7

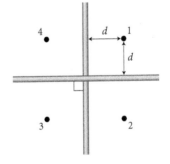

8. Two of the three wires in Figure P28.8 carry current I, and the third wire carries current $6I$. The location labeled P is a distance d from each of the wires carrying current I. What is the direction of the magnetic field at P? ••

Figure P28.8

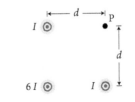

9. Two positively charged particles 1 and 2 are moving in the same plane, with the velocity of particle 1 perpendicular to the velocity of particle 2. At the instant shown in Figure P28.9, particle 2 is on the line that defines the velocity of particle 1. For this instant, describe and sketch the direction of the magnetic force that each particle exerts on the other. ●●●

Figure P28.9

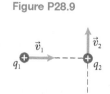

10. In Figure P28.10, (a) specify the direction of the magnetic field at the location labeled P due to each of the four sides 1–4 of the current loop. (b) Which side produces the strongest magnetic field at P? (c) What additional information is needed to determine the direction of the magnetic field at P due to the loop? ●●●

Figure P28.10

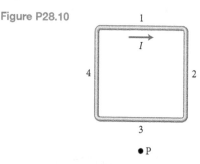

28.2 Current loops and spin magnetism

11. Where do you expect the magnitude of the magnetic field due to a circular current loop to be greatest? ●

12. Could Figure P28.12 represent the magnetic field due to a bar magnet that has a rectangular cross section rather than a circular cross section? ●

Figure P28.12

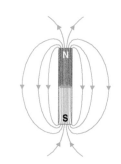

13. A loop of wire carries a current I as shown in Figure P28.13. Determine the direction of the magnetic field at the points labeled. ●

Figure P28.13

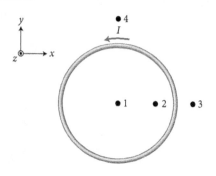

14. Figure P28.14 shows a positively charged spherical object that is spinning. For each of the labeled points, state the direction of the magnetic field. Assume all points lie in the xy plane. ●●

Figure P28.14

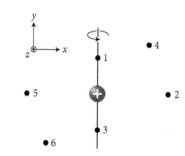

15. Sometimes when a current loop is constructed, a rectangular geometry is more convenient than a circular geometry. How would the magnetic field from a small square current loop compare with that from a small circular current loop? ●●

16. Consider two charged particles 1 and 2, each of them able to translate (move from place to place) and to spin. In which of the following circumstances is there a magnetic interaction between the particles: (a) neither particle translating, neither particle spinning; (b) neither translating, only particle 1 spinning; (c) neither translating, both spinning; (d) 1 at rest and not spinning, 2 translating and not spinning; (e) 1 at rest and not spinning, 2 translating and spinning; (f) 1 spinning and not translating, 2 translating and not spinning; (g) 1 spinning and not translating, 2 translating and spinning; (h) both translating, neither spinning; (i) both translating, only 2 spinning; (j) both translating, both spinning. ●●

17. A circular current-carrying wire loop produces a magnetic field. A spinning disk of uniformly distributed charge produces a similar magnetic field. How would you expect the field due to a spinning disk to compare to the field due to a current-carrying wire loop? ●●

18. For the bar magnet in Figure P28.18, which of the four locations labeled 1, 2, 3, 4 has the greatest density of magnetic field lines? ●●

Figure P28.18

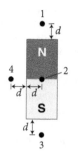

19. A negatively charged particle located at the origin of an xyz coordinate system is spinning clockwise about the x axis (that is, clockwise when you look at the particle while standing somewhere on the positive x axis). What is the direction of its magnetic field at all positions along (a) the x axis, (b) the y axis, and (c) the z axis? ●●

20. Figure P28.20 shows a wire segment bent into a half-circle, with the center of curvature labeled P. If the wire of which this segment is a part is extremely long and carries a current I, what is the direction of the magnetic field at P? ••

Figure P28.20

21. In the Bohr model of the hydrogen atom, an electron orbits a nucleus consisting of one proton. Given that the electron and proton are both spinning, describe the types of magnetic interactions you expect to be associated with the hydrogen atom. •••

28.3 Magnetic dipole moment and torque

22. In the space surrounding Earth, the main component of the planet's magnetic field is the field due to a magnetic dipole. In what direction is Earth's magnetic dipole moment? •

23. Earth's magnetic field is thought to be generated by currents in the planet's core. In what direction (clockwise or counterclockwise, when viewed along the rotation axis from north to south) does this current circulate? •

24. The disk shown in Figure P28.24 is charged with electrons and spins counterclockwise when viewed from above. From this perspective, what is the direction of the magnetic dipole moment of the disk? •

Figure P28.24

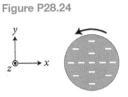

25. In the open wire loop of Figure P28.25, end 1 is held at a higher potential than end 2. (*a*) In which direction do electrons move through the loop? (*b*) What is the direction of the current? (*c*) What is the direction of the loop's magnetic dipole moment? ••

Figure P28.25

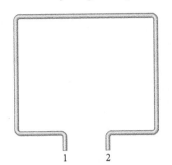

26. Figure P28.26 shows part of the rotation of an electric motor, during which the magnetic dipole moment of the loop points to the left or has some component to the left. If the entire rotation were shown, during what fraction of the rotation would the magnetic dipole moment have some component pointing to the right? ••

Figure P28.26

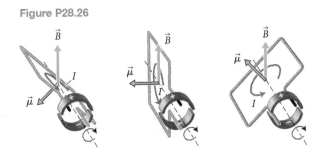

27. A current loop lying in the *xy* plane of an *xyz* coordinate system experiences a torque that is clockwise about the *y* axis when viewed looking down from the positive *y* axis toward the origin. This torque is due to a uniform external magnetic field that points in the positive *x* direction. What is the direction of the current in the loop? ••

28. A current loop lies in the *xy* plane of an *xyz* coordinate system, with the current circulating counterclockwise when viewed looking down the positive *z* axis toward the origin. The loop experiences a torque about the *x* axis that is counterclockwise when viewed looking down the positive *x* axis toward the origin. Describe the direction of the uniform external magnetic field responsible for this torque. ••

29. Determine the direction of the magnetic dipole moment in each current loop or charge distribution in Figure P28.29. In (*c*), the higher potential end of the loop is marked $+$. ••

Figure P28.29

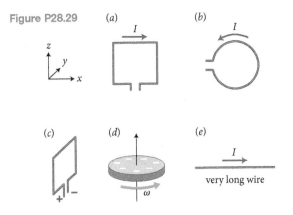

30. (*a*) As the electric motor shown schematically in Figure P28.30 operates, which of the arrows shown could represent the magnetic dipole moment at various instants? (*b*) If there are any arrows that are not possible magnetic dipole moment vectors, state why they are not allowed. ••

Figure P28.30

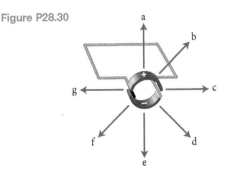

31. Figure P28.31 shows a rectangular loop of current in an external magnetic field. Initially the plane of the loop makes a 65° angle with the magnetic field. (*a*) Determine the direction of the magnetic force exerted on each side of the loop. Treat side 4 as though it were one unbroken wire. (*b*) Determine the direction of the torque on the loop about the axis shown as a dashed line. (*c*) What is the orientation of the loop once the system reaches equilibrium? ••

Figure P28.31

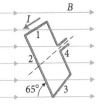

32. *Principles* Figure 28.10 shows a current loop in an external magnetic field and the forces exerted on the different lengths of the wire. Assume that the loop is attached to a pivot that allows it to spin (as between *Principles* Figures 28.10 and 28.11). (*a*) Determine the directions of all the forces on the loop if the current were reversed. (*b*) Is this new situation any different from that shown in *Principles* Figure 28.11? ●●●

33. A negatively charged particle is held in position and then released in a region where a uniform magnetic field points in the positive x direction and a uniform electric field points in the positive y direction. The particle is spinning about an axis parallel to the z axis, and the spin is clockwise when viewed looking down from the positive z axis toward the origin. (*a*) Is the electromagnetic force exerted on the particle different from what it would be if the particle were not spinning? (*b*) Would there be any other changes if the particle were not spinning? If so, describe them. ●●●

28.4 Ampèrian paths

34. The current loop in Figure P28.34 lies in the xy plane. For each of the Ampèrian paths (*a*)–(*e*), is the line integral of the magnetic field positive, negative, or zero? ●

Figure P28.34

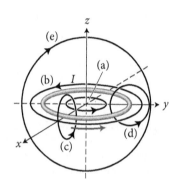

35. Wires 1 to 5 in Figure P28.35 carry current either into or out of the page. What is the magnitude of the current enclosed by the Ampèrian path indicated? Is the line integral of the magnetic field around this path, in the direction indicated, positive, negative, or zero? ●

Figure P28.35

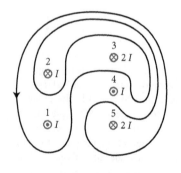

36. Is the line integral of the magnetic field along the closed path in Figure P28.36 positive, negative, or zero? The direction of integration is shown with arrows on the path. ●

Figure P28.36

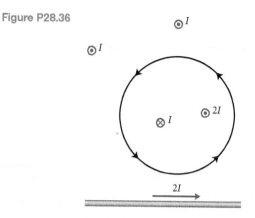

37. Figure P28.37 shows a series of current-carrying wires, and in each case an Ampèrian path is shown. Rank the six cases according to the magnitude of the line integral of the magnetic field calculated along the Ampèrian path shown in each case, smallest value of $|\oint \vec{B} \cdot d\vec{\ell}|$ first. ●●

Figure P28.37

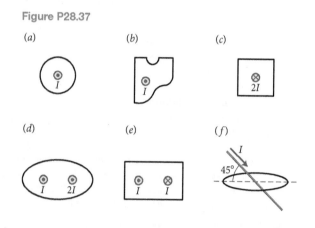

38. The line integral of the magnetic field around a certain closed path is initially L. The current that penetrates this path is then doubled. What can you say about the current through the path if the new integral of the magnetic field around the closed path is (*a*) L and (*b*) $2L$? ●●

39. Each of the wires 1 to 3 in Figure P28.39 carries a current perpendicular to the page. The line integrals of the magnetic field around the three Ampèrian paths shown all have the same positive value. How do the magnitudes and directions of the three currents compare? ●●

Figure P28.39

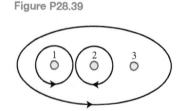

40. A positively charged particle located at the origin of an xyz coordinate system spins about the z axis, and the spin is counterclockwise when viewed looking down from the positive z axis toward the origin. Is the line integral of the magnetic field positive, negative, or zero for an Ampèrian path going (*a*) clockwise around the origin in the xy plane when viewed looking down from the positive z axis, (*b*) clockwise around the origin in the yz plane when viewed looking from the positive x axis, and (*c*) clockwise around the origin in the xz plane when viewed looking from the positive y axis? ●●

41. Eleven wires and one Ampèrian path are shown in Figure P28.41, with current values and directions as indicated. Is the line integral of the magnetic field along the Ampèrian path shown greater than, smaller than, or equal to zero? ••

Figure P28.41

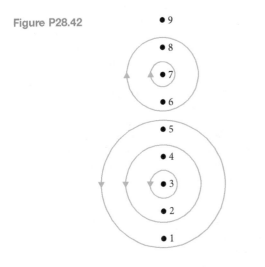

42. Figure P28.42 shows magnetic field lines in a certain region. Are there any locations where there must be a current directed into or out of the plane of the diagram? (Consider locations near the numbers on the vertical axis.) At which of the locations 1–9 does a current exist? What is the current direction in each case? ••

Figure P28.42

43. Figure P28.43 shows two paths (A and B) around a wire that carries current I. (a) Along which path is the line integral of the magnetic field greater? (b) Along which path is the average magnetic field greater? (c) Explain how your answers to parts a and b are consistent. •••

Figure P28.43

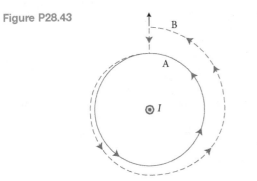

44. Figure P28.44 shows a very long wire that carries a current I in the z direction and is centered in the xy plane at the position (0, 0). The line integral of the magnetic field along Ampèrian path 1 is -5.50 T·m. Determine the line integral of the magnetic field along path 2. •••

Figure P28.44

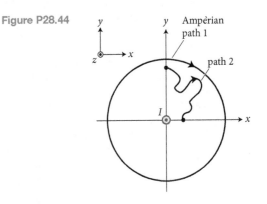

28.5 Ampère's law

45. At a location 25 mm away from a long, straight current-carrying wire, the magnitude of the magnetic field due to the wire is 2.0×10^{-5} T. Calculate the magnitude of the current in the wire. •

46. A long, straight wire carrying 1.5 A of current to the left is placed above a large, flat sheet through which the current per unit width is 3.0 A/m to the left. What are the magnitude and direction of the magnetic force exerted on each 1.0-m length of the wire? •

47. The magnetic field magnitude is 4.0 mT at a position 6.2 mm radially away from a long current-carrying wire. Calculate (a) the current in the wire and (b) the magnetic field magnitude at a position 77 mm radially away from the wire. •

48. Two straight wires separated by a very small distance run parallel to each other, one carrying a current of 3.0 A to the right and the other carrying a current of 4.0 A to the left. Give the approximate value for the magnitude of the magnetic field a large distance r from both wires. ••

49. A moving particle carrying charge e traveling to the right at 2.5×10^7 m/s initially feels no magnetic force. When a long current-carrying wire is placed parallel to the line of motion of the particle at a location 3.0 μm away from the particle, an initial force of magnitude 7.0×10^{-13} N is exerted on the particle. What is the magnitude of the current in the wire? ••

50. An electric current is uniformly distributed throughout a long, straight wire that has a diameter of 50 mm. If the current through the wire is 6.0 A, calculate the magnitude of the magnetic field (a) 20 mm radially away from the wire center and (b) 50 mm radially away from the wire center. (c) What must the current be to create a magnetic field of magnitude 1.0 T 50 mm radially away from the wire center? ••

51. Two large, flat current-carrying sheets are placed parallel to each other, one sheet above the other. The upper sheet carries a current 2.0 A per unit of width to the left, and the lower sheet carries a current 5.0 A per unit of width to the right. Calculate the magnitude of the magnetic field (a) between the sheets, (b) above the upper sheet, and (c) below the lower sheet. (d) Draw a diagram showing the direction of the magnetic field in each of these regions. ••

52. A electron travels to the right at 3.0×10^6 m/s between two large, flat sheets that are parallel to each other and to the electron's line of motion. If currents per unit width of 8.0 A/m to the right through the top sheet and 8.0 A/m to the left through the bottom sheet are then generated, what is the magnitude of the magnetic force exerted on the electron? Draw a diagram showing the direction of the magnetic field between the sheets and the direction of the magnetic force exerted on the electron. ••

53. A certain wire has a circular cross section of radius R and carries a current I. Suppose that the charge carriers all move along the cylindrical surface of the wire, not through its cross-sectional area. (a) Derive an expression for the magnetic field magnitude $B(r)$ as a function of distance r from the center of the wire; check that your expression makes sense for $r < R$ and for $r > R$. (b) Make a graph showing the magnitude of the magnetic field in and around the wire as a function of the radial distance r from the center. Mark the wire radius R on your graph. ••

54. Point P is a distance $d_1 = 4.0$ mm above a large sheet of metal that carries a current of 40 A in the positive x direction and a distance $d_2 = 3.0$ mm below a very long wire that carries a current of 0.35 A in the positive x direction. If the magnetic field magnitude at P is zero, calculate the width of the metal sheet. ••

55. Two large, parallel, current-carrying plates are oriented horizontally and the vertical distance between them is 5.0 mm. The current per unit width in each plate is 100 A/m, and both currents are in the positive x direction. Determine the magnitude and direction of the magnetic force per unit area exerted by the lower plate on the upper plate. ••

56. A coaxial cable carries a current I_{wire} in its inner conducting wire and a current I_{shell} in its outer conducting shell. The radius of the wire is R_{wire}, the distance from the cable center to the inside of the shell is R_{shell}, and the distance from the center to the outer edge of the shell is $2R_{shell}$. Determine all locations (if any exist) at which the magnetic field magnitude is zero if (a) $I_{wire} = I_{shell}$, (b) $I_{wire} = -I_{shell}$, and (c) $I_{wire} = -I_{shell}/2$. •••

57. A particle of mass 9.1×10^{-31} kg and carrying an unknown quantity of charge is shot at a velocity of 2.0×10^4 m/s to the right and enters the magnetic field generated by a large, flat current-carrying sheet. The current in the sheet is parallel to the particle's initial line of motion. The particle exits the magnetic field 90 mm directly above the location where it enters. If the sheet carries a current of 4.0 A per unit width, what is the magnitude of the charge of the particle? •••

28.6 Solenoids and toroids

58. A long solenoid with 300 windings per meter of length carries a current of 1.0 A. Calculate the magnitude of the magnetic field inside the solenoid. •

59. You need to use a long solenoid to produce a magnetic field of magnitude 0.070 T. If the maximum current you are able to run through the windings is 20 A, what is the minimum number of windings per meter the solenoid must have? •

60. A small solenoid is inserted into a larger solenoid (Figure P28.60). The current in the small solenoid is from A to B. (a) Determine the initial direction of the magnetic dipole moment of the small solenoid. (b) Assuming the large solenoid is fixed in place and the small solenoid is free to rotate, determine the equilibrium direction of the magnetic dipole moment of the small solenoid. •

Figure P28.60

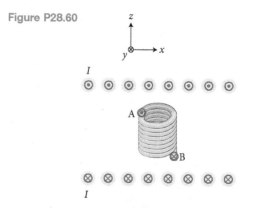

61. A long, straight wire carrying a current of 2.5 A to the left is placed directly below and parallel to the central axis of a solenoid that has 1000 windings per meter of length and a current of 45 mA. Calculate the magnitude and direction of the magnetic field at the center of the solenoid if the wire is 50 mm away from the solenoid center. Does it matter whether the wire is inside or outside the solenoid coils? ••

62. Calculate the magnitude of the magnetic force exerted on a wire that is 20 mm long and carries a current of 4.0 A when it is suspended inside a solenoid at an angle of 45° to the magnetic field. The solenoid has 700 turns per meter of length and carries a current of 3.0 A. ••

63. A toroid has 250 square windings carrying a current of 3.0 mA. Each side of each square winding is 50 mm long, and the distance from the toroid center to the inner surface of the windings is 120 mm. What is the magnitude of the magnetic field (a) at the center of any square winding, (b) midway between the toroid center and the inner surface of the windings, and (c) 30 mm beyond the outer surface of the windings? ••

64. At what radial distance r from the center of a toroid of 200 windings does the magnitude of the magnetic field equal that found inside a solenoid that has 500 turns per meter of length? Assume that the current is the same through both devices. ••

65. A toroid carries a current I and has n circular windings per unit length measured along the inside edge of the windings. The radius of each circular winding is $R_{winding}$, and the inner radius of the toroid is R_{toroid}. Derive an expression for the magnetic field magnitude at any location inside the circular windings. ••

66. An electron is fired into one end of the solenoid in Figure P28.66. Viewed along the positive x axis from a negative x coordinate, the electron enters from below at a 65° angle to the horizontal, just inside the bottom edge of the solenoid. From this viewpoint the solenoid carries a 10-A clockwise current. The solenoid is made from a 33.0-m length of wire, and it has 400 turns along the 200-mm length shown in the figure. (a) Ignoring end effects, what is the smallest time interval required for the electron to pass through the solenoid without striking the coils? (b) If the electron follows the quickest path through the solenoid as determined from the time interval you calculated in part a, how many revolutions does the electron's path make around the solenoid axis? •••

Figure P28.66

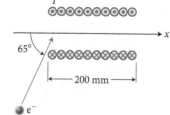

67. You are calibrating magnetic coils for a particle detector. One step involves checking the magnetic field at different positions inside a toroid, and you are asked to measure the field at the positions labeled 1, 2, 3, 4 in Figure P28.67. Your partner, knowing that the magnetic field inside a *solenoid* is uniform, asks why anyone would measure more than one position inside the toroid, which is a solenoid bent into a ring. How can you explain the need to compare the field magnitudes at positions 1 and 2? Why compare the magnitudes at positions 3 and 4? Can you explain to your partner why the magnetic field is not uniform in a toroid even though a toroid is nothing more than a solenoid bent into a donut shape? •••

Figure P28.67

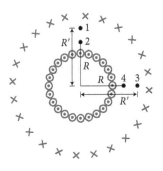

28.7 Magnetic fields due to currents

68. Calculate the magnitude of the magnetic field at the center of a circular arc of radius 25 mm spanning an angle of $\pi/2$ and carrying a current of 3.0 A. •

69. Wire 1, 5.0 m long and carrying a current of 3.0 A, experiences a magnetic force of magnitude 4.0×10^{-7} N when placed 90 mm away from wire 2 running parallel to wire 1. What must the magnitude of the current in wire 2 be? •

70. Use the Biot-Savart law to determine the magnetic field 70 mm above the center of a loop of wire that has a radius of 0.22 m and carries 3.0 A of current. ••

71. Wire 1, 3.0 m long and of linear mass density 0.010 kg/m, is initially held in place and carries 10 A of current to the right. Very long wire 2 is placed parallel to and 5.0 mm directly above wire 1. When wire 1 is released, it stays in place. What are the magnitude and direction of the current in wire 2? ••

72. Suppose that we can use wire of 1.0-mm diameter to make either a single loop of wire or a solenoid, and we wish to compare, for a given current, the magnetic fields at the center of each. (*a*) Use the Biot-Savart law to derive an expression for the magnetic field magnitude at the center of a circular current loop. (*b*) Compare the magnitude of the magnetic field at the center of a circular current loop of radius 10 mm with the magnitude of the magnetic field at the center of a solenoid of the same radius and with 1.0 turn per millimeter. Assume the current is the same through the current loop and the solenoid. ••

73. In Figure P28.73, point P is the common center of two circular arcs of wire, the larger of radius 70 mm and the smaller of radius 20 mm. What are the magnitude and direction of the magnetic field at P if the current through the wire is 3.0 mA? ••

Figure P28.73

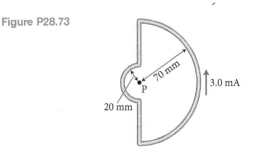

74. A current-carrying wire has been bent into the form shown in Figure P28.74, with a half-circle of radius R_1 lying in the *xy* plane connected via two straight segments to a half-circle of radius R_2 lying in the *yz* plane. The current direction is as indicated. If $R_2 = 1.5 R_1$, what is the direction of the magnetic field at P, which lies at the common center of the half-circles? ••

Figure P28.74

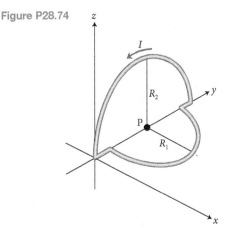

75. A wire carrying a 3.0-A current lies along the *x* axis of an *xy* coordinate system, extending from $x = 0$ to $x = 10$ m. What is the magnitude of the magnetic field at point P located at $x = 0$, $y = 2.0$ m? •••

76. The horizontal portion of the wire in Figure P28.76 has a length $\ell = 0.100$ m, and position P is a perpendicular distance $d = 30.0$ mm above the center of the horizontal portion. The wire carries a 45.0-A current, and the two slanted portions of the wire are extremely long. Calculate the magnitude of the magnetic field at P. •••

Figure P28.76

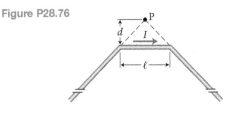

28.8 Magnetic field of a moving charged particle

77. An electron moves in a straight line at a speed of 6.0×10^7 m/s. Calculate the magnitude and direction of the magnetic field at a position 5.0 mm behind the electron and 15 mm below its line of motion. •

78. A proton moves in the positive x direction at 4.00×10^4 m/s. Calculate the magnitude of the magnetic field at the point $(x, y) = (+2.00$ mm, $+1.00$ mm$)$ as the proton passes through the origin. ●

79. Express the magnetic field due to a uniformly moving charged particle in terms of the electric field of the particle. ●●

80. Two electrons 1 and 2 move along antiparallel paths separated by a distance of 10 nm, traveling at speeds $v_1 = 4.0 \times 10^7$ m/s and $v_2 = 7.0 \times 10^6$ m/s. What is the magnitude of the magnetic force exerted by electron 2 on electron 1? ●●

81. Proton 1, traveling in the negative x direction at speed v_1, is directly below proton 2, which is traveling at speed v_2 at an angle of $45°$ above the positive x axis. If the protons are separated by a distance r, calculate the magnitude of the magnetic force each proton exerts on the other. ●●

82. A charged particle is traveling through a uniform magnetic field, with its velocity perpendicular to the field direction. In Section 27.7 you learned that such a particle experiences a magnetic force that causes it to move in a circular path. Also, because it is moving, the charged particle creates its own magnetic field $\vec{B}_\text{p}$. (a) Derive an expression for the magnetic field magnitude B_p at the center of the circular path in terms of the magnitude B_ext of the external uniform magnetic field, the particle's orbit radius R, the charge q on the particle, and the particle's mass m. (b) Using $c_0 = 1/\sqrt{\mu_0\epsilon_0}$, show that your expression can be cast in the form below. ●●

$$\frac{q^2}{4\pi\epsilon_0 R}\frac{1}{mc_0^2}B_\text{ext}$$

83. Electron 1, initially traveling to the right at 1.5×10^6 m/s, is accelerated upward at 900 m/s² by the electromagnetic force exerted by electron 2, which is directly beneath electron 1 and traveling to the left at 4.0×10^6 m/s. What must the distance between the electrons be? ●●

84. An electron and a proton are fired in opposite directions, and at the instant they are nearest each other, their separation distance is 3.0 μm (Figure P28.84). At that instant, the two particles are both moving at 3.0×10^4 m/s but in opposite directions. (a) Determine the magnitude and direction of the magnetic force exerted by the proton on the electron at this instant. (b) Show that the ratio of the magnetic to electric forces at this instant equals v^2/c_0^2, where $v = 3.0 \times 10^4$ m/s and c_0 is the speed of light. ●●

Figure P28.84

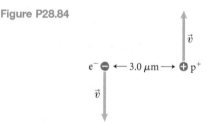

85. Two electrons move near each other and at the instant shown in Figure P28.85 are 2.0 mm apart. The speed of electron 1 is $v_1 = 300$ m/s, that of electron 2 is $v_2 = 500$ m/s, and the directions of motion are as shown in Figure P28.85. Determine the magnitude and direction of (a) the magnetic force exerted by electron 1 on electron 2 and (b) the magnetic force exerted by electron 2 on electron 1. ●●

Figure P28.85

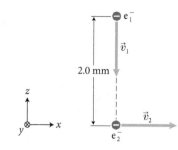

86. At $t = 0$, electron 1 is shot out of an accelerator at a speed of 2.0×10^3 m/s. At $t = 1.0$ μs, electron 2 is shot out of the accelerator and travels on a path that is parallel to and 10 mm below the path of electron 1. The speed of electron 2 is 5.0×10^3 m/s. (a) At $t = 3.0$ μs, what is the magnitude of the magnetic field at a point that is 3.0 mm ahead of electron 1 and 5.0 mm below it? Assume that the magnetic forces the electrons exert on each other for the 2.0 μs before you make your calculations do not alter the electrons' paths significantly. (b) Show whether or not it is valid to assume that the magnetic forces the electrons exert on each other during the interval from $t = 1.0$ μs to $t = 3.0$ μs do not alter the electrons' paths significantly. ●●●

Additional Problems

87. A current loop lies in the xy plane, with the current circulating counterclockwise when viewed from the positive z axis. Is there a torque on the loop, and if so, in what direction, if a uniform magnetic field is applied along the positive (a) x axis, (b) y axis, and (c) z axis? ●

88. A solenoid that is 200 mm long has 200 turns. What current I in the solenoid is required to produce a magnetic field of magnitude 1.0 T inside the solenoid? ●

89. Wire 1 is 2.3 m long and carries a current of 2.2 A to the right. Wire 2 is also 2.3 m long, and it carries a current of 3.0 A to the left. The wires are parallel to each other and separated by a distance of 0.25 m. Determine the direction and magnitude of the magnetic force exerted by wire 2 on wire 1. ●●

90. Figure P28.90 shows two square loops of wire. The loop on the right is fixed in place, and the one on the left is free to pivot in any direction. Both loops carry a current that is counterclockwise when viewed from above. (a) What is the direction of the magnetic field created by the right loop at the left loop? (b) What is the initial direction of the magnetic dipole moment of the left loop? (c) How does the left loop rotate? (d) After the left loop is allowed to rotate and the system reaches equilibrium, are the magnetic dipole moments of the two loops parallel, antiparallel, or neither? ●●

Figure P28.90

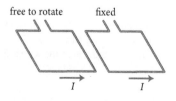

91. Wire 1, with mass 0.010 kg and length 1.0 m, has a square cross section and is initially at rest on a table. It is connected by flexible leads to a battery and carries a steady current of 1.5 A. When wire 2 is placed parallel to wire 1 a distance 2.0 mm away, wire 1 begins to slide across the table away from wire 2. If the coefficient of static friction between wire 1 and the table is 0.050, what must be the minimum current through wire 2? ●●

92. Two of your friends separately calculated a magnetic field line integral around a long, straight current-carrying wire in a homework problem, but they arrived at different answers. Now they want your help, so they send you a copy of their work. Andy chose a square path for his line integral, a path centered on the wire in a plane perpendicular to the wire. Beth chose a path in the shape of an equilateral triangle encircling the wire in the same plane, with one side exactly equal in length to and aligned with one side of Andy's square path. The wire penetrates the center of the square but not the center of the triangle. Andy came up with a value of 64 T · m for the line integral, and Beth calculated 89 T · m. Andy's integral along the common side was 10 T · m, and Beth's integral along this side was 45 T · m. Unfortunately they forgot to send you any details about the current in the wire. You begin to text them for more information, but you suddenly realize that you need nothing more to evaluate quite a bit about their work. ●●● CR

93. Your design team is working on an air-core toroid that is to have the greatest feasible magnetic field per ampere of current but in which the greatest magnetic field magnitude must be exactly four times the smallest magnetic field magnitude. Because of space and cost restrictions, the maximum length of wire you can use is 100 m and the core radius must be at least 30 mm. You begin to speculate about how many turns the toroid needs to have, its inner and outer radii, and how much magnetic field you might achieve. ●●● CR

Answers to Review Questions

1. Particles in motion—either moving in a straight line or spinning about an axis—cause magnetic fields.

2. Magnetic forces are generally not central; that is, they do not point along the line joining two source elements.

3. Yes. For example, the magnetic field due to a charged particle moving in a straight line has no poles.

4. The two field line patterns are similar to each other, and both resemble the pattern of the magnetic field due to an infinitesimally small magnetic dipole.

5. The magnetic field due to a spinning charged particle is identical to the magnetic field due to an infinitesimally small magnetic dipole.

6. The direction of the magnetic dipole moment vector is the same as the direction of the magnetic field line passing through the center of the dipole. This is from S to N in a bar magnet or according to the right-hand dipole rule for a current loop.

7. The right-hand current rule gives magnetic field direction when current direction is known, and vice versa. The right-hand force rule gives magnetic force direction when current direction and magnetic field direction are known, and vice versa. The right-hand dipole rule gives magnetic dipole moment direction when current direction is known, and vice versa. These rules are illustrated in *Principles* Figure 28.9.

8. The vector sum of forces exerted on the current loop is zero, but there is a nonzero vector sum of torques that tends to align the loop's magnetic dipole moment vector with the external magnetic field.

9. The commutator reverses the direction of the current through the motor's current loop every time the loop rotates one-half turn (just as the loop's magnetic dipole moment aligns with the external field), so that the magnetic torque keeps the loop always rotating in the same direction.

10. Electrostatic field lines originate and terminate on charged particles; magnetic field lines form closed loops. Therefore, the electric flux through a closed surface is proportional to the amount of charge inside, but the corresponding magnetic flux through the surface is always zero.

11. The line integral of the electrostatic field is always zero, regardless of the quantity of charge; that of the magnetic field depends on the amount of current encircled.

12. The line integral of the magnetic field along a closed path is proportional to the current encircled by the path.

13. If the direction in which the Ampèrian path encircles the current is the same as the direction of the magnetic field created by the current, the current makes a positive contribution to the line integral; otherwise, the current makes a negative contribution.

14. The constant shows the relationship between the line integral of the magnetic field around an Ampèrian path and the amount of current encircled by the path.

15. The wire has cylindrical symmetry. Because of its cylindrical symmetry, the magnetic field lines are concentric circles with constant magnitude at each radius. In using Ampère's law to determine this magnitude, you should choose an Ampèrian path that coincides with one of the field lines.

16. The magnitude of the magnetic field at any point outside the wire is inversely proportional to the radial distance from the wire axis. This is true because all the current in the wire is encircled by the Ampèrian path, and the length of the path is proportional to the radial distance from the axis. At points inside the wire, the magnitude is directly proportional to the radial distance from the axis because in this case only a fraction of the current is encircled by the magnetic field line used as the Ampèrian path. How large that fraction is depends on the ratio of the area encircled by the Ampèrian path to the cross-sectional area of the wire (see *Principles* Checkpoint 28.12).

17. The magnetic field is uniform on either side of the sheet; in other words, it has the same magnitude at all distances above and below the sheet, with the field magnitude given by the result of *Principles* Example 28.4: $B = \frac{1}{2}\mu_0 K$, where K is the current per unit width carried by the sheet. The field direction lies in the plane of the sheet and is perpendicular to the current, as given by the right-hand current rule. The field direction is diametrically opposite on the two sides.

18. A solenoid is a tightly wound, long coil of wire used to produce a magnetic field. The field pattern is like that of a bar magnet oriented along the axis of the solenoid, and the field is much greater inside the solenoid than outside. The field is approximately uniform inside, proportional to the current and the number of turns per unit length (Eq. 28.6), and approximately zero outside.

19. A toroid is a tightly wound, donut-shaped coil of wire, as would result from bending a solenoid into a circle so that it ends meet. Its magnetic field is confined to the donut-shaped interior cavity, with magnitude inversely proportional to the distance from the center of the circle (the distance from the central axis of the donut hole), and direction in accordance with the right-hand current rule.

20. The magnetic field inside the solenoid is approximately uniform, but the field inside the toroid is not—it depends inversely on the distance from the axis about which the toroid would roll if it were a car tire.

21. Both fields are directly proportional to the strength of the source ($I\,d\vec{\ell}$ for the magnetic field, dq_s for the electrostatic field) and inversely proportional to the square of the radial separation distance, but the electrostatic field is directed along the unit vector to the field point, while the magnetic field depends on the vector product of the current segment and this unit vector.

22. First use Ampère's law (Eq. 28.1) along a circular path of radius d centered on wire 1, to determine the magnetic field at the location of wire 2 due to the current in wire 1. Then use the magnetic force law (Eq. 27.8) to calculate the force exerted on wire 2 due to the magnetic field of wire 1. The result is $F_{12}^B = \mu_0 \ell I_1 I_2 / (2\pi d)$ (Eq. 28.16).

23. Ampère's law is useful only in situations where the field direction is known from symmetry and only the magnitude must be determined. The Biot-Savart law is not limited to symmetrical situations and can be used to compute the magnetic field due to a steady current circulating in any closed circuit, provided, of course, that the integral of Eq. 28.10 is amenable to analytic or numerical evaluation.

24. The vector product $\vec{v}_1 \times \hat{r}_{12}$ comes from the magnetic field produced by particle 1 at the location of particle 2, as given by the Biot-Savart law. The vector product $\vec{v}_2 \times (\vec{v}_1 \times \hat{r}_{12})$ comes from the magnetic interaction between the particles: Particle 2 is subject to the magnetic field created by particle 1.

25. $\epsilon_0\mu_0 = (8.85 \times 10^{-12}\ \mathrm{C^2/N \cdot m^2})(4\pi \times 10^{-7}\ \mathrm{T \cdot m/A}) = 1.11 \times 10^{-17}\ \mathrm{s^2/m^2} = 1.11 \times 10^{-17}\,\mathrm{(m/s)^{-2}} = 1/(8.99 \times 10^{16}\ \mathrm{m^2/s^2}) = 1/(3.00 \times 10^8\ \mathrm{m/s})^2$. This is the reciprocal of the square of the speed of light.

26. No. Newton's third law requires that the forces exerted by two objects on each other be equal in magnitude and opposite in direction. The magnetic forces exerted by two moving charged particles on each other are typically neither equal in magnitude nor oriented in opposite directions, although some special cases (e.g. two charged particles moving in parallel, side by side) can satisfy $\vec{F}_{12}^B = -\vec{F}_{21}^B$. The reason is that Newton's law, $\vec{F}_{12} = -\vec{F}_{21}$, requires that the system's momentum be constant, and when fields are involved it is not enough to consider only the particles in doing a third-law analysis. Instead, the system for this analysis must include both the particles and their electric and magnetic fields.

Answers to Guided Problems

Guided Problem 28.2

$$\frac{\mu_0 I}{2\pi R} + \frac{(\mu_0 I)(\pi/2)}{4\pi R} = 1.9 \times 10^{-5} \text{ T, pointing into the plane of the page.}$$

Guided Problem 28.4

$$F = \frac{\mu_0 I^2 \ell}{2\pi}\left(\frac{1}{x} - \frac{1}{x+w}\right) = 4.3 \times 10^{-9} \text{ N, attracting the loop toward the wire.}$$

Guided Problem 28.6

For $R_{\text{wire}} < r < R_{\text{shell}}$, $B(r) = \dfrac{\mu_0 I}{2\pi r}$. For $r > R_{\text{shell}}$, $B(r) = 0$ because $I_{\text{enc}} = 0$.

Guided Problem 28.8

(a) $B = 0$. (b) $B = \dfrac{\mu_0 I}{2\pi r}\dfrac{(r^2 - R_{\text{in}}^2)}{(R_{\text{out}}^2 - R_{\text{in}}^2)}$. (c) $B = \dfrac{\mu_0 I}{2\pi r}$.

PRACTICE

29

Changing Magnetic Fields

PRACTICE

Chapter Summary

Induced emf and current (Sections 29.1, 29.2, 29.4, 29.5)

Concepts A changing magnetic flux through the area enclosed by a conducting loop causes an **induced current** through the loop. This process is called **electromagnetic induction.**

According to **Lenz's law,** the direction of an induced current is always such that the magnetic flux produced by the induced current opposes the change in the magnetic flux that induces the current.

Quantitative Tools If a straight rod of length ℓ moves with speed v perpendicular to a magnetic field of magnitude B, the magnitude of the **induced emf** across the ends of the rod is

$$|\mathcal{E}_{ind}| = B\ell v. \tag{29.3}$$

According to **Faraday's law,** the induced emf in a closed path due to a changing magnetic flux through the area enclosed by the path is

$$\mathcal{E}_{ind} = -\frac{d\Phi_B}{dt}, \tag{29.8}$$

where $d\Phi_B/dt$ is the rate at which the magnetic flux changes. The **induced current** in a conducting loop of resistance R is

$$I_{ind} = \frac{\mathcal{E}_{ind}}{R}. \tag{29.4}$$

Reminder: The **magnetic flux** Φ_B through a surface is

$$\Phi_B \equiv \int \vec{B} \cdot d\vec{A}, \tag{27.10, 29.5}$$

where the integral is taken over the surface. Magnetic flux is measured in **webers** (Wb), where $1\ \text{Wb} \equiv 1\ \text{T} \cdot \text{m}^2$.

The electric field accompanying a changing magnetic field (Sections 29.3, 29.6)

Concepts A changing magnetic field is accompanied by an electric field. Unlike an electrostatic field, this electric field does not necessarily do zero work on a charged particle that travels around a closed path.

Quantitative Tools The integral around any closed path of the electric field that accompanies a changing magnetic field is given by

$$\oint \vec{E} \cdot d\vec{\ell} = -\frac{d\Phi_B}{dt}, \tag{29.17}$$

where the line integral is around a closed path, and the magnetic flux is through a surface bounded by that same closed path.

Inductance (Section 29.7)

Quantitative Tools If an emf $\mathcal{E}_{ind}$ is induced in a loop when the current through it changes at the rate dI/dt, the **inductance** L of the loop is given by

$$\mathcal{E}_{ind} = -L\frac{dI}{dt}. \tag{29.19}$$

See the Procedure box for guidance on how to calculate L. The SI unit of inductance is the **henry** (H):

$$1\ \text{H} \equiv 1\ \text{V} \cdot \text{s/A} = 1\ \text{kg} \cdot \text{m}^2/\text{C}^2. \tag{29.20}$$

The inductance of a solenoid of length ℓ and cross-sectional area A with N turns is

$$L = \frac{\mu_0 N^2 A}{\ell}.$$

Magnetic energy (Section 29.8)

Quantitative Tools The **magnetic potential energy** U^B stored in the magnetic field of an inductor that has inductance L and carries a current I is

$$U^B = \tfrac{1}{2}LI^2. \qquad (29.25)$$

The **energy density** u_B of the potential energy stored in a magnetic field of magnitude B, defined as the magnetic potential energy per unit volume, is

$$u_B \equiv \tfrac{1}{2}\frac{B^2}{\mu_0}. \qquad (29.29)$$

Review Questions

Answers to these questions can be found at the end of this chapter.

29.1 Moving conductors in magnetic fields

1. What happens when a vertical conducting rod moves east through an external magnetic field that points north?
2. What happens when a conducting loop, moving east, gradually leaves a region of zero magnetic field and enters a region of uniform, north-pointing magnetic field? Assume that the area vector of the loop points north.
3. What is an induced electric current?
4. Do the effects induced in a conducting object that is moving in an external magnetic field depend on the direction of the object's motion relative to the field direction?

29.2 Faraday's law

5. How does changing the reference frame from which you make your measurements affect your explanation of induced current in a conducting loop that is moving from a region of zero magnetic field into a region of uniform external magnetic field?
6. What is Faraday's law?
7. What is electromagnetic induction?

29.3 Electric fields accompany changing magnetic fields

8. Must a magnetic force be exerted on the charge carriers in a conducting loop in order for a current to be induced in the loop?
9. Does the nature of the force that causes electromagnetic induction depend on the choice of reference frame? If so, how? If not, why?
10. What is the difference, if any, between the field lines of the electric field that accompanies a changing magnetic field and the field lines of the electric field of a stationary charged particle?

29.4 Lenz's law

11. What does Lenz's law say about the direction of a current induced in a conducting loop?
12. What general physical principle underlies Lenz's law (that is, why would it make no sense to reverse the direction of Lenz's law)?
13. What are eddy currents?

29.5 Induced emf

14. What is induced emf?
15. When a conducting loop moves through a nonuniform external magnetic field, a current is induced as charge carriers inside the loop start moving. This is true even when the loop is oriented such that the direction of the magnetic force is perpendicular to the direction of the induced current, so the magnetic force does no work on the charge carriers. Where does the energy that causes the charge carriers to move come from?
16. What are (a) the quantitative statement of Faraday's law and (b) the significance of the negative sign in the equation?
17. Describe two differences between induced emf and potential difference.
18. How does the emf induced in a flat conducting loop that is rotating at a constant rotational speed ω in a uniform magnetic field change as the loop rotates?

29.6 Electric field accompanying a changing magnetic field

19. How is the electric field that accompanies a changing magnetic field related to the induced emf in the region of changing magnetic flux?
20. How does the direction of the electric field vary inside and outside a solenoid whose magnetic field is changing with time?
21. How does the magnitude of the electric field that accompanies the changing magnetic field described in Review Question 18 vary inside and outside the solenoid?

29.7 Inductance

22. Does changing the current in a conducting loop induce an emf in the loop?
23. What is the SI unit of inductance?
24. What is an inductor, and what purpose does it serve in electric circuits?
25. What characteristic of a conducting loop or device does inductance describe? On what properties of the conducting loop or device does inductance depend?

29.8 Magnetic energy

26. Work must be done against the induced emf in an inductor in order to change the current in it. What change in energy occurs to account for the work done?
27. How does the magnetic potential energy stored in an inductor depend on the current through the inductor? Does this energy also depend on other properties of the inductor?
28. How does the magnetic potential energy stored in the magnetic field of an inductor depend on the field magnitude? Is this relationship applicable to magnetic fields other than those of inductors?

Developing a Feel

Make an order-of-magnitude estimate of each of the following quantities. Letters in parentheses refer to hints below. Use them as needed to guide your thinking.

1. The emf you can generate along a rotating metal clothes hanger without using magnets (P, K, G, B)
2. The maximum potential difference developed when you swing a metal curtain rod around your body (H, S, K, G)
3. The maximum current induced when you drop a small but powerful bar magnet through a metal key ring of resistance $R = 0.1$ V/A (R, I, M)
4. The magnetic potential energy stored in a volume of 1 m³ near Earth's surface (G)
5. The maximum emf induced around the loop formed by your metal key ring when you walk under a 100-A residential power line (W, A, Q, L, F)
6. The maximum magnetic potential energy stored in a doghouse placed under a 100-A neighborhood power line (W, A, Q, C)
7. The magnitude of the electric field due to changing magnetic fields around the outside of your car when you park it under a high-tension power line leading away from a nuclear-powered electricity-generating plant (W, D, J, Q, U, F, X)
8. The magnetic field magnitude needed to have the same energy density as gasoline (N)
9. The length of wire needed to make a 1-H inductor in the form of a solenoid wrapped on a pencil (E, O, V)
10. The maximum potential difference between the two ends of a 2-m metal rod dropped from the top of a 10-story building so that it maintains a horizontal orientation as it falls (K, G, T)

Hints

A. How far above you is the power line?
B. How rapidly can you rotate the loop?
C. What is the volume of a doghouse?
D. What is the magnitude of the current carried by a power line?
E. How is inductance related to the radius and length of the pencil?
F. How does the current vary with time?
G. What is the magnetic field magnitude?
H. What is a typical length of a curtain rod?
I. Over what area is the magnetic flux changing?
J. How far above the car is the power line?
K. What is the source of the magnetic field?
L. What is the area of the conducting loop?
M. What is the smallest likely time interval for the change in flux?
N. What is the energy content of a liter of gasoline?
O. What are the length and radius of a standard pencil?
P. What is the area enclosed by the loop formed by the hanger?
Q. How can you estimate the maximum magnetic field strength?
R. What is the magnetic field strength near a pole of the magnet?
S. What is the average translational speed of points on the rod?
T. What is the maximum speed of the rod?
U. What is the "radius" of the car?

V. What is the circumference of each winding?
W. How should you model the power line?
X. How are the induced emf and electric field related for a circular path of radius R that encircles a changing magnetic flux?

Key (all values approximate)

A. 6 m; B. spinning at the end of a string—say, three times/s; C. 1 m³; D. for a 1-GW nuclear plant, about 1×10^3 A; E. $L = \mu_0 N^2 (\pi R^2)/\ell$; F. it goes from positive maximum to negative maximum and back in $\frac{1}{60}$ s; G. 5×10^{-5} T; H. 1 m; I. the magnet cross section—say, 10^{-4} m²; J. 20 m; K. Earth; L. 10^{-3} m²; M. the time interval during which the magnet passes through the ring, 10^{-2} s; N. about 3×10^7 J; O. $\ell = 0.2$ m, $R = 3 \times 10^{-3}$ m; P. 3×10^{-2} m²; Q. from the form of Ampere's law given in *Principles* Example 28.3: $B = \mu_0 I/2\pi d = (2 \times 10^{-7}$ T·m/A$)I/d$; R. 1 T; S. 5 m/s, assuming a rotation rate slower than 2 rev/s; T. 2×10^1 m/s; U. 1 m; V. $2\pi R$; W. as a long, straight current-carrying wire; X. $\mathscr{E} = 2\pi RE$

Worked and Guided Problems

Procedure: Calculating inductances

The inductance of a current-carrying device or current loop is a measure of the emf induced in the device or loop when current is changed. To determine the inductance of a particular device or current loop, follow these four steps.

1. Derive an expression for the magnitude of the magnetic field in the current-carrying device or current loop as a function of the current. Your expression should depend only on the current I and possibly—but not necessarily—the position within the device or current loop.
2. Calculate the magnetic flux Φ_B through the device or current loop. If the expression you derived in step 1

depends on position, you will have to integrate that expression over the volume of the device or circuit. Use symmetry to simplify the integral and divide the device into segments on which B is constant.
3. Substitute the resulting expression you obtained for Φ_B into Eq. 29.21. As you take the derivative with respect to time, keep in mind that only the current varies with respect to time, so you should end up with an expression that contains the derivative dI/dt on both sides of the equal sign.
4. Solve your expression for L after eliminating dI/dt.

These examples involve material from this chapter but are not associated with any particular section.
Some examples are worked out in detail; others you should work out by following the guidelines provided.

Worked Problem 29.1 Rectangular loop near a wire

The long, straight wire in Figure WG29.1 carries a current i that varies as a function of time according to $i(t) = a + bt$, where $a = 0.50$ A and $b = 4.0$ A/s during the time interval $0 < t \leq 2.0$ s. For all instants $t > 2.0$ s, the current is constant. The wire is placed a distance $h = 0.040$ m above and in the plane of a stationary rectangular loop of wire. The loop dimensions are width $w = 0.10$ m and length $\ell = 0.60$ m, and its resistance is $R = 2.8$ V/A. For the time interval $0 < t \leq 2.0$ s and for all instants $t > 2.0$ s, determine the induced emf in the loop and the magnitude and direction of the induced current in the loop.

Figure WG29.1

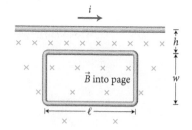

① GETTING STARTED We are given a description of a current-carrying, straight wire positioned above a rectangular loop made of conducting material, with the wire sitting in the plane defined by the loop. Our tasks are to obtain values for the emf and the current induced in the loop and to determine the direction of that induced current. We know that the emf and current are induced by a changing magnetic flux, and we know that the magnetic flux through the loop is changing because that flux is due to the magnetic field created by the current in the wire. Because that current changes during the time interval $0 < t \leq 2.0$ s, the magnetic field around the wire is also changing.

② DEVISE PLAN We can calculate the magnetic field created by the current in the straight wire using Ampere's law. Recall from *Principles* Example 28.3 that the magnitude of this magnetic field is inversely proportional to the perpendicular distance r from the wire: $B = \mu_0 I/(2\pi r)$. Because the field lines of this magnetic field form circles around the wire, there is a magnetic flux through the rectangular loop, given by Eq. 29.5:

$$\Phi_B = \int \vec{B} \cdot d\vec{A}.$$

Because the magnetic field magnitude at any location enclosed by the loop is a function of how far from the wire that location is, we need to integrate the magnetic field over the loop area in order to calculate the magnetic flux.

Once we have the changing magnetic flux, we can use Faraday's law to calculate the induced emf, which depends on a time-varying magnetic flux. Hence we need to analyze the derivative of the magnetic flux with respect to time for the interval $0 < t \leq 2.0$ s in order to calculate the emf induced in the loop:

$$\mathcal{E}_{\text{ind}} = -\frac{d\Phi_B}{dt} = -\frac{d}{dt}\int \vec{B} \cdot d\vec{A}.$$

Our final step is to use Eq. 29.4, $I_{\text{ind}} = \mathcal{E}_{\text{ind}}/R$, to calculate the magnitude of the induced current and to use Lenz's law to establish its direction.

③ EXECUTE PLAN The current in the wire and hence the magnetic flux are changing only during the interval $0 < t \leq 2.0$ s. For all instants $t > 2.0$ s, the current in the wire, the magnetic field this current creates, and the magnetic flux through the loop are all constant, and therefore both the induced emf and the induced current are zero for $t > 2.0$ s. ✔

For the time interval $0 < t \leq 2.0$ s, the magnitude of the magnetic field due to a current-carrying wire is given by

$$B = \frac{\mu_0 i}{2\pi r} = \frac{\mu_0(a + bt)}{2\pi r},$$

where r is a perpendicular distance away from the wire. We begin by drawing, across the loop area, a thin strip of width dr, length ℓ, and area $dA = \ell \, dr$ (Figure WG29.2). We can consider the magnetic field to be essentially constant over the area of this infinitesimal strip. The differential magnetic flux $d\Phi_B$ through the differential area element dA is then

$$d\Phi_B = B \, dA = B\ell \, dr = \frac{\mu_0(a + bt)}{2\pi r}\ell \, dr.$$

Figure WG29.2

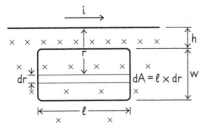

The magnetic flux through the loop is found by integrating this expression from $r = h$ to $r = h + w$:

$$\Phi_B = \int \vec{B} \cdot d\vec{A} = \frac{\mu_0(a + bt)}{2\pi} \int_{r=h}^{r=h+w} \frac{\ell \, dr}{r}$$

$$= \frac{\mu_0(a + bt)\ell}{2\pi} \ln\left(\frac{h + w}{h}\right).$$

Applying Faraday's law gives us

$$\mathcal{E}_{\text{ind}} = -\frac{d\Phi_B}{dt} = -\frac{d}{dt}\left[\frac{\mu_0(a + bt)\ell}{2\pi}\ln(1 + w/h)\right]$$

$$= -\frac{\mu_0 b\ell}{2\pi}\ln(1 + w/h).$$

The magnitude of the induced emf is thus

$$|\mathcal{E}_{\text{ind}}| = (2 \times 10^{-7} \text{ T} \cdot \text{m/A})(4.0 \text{ A/s})(0.60 \text{ m})$$
$$\times \ln[1 + (0.10 \text{ m}/0.040 \text{ m})]$$
$$= 6.0 \times 10^{-7} \text{ T} \cdot \text{m}^2/\text{s}.$$

(Note that the induced emf is independent of t for the interval $0 < t \leq 2.0$ s.)

Because the volt is the unit of emf, we need to check the unit in this equation before we can say we are done. Using the substitution $1 \text{ T} = 1 \text{ N}/(\text{A} \cdot \text{m})$ gives us

$$\frac{\text{T} \cdot \text{m}^2}{\text{s}} = \frac{\text{N} \cdot \text{m}^2}{\text{A} \cdot \text{m} \cdot \text{s}} = \frac{\text{N} \cdot \text{m}}{\text{A} \cdot \text{s}} = \frac{\text{N} \cdot \text{m}}{\text{C}} = \frac{\text{J}}{\text{C}} = \text{V}.$$

Thus the magnitude of the induced emf is

$$|\mathcal{E}_{\text{ind}}| = 6.0 \times 10^{-7} \text{ V.} ✔$$

The current $i(t)$ in the wire produces a magnetic flux that within the area of the loop is directed into the page in Figure WG29.2. The magnetic field increases as time passes, and hence the magnetic flux through the loop also increases. By Lenz's law, the direction of the current induced in the loop must be counterclockwise in order to produce an induced magnetic field out of the plane of the page to counteract the increase in flux due to the time-varying magnetic field. ✔

The magnitude of the induced current is

$$I_{\text{ind}} = \frac{|\mathcal{E}_{\text{ind}}|}{R} = \frac{6.0 \times 10^{-7} \text{ V}}{2.8 \text{ V/A}} = 2.1 \times 10^{-7} \text{ A.} ✔$$

❹ EVALUATE RESULT Moving a magnet through the many windings of a solenoid induces a current on the order of microamperes, so we should not be surprised that the current through one turn of wire is about 0.2 μA even though the current in the wire is fairly great and the loop is close to the wire. Inductive effects are small.

Looking at the loop center gives us a way of checking our $\mathcal{E}_{\text{ind}}$ value. The distance from the wire to the center of the loop is $r = h + (w/2) = 0.090$ m, and we can use Ampere's law to obtain the magnetic field magnitude at this location at $t = 0$:

$$B(t = 0) = \frac{\mu_0 i}{2\pi r} = \frac{\mu_0(a + bt)}{2\pi r}$$

$$= (2 \times 10^{-7} \text{ T} \cdot \text{m/A})\left(\frac{0.50 \text{ A}}{0.090 \text{ m}}\right)$$

$$= 1.1 \times 10^{-6} \text{ T}.$$

At $t = 2.0$ s, the magnetic field at the loop center is 17 times greater than this value: $B(t = 2.0 \text{ s}) = 1.9 \times 10^{-5}$ T. [The factor 17 is the ratio of the currents at these two values of t: $(8.5 \text{ A})/(0.50 \text{ A}) = 17$.] The average change in the magnetic field at the center is then

$$\frac{\Delta B}{\Delta t} = \frac{(17 - 1)(1.1 \times 10^{-6} \text{ T})}{2.0 \text{ s}}$$

$$= 8.9 \times 10^{-6} \text{ T/s}.$$

We can estimate the average time derivative of the magnetic flux by multiplying this value by the area of the loop:

$$\frac{\Delta \Phi_B}{\Delta t} \approx \left(\frac{\Delta B}{\Delta t}\right)(\ell w) = (8.9 \times 10^{-6} \text{ T/s})(0.60 \text{ m})(0.10 \text{ m})$$

$$= 5.3 \times 10^{-7} \text{ V}.$$

This is close to our calculated value, $\mathcal{E}_{\text{ind}} = 6.0 \times 10^{-7}$ V, which gives us some assurance that our work is correct.

PRACTICE

Guided Problem 29.2 Moving loop

A rectangular loop of length ℓ and width w moves at constant velocity $\vec{v}$ away from a long, straight wire carrying a current I (Figure WG29.3). The wire lies in the plane defined by the loop, and the loop's resistance is R. What are the direction and magnitude of the current induced in the loop at the instant the side nearest the wire is a perpendicular distance r away from the wire?

Figure WG29.3

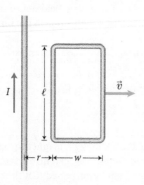

① GETTING STARTED

1. Look for similarities and differences between this problem and Worked Problem 29.1. Will a modification of the approach we used in that problem work here?
2. Which portions of the results of Worked Problem 29.1 can be used directly?

② DEVISE PLAN

3. Determine an expression for the magnetic field at a perpendicular distance r from the wire.
4. Do you need to integrate the magnetic field over the loop in order to calculate the magnetic flux? If so, can you use the same differential area element we used in Worked Problem 29.1?

5. You will likely need to differentiate the magnetic flux through the loop with respect to t to determine the rate of change of the magnetic flux. Remember that because the loop is moving, r is a function of time.
6. Will calculating the time derivative of the magnetic flux allow you to express the induced emf in terms of the loop velocity? If so, will that result lead you to the induced current?

③ EXECUTE PLAN

7. What are the appropriate limits of integration for the flux integral?
8. Here are two possibly useful derivatives:

$$\frac{d}{dt}\ln(r + w) = \frac{1}{r + w}\frac{dr}{dt} \quad \text{and} \quad \frac{d}{dt}\ln(r) = \frac{1}{r}\frac{dr}{dt}.$$

9. Use Lenz's law to determine the direction of I_{ind}. Remember to consider not only the direction of the magnetic field through the loop but also whether the magnetic flux is *increasing* or *decreasing* over time.

④ EVALUATE RESULT

10. Check that the current direction you found opposes the change in the magnetic flux. You can check by determining which way the magnetic force exerted by the wire on the loop points according to your direction for the induced current. The magnetic force exerted on the loop must oppose the loop's motion.
11. How does your result for emf compare with the value obtained in Worked Problem 29.1? Is this reasonable?

Worked Problem 29.3 Electric field accompanying a changing magnetic field

Figure WG29.4 shows three conducting loops, A, C, and D, positioned in a uniform magnetic field whose magnitude increases with time. The concentric circles are all equidistant from one another, at radii R, $2R$, $3R$, and $4R$, and the radial lines divide each circle into 12 equal segments. The region of nonzero magnetic field ends at $r = \frac{5}{2}R$. Obtain expressions for the magnitude of the induced emf

Figure WG29.4

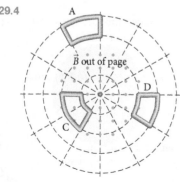

in each of the three conducting loops A, C, and D. Then use Lenz's law to determine the direction of the induced current in each of the three loops.

① **GETTING STARTED** The figure shows three conducting loops, each perpendicular to a changing magnetic field. We need to determine the induced emf, induced current, and direction of the induced current in each loop. It looks as if there is a changing magnetic flux through two of the three loops, so we expect to obtain a nonzero induced emf and therefore an induced current in loops C and D. We also expect that we will be able to simplify the problem by exploiting the cylindrical symmetry of the shaded region of the figure and by using the fact that the magnetic field is uniform within this shaded region. Finally, we remember seeing a similar example of cylindrical symmetry worked out in *Principles* Example 29.7.

② **DEVISE PLAN** Because of the cylindrical symmetry of the changing magnetic field, we know that the electric field lines that accompany this changing magnetic field must be concentric circles, such as the circles drawn in the figure.

The magnitude $E(r)$ of the electric field that accompanies the changing magnetic field can be obtained using Eq. 29.17, $\oint \vec{E} \cdot d\vec{\ell} = -d\Phi_B/dt$. We compute the line integral around each of the four circles at radii $r = R, 2R, 3R, 4R$. Because each of the circles lies along an electric field line, and the electric field magnitude is constant along any field line, we can write $|\oint \vec{E} \cdot d\vec{\ell}| = 2\pi r E(r)$ for the circular path at radius r, leaving us with

$$2\pi r E(r) = \left| -\frac{d\Phi_B}{dt} \right|. \qquad (1)$$

We take the absolute value because $E(r)$ is a magnitude and therefore must be non-negative.

Because the magnetic field is uniform within the shaded region of the diagram, we can write the magnetic flux through each circle simply as the product $\Phi_B = BA$, where B is the magnetic field magnitude and A is the *shaded* area enclosed by the circle. If we call the radius of the shaded area $R_{shaded} = \frac{5}{2}R$, then for $r \leq R_{shaded}$, we have $\Phi_B = \pi r^2 B$, and for $r \geq R_{shaded}$, we have $\Phi_B = \pi R_{shaded}^2 B$.

Once we have the electric field magnitude $E(r)$, we can combine Eqs. 29.8 and 29.17 to determine the emf induced around each of the three conducting loops: $\mathcal{E}_{ind} = \oint \vec{E} \cdot d\vec{\ell}$. We must break the line integral around each conducting loop into four parts: the two radial sides and the two arc sides. Because the electric field lines are concentric circles, the line integral of the electric field for each loop is zero along the radial sides and nonzero along the arcs.

Finally, we can apply Lenz's law to determine the direction of the induced current in each loop.

❸ **EXECUTE PLAN** Combining Eq. 1 with our expressions for the magnetic flux Φ_B through each of the concentric circles, we see that for $r \leq R_{shaded}$, we have $2\pi r E = \pi r^2 |dB/dt|$, so $E(r) = (r/2)|dB/dt|$. For $r \geq R_{shaded}$, we have $2\pi r E = \pi R_{shaded}^2 |dB/dt|$, and thus $E(r) = (R_{shaded}^2/2r)|dB/dt|$. Because the magnetic field points out of the page and increases in magnitude with time, by Lenz's law the electric field must point clockwise around each circle.

Loop A is entirely outside the magnetic field, which means there is no magnetic flux through this loop and therefore no induced emf and no induced current. (Note that there is a nonzero electric field along the two arcs of loop A. However, the integral of the electric field along the inner arc must be the negative of the integral along the outer arc, so the line integral around the closed path is zero. We can see that the two canceling contributions to the emf are equal in magnitude because (for $r > R_{shaded}$) the arc length $\propto r$, and the electric field $\propto 1/r$.) ✔

Loop C lies entirely inside the magnetic field. The radius of the inner arc is R, and the radius of the outer arc is $2R$. Moving clockwise around loop C as we evaluate the line integral $\mathcal{E}_{ind} = \oint \vec{E} \cdot d\vec{\ell}$, we determine a positive contribution for the outer arc ($\vec{E}$ points in the same direction as $d\vec{\ell}$), zero for the radial segment ($\vec{E} \perp d\vec{\ell}$), a negative contribution for the inner arc ($\vec{E}$ points opposite $d\vec{\ell}$), and

zero again for the second radial segment, thus completing the loop. Because each arc subtends $\frac{1}{6}$ of a circle, the arc lengths are $2\pi r/6$ for $r = 2R$ and $r = R$. Adding the four contributions gives

$$\mathcal{E}_C = \frac{2\pi(2R)E(2R)}{6} + 0 - \frac{2\pi R E(R)}{6} + 0.$$

Then substituting $E(r) = (r/2)(dB/dt)$ at both $r = 2R$ and $r = R$ gives us

$$\mathcal{E}_C = \frac{2\pi}{6}\left(\frac{4R^2}{2} - \frac{R^2}{2}\right)\frac{dB}{dt} = \frac{\pi R^2}{2}\frac{dB}{dt}$$

for the magnitude of the emf induced in loop C. Because the magnetic flux through the loop points out of the page and is increasing in magnitude, the direction of the induced current must be clockwise around loop C. ✔

We determine the induced emf for loop D in a similar manner. In this case, the outer arc, at $r = 3R$, is outside the magnetic field, while the inner arc, at $r = 2R$, is inside the magnetic field. Also, each arc subtends only $\frac{1}{12}$ of a circle, so the arc lengths are $2\pi r/12$ for $r = 3R$ and $r = 2R$. Integrating $\mathcal{E}_{ind} = \oint \vec{E} \cdot d\vec{\ell}$ clockwise over the four sides of loop D (outer arc, radial segment, inner arc, and radial segment) gives us

$$\mathcal{E}_D = \frac{2\pi(3R)E(3R)}{12} + 0 - \frac{2\pi(2R)E(2R)}{12} + 0.$$

For the inner arc, because $2R < R_{shaded}$, we again use $E(r) = (r/2)(dB/dt)$ and obtain $E(2R) = R(dB/dt)$. For the outer arc, because $3R > R_{shaded}$, we instead use $E(r) = (R_{shaded}^2/2r)(dB/dt)$, so then

$$E(3R) = \frac{(5R/2)^2}{6R}\frac{dB}{dt} = \frac{25R}{24}\frac{dB}{dt}.$$

Substituting these values for the electric field, we obtain the magnitude of the induced emf in loop D:

$$\mathcal{E}_D = \frac{2\pi}{12}\left[(3R)\frac{25R}{24} - (2R)R\right]\frac{dB}{dt} = \frac{3\pi R^2}{16}\frac{dB}{dt}.$$

Because the magnetic flux through the loop again points out of the page and is increasing in magnitude, the induced current must be clockwise around loop D. ✔

❹ **EVALUATE RESULT** Because loop A is completely outside the magnetic field, it is reasonable that this loop has no induced emf. Loops C and D experience the changing magnetic flux to different degrees, so we expect their induced emfs to differ. Loop D, with the smaller area affected by the magnetic flux, has the smaller induced emf, as we expect.

Guided Problem 29.4 A falling loop

Under the influence of gravity, a rectangular wire loop of mass m, width w, length ℓ, and resistance R falls out of a uniform magnetic field $\vec{B}$ (Figure WG29.5 on the next page). The loop is released from rest at the instant its lower edge is just barely inside the magnetic field. At the instant shown in the figure, the loop is exiting

the magnetic field at speed $v(t) > 0$ (that is, the loop is moving downward). Obtain an expression for the speed of the loop as a function of time, for the time interval from the instant the loop is released to the instant just before its top edge exits the magnetic field. What happens after the top edge of the loop has left the field?

Figure WG29.5

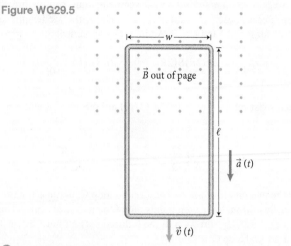

① GETTING STARTED

1. As the loop falls, the magnetic flux through the loop changes, and that change in flux induces a current in the loop. The induced current slows the loop down (Lenz's law). A good first step is to seek a relationship between the magnetic flux through the loop at some instant t and the downward velocity of the loop. Be careful, though; at any instant, the magnetic field is zero over the lower region of the loop area and uniform and nonzero over the upper region.

2. Induced emf and induced current may be more useful here than simple magnetic flux.

3. You may need additional information to solve for the speed, so consider force analysis or energy analysis. Remember that you seek a relationship between speed and time.

4. It may be necessary to solve a differential equation to determine $v(t)$, so do not rule out acceleration as a useful quantity.

② DEVISE PLAN

5. Obtain an expression for $d\Phi_B/dt$ that involves $v(t)$.

6. Current may relate to both magnetic flux and magnetic force. What is the magnitude of the induced current in the loop at the instant shown in Figure WG29.5? (Use $I_{ind} = \mathscr{E}_{ind}/R$.)

7. Would a free-body diagram for all the vertical forces exerted on the loop be helpful? Recall that a magnetic force is exerted on the loop. Express the magnitude and direction of this force in terms of the quantities given. (Hint: Use Eq. 28.13, $\vec{F} = I_{ind}\vec{\ell} \times \vec{B}$.) Use the vertical component of this force to obtain an expression for the vertical motion of the loop.

8. You know that $a = dv/dt$, so is it possible to write a differential equation for the speed as a function of time?

③ EXECUTE PLAN

9. If you get a differential equation of the form $dv/dt = \alpha - \beta v$, where $v(0) = 0$, you might want to try a solution of the form $v = (\alpha/\beta)(1 - e^{-\beta t})$.

④ EVALUATE RESULT

10. Taking a derivative of your expression for $v(t)$ should yield acceleration, giving you a test of the reasonableness of your result.

Worked Problem 29.5 Inductance of a toroid

Determine an expression for the inductance L of a toroid (see Section 28.6) for which the windings have a circular cross section of radius R_w and the toroid radius is $R_t \gg R_w$.

① GETTING STARTED

We begin by making a sketch of the toroid (Figure WG29.6). We know from *Principles* Section 28.6 that the magnetic field is entirely contained within the cavity formed by the windings of the toroid and that the magnetic field lines are circular loops centered on the toroid's central axis (an axis perpendicular to the plane of the figure).

Figure WG29.6

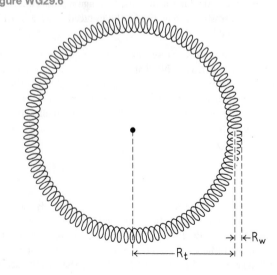

② DEVISE PLAN

To calculate the inductance of the toroid, we can follow the steps in the Procedure box at the beginning of this *Practice* chapter. We first need to determine the magnetic field magnitude in terms of the current I through the toroid. We derived this expression in Section 28.6 and found that at a radial distance r from the center of a toroid that has N windings, $B = \mu_0 NI/(2\pi r)$ (Eq. 28.9). The condition $R_t \gg R_w$ means that r in Eq. 28.9 can be approximated as $r \approx R_t$, so we have $B = \mu_0 NI/(2\pi R_t)$. Having this expression for B, we can calculate the magnetic flux as a function of the current. We can then substitute this result into Eq. 29.21, $d\Phi_B/dt = L(dI/dt)$, and solve for L.

③ EXECUTE PLAN

The magnetic flux through one winding is the area of one winding, πR_w^2, multiplied by the magnetic field magnitude B inside the winding. For the entire toroid, therefore, the magnetic flux is

$$\Phi_B = N(\pi R_w^2)B = \frac{\mu_0 N^2 I R_w^2}{2R_t}.$$

Substituting this expression for Φ_B into Eq. 29.21 yields

$$\frac{d}{dt}\frac{\mu_0 N^2 I R_w^2}{2R_t} = L\frac{dI}{dt}.$$

The only time-dependent factor on the left is the current, so

$$L = \frac{\mu_0 N^2 R_w^2}{2R_t}. \checkmark$$

④ EVALUATE RESULT Our result shows that the inductance of a toroid increases as the square of the number of windings N. This makes sense because both the magnetic field in the toroid cavity and the magnetic flux through the toroid windings increase with N. That inductance also depends on the square of the winding radius R_w makes sense because increasing R_w increases the area enclosed by each winding and therefore increases the magnetic flux by the factor R_w^2.

Finally, the inductance is inversely proportional to the radius R_t of the toroid, which makes sense because the magnetic field and therefore the magnetic flux decrease as $1/R_t$. (Note: This expression for inductance is valid only for toroids in which $R_t \gg R_w$.)

Guided Problem 29.6 Coaxial cable inductance and magnetic energy

Figure WG29.7 shows a coaxial cable that consists of two concentric long, hollow cylinders of negligible resistance. The inner cylinder has radius R_{inner}, the outer cylinder has radius R_{outer}, and the length of both cylinders is $\ell \gg R_{outer}$. There is a current I in the cable, and the current direction is from the battery into the inner cylinder and then through the outer cylinder to the battery. What is the magnetic potential energy stored in the magnetic field? What is the inductance of the cable?

Figure WG29.7

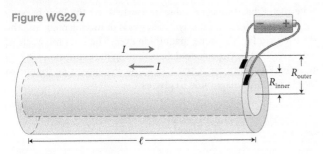

① GETTING STARTED

1. We must know the magnetic field magnitude as a function of the radius in order to determine the amount of magnetic potential energy stored. Is Ampere's law (Eq. 28.1) useful for this?
2. What is the relationship between the energy stored in the magnetic field of an inductor and the inductance?

② DEVISE PLAN

3. To obtain expressions for the magnetic field magnitude everywhere, apply Ampere's law, $\oint \vec{B} \cdot d\vec{\ell} = \mu_0 I_{enc}$ (Eq. 28.1), outside the cable, where the radial distance $r > R_{outer}$; then inside the inner cylinder, where $r < R_{inner}$; and finally between the cylinders, where $R_{inner} < r < R_{outer}$.
4. For the region where the magnetic field magnitude is nonzero, use Eq. 29.29 to determine the magnetic energy density.
5. The quantity of magnetic potential energy stored can be found by integrating the magnetic energy density over the volume of space where $B \neq 0$. Is the magnetic field uniform or nonuniform in this region? You may need to choose a volume element for your integral. Based on the symmetry in the problem, the volume element for a cylindrical shell of radius r, thickness dr, and length ℓ is $dV = 2\pi r\ell\, dr$.
6. What are the appropriate limits of integration?
7. Once you have U^B, you can use it and Eq. 29.25 to determine the inductance in the cable.

③ EXECUTE PLAN

④ EVALUATE RESULT

8. Consider what happens to the stored energy as the dimensions of the coaxial cable are changed.

Worked Problem 29.7 Electric fields and Faraday's law

A solenoid is made by wrapping a wire 100 times around a hollow, nonmagnetic cylinder (Figure WG29.8). The solenoid's length is $\ell = 2.5 \times 10^{-1}$ m, and its radius is $a = 3.0 \times 10^{-2}$ m. A small wire loop of radius $r_{loop} = 1.0 \times 10^{-2}$ m is placed at the midpoint of the solenoid's length and concentric with the solenoid. The loop has resistance $R = 5.0$ V/A. During the time interval $t = 0$ to $t = 2.0$ s, the current through the solenoid increases as $I(t) = bt$, where $b = 2.0 \times 10^{-1}$ A/s. After $t = 2.0$ s, the current remains

Figure WG29.8

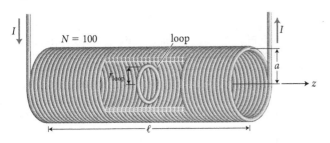

constant. For $0 < t < 2.0$ s and for $t > 2.0$ s, what are (a) the emf induced in the loop, (b) the magnitude and direction of the electric field that accompanies the changing magnetic flux in the loop, and (c) the magnitude and direction of the current induced in the loop?

① GETTING STARTED For $t > 2.0$ s, the current is not changing, so the induced emf, electric field, and induced current are all zero. Thus we have already completed one part of our task. ✔

All we need to consider now is what happens during the interval $0 < t < 2.0$ s, when the current *is* changing. During this interval, there is a changing magnetic flux through the solenoid cavity and hence through the area enclosed by the loop. Therefore, by the Eq. 29.17 form of Faraday's law, there must be an electric field accompanying the changing magnetic flux through the loop area. This electric field is responsible for the emf that drives the induced current around the loop. We can determine the direction of the induced current by using Lenz's law or by determining the direction of the electric field. Note that the direction of the current through the solenoid is shown in Figure WG29.8.

❷ DEVISE PLAN In order to determine the induced emf in the loop, we must first calculate the magnetic field inside the solenoid. For this we can use Eq. 28.6, $B = \mu_0 nI$, where n is the number of windings per unit length of the solenoid:

$$B = \mu_0 nI = \mu_0 \frac{N}{\ell} I.$$

We can integrate this expression for B to determine the magnetic flux inside the loop from Eq. 29.5:

$$\Phi_B = \int \vec{B} \cdot d\vec{A},$$

where $d\vec{A}$ is the area vector perpendicular to the solenoid axis. Then the Eq. 29.8 form of Faraday's law gives us the emf induced in the loop:

$$\mathscr{E}_{ind} = -\frac{d\Phi_B}{dt} = -\frac{d}{dt}\left(\int \vec{B} \cdot d\vec{A}\right).$$

We should then be able to obtain the electric field magnitude by using the definition of emf as the line integral of the electric field around the loop. Combining Eqs. 29.8 and 29.17, we have

$$\mathscr{E}_{ind} = \oint_{loop} \vec{E} \cdot d\vec{l} = -\frac{d}{dt}\int \vec{B} \cdot d\vec{A}, \qquad (1)$$

where the line integral is taken along the circle of radius r, centered on the solenoid axis, around which we wish to determine the electric field magnitude $E(r)$ due to the changing magnetic field. To determine the direction of the electric field, we infer by analogy with *Principles* Checkpoint 29.12 that the electric field lines will form circles centered around the solenoid axis, in the direction required by Lenz's law.

Finally, we can use Eq. 29.4 to obtain the induced current in the loop from the emf and the resistance of the loop:

$$I_{ind} = \frac{|\mathscr{E}_{ind}|}{R}.$$

❸ EXECUTE PLAN (*a*) The magnetic field inside the solenoid is

$$\vec{B} = \mu_0 nI\,\hat{k} = \frac{\mu_0 NI}{\ell}\,\hat{k} = \frac{\mu_0 Nbt}{\ell}\,\hat{k}.$$

(From the orientation of the solenoid loops and the direction of the current in Figure WG27.8, we see that the magnetic field produced by the solenoid is in the positive z direction, so the direction of $\vec{B}$ is given by $\hat{k}$.) We choose the orientation of the area element $d\vec{A}$ in the magnetic flux integral to point in the positive $\hat{k}$ direction, parallel to the magnetic field: $d\vec{A} = dA\,\hat{k}$. The magnetic flux integral through the loop is then

$$\Phi_B = \int \vec{B} \cdot d\vec{A} = \int B\,\hat{k} \cdot dA\,z = \int B\,dA.$$

Because the magnetic field is constant inside the solenoid and the area of the loop is $A = \pi r_{loop}^2$, the magnetic flux inside the loop is given by

$$\Phi_B = \int B\,dA = \frac{\mu_0 Nbt}{\ell}\int dA = \frac{\mu_0 Nbt}{\ell}\pi r_{loop}^2.$$

The induced emf is then

$$\mathscr{E}_{ind} = -\frac{d\Phi_B}{dt} = -\frac{d}{dt}\left(\frac{\mu_0 Nbt}{\ell}\right)\pi r_{loop}^2 = -\frac{\mu_0 Nb\pi r_{loop}^2}{\ell} \qquad (2)$$

$$= -\frac{(4\pi \times 10^{-7}\ \text{T}\cdot\text{m/A})(100)(2.0 \times 10^{-1}\ \text{A/s})\pi(1.0 \times 10^{-2}\ \text{m})^2}{(2.5 \times 10^{-1}\ \text{m})}$$

$$= -3.2 \times 10^{-8}\ \text{T}\cdot\text{m}^2/\text{s} = -3.2 \times 10^{-8}\ \text{V.}\ ✔$$

(*b*) We obtain the electric field that accompanies the changing magnetic flux by extracting $\vec{E}$ from the line integral of Eq. 1. For this case, that equation becomes

$$\mathscr{E}_{ind} = \oint_{loop} \vec{E} \cdot d\vec{l} = E(2\pi r_{loop}). \qquad (3)$$

Note that E has the same value everywhere on the loop because the loop is centered on the symmetry axis of the solenoid, and the electric field has the same magnitude everywhere on the circle of radius r_{loop} inside the solenoid. Substituting the expression for $\mathscr{E}_{ind}$ given by Eq. 2 into Eq. 3 and taking the absolute value (to obtain the electric field magnitude E) give us

$$E(2\pi r_{loop}) = \frac{\mu_0 Nb\pi r_{loop}^2}{\ell}$$

$$E = \frac{1}{2\pi r_{loop}}\frac{\mu_0 Nb\pi r_{loop}^2}{\ell} = \frac{\mu_0 Nbr_{loop}}{2\ell}$$

$$= \frac{(4\pi \times 10^{-7}\ \text{T}\cdot\text{m/A})(100)(2.0 \times 10^{-1}\ \text{A/s})(1.0 \times 10^{-2}\ \text{m})}{2(2.5 \times 10^{-1}\ \text{m})}$$

$$= 5.0 \times 10^{-7}\ \text{T}\cdot\text{m/s.}\ ✔$$

Because $\vec{B}$ points along the z axis and increases with time, the resulting electric field lines must loop around clockwise, as viewed from the positive z axis: This is the direction in which our fingers curl if we point our right thumb in the $-z$ direction, to oppose $d\vec{B}/dt$ (using the right-hand dipole rule). ✔

(*c*) The direction of the induced current is the same direction as the electric field. So the direction of the induced current in the loop is opposite the direction of the current in the solenoid. ✔

The magnitude of the induced current in the loop is

$$I_{ind} = \frac{|\mathscr{E}_{ind}|}{R} = \frac{\mu_0 Nb\pi r_{loop}^2}{R\,\ell} = \frac{3.2 \times 10^{-8}\ \text{V}}{5.0\ \text{V/A}}$$

$$= 6.4 \times 10^{-9}\ \text{A.}\ ✔$$

❹ EVALUATE RESULT The direction of the induced current can also be determined from Lenz's law. The magnetic flux through the loop is positive (the magnetic field points in the positive z direction) and increases as the current in the solenoid increases. So, the direction of the induced current is opposite the direction of the current in the solenoid in order to oppose the change that created it.

Guided Problem 29.8 Betatron

An electron of mass m and charge $q = -e$ located in a non-uniform magnetic field between the north and south poles of a magnet travels in a circular orbit of radius R (Figure WG29.9, illustrating a type of particle accelerator known as a betatron). The magnetic field magnitude is $B(r)$, where r is radial distance from an axis that is perpendicular to the plane defined by the circular orbit and passes through the center of the circle. Although B varies with r, the field is symmetrical about this axis. The magnetic field direction is perpendicular to the plane of the orbit. The average value of the field magnitude over the area bounded by the orbit is

$$B_{av} = \frac{1}{\pi R^2} \int_{area} B(r)\, dA.$$

Suppose that $B(r)$ varies with time. What relationship between dB_{av}/dt, the rate of change of the average magnetic field enclosed by the electron's orbit, and $dB(R)/dt$, the rate of change of the magnetic field at the orbit radius $r = R$, is necessary for the electron to stay in its circular orbit?

Figure WG29.9

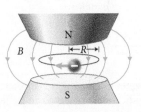

❶ GETTING STARTED

1. Assume that the electron moves in a circular orbit at constant radius R, but that the electron's speed may vary with time. (Changing the electron's speed is the purpose of a particle accelerator.) To keep the electron moving in a circle, what must be the direction of the magnetic force exerted by the magnetic field on the moving electron?

2. If the magnitude $B(R)$ of the magnetic field at the orbit radius R varies with time, what must happen to the electron's speed in order to maintain the circular motion in the orbit?

3. What relates speed to force for circular motion? Is the magnetic force exerted on the electron related to the magnetic field magnitude?

❷ DEVISE PLAN

4. Write an expression for the magnetic force exerted on the electron in terms of the electron's speed v, orbit radius R, and magnetic field magnitude $B(r)$ when $r = R$.

5. What radial force (perpendicular to the particle's velocity) is needed to keep a particle traveling in circular motion at a given speed?

6. Use the relationship between force and acceleration to obtain an expression for the speed of the electron.

7. Differentiate the electron's speed with respect to time to obtain an expression for the time rate of change of the electron's speed in terms of $dB(r)/dt$, R, $-e$, and m.

8. When the magnetic field magnitude starts to increase at a rate $dB(r)/dt$, the changing magnetic flux is accompanied by an electric field. Can you express the changing magnetic flux in terms of dB_{av}/dt and R?

9. Write an expression that gives the electric field a distance R from the center of the orbit in terms of dB_{av}/dt and R. Does the electric field point in the direction of the electron's velocity or in the opposite direction?

10. Relate dv/dt to the electric field magnitude a distance R from the orbit center.

11. Determine an expression for dv/dt in terms of dB_{av}/dt, R, $-e$, and m.

❸ EXECUTE PLAN

12. Compare your two expressions for dv/dt to obtain a condition that relates B_{av} and $B(r)$ and is mandatory in order for the electron to stay in its circular orbit at radius R.

❹ EVALUATE RESULT

13. Consider limiting cases.

Questions and Problems

For instructor-assigned homework, go to MasteringPhysics®   (MP)

Dots indicate difficulty level of problems: • = *easy*, •• = *intermediate*,
••• = *hard*; CR = *context-rich problem.*

29.1 Moving conductors in magnetic fields

1. What happens if the conducting rod in Figure P29.1 moves
(a) in either direction along the *z* axis and (b) in either direction along the *y* axis? •

Figure P29.1

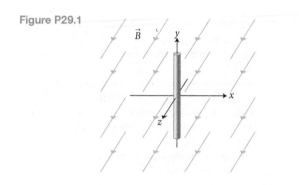

2. The Air Force Thunderbirds aerial demonstration team is
performing at an air show located on Earth's magnetic equator. In what directions can the airplanes fly so that there is no
charge separation on their metal surfaces? •

3. How should any one of the airplanes described in Problem 2
fly in order to produce the maximum charge separation between its wing tips? (Consider both the direction of motion
and the orientation of the wings.) ••

4. Figure P29.4 shows a square conducting loop centered on
the *x* axis, with its sides parallel to the *y* and *z* axes. The loop
moves with constant velocity in the negative *x* direction toward a small bar magnet that is centered on the origin and
has its polar axis aligned along the *x* axis. At the instant
shown, what is the direction of the magnetic force exerted on
an electron sitting at the midpoint of each side? Does the motion of the loop cause any separation of the charge carriers in
the loop? Does the motion induce a current in the loop? If so,
what is the direction of that current? ••

Figure P29.4

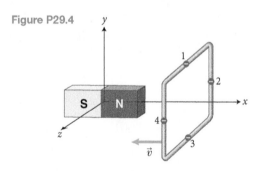

5. What happens if the conducting rod in Figure P29.1 rotates
(a) clockwise about the *z* axis as viewed looking down the
positive *z* axis toward the origin, (b) clockwise about the *x* axis
as viewed looking down the positive *x* axis toward the origin,
and (c) clockwise about the *y* axis as viewed looking down the
positive *y* axis toward the origin? ••

29.2 Faraday's law

6. The large loop of wire in Figure P29.6a carries into and out
of a lamp an electric current whose direction alternates back
and forth with time. A circular ring of wire of radius *R* is at
one of the three positions labeled A, C, and D. (a) At which
position is the induced current in the ring greatest? At which
position is it smallest? (b) Instead of being spread out in large
loops, the actual wiring in houses and other buildings has the
wires entering and leaving the lamp close and parallel to each
other, as shown in Figure P29.6b. How is the induced current
in the ring affected by this geometry? •

Figure P29.6

(a)   (b)

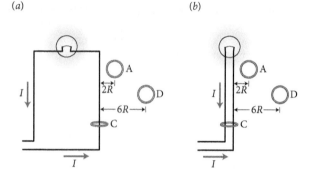

7. The bar magnet in Figure P29.7 is rotated about an axis that
runs perpendicular to the page and passes through the center
of the magnet. The magnet rotates with rotational speed *ω*.
A loop of wire is placed alongside the magnet as shown. The
loop is positioned so that the axis that runs perpendicular to
the face of the loop and that passes through the center of the
loop lies in the plane in which the magnet rotates. (a) Is a
current induced in the loop? (b) If so, is the induced current
constant, or does it vary with time? •

Figure P29.7

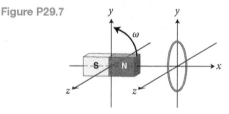

8. Suppose you used a circular loop of the same area rather than
the rectangular loop in *Principles* Example 29.1. What similarities and differences would you observe in each portion of
Figure P29.8 parts *a–e*? ••

Figure P29.8

(a)   (b)   (c)   (d)   (e)

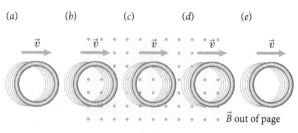

9. A large region of space contains a uniform magnetic field that is increasing with time. You have a piece of wire of length ℓ and want to form a coil from it. What shape should you use for your windings and how many windings should you have to generate the maximum induced current in the coil when it is placed in the changing magnetic field? ••

10. A 1.00-m length of wire is shaped into a rectangle, and another 1.00-m length of identical wire is shaped into a circle. Both wires then move at the same speed into and then out of a region of uniform magnetic field. Is the induced current in the rectangle greater than, smaller than, or the same as the induced current in the circle? •••

29.3 Electric fields accompany changing magnetic fields

11. You observe a small charge separation between the ends of a conducting rod that is lying on the table in front of you. This is puzzling because the rod is not connected to a battery or other power source; it is at rest on the nonconducting table, pointed toward a nearby window. You call your friend, who calmly asks where you are. You reply that you are riding the high-speed train between Paris and Avignon. Your friend offers explanations for the charge separation in two different inertial reference frames. What are those explanations? •

12. A flat conducting plate lies in the xy plane of an xyz coordinate system in which the xy plane is horizontal. A bar magnet is lowered vertically toward the plate. If the magnet is oriented so that its north pole faces the origin as the magnet moves toward the plate, what do the electric field lines in the plate look like? What do the field lines look like if the south pole faces the origin as the magnet moves? •

13. A metal pipe is held vertically, and a bar magnet is dropped into it. What do the electric field lines in the pipe look like as the magnet falls through it? ••

14. You have a bar magnet and a circular conducting loop, and you wish to induce a current in the loop that changes direction regularly: clockwise, counterclockwise, clockwise, and so on. Explain how to do this while the loop remains at rest on a wooden table. ••

29.4 Lenz's law

15. You have a bar magnet and a loop of wire. The loop lies in the plane of this page, and we define a positive current as one for which the current direction is clockwise around the loop as viewed from above. How can you move the magnet so as to induce a positive current in the loop? (There are several answers to this question; provide as many as you can.) •

16. If you drop a magnet through a length ℓ of copper pipe, the time interval needed for the magnet to travel through the pipe (even if the magnet never touches the sides of the pipe) is much greater than the time interval the magnet takes to drop the same distance ℓ in air. Why? •

17. The long straight wire in Figure P29.17 carries a current I that varies in time as $I = I_0 \sin(\omega t)$, and a loop of wire is held stationary near the straight wire. When is the induced current in the loop clockwise? When is it zero? When is it counterclockwise? ••

Figure P29.17

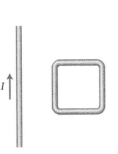

18. A pendulum consists of a rod with an aluminum disk attached, suspended from a pivot. First the pendulum is held at a 30° angle to the vertical and released so that it begins to swing. The disk passes between the poles of a powerful magnet on each swing (Figure P29.18a). Next a series of vertical slits are cut completely through the disk (Figure P29.18b). The pendulum is again held at a 30° angle and released, and the disk again passes between the magnet's poles on each swing. Describe the motion of the pendulum in each case and explain your answer. Ignore any frictional force exerted at the pivot. ••

Figure P29.18

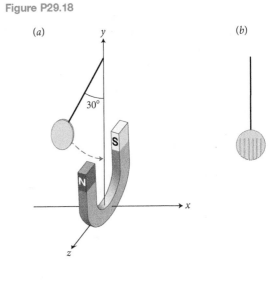

29.5 Induced emf

19. The magnetic flux through a conducting loop increases at a rate of 3.0 T·m²/s. What is the magnitude of the induced emf in the loop? •

20. Initially there is no magnetic flux through a conducting loop. A magnetic field near the loop is then suddenly turned on, and 5.0 s later the magnetic flux through the loop is 1.0 T·m². What is the average magnitude of the induced emf in the loop during the 5.0-s time interval? •

21. A rectangular loop of length $\ell = 80$ mm, width $w = 60$ mm, and internal resistance $R = 20$ V/A is located in a homogeneous magnetic field of magnitude $B = 0.50$ T. The area vector of the loop makes a 45° angle with the magnetic field direction. In 0.40 s, the magnetic field completely reverses direction. What is the average current in the loop during this time interval? •

22. You are building an instrument to measure the orientation of Earth's magnetic field. Your device consists of a single conducting coil that encloses an area $A = 400$ mm² and rotates

at a speed of 10,000 rotations/min. What peak induced emf should you expect if the magnitude of Earth's magnetic field is 50 μT? •

23. A circular coil of radius $R = 50$ mm rotates about an axis that is perpendicular to a uniform magnetic field of magnitude $B = 0.50$ T (Figure P29.23). If the coil completes 60 rotations each second, how many windings must the coil have in order to power an appliance that requires an emf that varies as $\mathcal{E}_{ind}(t) = V_{max} \sin(\omega t)$, where $V_{max} = 155$ V? ••

Figure P29.23

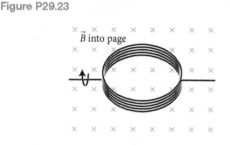

24. The square conducting loop in Figure P29.24 lies in the xy plane of an xyz coordinate system. The loop is in a uniform magnetic field that points in the positive z direction and is decreasing at a rate of 0.070 T/s. What are (a) the magnitude of the induced emf in the loop and (b) the direction of the induced current in the loop? ••

Figure P29.24

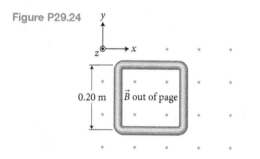

25. An increasing number of products, such as passports and credit cards, contain an embedded radio-frequency identification chip that both stores and transmits information. The chips do not have their own power sources. Instead, they receive their power through induction from the device used to read the stored information. The reading device generates a magnetic field, and the passport or credit card containing a coil is passed through this field. If a certain chip needs a peak induced emf of 4.0 V to operate and the magnetic field varies with time as $B(t) = B_{peak} \sin(\omega t)$, where $B_{peak} = 5.0$ mT is the maximum magnetic field and $\omega = 8.52 \times 10^7$ s^{-1}, what value must the product AN have in order for the chip to operate, where A is the coil's surface area and N is number of turns in the coil? ••

26. A 100-mm-long metal rod is placed in a uniform magnetic field with the rod length perpendicular to the field direction (Figure P29.26). The rod moves at 0.20 m/s, and its velocity vector makes an angle of 60° with the rod length. If the magnitude of the magnetic field is 0.40 T, what is the potential difference between the two ends of the rod? ••

Figure P29.26

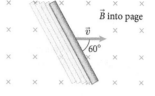

27. The very long cylindrical solenoid of Figure P29.27 has a radius of 0.50 m and 1000 windings per meter along its length. A circular conducting loop of radius 1.0 m encircles the solenoid, with the long central axis of the solenoid passing through the center of the loop, and with the area vector of the loop parallel to the solenoid axis. The solenoid initially carries a steady current I, but the current is then reduced to zero during a 0.100-s time interval. If the average emf induced in the loop during that interval is 0.10 V, what was the initial current magnitude? ••

Figure P29.27

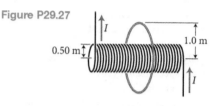

28. The space to the right of the y axis in Figure P29.28 contains a uniform magnetic field of unknown magnitude that points in the positive z direction. As a conducting square loop placed in the xy plane (oriented with its horizontal and vertical sides parallel to the x and y axes) moves to the right across the y axis at a constant speed of 2.0 m/s, a 0.24-V emf is induced in the loop. (a) If the side length of the loop is 0.30 m, what is the magnitude of the magnetic field? (b) What is the direction of the induced current in the loop? ••

Figure P29.28

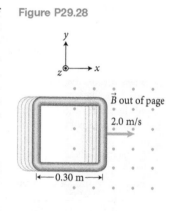

29. A region of space contains a changing magnetic field given by $\vec{B}(t) = B_0 e^{-t/\tau} \hat{k}$, and a circular conducting loop of radius R lies in this region in the xy plane. (a) Calculate the magnetic flux through the loop as a function of time. Is the flux increasing or decreasing as time passes? (b) Calculate the induced emf in the loop as a function of time. (c) Determine the current direction in the loop. ••

30. The coil in a generator has 100 windings and a cross-sectional area of 0.0100 m^2. (a) If the coil turns at a constant rotational speed and the magnetic field in the generator is that of Earth ($B = 0.500 \times 10^{-4}$ T), how many 360° rotations must the coil complete each second to generate a maximum induced emf of 1.00 V? (b) Based on this calculation, does it seem practical to use Earth's magnetic field in electric generators? ••

31. You have two cylindrical solenoids, one inside the other, with the two cylinders concentric. The outer solenoid has length $\ell_{outer} = 400$ mm, radius $R_{outer} = 50$ mm, and $N_{outer} = 1000$ windings. The inner solenoid has length $\ell_{inner} = 40$ mm,

radius $R_{inner} = 20$ mm, and $N_{inner} = 150$ windings. The inner solenoid is centered within the outer solenoid. When the outer solenoid carries a current given by $I(t) = I_0 \sin(\omega t)$, with $I_0 = 600$ mA and $\omega = 100$ s^{-1}, what is the peak emf in the inner solenoid? ●●

32. A rectangular wire loop enclosing an area $A = 0.40$ m^2 is inside a long cylindrical solenoid with two windings per mm. The area vector of the loop is aligned with the axis of the solenoid, and the current in the solenoid varies according to the graph shown in Figure P29.32. What is the induced emf in the loop at $t = 10$ s? ●●

Figure P29.32

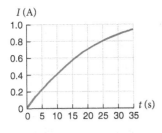

33. A circular metal disk with a shaft through its center rotates about a central axis as shown in Figure P29.33. The unit is placed in a uniform magnetic field of magnitude 1.5 T, directed parallel to the shaft. Two small sliding contacts are placed against the unit, one touching the edge of the disk and the other touching the end of the shaft. (a) If the disk radius is 100 mm and the disk completes 300 rotations per minute, what is the value of the emf induced between the two contacts? (b) Which contact is at the greater potential? ●●

Figure P29.33

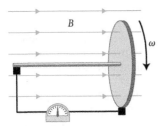

34. The dimensions of the rectangular loop of wire in Figure P29.34 are $\ell = 50$ mm and $w = 40$ mm. The loop moves at speed $v = 30$ mm/s through the magnetic field shown. The field magnitude increases linearly from $B_i(x_i) = 10$ mT at $x_i = 300$ mm to $B_f(x_f) = 60$ mT at $x_f = 900$ mm. The area vector of the loop is parallel to the magnetic field direction. What is the induced emf in the loop? ●●●

Figure P29.34

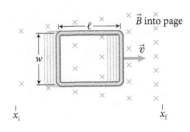

35. The dimensions of the rectangular loop of wire in Figure P29.35 are $\ell = 400$ mm and $w = 120$ mm. The mass of the loop is 10 g, its resistance is 5.0 V/A, and before entering the magnetic field shown the loop is moving at a constant speed v_i. The magnetic field magnitude is 5.0 T, and the loop's area vector is parallel to the field direction. How many seconds after the leading edge of the loop enters the magnetic field is the loop's speed half its initial value? Ignore any friction effects. ●●●

Figure P29.35

36. (a) A rectangular loop of wire is $\ell = 800$ mm long and $w = 500$ mm wide. You bend the ℓ sides into a semicircle while keeping the w sides straight, as shown in Figure P29.36, and then move the curved loop at speed $v = 0.800$ m/s into a uniform magnetic field of magnitude $B = 0.600$ T. One of the sides labeled w is the leading edge of the moving loop, and the magnetic field direction is perpendicular to those sides. What is the value of the emf induced in the loop? (b) What is the induced emf if the loop is rotated 90° so that the side leading into the magnetic field is one of the curved sides? ●●●

Figure P29.36

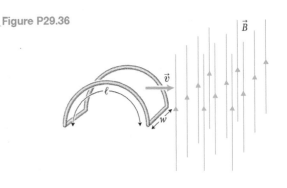

37. A bar is sliding along a set of connected conducting rails as shown in Figure P29.37. The bar is given an initial velocity $\vec{v}_i$ to the right and then allowed to move freely. The bar has mass m, and the distance between the rails (which is also the bar length) is ℓ. The resistance of the conducting loop comprising the bar and conducting rails is R. Show that the speed of the bar decreases exponentially with time, and determine the time constant. ●●●

Figure P29.37

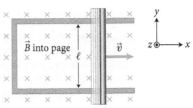

38. The area vector of a rectangular loop that is initially ℓ_i = 300 mm long and w_i = 200 mm wide is aligned with the direction of a uniform magnetic field that has initial magnitude B_i = 500 mT. You want to increase the field magnitude smoothly to B_f = 700 mT in 10 s, but you want to have zero induced current in the loop. You plan to accomplish this by changing the loop's length ℓ as you increase the magnetic field. In order to have I_{ind} = 0, what must the loop length be after 3.00 s and after 10.0 s? •••

29.6 Electric field accompanying a changing magnetic field

39. A uniform magnetic field exists in a circular area. A particle carrying charge q = 5.0 mC is placed in the field a distance r_p = 20 mm from the center of the circular area. If the particle experiences a force that has magnitude F = 4.00 μN and is perpendicular to the direction of the magnetic field, at what rate is the magnetic field changing? •

The next four problems are based on the situation illustrated in Figure P29.40. A uniform magnetic field pointing in the positive z direction fills a cylindrical volume of space of radius R whose central axis is the z axis. Outside this region, there is no magnetic field.

Figure P29.40

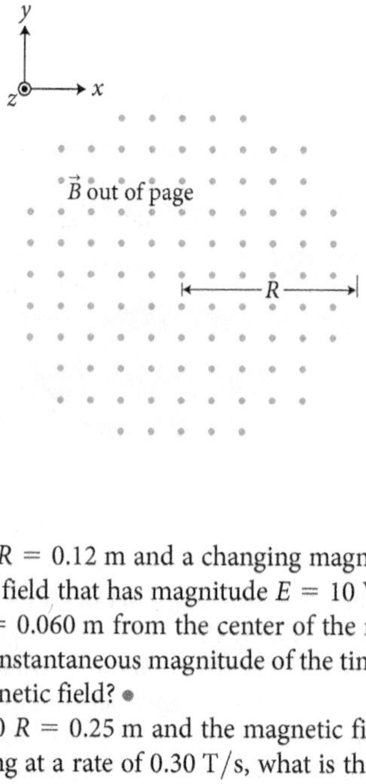

$\vec{B}$ out of page

40. In Figure P29.40, R = 0.12 m and a changing magnetic field creates an electric field that has magnitude E = 10 V/m at a radial distance r = 0.060 m from the center of the magnetic field. What is the instantaneous magnitude of the time rate of change of the magnetic field? •

41. If in Figure P29.40 R = 0.25 m and the magnetic field magnitude is decreasing at a rate of 0.30 T/s, what is the magnitude of the electric field created by this changing magnetic field (a) at radial distance r = 0.20 m from the magnetic field center and (b) at r = 0.50 m from the center? (c) Do the electric field lines encircle the z axis clockwise or counterclockwise, when viewed looking down the positive z axis toward the origin? ••

42. If the magnitude of the magnetic field in Figure P29.40 changes with time as $B = B_{max} \sin(\omega t)$, calculate the magnitude of the electric field that accompanies this changing magnetic field as a function of time t and radial distance r from the center of the magnetic field for (a) $r < R$ and (b) $r > R$. (c) At t = 0, what is the direction of the electric field? ••

43. The magnitude of the magnetic field in Figure P29.40 changes with time, and the magnitude of the accompanying electric field inside the magnetic field is given by $E(r, t) = 3Crt^2$, where C is a positive constant and r is the radial distance from the center of the magnetic field. For the case where B = 0 at t = 0, derive an expression for the magnitude of the magnetic field as a function of time for $t > 0$. ••

44. A uniform magnetic field fills a cylindrical volume of radius R, and the field magnitude changes with time at an unknown rate. At a certain instant, the electric field magnitude at a radial distance $r_1 < R$ from the magnetic field center is E_1. At this instant, at what radial distance r from the magnetic field center is the electric field magnitude E equal to $E_1/3$ (a) if $r < R$ and (b) if $r > R$? ••

45. It takes an electric field magnitude of about 10^6 V/m to ionize atoms in the air and produce a spark. Is it possible to increase the magnetic field inside a long solenoid quickly enough to generate a spark inside? Take the solenoid radius to be 30 mm. •••

29.7 Inductance

46. A 2.0-H inductor carries a current that is increasing at a rate of 0.40 A/s. What is the magnitude of the emf induced in the inductor? Does this induced emf aid or oppose the flow of the charge carriers? •

47. When the current through an inductor is decreasing at a rate of 2.0 A/s, the magnitude of the induced emf is 6.0 V. What is the inductance of the inductor? •

48. The radius of a toroid is R_t = 0.10 m, and the windings have a circular cross section. The radius of each winding is R_w = 10 mm, and the number of windings is N = 400. Calculate the inductance of the toroid. •

49. The current through an inductor of inductance L is given by $I(t) = I_{max} \sin(\omega t)$. (a) Derive an expression for the induced emf in the inductor as a function of time. (b) At t = 0, is the current through the inductor increasing or decreasing? (c) At t = 0, is the induced emf opposing or aiding the flow of the charge carriers? (Remember that the direction of a positive induced emf is the same as the current direction and the direction of a negative induced emf is opposite the current direction.) (d) How are the answers to parts b and c consistent with the behavior of inductors discussed in the text? ••

50. The induced emf in an inductor of inductance L varies with time according to $\mathcal{E}_{ind}(t) = -2Ct$, where C is a positive constant. (a) If there is no current through the inductor at t = 0, calculate the current as a function of time for $t > 0$. (b) Is the current increasing or decreasing when $t > 0$? (c) Discuss how your answer to part b is consistent with the sign of $\mathcal{E}_{ind}$ and what you know about the behavior of inductors. ••

51. You and a friend have a 0.65-m length of copper wire that has a diameter of 4.115 mm and a wooden rod that is 85 mm long and has a diameter of 10 mm. You're aiming to wind the wire around the rod about 40 times to form an inductor. (a) What is the maximum inductance you can achieve with this device? (b) Your friend solves this problem by reasoning that a cylindrically wound wire whose length greatly exceeds its radius is a solenoid, and therefore he can use the equation from *Principles* Example 29.8 to determine the inductance:

$$L = \frac{\mu_0 N^2 A}{\ell} = \frac{(4\pi \times 10^{-7} \text{ T} \cdot \text{m/A})(40^2)\pi(0.0020575 \text{ m})^2}{0.65 \text{ m}}$$

$$= 4.1 \times 10^{-8} \text{ H}.$$

Evaluate your friend's work. ●●

52. The toroid in Figure P29.52 has 200 rectangular windings, and the toroid radii are $R_{in} = 160$ mm and $R_{out} = 240$ mm. The height of each winding is $h = 20$ mm, such that the rectangular cross section of each winding is $(R_{out} - R_{in}) \times h = (80 \text{ mm}) \times (20 \text{ mm})$. What is the inductance of the toroid? ●●●

Figure P29.52

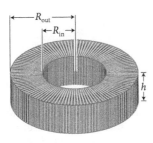

29.8 Magnetic energy

53. Calculate the amount of magnetic potential energy stored in a 0.60-H inductor when the current in the inductor is 6.0 A. ●

54. If 10 J of magnetic potential energy is stored in a 5.0-H inductor, what is the current in the inductor? ●

55. A cylindrical volume of space contains a uniform magnetic field of magnitude 0.12 T but unknown direction. If the dimensions of the cylindrical volume are length $\ell = 0.060$ m and radius $R = 0.040$ m, how much magnetic potential energy is stored in the field? ●●

56. When you unplug a coffee maker that plugs into the utility outlet of your car, you notice a spark. Worried that the coffee maker might be broken, you take it apart and find that the heating element is a tungsten wire that, according to the label, is wound 600 times around what appears to be a nonmagnetic core. The core has radius $R = 2.0$ mm and length $\ell = 200$ mm. On the outside of the coffee maker, it says 12 V, 3.2 A. Where does the spark come from? ●●

57. The magnitude of the magnetic field in a magnetic resonance imaging (MRI) machine can be as great as $B = 3.0$ T. Under normal circumstances, this field cannot be shut off by just flipping a switch. Instead the magnitude needs to be carefully decreased to zero. In an emergency, however, the magnet can be "quenched" so that B reduces to zero in 20 s. Such a quench can cost thousands of dollars and likely damages the magnets. Assume that the magnetic field exists inside a cylinder of radius $R = 300$ mm and length $\ell = 200$ mm. How much magnetic potential energy is dissipated when the magnetic field is quenched in this way, and what is the average rate at which energy is dissipated? ●●

58. What is the magnetic potential energy stored in a cylindrical volume of height $h_{cylin} = 50$ mm and radius $R_{cylin} = 24$ mm that symmetrically surrounds an infinitely long wire that has radius $R_{wire} = 2.1$ mm and carries current $I = 2.3$ A? ●●●

59. A cylindrical solenoid of length ℓ and radius R has n windings per unit length and carries a current I. (a) Use the inductance expression $L = (\mu_0 N^2 A)/\ell$ from *Principles* Example 29.8 and Eq. 29.25, $U^B = LI^2/2$, to derive an expression for the magnetic potential energy in the solenoid as a function of the current and the solenoid's dimensions. (b) Derive this same expression by beginning with Eq. 29.30, $U^B = \int u_B \, dV$. ●●●

Additional problems

60. Calculate the inductance of a 2000-windings cylindrical solenoid that is 0.20 m long if the radius of each winding is 0.03 m. ●

61. The current in a cylindrical solenoid is increased smoothly from $I_i = 0.40$ A at $t_i = 3.0$ s to $I_f = 1.2$ A at $t_f = 5.0$ s. What is the induced emf during this time interval if the solenoid length is $\ell = 150$ mm, the radius of each winding is $R = 20$ mm, and there are 400 windings? ●

62. A uniform magnetic field exists in a cubic volume of space with a 50-mm side length. If the magnetic energy stored in this volume is 12 J, what is the magnetic field magnitude? ●

63. In a large laboratory electromagnet, the poles have a circular cross section with a diameter of 100 mm and are 25 mm apart. If there is a uniform 1.3-T magnetic field between the poles, how much magnetic potential energy is stored in the magnetic field? ●

64. The rate at which the magnetic flux inside a wire loop decays is given by $\Phi_B(t) = \Phi_{B,i}e^{-\beta t}$, where $\beta = 0.50/\text{s}$ and $\Phi_{B,i} = 4.0$ Wb. What is the magnitude of the induced current at $t = 10$ s if the resistance of the wire is $R = 2.0$ V/A? ●●

65. You build a solenoid containing 400 windings over a 0.20-m length, with a loop radius of 0.025 m for each winding. If the current in the unit is 3.0 A, what are (a) the magnitude of the magnetic field produced and (b) the inductance of the solenoid? (c) Use your value of B from part a to calculate the amount of magnetic potential energy stored in the solenoid. (d) Use your value of L from part b to calculate the amount of magnetic potential energy stored. ●●

66. A conducting bar that is $\ell = 40$ mm long can slide with negligible friction on two parallel conducting rails positioned at an incline of $\theta = 15°$ (Figure P29.66). Initially, the bar is at rest in a magnetic field of magnitude $B = 0.60$ T. What is the emf between the rails 0.20 s after the bar starts sliding while it is still inside the magnetic field? ●●

Figure P29.66

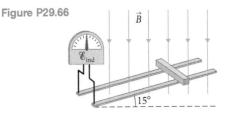

67. You have a circular wire loop of radius $a = 0.50$ m. It carries a current that increases linearly from 0 to 4.5 A in 0.30 s. At the center of this loop is a wire loop of radius $b = 0.0020$ m and resistance $R = 0.80$ V/A. The loops are coplanar. What is the current induced in the smaller loop? ●●

68. You shape a flexible wire into a loop of initial radius $r_i =$ 30 mm. You then place the loop in a uniform magnetic field and pull the two ends of the wire in opposite directions at $v =$ 6.0 mm/s so that the loop starts closing up (Figure P29.68). If the field magnitude is $B = 0.70$ T, what is the emf between the ends of the wire 2.0 s after you begin pulling? ••

Figure P29.68

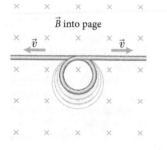

$\vec{B}$ into page

69. A rod of length ℓ rotates about one end at a constant rotational speed ω. The rod is in a uniform magnetic field $\vec{B}$, and the axis of rotation is parallel to $\vec{B}$ (Figure P29.69). (a) In terms of ℓ, B, and ω, what potential difference develops between the two ends of the rod? (b) Which end of the rod has a greater potential? (c) If $\ell = 0.15$ m, $B = 1.0$ T, and $\omega = 377$ s^{-1}, what is the potential-difference value? ••

Figure P29.69

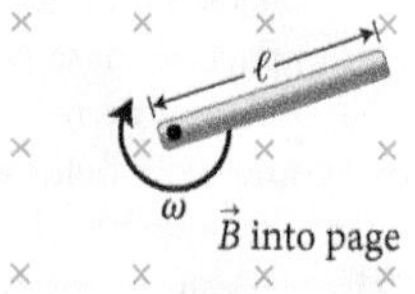

ω $\vec{B}$ into page

70. A uniform magnetic field of magnitude B fills all space and points in the positive z direction (Figure P29.70). A circular conducting loop in the xy plane is growing larger, with its radius as a function of time given by $r(t) = vt$, where v is a positive constant. (a) Derive an expression for the magnitude of the emf induced in the loop as a function of time. (b) What is the direction of the induced current? ••

Figure P29.70

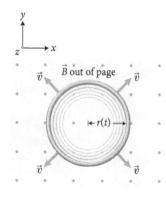

$\vec{B}$ out of page

71. A conducting bar of width $w = 0.12$ m and mass $m = 8.0$ g can slide freely on two parallel conducting rails positioned at an incline of $\theta = 15°$ (Figure P29.71). The rails are connected at their base by a piece of conducting material. The distance between the rails is w, and the resistance in the rails is $R = 0.20$ V/A. A uniform magnetic field $\vec{B}$ is exactly vertical as indicated in the drawing, with $B = 0.50$ T. At what constant (terminal) speed does the bar slide down the incline? Ignore friction. ••

Figure P29.71

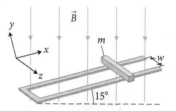

72. For the system described in Problem 71, you measure a constant speed of 1.0 m/s. Because this is not the value you calculated when you ignored friction in the system, you conclude that the friction in the rails is too great to be ignored. What value for the coefficient of kinetic friction μ_k yields the 1.0-m/s speed you measured? •••

73. A square loop of wire of side length a and resistance R lies a distance x to the right of a long, straight wire that carries a current I. The straight wire lies in the plane defined by the loop, parallel to one side of the square, and the current direction in the wire is upward. The loop is held stationary, and the current in the wire varies sinusoidally as $I = I_{max} \sin(\omega t)$. Derive an expression for the emf induced in the loop as a function of I_{max}, ω, a, x, and t. •••

74. You are working for a company that is interested in mapping geological formations in Earth's crust by examining variations in the magnitude of the magnetic field at Earth's surface. Your assignment is to design a device that can detect small variations in this magnetic field at ground level. Deciding on a system that uses a rotating coil, you realize that the design (number of windings, winding cross-sectional area, rotational speed, and so forth) must give a 1-mV signal in Earth's magnetic field in order to be useful. ••• CR

75. On the fifth floor of the physics building, you are in a laboratory class studying induction. You are using a computer to measure emf values from a solenoid when suddenly a thunderstorm breaks out. You see a large blip on the computer screen and 2.0 s later hear a loud thunderclap. Looking out the window, you see that straight ahead a tree was struck by lightning. You quickly save the data on your computer (plotted in Figure P29.75) and note that the solenoid happens to be oriented at an angle of $\theta = 40°$ with respect to your line of sight to the tree. The solenoid windings have cross-sectional area $A = 0.10$ m^2, and there are $N = 100$ windings. You wonder about the current involved in the lightning flash that struck the tree. ••• CR

Figure P29.75

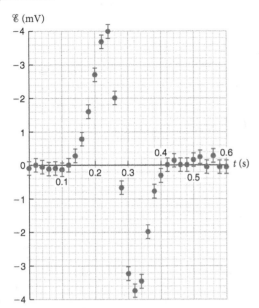

76. An electromagnet in a physics laboratory is damaging electronic apparatus in its vicinity. You suspect that the damage is due to unusually large induced currents created each time the electromagnet power supply is turned on, so you decide to monitor the magnet's magnetic field. Figure P29.76 shows the field magnitude as a function of time during the first 18 s after you connect the magnet to a power supply. Instead of smoothly increasing to its designed value of 0.90 T, the field magnitude starts to decrease after about 3.0 s, very likely due to fluctuations in its power supply. What is not clear is whether these fluctuations can account for the damage, because the electronic apparatus is designed with the expectation that the change in magnetic field strength will be linear with time. ••• CR

Figure P29.76

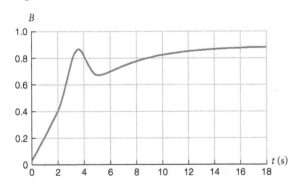

77. Analog cassette players read sound recorded on magnetic tape. The sound is recorded by magnetizing the tape longitudinally (magnetization parallel to the tape's length) with varying magnetic field magnitudes in either direction. The tape is usually divided into longitudinal tracks so that different signals can be recorded in parallel. In the player, as the tape is pulled across the reading head, a varying emf is induced in a coil wound around the C-shaped metal core of the head (Figure P29.77). This emf is then amplified and sent to the speakers. Trying to learn more about the physics of this technology, you read that the recorded signal magnitude is usually given in terms of *fluxivity,* which is the peak magnetic flux per track width. In particular, you find a paper that gives a fluxivity of 320 nWb/m for a 1000-Hz sine wave recorded on a track 6.3 mm wide [O. Schmidbauer, *J. Audio Eng. Soc.,* 46(10), 859 (1998)]. Naturally, not all of the flux generated threads through the coil, but your search shows that reading heads can have a "flux efficiency" of 98% [J. G. McKnight, B. E. Cortez, and J. A. McKnight, *J. Audio Eng. Soc.,* 46(10), 845 (1998)] and that 250 coil windings are typical. You begin to wonder about the emf induced in the coil and how the frequency of the recorded sound relates to the speed v with which the tape runs. ••• CR

Figure P29.77

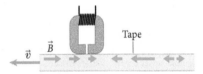

Answers to Review Questions

1. The magnetic force exerted by the external magnetic field on the charge carriers that move with the rod drives the positive carriers upward and the negative carriers downward. The result is a separation of charge and a small potential difference between the bottom and top of the rod.

2. For the portion of the loop that is in the nonzero-field region, the magnetic force exerted by the magnetic field on the charge carriers drives the positive carriers upward and the negative carriers downward. As long as part of the loop is in the nonzero-field region and part of the loop is in the zero-field region, the result is to create an electric current in the loop. When the entire loop is within the region of nonzero, uniform magnetic field, the current is no longer induced.

3. An induced electric current is the flow of charge carriers caused by electromagnetic induction, as opposed to a current that is caused by a source of potential difference such as a battery. Although the causes are different, there is no *physical* difference between induced currents and other currents.

4. Yes. The induced effects are reversed when the direction of the object's velocity is reversed, and the effects are zero when the object's velocity is parallel to the magnetic field.

5. Changing the reference frame does not affect the explanation. Whether you say the loop moves through the external magnetic field created by a stationary source or the external source moves and the loop is stationary, the result is the same: An electric current is induced in the loop as it moves between regions of differing magnetic fields.

6. Whenever the magnetic flux through a conducting loop changes, an electric current is induced in the loop.

7. Electromagnetic induction is the process by which a changing magnetic flux causes charge carriers in a conducting object to move. When the magnetic flux through a conducting loop changes, a current is induced in the loop.

8. No. In the reference frame in which the loop is at rest, there is no magnetic force to create the current in the loop. Rather, the changing magnetic field is accompanied by an electric field, and this electric field is the source of an electric force exerted on the charge carriers, creating a current in the loop.

9. Yes. In a reference frame in which a conducting loop is at rest and a magnetic field source is moving, the electric field caused by the time-varying magnetic flux is the source of the electromagnetic induction. In a reference frame in which the conducting loop moves through a nonuniform external magnetic field, the magnetic force exerted on the charge carriers in the loop is the source of the electromagnetic induction.

10. The field lines of an electric field that accompanies a changing magnetic field form closed loops, whereas the field lines of the field of stationary charged particles, which originate on positively charged particles and terminate on negatively charged ones, do not.

11. The current is induced by a changing magnetic flux through the loop, and Lenz's law says that the direction of the induced current is the direction that makes the magnetic field created by the induced current oppose the changing magnetic flux through the loop.

12. The law of conservation of energy underlies Lenz's law. If the direction of an induced current were to enhance the change in the magnetic flux rather than oppose that change, the result would be an increase in the system's energy without any work being done on the system.

13. Eddy currents are electric currents induced in a conducting object by a changing external magnetic field near the object. These currents are generally not confined to a single path, as in a wire, but circulate as tiny whirlpools.

14. Induced emf is the emf (work per unit charge done in separating positive and negative charge carriers by nonelectrostatic means) associated with changing magnetic flux through a closed path.

15. The energy acquired by the charge carriers comes from the agent that causes the loop to move. If the loop is being pulled through the magnetic field, for example, that mechanical work done on the loop is transferred to the charge carriers.

16. (*a*) Faraday's law states that the emf induced around a closed path is equal to the negative of the time rate of change of magnetic flux through an area bounded by the path: $\mathcal{E}_{ind} = -d\Phi_B/dt$. (*b*) The negative sign reflects Lenz's law by making the expression say that the direction of $\mathcal{E}_{ind}$ is such that the induced current opposes the magnetic-flux change generating that current.

17. (1) Both induced emf and potential difference are related to the work done per unit charge on charged particles. In the case of potential difference, the work is done by electrostatic forces, but the work is done by nonelectrostatic forces in the case of emf. (2) Potential difference is path-independent, which means that the work done by electrostatic forces on charged particles depends only on the particles' starting and ending locations, not on the path they take to get to those locations. The work done by the emf induced by a changing magnetic field does depend on the path taken by the charged particles; that is, the work done by nonelectrostatic forces depends on the shape of the loop in which the emf is induced.

18. The induced emf oscillates sinusoidally according to the expression $\mathcal{E}_{ind} = \omega BA \cos \omega t$ (where A is the area enclosed by the loop).

19. The induced emf is the line integral of the electric field that accompanies the changing magnetic field, around the path bounding the area through which the magnetic flux is changing.

20. The direction of the electric field is tangent to the electric field lines, which form loops centered on the solenoid axis. The electric field lines lie in planes perpendicular to the solenoid axis and point in the direction dictated by Lenz's law. This is true both inside and outside the solenoid.

21. The magnitude of the electric field is proportional to the time derivative of the magnetic field strength, $E \propto (dB/dt)$. From *Principles* Example 29.7 you know that inside the magnetic field region E varies directly with distance from the solenoid axis, and from Checkpoint 29.13 you know that outside the magnetic field region E varies inversely with the distance from the solenoid axis.

22. Yes. The changing current changes the magnetic flux through the loop, and Faraday's law tells you that the changing magnetic flux induces an emf to oppose the flux change.

23. The SI unit is the henry, which equals one volt-second per ampere.

24. An inductor is an electrical component that has a specified inductance, such that a given dI/dt results in a known, specified emf. Because the induced emf opposes changes in current, one use of an inductor is to even out any current fluctuations in a current-carrying loop.

25. The inductance of a conducting loop or device describes how much the magnetic flux through it changes when the current changes. The inductance depends only on the geometric properties of the loop or device—that is, on its size and shape. For example, the inductance of a solenoid depends on its length, cross-sectional area, and the number of windings: $L \propto N^2A/\ell$.

26. The work done to change the current in an inductor goes into, or comes out of, the magnetic potential energy stored in the magnetic field of the inductor. That is, a reduction in the current is accounted for by a decrease in the stored magnetic potential energy. Some external source is needed to account for the work done to increase the current, work that increases the stored magnetic potential energy.

27. The magnetic potential energy depends on the square of the current in the inductor and on the inductance: $U^B = LI^2/2$. Because inductance depends on the physical dimensions of the inductor, you can also say that the magnetic potential energy stored in an inductor depends on the square of the current and on the size and shape of the inductor; for a solenoidal inductor, for example, $U^B \propto N^2 A I^2/\ell$.

28. The magnetic potential energy in an inductor is equal to the volume integral of the energy density in the magnetic field: $U^B = \int u_B dV$. The energy density is proportional to the square of the field strength, $u_B = B^2/(2\mu_0)$, which is a general relationship for any magnetic field. (If the field strength is approximately uniform over the volume of the inductor, the energy is just the product of the energy density and the volume.)

Answers to Guided Problems

Guided Problem 29.2 $I_{ind} = \dfrac{\mathscr{E}_{ind}}{R} = \dfrac{\mu_0 I \ell v}{2\pi R}\left(\dfrac{1}{r} - \dfrac{1}{r + w}\right)$. In the configuration of Figure WG29.3, the direction of the induced current is clockwise around the loop.

Guided Problem 29.4 While the top of the loop is still in the magnetic field, $v = (g\tau)(1 - e^{-t/\tau})$, with $\tau = (mR/w^2 B^2)$. After the top edge of the loop has left the magnetic field, v increases with time at constant acceleration g.

Guided Problem 29.6 $U^B = \dfrac{\mu_0 \ell I^2}{4\pi}\ln\left(\dfrac{R_{outer}}{R_{inner}}\right)$, $L = \dfrac{\mu_0 \ell}{2\pi}\ln\left(\dfrac{R_{outer}}{R_{inner}}\right)$

Guided Problem 29.8 $\dfrac{dB(R)}{dt} = \dfrac{1}{2}\left(\dfrac{dB_{av}}{dt}\right)$

30

PRACTICE

Changing
Electric Fields

PRACTICE

Chapter Summary

Changing electric fields (Sections 30.1, 30.4)

Concepts A changing electric field is accompanied by a magnetic field, and a changing magnetic field is accompanied by an electric field.

Table 30.1 Properties of electric and magnetic fields

	Electric field	Magnetic field
associated with	charged particle	moving charged particle
	changing magnetic field	changing electric field
exerts force on	any charged particle	moving charged particle

Quantitative Tools The **displacement current** due to a changing electric flux through a surface is

$$I_{disp} \equiv \epsilon_0 \frac{d\Phi_E}{dt}. \tag{30.7}$$

The *Maxwell-Ampère law* is

$$\oint \vec{B} \cdot d\vec{\ell} = \mu_0 (I_{int} + I_{disp}), \tag{30.8}$$

where I_{int} is the current intercepted by a surface spanning an Ampèrian path.

Maxwell's equations (Section 30.5)

Concepts **Maxwell's equations** provide a complete mathematical description of electric and magnetic phenomena and the relationship between the two.

Quantitative Tools **Maxwell's equations** are

$$\Phi_E \equiv \oint \vec{E} \cdot d\vec{A} = \frac{q_{enc}}{\epsilon_0} \tag{30.10}$$

$$\Phi_B \equiv \oint \vec{B} \cdot d\vec{A} = 0 \tag{30.11}$$

$$\oint \vec{E} \cdot d\vec{\ell} = -\frac{d\Phi_B}{dt} \tag{30.12}$$

$$\oint \vec{B} \cdot d\vec{\ell} = \mu_0 I_{int} + \mu_0 \epsilon_0 \frac{d\Phi_E}{dt}. \tag{30.13}$$

Electromagnetic waves (Sections 30.2, 30.3, 30.6, 30.7)

Concepts An **electromagnetic wave** is a propagating disturbance in a combined electric and magnetic field. The electric and magnetic fields in these waves are perpendicular to each other, and the direction of wave propagation is the direction of $\vec{E} \times \vec{B}$.

A **planar electromagnetic wave** is one in which the wavefronts are planes perpendicular to the direction of propagation. At each point on a planar wavefront, the instantaneous magnitude of the electric field has the same value, as does the instantaneous magnitude of the magnetic field.

Oscillating dipoles and antennas to which an alternating potential is applied emit electromagnetic waves.

The **polarization** of an electromagnetic wave is the orientation of the electric field as seen by an observer looking in the direction of propagation.

Quantitative Tools The speed of an electromagnetic wave in vacuum is

$$c_0 = \frac{1}{\sqrt{\epsilon_0 \mu_0}}. \tag{30.26}$$

The speed of an electromagnetic wave in a dielectric of dielectric constant κ is

$$c = \frac{c_0}{\sqrt{\kappa}}.$$

The **Poynting vector** $\vec{S}$ gives the energy transported by an electromagnetic wave per unit time across a unit area perpendicular to the direction of propagation of the wave:

$$\vec{S} \equiv \frac{1}{\mu_0} \vec{E} \times \vec{B}. \tag{30.37}$$

The power transported by an electromagnetic wave crossing a surface is

$$P = \int_{surface} \vec{S} \cdot d\vec{A}. \tag{30.38}$$

Review Questions

Answers to these questions can be found at the end of this chapter.

30.1 Magnetic fields accompany changing electric fields

1. What besides electric current produces a magnetic field?
2. How is the direction of the magnetic field that accompanies a changing electric field related to the direction of the changing electric field?
3. Describe the similarities and differences in the sources that produce electric and magnetic fields.
4. What is the main difference between the effects of electric fields on charged particles and the effects of magnetic fields on charged particles?
5. Describe the main similarity and the main difference in the spatial appearance of electric and magnetic field lines.

30.2 Fields of moving charged particles

6. Is the electric field surrounding a charged particle moving with constant velocity spherically symmetrical or asymmetrical? If asymmetrical, describe what the field looks like.
7. What determines how asymmetrical the electric field surrounding a charged particle moving at constant velocity is?
8. When do kinks appear in the field line pattern of the electric field that surrounds a charged particle? What two regions of a given field line does a kink join?
9. What are the two components of an electromagnetic wave?

30.3 Oscillating dipoles and antennas

10. Describe at the instant $t = T$ the electric field lines in three regions of interest near an electric dipole whose polarity changes once (from positive above negative to negative above positive) during the time interval $t = 0$ to $t = T/2$ and then remains fixed from $t = T/2$ to $t = T$.
11. In a transverse electromagnetic wave, how are the electric and magnetic fields oriented relative to each other and relative to the direction in which the wave propagates?
12. What does it mean to say that the electric and magnetic fields in an electromagnetic wave are *in phase*?
13. How is the polarization of an electromagnetic wave defined?
14. What is an antenna?
15. How is an oscillating current created in an emitting antenna?

30.4 Displacement current

16. What electrical device can be used to demonstrate that the form of Ampère's law given in Chapter 28, $\oint \vec{B} \cdot d\vec{\ell} = \mu_0 I_{enc}$, is incomplete? Describe an Ampèrian path around the device and a surface spanned by the path that you can use to illustrate this incompleteness.
17. What is the generalized form of Ampère's law, which applies when electric fields are changing?
18. In the generalized form of Ampère's law, what does each term to the right of the equal sign represent?
19. Is displacement current really a current? If not, why is it called a current?

20. How must the displacement-current term in the generalized form of Ampère's law be modified when the capacitor being analyzed contains a dielectric between its plates?

30.5 Maxwell's equations

21. Write the four equations from the *Principles* text that are collectively called Maxwell's equations, and name each one.
22. Given that all four of the laws for electric and magnetic fields were discovered before Maxwell modified one of them, why is it still fitting to refer to all of them as Maxwell's equations?
23. Describe the experimental evidence for each of Maxwell's equations.

30.6 Electromagnetic waves

24. For an electromagnetic wave pulse emanating from an accelerated charge carrier, what does the transverse (kinked) portion of the pulse look like far from the location where the acceleration occurred?
25. What is the relationship between the magnitudes of the electric and magnetic fields for an electromagnetic wave pulse traveling in vacuum?
26. What is the relationship between the magnitudes of the electric and magnetic fields for an electromagnetic wave pulse traveling through a dielectric material?
27. In terms of the electric constant ϵ_0 and the magnetic constant μ_0, what is the speed of an electromagnetic wave pulse traveling in vacuum and traveling through a dielectric?
28. For a planar electromagnetic wave, what is the directional relationship among the magnetic field, the electric field, and the wave's propagation velocity?
29. Do electromagnetic waves of different frequencies travel at different speeds in vacuum?
30. How is the speed at which an electromagnetic wave travels in vacuum related to the wave's frequency and wavelength?
31. What are the names of the major divisions of the electromagnetic spectrum?

30.7 Electromagnetic energy

32. How do the energy densities in the electric and magnetic fields of a planar electromagnetic wave in vacuum compare with each other?
33. (*a*) What is the expression for the energy density u of an electromagnetic wave in vacuum in terms of its electric and magnetic components? (*b*) How can you express the energy density if you know the electric component of the wave but do not know the magnetic component? (*c*) How can you express the energy density if you know the magnetic component but not the electric component?
34. What is the Poynting vector of an electromagnetic wave in vacuum, and what properties of the wave does this vector represent?
35. What is the intensity of an electromagnetic wave?
36. What is the relationship between the intensity of an electromagnetic wave and its energy density?

Developing a Feel

Make an order-of-magnitude estimate of each of the following quantities. Letters in parentheses refer to hints below. Use them as needed to guide your thinking.

1. The shortest-wavelength electromagnetic wave you can generate by waving a charged rod (T, F, B)
2. The wavelength of a radio station that is called FM 104 (A, K, F, B)
3. The frequency of a radio wave if one wavelength occupies the length of a tennis court (F, B, U)
4. The maximum magnitude of the electric field 1 m from an electron that has 10^{-12} J of energy and is moving at a constant speed $v \approx c_0$ (W, G, DD, S, FF)
5. The time interval needed for a radio wave pulse emitted from ground level to travel to and then back from a communications satellite moving in a geostationary orbit at 3×10^3 m/s (A satellite in geostationary orbit moves at a translational speed equal to the product of Earth's rotational speed and the orbit's radius, so it always stays above a single location on Earth's surface.) (B, P, CC, N, H)
6. The average displacement current caused when a 1-μF capacitor is charged to 10 V in 0.1 s (J, O)
7. The root mean square (rms) value of the electric field magnitude 1 km from an AM radio station emitting antenna (E, I, X, Q, V, M)
8. The maximum magnetic field magnitude 100 mm from a 125-mW cell phone (E, Z, X, Q, BB)
9. The change in electric flux in the region between your finger and a metal doorknob when a spark jumps from your finger to the knob (Y, EE, C, R)
10. The power radiated by all the AM radio stations in the United States (M, D, L, AA)

Hints

A. What does the radio station number refer to?
B. What is the wave speed?
C. What is the electric field magnitude at which air breaks down (that is, when sparks form)?
D. How many AM stations are there in an average-size city?
E. What is the relationship between the rms values of the electric and magnetic field magnitudes?
F. What is the relationship between wavelength and frequency?
G. What is the electric field magnitude 1 m from an electron at rest?
H. What is the height above Earth's surface to geostationary orbit?
I. What is the relationship between E_{rms} and the average intensity of the wave?
J. What is the quantity of charge on each plate when the capacitor is fully charged?
K. What is the frequency unit for FM radio?
L. How many average-size cities are in the United States?
M. What power is radiated by a typical commercial radio station?
N. What is Earth's radius?
O. What is the conventional current required to charge the capacitor?
P. What is the orbital period of a geostationary orbit?
Q. What is the relationship between the average intensity of the wave and the average power of the wave source at a radial distance $r = R$ from the source?
R. What is the cross-sectional area where the electric field magnitude is greatest?
S. For a moving electron, how does the magnitude of the component of the electric field perpendicular to the line of motion 1 m from the electron compare with the magnitude of the electric field 1 m from an electron at rest?
T. At what maximum frequency can you wave the rod?
U. What is the length of a tennis court?
V. What is the relationship between P_{av} and E_{rms}?
W. What is the charge on the electron?
X. What is the area of a sphere of radius R?

Y. How should you model this situation to relate it to material covered in the *Principles* text?
Z. What is the relationship between B_{rms} and the average intensity of the wave?
AA. What is a reasonable value for the number of AM stations in the United States that are outside cities?
BB. What is the relationship between P_{av} and B_{rms}?
CC. How does the period of an object in circular motion at constant speed relate to the circle's radius?
DD. Where is the electric field due to the electron's motion greatest?
EE. Is the electric field between the plates of a charged capacitor uniform or nonuniform?
FF. What is the γ factor for a 10^{-12}-J electron?

Key (all values approximate)

A. the frequency of the electromagnetic waves emitted by the station's emitting antenna; B. 3×10^8 m/s; C. 3×10^6 V/m; D. 30 stations; E. $B_{rms} = E_{rms}/c_0$; F. $f = c_0/\lambda$; G. $ke/r^2 = 1 \times 10^{-9}$ V/m ($k = 9 \times 10^9$ N·m^2/C^2, Coulomb's law); H. $R - R_E \sim 4 \times 10^7$ m; I. $S_{av} = E_{rms}^2/c_0\mu_0$; J. $q_{max} = CV = 10^{-5}$ C; K. megahertz; L. at least one per state, and more in populous states—say 100 cities; M. 10^4 W; N. 6×10^6 m; O. $I = \Delta q/\Delta t = 10^{-4}$ A; P. $T = 1$ day $= 9 \times 10^4$ s; Q. $P_{av} = S_{av}A = S_{av}4\pi R^2$; R. the cross-sectional area of the smaller object, your finger—10^{-4} m^2; S. the two magnitudes differ by the same factor that scales length contraction: $\gamma = 1/\sqrt{1 - v^2/c_0^2}$; T. 5 Hz; U. 3×10^1 m; V. $P_{av} = E_{rms}^2 4\pi R^2/c_0\mu_0$; W. -1.6×10^{-19} C; X. $A = 4\pi R^2$; Y. as a parallel-plate capacitor with your finger as one plate and the knob as the other plate; Z. $S_{av} = c_0 B_{rms}^2/\mu_0$; AA. 20 in each state = 1000 stations; BB. $P_{av} = c_0 B_{rms}^2 4\pi R^2/\mu_0$; CC. $T = 2\pi R/v$ (Eq. 11.20); DD. perpendicular to the line of motion; EE. uniform; FF. 1×10^1

Worked and Guided Problems

These examples involve material from this chapter but are not associated with any particular section.
Some examples are worked out in detail; others you should work out by following the guidelines provided.

Worked Problem 30.1 Magnetic from electric

The electric field of a planar sinusoidal electromagnetic wave is given by $\vec{E}(z, t) = E \sin(kz - \omega t)\hat{\imath}$, where $k = 9.0$ m^{-1} and $E = 6.0 \times 10^2$ V/m. (*a*) What are the wavelength and angular frequency of the wave? (*b*) What are the magnitude and direction of the magnetic field associated with this electric field?

❶ GETTING STARTED We are given the equation that describes the electric field of an electromagnetic wave and the values for the field magnitude E and the wave number k. From the z and the minus sign in the argument of the sine function, we know that the wave is traveling in the positive z direction (Eq. 16.12). Because the wave is planar, we see from *Principles* Figure 30.38 that, on each planar surface $z = a$, the electric field has a uniform value and lies along the x direction.

❷ DEVISE PLAN For part *a* we can determine the wavelength from Eq. 16.7, $k = 2\pi/\lambda$, and the angular frequency from Eqs. 16.11 and 16.9, $\omega = 2\pi/T$ and $\lambda = cT$, where in this case $c = c_0 = 3.0 \times 10^8$ m/s. For part *b* we use our knowledge that in a planar sinusoidal electromagnetic wave, the electric and magnetic fields are perpendicular to each other and the direction in which the wave they constitute travels is given by $\vec{E} \times \vec{B}$. We also know that the relationship between the field magnitudes is $B = E/c_0$ (Eq. 30.24) and that the fields are in phase.

❸ EXECUTE PLAN (*a*) From Eq. 16.7 $k = 2\pi/\lambda$, the wavelength is $\lambda = 2\pi/k = 2\pi/(9.0$ m$^{-1}) = 7.1 \times 10^{-2}$ m. ✔

The angular frequency of the wave is therefore

$$\omega = \frac{2\pi c_0}{\lambda} = \frac{2\pi(3.0 \times 10^8 \text{ m/s})}{(2\pi/9.0) \text{ m}} = 2.7 \times 10^9 \text{ s}^{-1}. ✔$$

(*b*) Consider a pair of values (z, t) such that $0 < kz - \omega t < \pi/2$. At the location and instant specified by (z, t), the sine function is positive

and so the electric field points in the positive x direction. The wave travels in the positive z direction. Therefore, at (z, t), $\vec{E} \times \vec{B}$ must point in the positive z direction. We know that $\hat{\imath} \times \hat{\jmath} = \hat{k}$, so we know that the magnetic field must point in the positive y direction and be of the form

$$\vec{B}(z, t) = B \sin(kz - \omega t)\hat{\jmath}.$$

The magnitude of the magnetic field is

$$B = \frac{E}{c_0} = \frac{6.0 \times 10^2 \text{ V/m}}{3.0 \times 10^8 \text{ m/s}} = 2.0 \times 10^{-6} \text{ V} \cdot \text{s/m}^2.$$

We know that 1 V $= 1$ N $\cdot$ m/C, so 1 V $\cdot$ s/m$^2 = 1$ N $\cdot$ s/C $\cdot$ m. We also know that the unit of magnetic field is the tesla, where 1 T $= 1$ N $\cdot$ s/m $\cdot$ C. So the magnitude of the magnetic field is $B = 2.0 \times 10^{-6}$ T, and if we include its direction the result is

$$\vec{B}(z, t) = (2.0 \times 10^{-6} \text{ T}) \sin[(9.0 \text{ m}^{-1})z - (2.7 \times 10^9 \text{ s}^{-1})t]\hat{\jmath}. ✔$$

❹ EVALUATE RESULT The values we calculated in part *a* lie in the range between commercial radio waves and microwaves and satisfy $c_0 = \lambda f$. In part *b* our calculated magnetic field magnitude is about $1/25$ the magnitude of Earth's magnetic field near the equator. The electric field magnitude of this wave is about six times the magnitude of typical atmospheric electric fields, 100 V/m. Thus the results we obtained are not unreasonable.

Guided Problem 30.2 Electric from magnetic

The magnetic field vector of a planar electromagnetic wave is given by

$$\vec{B}(y, t) = B \cos(ky + \omega t)\hat{k},$$

where $B = 2.0 \times 10^{-5}$ T, $\omega = 3.0 \times 10^9$ s^{-1}, and $\hat{k}$ is the unit vector in the z direction. What are (*a*) the value of the wave number k and (*b*) the expression for the magnitude and direction of the electric field associated with this magnetic field?

❶ GETTING STARTED

1. Is the approach used in Worked Problem 30.1 useful here?
2. In which direction is the wave traveling?
3. Along which axis does the direction of the magnetic field oscillate?

❷ DEVISE PLAN

4. How is the wave number k related to the angular frequency ω?

5. Along which axis does the electric field oscillate?
6. How are the magnitudes of the electric and magnetic fields related?
7. You should now be able to write an expression for the electric field.

❸ EXECUTE PLAN

8. Calculate the value of k.
9. Write an expression for the wave's electric-field component.
10. What is the magnitude of the electric field?
11. Do you have the correct units for the electric field?

❹ EVALUATE RESULT

12. How do your values for E and B compare with the magnitude of Earth's magnetic field near the equator and the magnitude of a typical atmospheric electric field, which is about 100 V/m?

PRACTICE

Worked Problem 30.3 Antenna reach

A certain type of FM radio receiver requires a minimum radio signal with a root-mean-square electric field magnitude of 1.2×10^{-2} N/C to operate. How far from a radio station broadcasting its electromagnetic signal at an average power of 100 kW can this receiver be used?

❶ GETTING STARTED We are given the power at which a radio station broadcasts its signal, 100 kW, and we must calculate the distance from the emitting antenna to the position at which the electric-field portion of the electromagnetic waves has a root-mean-square magnitude of 1.2×10^{-2} N/C. We begin by assuming that the waves are broadcast uniformly in all directions, which allows us to model the power at any instant as being distributed on a spherical surface. Thus the distance we seek is the radius r of the sphere at the position where $E_{rms} = 1.2 \times 10^{-2}$ N/C.

❷ DEVISE PLAN We can use Eq. 30.38 to obtain the relationship between the area of any spherical surface through which the waves pass and the average power and average intensity of the waves. Thus from $A_{sphere} = 4\pi r^2$ we can obtain a value for r, the distance we seek. In order to use Eq. 30.38, however, we must know the average intensity of the waves, so our first step should be to calculate that value from Eq. 30.40, $S_{av} = E_{rms} B_{rms} / \mu_0$.

❸ EXECUTE PLAN Substituting E_{rms}/c_0 for B_{rms} in Eq. 30.40, we get for the average intensity

$$S_{av} = \frac{E_{rms}^2}{\mu_0 c_0} = \frac{(1.2 \times 10^{-2} \, \text{N/C})^2}{(4\pi \times 10^{-7} \, \text{N} \cdot \text{s}^2/\text{C}^2)(3.0 \times 10^8 \, \text{m/s})}$$

$$= 3.8 \times 10^{-7} \, \text{N/m} \cdot \text{s}.$$

Recall that 1 W = 1 N·m/s, so $S_{av} = 3.8 \times 10^{-7}$ W/m². The time-average version of Eq. 30.38 is

$$P_{av} = \int \vec{S}_{av} \cdot d\vec{A} = S_{av} 4\pi r^2.$$

Therefore the distance r at which $E_{rms} = 1.2 \times 10^{-2}$ N/C is

$$r = \sqrt{\frac{P_{av}}{4\pi S_{av}}} = \sqrt{\frac{1.0 \times 10^5 \, \text{W}}{(4\pi)(3.8 \times 10^{-7} \, \text{W/m}^2)}} = 1.4 \times 10^5 \, \text{m.} \checkmark$$

❹ EVALUATE RESULT Our result—about 100 miles—is close to the distance at which FM stations fade out when we are driving across the country and therefore in agreement with our experience.

Guided Problem 30.4 Beam from outer space

A spacecraft 120 AU above Earth (1 AU = 1 astronomical unit = 1.5×10^8 km) has a 20-W directional dish antenna emitting at 8.0 GHz (Figure WG30.1). This emitting antenna is aimed at a 34-m-diameter receiving antenna located on Earth. Suppose you want the signal to have a root-mean-square electric field magnitude of 1.0×10^{-3} V/m at the receiving dish on Earth's surface. What must the beam width angle θ be?

Figure WG30.1

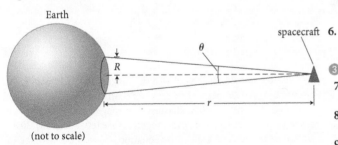

(not to scale)

❶ GETTING STARTED

1. How does a directional antenna differ from an antenna that emits waves equally in all directions?
2. What assumptions should you make about how the power is emitted directionally?
3. Assume the signal projects to a circular area on Earth's surface. Draw a diagram showing how the beam width is related to the radius R of that circular area and to r, the distance from the spacecraft to Earth.

❷ DEVISE PLAN

4. How can you calculate the average intensity of the signal's electromagnetic waves?
5. What relationship can you use to determine the maximum area on Earth that the signal is directed toward in order to be detected? What relationship can you use to determine the maximum area on Earth's surface that the beam can cover and still be detectable?
6. How can you determine the maximum beam width once you know the maximum area that the signal should cover on Earth?

❸ EXECUTE PLAN

7. Calculate the maximum intensity associated with the signal root-mean-square electric field magnitude.
8. Calculate the maximum area on Earth's surface that the beam can cover and still be detectable.
9. Calculate the radius R of the circular area on Earth's surface covered by the signal.
10. Use your values for R and r and your diagram from step 3 to obtain the beam width angle.

❹ EVALUATE RESULT

11. With the beam angle you calculated, do you think the 34-m-diameter receiving antenna can detect the signal?

Worked Problem 30.5 Discharge radiation

A capacitor consists of two circular parallel plates of radius R = 150 mm separated by distance d = 20 mm. The initial magnitude of the charge on the capacitor is $q_0 = 9.0 \times 10^{-8}$ C, and after discharge is initiated, it discharges via a steady current I = 3.0 mA. What is the power that crosses the closed cylindrical surface surrounding the space between the plates 2.0×10^{-5} s after discharge begins?

① GETTING STARTED We begin with a sketch showing the discharging capacitor and a few of the associated electric and magnetic field lines (Figure WG30.2). The closed cylindrical surface surrounding the space between the capacitor plates consists of two end faces, one coinciding with each plate, and a curved surface that joins the end faces and encloses the space between the plates. Because the distance between the plates is small relative to the radius of the plates, we assume that at any instant t, the charge $q(t)$ on the plates is uniformly distributed and the electric field $\vec{E}(t)$ is uniform between the plates (that is, we ignore edge effects). We show this uniform field in our sketch. While the capacitor is discharging, the magnitude of $\vec{E}$ is decreasing, and therefore there is a displacement current I that points in the direction of $\Delta\vec{E}$, which is opposite the direction of $\vec{E}$.

Figure WG30.2

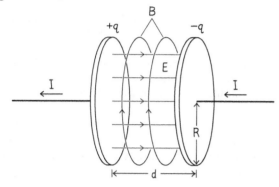

While the electric field is changing, there is an associated magnetic field $\vec{B}(t)$ between the plates, and we know that the magnetic field lines form circular loops. We determine the direction of these loops by applying the right-hand current rule to the displacement current and add the loops to our Figure WG30.2.

At each location in the space between the plates, the electric and magnetic fields are perpendicular to each other. Because the electric field is decreasing, the energy stored in this field is also decreasing. Using our drawing and this information, we must determine, at $t = 2.0 \times 10^{-5}$ s, the power P that crosses the closed cylindrical surface defined by the capacitor volume.

② DEVISE PLAN In order to calculate P, we must determine the flux of the Poynting vector (Eq. 30.38). We know from Eq. 30.37 that this vector is proportional to $\vec{E} \times \vec{B}$, and so we must determine the magnitudes of the electric and magnetic fields between the plates. We can use Gauss's law (Eq. 30.10) to obtain E, which depends on the charge on the plates. Because the current is steady, we can determine the charge on the plates as a function of time. After we use Eq. 30.8 to determine B, we can calculate the flux of the Poynting vector on the closed cylindrical surface and obtain the power that crosses the surface.

③ EXECUTE PLAN Figure WG30.3 shows a circle of radius R that is centered on and perpendicular to the line passing through the centers of the two circular plates. Consider a point Z lying on this circle. Our first task is to use Gauss's law to calculate the magnitude of $\vec{E}(t)$ at Z. We choose as our Gaussian surface the closed cylinder shown in Figure WG30.4a. Note that the cylinder lies partly inside the space between the capacitor plates and partly outside that space and that Z lies on the end face that is in the space between the plates, as shown in Figure WG30.4b. In this space, there is nonzero

Figure WG30.3

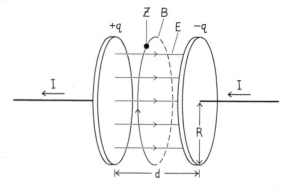

flux only through this end face. Thus with $A_{endface}$ as the face area, Gauss's law, $\Phi_E = \oint \vec{E} \cdot d\vec{A} = q_{enc}/\epsilon_0$ (Eq. 24.8), becomes

$$EA_{endface} = \frac{\sigma A_{endface}}{\epsilon_0} = \frac{q(t)A_{endface}}{\pi R^2 \epsilon_0}$$

$$E(t) = \frac{q(t)}{\pi R^2 \epsilon_0}. \tag{1}$$

Figure WG30.4

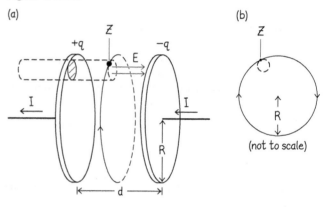

(not to scale)

We now use Eq. 30.8 to obtain the magnitude of $\vec{B}(t)$ at Z. We choose as our (Ampèrian) integration path the circle of radius R shown in Figure WG30.3. Because the magnitude B is constant along this integration path, the integral on the left side of Eq. 30.8 is $B(2\pi R)$. On the right side of the equation, $I_{int} = 0$ because the integration path defines an open surface, a disk of radius R, and there is no current through the disk. Because the electric field is uniform, its flux is $\Phi_E = E(\pi R^2)$, so the magnitude of the displacement current is, from Eq. 30.7,

$$I_{disp} = \epsilon_0 \frac{dE}{dt}\pi R^2.$$

Substituting Eq. 1 for E gives us

$$I_{disp} = \epsilon_0 \frac{d}{dt}\left[\frac{q(t)}{\pi R^2 \epsilon_0}\right]\pi R^2 = \frac{dq(t)}{dt}.$$

Because the current is steady and the charge is decreasing, the steady current $I = -dq(t)/dt$. Thus the magnitude of the displacement current is equal to the magnitude of the steady current. Therefore Eq. 30.8 becomes $B(2\pi R) = \mu_0 I$, and we have

$$B = \frac{\mu_0 I}{2\pi R}. \tag{2}$$

We now apply Eq. 30.37 to calculate the magnitude and direction of the Poynting vector $\vec{S}(t)$ at point Z. Because point Z could be chosen on any circle inside the capacitor, the expression for the Poynting vector should be general. Applying the right-hand rule for the vector product $\vec{E} \times \vec{B}$ in Figure WG30.5a, we see that the direction of the vector product points away from the curved part of the closed cylinder—that is, radially outward at Z in Figure WG30.5b. This is therefore the direction of $\vec{S}$. From Eqs. 1 and 2, the magnitude is

$$S(t) = \frac{1}{\mu_0} EB = \frac{q(t)}{\pi R^2 \epsilon_0} \frac{I}{2\pi R}.$$

Figure WG30.5

(a)   (b)

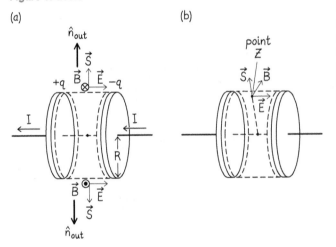

Note that the Poynting vector is directed radially outward at each point inside the capacitor, so energy will not cross the flat ends of the cylindrical space. The power that crosses the curved part of our closed cylindrical surface can be computed using Eq. 30.38. For a closed surface, we always choose $\hat{n}_{out}$ as the outward-pointing normal to the surface. Because $\vec{S}(t)$ points outward on all portions of our curved surface, the only thing we need to do is multiply S by the area of that curved surface, $A = 2\pi Rd$. The power that crosses the surface is then

$$P(t) = S(t)A = \frac{q(t)}{\pi R^2 \epsilon_0} \frac{I}{2\pi R} 2\pi Rd = \frac{q(t)I}{\pi R^2 \epsilon_0} d.$$

Because the current is steady, the charge on the plates as a function of time is given by $q(t) = q_0 - It$. Therefore the power that crosses the curved part of our closed cylindrical surface as a function of time is given by

$$P(t) = \frac{(q_0 - It)I}{\pi R^2 \epsilon_0} d,$$

and at $t = 2.0 \times 10^{-5}$ s the power is

$$P = \frac{[(9.0 \times 10^{-8}\,\text{C}) - (3.0 \times 10^{-3}\,\text{A})(2.0 \times 10^{-5}\,\text{s})]}{\pi (0.150\,\text{m})^2 (8.85 \times 10^{-12}\,\text{C}^2/\text{N} \cdot \text{m}^2)}$$

$$\times (3.0 \times 10^{-3}\,\text{A})(2.0 \times 10^{-2}\,\text{m}) = 2.9\,\text{W}. ✔$$

④ **EVALUATE RESULT** In *Principles* Example 30.10, a parallel-plate capacitor with circular plates of radius $R = 0.10$ m, plate separation distance $d = 0.10$ mm, and a steady charging current of 1.0 A had $(3.6 \times 10^8\,\text{W/s})\Delta t$ of power crossing into the cylindrical space between the plates. For that capacitor, therefore, the power at $\Delta t = 2.0 \times 10^{-5}$ s would be 7.2×10^3 W. From Example 30.10, we know that the power is proportional to I^2 and to d and inversely proportional to R^2. Using that relationship for our capacitor, where $I_{discharging} = 3.0$ mA, $R = 150$ mm, and $d = 20$ mm, we expect a power of

$$\frac{P_{discharging}(\Delta t = 2.0 \times 10^{-5}\,\text{s})}{P_{charging}(\Delta t = 2.0 \times 10^{-5}\,\text{s})} =$$

$$\frac{(q_0 - I_{discharging}\Delta t)I_{discharging}}{(I_{charging}\Delta t)I_{charging}} \frac{d_{discharging}}{d_{charging}} \frac{(R_{charging})^2}{(R_{discharging})^2}$$

$$P_{discharging}(\Delta t = 2.0 \times 10^{-5}\,\text{s}) =$$

$$(7.2 \times 10^3\,\text{W}) \frac{(3.0 \times 10^{-8}\,\text{C})}{(2.0 \times 10^{-5}\,\text{C})} \frac{(3.0 \times 10^{-3}\,\text{A})}{(1.0\,\text{A})}$$

$$\times \frac{(20\,\text{mm})}{(0.10\,\text{mm})} \frac{(0.10\,\text{m})^2}{(0.150\,\text{m})^2} = 2.9\,\text{W},$$

in excellent agreement with our result.

Guided Problem 30.6 Charge it!

A capacitor consists of two circular parallel plates, each with a radius $R = 200$ mm, separated by a distance $d = 15$ mm (Figure WG30.6). A steady current charges the capacitor for a time interval $\Delta t = 7.7 \times 10^{-6}$ s. During this time interval, the maximum magnitude of the magnetic field between the plates is $B_{max} = 1.2 \times 10^{-8}$ T. What is the maximum power that crosses the closed cylindrical surface surrounding the space between the plates?

Figure WG30.6

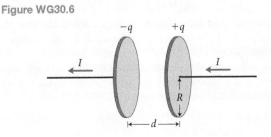

① GETTING STARTED

1. What quantities do you need to know in order to determine the maximum power that crosses the closed cylindrical surface that defines the space between the plates?
2. Which of these quantities are given in the problem statement?

② DEVISE PLAN

3. Which Maxwell equation gives you a relationship between the current and B_{max}?
4. Along what closed path does the magnetic field have its maximum magnitude?
5. Which Maxwell equation allows you to determine the maximum value of the electric field magnitude, E_{max}?
6. What is the relationship between the current and q_{max}, the maximum value of the charge on the capacitor plates?

7. How do you calculate the maximum power that crosses into the space between the plates?

③ EXECUTE PLAN

8. Write an expression for the current.
9. Write an expression for q_{max}.
10. Write an expression for E_{max}.
11. Determine the direction of the Poynting vector, and write an expression for the maximum value of the magnitude of the Poynting vector.
12. Determine the maximum value of the power that crosses the cylindrical surface.

④ EVALUATE RESULT

13. Does your value for the steady current seem reasonable?
14. Does your value for P_{max} seem reasonable?

Worked Problem 30.7 Solenoid antenna

The solenoid of Figure WG30.7 has radius $a = 0.10$ m and height $h = 0.60$ m. The current is decreasing as $I(t) = I_0 - bt$, where $I_0 = 0.40$ A and $b = 0.200$ A/s, and the current direction is as shown in the figure. If the solenoid has $N = 500$ windings, at what rate is electromagnetic energy leaving the cylindrical space inside the solenoid at $t = 1.0$ s?

Figure WG30.8

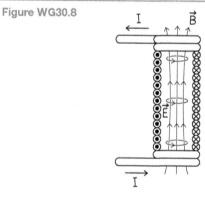

Figure WG30.7

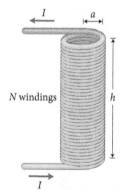

N windings

① GETTING STARTED The solenoid has N/h windings per unit of height, and the current in the solenoid is decreasing. While the current is decreasing, the magnetic field inside the solenoid is decreasing. This changing magnetic field is accompanied by an electric field. Because the magnetic field is decreasing, we expect electromagnetic energy to leave the inside of the solenoid, and our task is to determine the rate at which this energy leaves.

We can ignore edge effects because the height of the solenoid is much greater than its radius. We know from Section 28.6 that the magnetic field inside the solenoid is uniform and directed along the long (vertical) axis of the solenoid. The electric field forms circular loops centered on this axis, and at each location inside the solenoid, the electric and magnetic fields are perpendicular to each other. This information is illustrated in Figure WG30.8.

② DEVISE PLAN The rate at which electromagnetic energy leaves the cylindrical space inside the solenoid—the power—is given by the flux of the Poynting vector through the curved surface of the solenoid. Energy leaves the space inside the solenoid, and from this we know the direction of the Poynting vector—parallel to the end faces of the cylinder and directed outward, away from the long central axis.

We can use Eq. 30.36 to calculate the magnitude of the Poynting vector. In order to use this equation, we must know the magnitudes E and B. We can use the Eq. 30.12 form of Faraday's law to calculate E. Because the current decreases linearly with time, the rate of change of the magnetic flux in the solenoid, $d\Phi_B/dt$, is constant and therefore the electric field magnitude is constant. Thus there is no displacement current associated with the electric field. This means Eq. 30.6, the generalized form of Ampère's law, $\oint B \cdot d\ell = \mu_0 I_{int} + \mu_0\epsilon_0(d\Phi_E/dt)$, reduces to Eq. 28.1, so we can use the latter to calculate the magnetic field magnitude.

To determine the power, we must integrate the Poynting vector over the cylindrical surface just surrounding the space inside the solenoid. Because the electric and magnetic fields are perpendicular to each other, tangent to and uniform over this surface, the power is the product of the Poynting vector magnitude and the area of the cylindrical surface.

3 **EXECUTE PLAN** We begin with Ampère's law with no displacement current, $\oint \vec{B} \cdot d\vec{\ell} = \mu_0 I_{enc}$ (Eq. 28.1), where $d\vec{\ell}$ is a small segment of the Ampèrian path of length ℓ shown in Figure WG30.9. The direction of integration is clockwise. The magnetic field is zero outside the solenoid and points upward inside, so the left side of Eq. 28.1 is $\oint \vec{B} \cdot d\vec{\ell} = B\ell$. In the region of the solenoid we've chosen for our Ampèrian path, the current is into the plane of the page, so $I_{enc} = (N/h)\ell I$. Therefore the magnitude of the magnetic field is

$$B\ell = \frac{\mu_0 NI(t)\ell}{h} \Rightarrow B(t) = \frac{\mu_0 N(I_0 - bt)}{h}. \tag{1}$$

Figure WG30.9

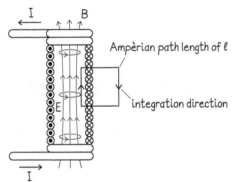

Ampèrian path length of ℓ

integration direction

Next, to obtain an expression for E, we apply the Eq. 30.12 form of Faraday's law, $\oint \vec{E} \cdot d\vec{\ell} = -d\Phi_B/dt$. This time $d\vec{\ell}$ represents a small segment of the circumference ℓ of the closed path of radius r shown in Figure WG30.10. Again we integrate clockwise (as viewed from below). The changing magnetic flux is

$$\frac{d\Phi_B}{dt} = \frac{dB}{dt}\pi r^2,$$

and we can use Eq. 1 to rewrite this equation in the form

$$-\frac{d\Phi_B}{dt} = -\frac{\mu_0 N\pi r^2}{h}\frac{d(I_0 - bt)}{dt} = \frac{\mu_0 N\pi r^2 b}{h}.$$

Because the electric field forms circular loops, the line integral of the electric field around this closed path is $\oint \vec{E} \cdot d\vec{\ell} = E2\pi r$. Therefore Faraday's law implies that the magnitude of the electric field is

$$E2\pi r = \frac{\mu_0 N\pi r^2 b}{h} \Rightarrow E = \frac{\mu_0 Nrb}{2h}. \tag{2}$$

Figure WG30.10

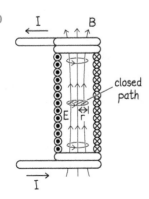

closed path

Because the sign of the electric field is positive in Eq. 2, the direction of the electric field is the same as the integration direction.

Now we have all we need to determine the rate at which electromagnetic energy leaves the region inside the solenoid. We do this by calculating the flux of the Poynting vector through the cylindrical surface of the solenoid, where $r = a$. First we check the direction of the Poynting vector by determining the direction of $\vec{E} \times \vec{B}$, which points radially away from the center of the solenoid. We now use Eqs. 1 and 2 in Eq. 30.36 to calculate the magnitude of the Poynting vector:

$$S(r = a) = \frac{1}{\mu_0}EB = \frac{\mu_0 N^2 ab(I_0 - bt)}{2h^2}.$$

To determine the power at $t = 1.0$ s, we multiply S by the area of the curved surface of the cylinder, $2\pi ah$:

$$P = 2\pi ahS(r = a) = \frac{\mu_0 N^2 b(I_0 - bt)}{h}\pi a^2$$

$$= \frac{(4\pi \times 10^{-7}\,\text{N} \cdot \text{s}^2/\text{C}^2)(500)^2(0.200\,\text{A/s})}{(0.60\,\text{m})}$$

$$\times \left[0.40\,\text{A} - (0.200\,\text{A/s})(1.0\,\text{s}) \right]\pi(0.10\,\text{m})^2$$

$$= 6.6 \times 10^{-4}\,\text{W.} \checkmark$$

4 **EVALUATE RESULT** This is a very small rate of energy leaving the solenoid. We have no clear standard of comparison for this value for the power. However, we expect that the electromagnetic energy leaving the cylindrical space inside the solenoid is equal to the time rate of change of the magnetic field energy stored in the space. The energy density of the magnetic field is given by Eq. 30.28, $u_B = B^2/2\mu_0$. Because the magnetic field is uniform, the energy U^B stored in it is the product of the energy density and the volume $\pi a^2 h$ of the cylindrical space:

$$U^B = \frac{B^2}{2\mu_0}\pi a^2 h = \frac{\mu_0 N^2 (I_0 - bt)^2}{2h^2}\pi a^2 h.$$

The time rate of change of the stored magnetic energy is thus

$$\frac{dU^B}{dt} = \frac{d}{dt}\left[\frac{\mu_0 N^2 (I_0 - bt)^2}{2h}\pi a^2 \right] = -\frac{\mu_0 N^2 b(I_0 - bt)}{h}\pi a^2.$$

This expression has the same magnitude as the one we obtained for P, the rate at which electromagnetic energy leaves the solenoid, giving us confidence that our calculation is correct. The minus sign makes sense because energy is leaving the solenoid interior and hence the stored energy decreases.

Guided Problem 30.8 Coiled again!

The solenoid in Figure WG30.7 has N windings, radius a, and height $h \gg a$. The current through the windings is given by $I(t) = bt$, where b is a positive constant and has units of amperes per second. At what rate does electromagnetic energy cross the cylindrical surface defined by the windings? In which direction is this energy transfer?

① GETTING STARTED

1. How does the situation in this solenoid differ from the situation in Worked Problem 30.7?
2. Do you have enough information to determine the magnitude and direction of the electric and magnetic fields inside the solenoid? Are any assumptions needed?
3. Make a sketch of the solenoid, showing the current direction and the directions you've determined or assumed for $\vec{E}$ and $\vec{B}$.

② DEVISE PLAN

4. What is a convenient generic location to choose in order to write an expression for the magnitudes of $\vec{B}(t)$ and $\vec{E}(t)$?
5. What equation can you use to calculate the direction and magnitude of $\vec{B}(t)$?
6. What equation can you use to determine $\vec{E}(t)$?
7. How can you determine the direction and magnitude of $\vec{S}(t)$?
8. What equation can you use to determine the power?

③ EXECUTE PLAN

④ EVALUATE RESULT

9. Write an expression for the energy stored in the magnetic field at instant t.
10. What is the time derivative of the stored magnetic energy?

Questions and Problems

For instructor-assigned homework, go to MasteringPhysics® (MP)

Dots indicate difficulty level of problems: • = easy, •• = intermediate, ••• = hard; CR = context-rich problem.

Unless directed otherwise, use $c_0 = 3.0 \times 10^8$ m/s for the speed of electromagnetic waves traveling in vacuum.

30.1 Magnetic fields accompany changing electric fields

1. The magnitude of the electric field of Figure P30.1 is changing with time. As a result of this change, there is an upward-pointing magnetic field at position P. Is the electric field magnitude increasing or decreasing? •

Figure P30.1

2. Figure P30.2 shows two electric fields, one in a region of circular cross-section and one in a long flat region. In both cases, the electric field decreases over time. What is the direction of the accompanying magnetic field in each case? •

Figure P30.2

3. A parallel-plate capacitor is charged until it carries charge $+q$ on one plate and charge $-q$ on the other plate. The capacitor is then disconnected from the power supply and isolated. What is the direction of the magnetic field that surrounds the charged capacitor? •

4. The uniform electric field shown in Figure P30.4 points out of the page and is contained in a cylindrical volume of space. If the electric field is rapidly turned off, a magnetic field is produced. (a) What is the direction of this magnetic field? (b) Does this magnetic field exist only in the volume where the electric field exists, only outside that volume, or both inside and outside that volume? ••

Figure P30.4

5. The capacitor of Figure P30.5 is being charged by a steady current I. What are the directions of (a) the electric field between the plates, (b) the change in the electric field, and (c) the magnetic field between the plates? ••

Figure P30.5

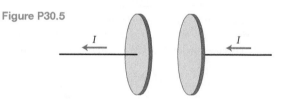

6. Figure P30.6 shows an increasing magnetic field and the electric field that accompanies it according to Faraday's law. If the magnetic field is increasing at an increasing rate, (a) is the electric field magnitude constant, increasing, or decreasing? (b) Does the behavior of the electric field produce an additional magnetic field? If so, what is the direction of the additional magnetic field? Does it reinforce or counteract the original magnetic field? ••

Figure P30.6

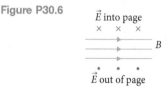

30.2 Fields of moving charged particles

7. Are the radiating electric field lines around a charged particle straight lines when the particle (*a*) is stationary, (*b*) moves at constant velocity, (*c*) accelerates? •

8. Which field line patterns in Figure P30.8 could represent (*a*) electric field lines and (*b*) magnetic field lines? •

Figure P30.8

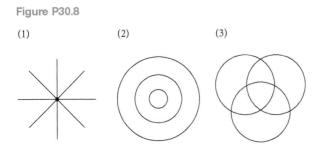

(1) (2) (3)

9. Would a charged particle moving at a high speed in a circle create kinks in its electric field? •

10. A positively charged particle moving to the right is stopped rapidly. Sketch the resultant radiated pulse. ••

11. Is any type of electric field produced when (*a*) a wire having zero surplus charge carries a constant current, (*b*) a wire having zero surplus charge carries a time-varying current, (*c*) a bar magnet moves translationally at constant velocity, (*d*) a bar magnet rotates about an axis that passes symmetrically through its poles? ••

12. Is any magnetic field produced when (*a*) a uniformly charged sphere rotates at constant rotational speed about an axis that passes through its fixed center, (*b*) a charged particle moves translationally at constant velocity, (*c*) a charged particle that is moving translationally accelerates? ••

13. Sketch the electric and magnetic field line patterns produced by the four situations shown in Figure P30.13: (*a*) a stationary charged rod carrying a linear charge density of $+\lambda$, (*b*) a charged rod carrying a linear charge density of $+\lambda$ that moves at constant velocity along the length of the rod, (*c*) a stationary charged rod carrying a linear charge density of $+\lambda$ that is infinitesimally close to a parallel stationary charged rod carrying a linear charge density of $-\lambda$, (*d*) a charged rod carrying a linear charge density of $+\lambda$ that moves at constant velocity along the length of rod and is infinitesimally close to a parallel charged rod carrying a linear charge density of $-\lambda$ and moving in the opposite direction. ••

Figure P30.13

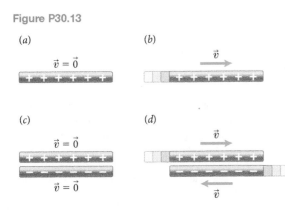

(*a*) $\vec{v} = \vec{0}$

(*b*) $\vec{v}$

(*c*) $\vec{v} = \vec{0}$

(*d*) $\vec{v}$ $\vec{v} = \vec{0}$ $\vec{v}$

30.3 Oscillating dipoles and antennas

14. What antenna length should be used to create a dipole antenna that emits 100-MHz electromagnetic waves, a frequency typical of FM radio broadcasts? •

15. An electromagnetic wave is traveling eastward. If at a given instant the magnetic field for one section of the wave points south, in which direction does the electric field for that section point at that instant? •

16. An electric dipole with its center located at the origin of a Cartesian coordinate system oscillates along the *x* axis, creating an electromagnetic wave. At a position on the *z* axis far from the origin, (*a*) what is the polarization of the wave and (*b*) which axis are the magnetic field lines parallel to? ••

17. Figure P30.17 shows a magnetic field line pattern radiating from an oscillating electric dipole. (*a*) What is the direction of the change, over the next infinitesimal time interval, in the magnetic field at P? (*b*) Use your answer to part *a* to determine the direction of the electric field loop around P. (*c*) Is the dipole oscillating right-left, up-down, or in-out of the page? ••

Figure P30.17

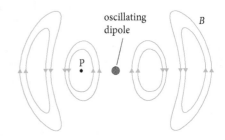

oscillating dipole

P

B

18. A router used for wireless Internet access follows the 802.11g standard, which operates at 2.4 GHz. (*a*) What is the wavelength of the electromagnetic waves emitted by the router? (*b*) How tall would a dipole antenna need to be? Is this length comparable to the length of any router antennas you've seen? ••

19. Why are radio transmission towers oriented vertically rather than laid horizontally on the ground? ••

20. To detect an incoming planar electromagnetic wave, we observe a single charged particle that begins at rest and is free to move only in the *xy* plane. If we observe the particle oscillating along the *y* axis, with no motion along the *x* axis, what can we say about the direction of the electric and magnetic fields and the direction of wave propagation? ••

21. In Figure P30.21, a charged particle has been suddenly accelerated downward, producing the electric field line pattern shown. When the kinks in the field lines reach the metal rod at the left, they produce a downward current in the rod. Is the particle that has been accelerated positively or negatively charged? ••

Figure P30.21

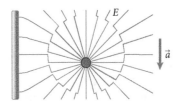

E

$\vec{a}$

22. As we saw in *Principles* Checkpoint 30.9, a receiving dipole antenna has to be aligned with the oscillating electric field in order to produce a measurable potential difference in the antenna. What if we wanted to detect the potential difference caused by the changing magnetic field? (*a*) What antenna shape would we need? (*b*) How would this antenna need to be oriented relative to the wave in order to maximize its ability to detect the wave? (*c*) Use Faraday's law to explain whether this antenna is a better detector for low-frequency waves or for high-frequency waves. ●●●

30.4 Displacement current

23. A parallel-plate capacitor with circular plates has a steady charging current of 5.0 A. The wires into and out of the plates attach to the plate centers. If the radius of each plate is 40 mm and there is no dielectric between the plates, what is the magnetic field magnitude at a position that lies between the plates and is 30 mm from the (imaginary) line joining their centers? ●

24. A specified volume of space contains an electric field for which the magnitude is given by $E = E_0 \cos(\omega t)$. Suppose that $E_0 = 10 \text{ V/m}$ and $\omega = 1.0 \times 10^7 \text{ s}^{-1}$. (*a*) What is the maximum displacement current through a 0.50-m² cross-sectional area of this volume? (*b*) How would this area have to be oriented relative to the electric field to get this maximum displacement current? ●

25. Instead of a capacitor in a circuit, we can get the same effect by slicing a thick wire in two, making our cut perpendicular to the wire's long axis. If the wire diameter is 10.0 mm and we place the two parallel circular surfaces of the cut wire 0.010 mm apart, what is the magnetic field magnitude at a position that lies between the two surfaces and is 2.0 mm from the long central axis of the wire at the instant the current in the wire is 2.0 A? Assume the charge carriers that create the current are uniformly distributed over the cross-sectional area of the wire. ●●

26. A parallel-plate capacitor has a steady charging current of 5.0 A. What are (*a*) the time rate of change of the electric flux between the plates and (*b*) the displacement current between the plates? (*c*) How do your answers to parts *a* and *b* change if there is a dielectric for which $\kappa = 1.5$ between the plates? Assume the area of the plates is much greater than the separation distance between them. ●●

27. A parallel-plate capacitor is charging with constant current *I*. At some instant, $B = 1.6 \times 10^{-8} \text{ T}$ at a position that is 7.0 mm from the center of the wire leading to the capacitor. (*a*) Calculate the current magnitude at that instant. (*b*) Draw the current in the left plate to show why you get the same value of *B* no matter where you place the surface bounded by your Ampèrian path. Draw the lengths of your current arrows to scale to show how the current magnitude does or does not change at various positions in the plate. ●●

28. For a capacitor of capacitance *C*, show that the displacement current between the capacitor's plates is given by $C(dV/dt)$, where *V* is the potential difference across the capacitor. ●●

29. The circular plates of a parallel-plate capacitor have a radius of 30 mm. A steady 2.0-A current is charging the initially uncharged capacitor, and the surface charge on the plates is distributed uniformly. (*a*) Derive an expression for the magnitude of the electric field between the plates as a function of time. (*b*) In Figure P30.29*a*, the flat circular surface between the capacitor plates has a radius of 10 mm. What is the displacement current through this flat circular surface? (*c*) Consider the open surface shown in Figure P30.29*b*, a cylindrical shell open at the right end that passes through the left capacitor plate. If the radius of the flat circular end is 10 mm, what is the displacement current through the open shell? (*d*) Why is your answer to part *c* different from your answer to part *b*? Why are both these answers different from $I = 2.0$ A, the current through the capacitor? ●●

Figure P30.29

(*a*)

(*b*)

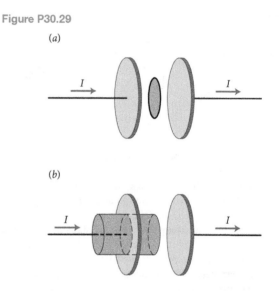

30. A short wire runs along an *x* axis from $x = a$ to $x = -a$ (Figure P30.30). At $t = 0$, there is a small sphere carrying charge $+q_0$ at $x = a$ and a small sphere carrying charge $-q_0$ at $x = -a$. As the spheres discharge and a current is established in the wire, show that, for $t > 0$, the generalized form of Ampère's law (Eq. 30.13) and the Biot-Savart law (Eq. 28.12) give the same result for the magnitude of the magnetic field a distance *b* up the *y* axis. (Hint: Obtain the electric flux through a circular disk in the *yz* plane, centered at the origin. Because the electric field is not constant over the surface of the disk, you must divide the disk into a nested set of rings of various radii and integrate. A representative ring should have radius *r* and radial extent *dr*.) ●●●

Figure P30.30

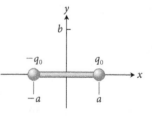

31. A parallel-plate capacitor has circular plates of radius $R = 0.300$ m and plate separation distance $d = 0.10$ mm. While it is charging, the potential difference across the plates is given by $V(t) = V_{max}(1 - e^{-t/\tau_0})$, where $V_{max} = 15$ V and $\tau_0 = 3.0$ ms. What is the magnitude of the magnetic field between the plates at a distance $r = 0.20$ m from the axis of the capacitor at $t = 1.30$ ms? ●●●

30.5 Maxwell's equations

32. When you use Maxwell's equations to determine electric and magnetic fields, a lot depends on making the "right" choice for the integration path. What happens if you choose the "wrong" path? Do the equations still hold? Consider a parallel-plate capacitor with circular plates, but use a rectangular integration path that has two sides parallel to the plates and two sides perpendicular to them, as in Figure P30.32. What do you get? ●

Figure P30.32

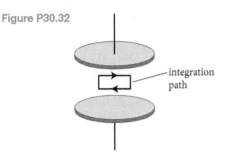

integration path

33. Using Eq. 30.11, show that the normal component of the magnetic field is continuous across any surface. ●●

34. In free space, Maxwell's equations simplify greatly. The two equations involving surface integrals of the fields (Eqs. 30.10 and 30.11) are zero, and the two equations involving line integrals of the fields (Eqs. 30.12 and 30.13) have values proportional to the rate of flux change of the other field. Because the fluxes are surface integrals of the fields, why don't all four equations reduce to zero? ●●

35. For a perfect conductor, $E = 0$ everywhere inside, and all the charge resides on the surface even when charge carriers are flowing. (a) Use Maxwell's equations to show that the magnetic field inside a conductor is constant. (b) Use Maxwell's equations to show that the magnetic flux through a perfect conducting loop is constant. (c) A superconductor is more than just a perfect conductor. It also has the property that $B = 0$ inside the superconductor. Use Maxwell's equations to show why the current in a superconductor is confined to the surface. ●●●

36. A physics teacher tries to build a device that illustrates Maxwell's generalization of Ampère's law. She drills a hole in the center of each plate of a parallel-plate capacitor and then runs a wire through the holes (Figure P30.36). There is no connection between the wire and the plates, and the potential difference across the plates can be controlled. Can the teacher adjust this potential difference so that there is no magnetic field at a distance r from the wire? In particular, what must be the rate of change of the potential difference if she wants no magnetic field at a distance $r = 20$ mm from the wire when it carries a steady current of 0.0200 A and the distance between the plates is $d = 3.0$ mm? ●●●

Figure P30.36

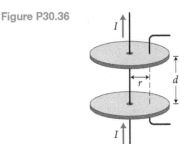

30.6 Electromagnetic waves

37. The frequency of AM radio channels is typically on the order of 10^5 Hz or 10^6 Hz. What is the wavelength of these waves? FM waves have wavelengths between 1.0 m and 10 m. What is the frequency of these waves? ●

38. The speed of light drops to 2.26×10^8 m/s in water. What is the dielectric constant of water? ●

39. The optical fibers used for telecommunications links have dielectric constant $\kappa = 1.6$. How long does a signal originating in California take to reach New York in a fiber-optic cable? ●

40. A phone call you make from the United States to Germany is routed via a satellite that is in a geostationary orbit at an altitude of 36,000 km. How long is the time interval between the instant you say "Hello" to the instant your greeting arrives in Germany? Ignore the distance between the United States and Germany. ●

41. The antenna of a WiFi access point has a length of about 80 mm. What does this say about the likely frequency of the wireless network? ●

42. (a) At a distance from an emitting antenna where the electric field has a maximum magnitude of 15 V/m when the air is dry, what is the maximum magnetic field magnitude? (b) How does the value of E_{max} change when the air is very damp, increasing the dielectric constant of the air? (c) How does the value of B_{max} change in the damp air? Assume that the antenna's potential difference is unaffected by the damp air. ●●

43. Using electromagnetic waves, you generally cannot resolve any structures that are smaller than the wavelength you are using. CD, DVD, and Blu-ray players use small "pits" that encode the 0s and 1s of the digital information stored on them—the smaller the pits, the more information you can store. A DVD can store 4.7 GB, and a Blu-ray can store 25 GB. If a DVD player typically uses lasers that emit red light in the wavelength range from 640 nm to 660 nm, what do you expect the wavelength and color of a Blu-ray laser to be? ●●

44. Blue light has a wavelength of 430 nm in vacuum. What is its wavelength after it enters a medium for which the dielectric constant $\kappa = 1.45$? ●●

45. *3K cosmic background radiation* is energy left over from events that occurred when the universe was in a very early stage of development. Given that the amount of energy associated with any radiation is linearly proportional to the radiation frequency and that the energy associated with a 10^6-Hz radio wave is 6.6×10^{-28} J, what is the frequency of the cosmic background radiation? Assume that the energy of this radiation can be approximated as $k_B T$, where $T = 3.0$ K (thus the name given to this radiation). ●●

46. If the electric field in an electromagnetic wave 100 mm from a radio-emitting antenna has a maximum magnitude of 6.0×10^5 V/m, what is the maximum magnetic field magnitude 500 m from the antenna? ●●

30.7 Electromagnetic energy

47. An electromagnetic wave has an average Poynting vector magnitude of 8.00×10^{-7} W/m². What is the maximum value of the magnitude of the electric field? ●

48. An electromagnetic wave has root-mean-square magnetic field magnitude $B_{rms} = 1.5 \times 10^{-6}$ T. What are the root-mean-square electric field magnitude and the average intensity of the wave? ●

49. The power of a laser is much smaller than the power of an incandescent light bulb, but the laser light does not spread out very much. Explain why this tendency not to spread has such an effect over long distances. •

50. A 1.0-mW laser has a beam radius of 0.6 mm. What is the intensity of this beam? •

51. The intensity of the HERCULES laser, one of the world's most powerful, is 2.0×10^{20} W/mm². Granted, the beam pulse lasts for only 30 fs, but if we assume the beam is an electromagnetic pulse, what is its average energy density, and what energy can one pulse deliver to a 1.0-μm² target? ••

52. Radio signals typically have a very small intensity. Imagine that a vehicle receives a signal of 10 μW/m². (a) What are the maximum magnitudes of the electric and magnetic fields? (b) If the tower emitting the radio waves is located 8.0 km away from the vehicle, how powerful is the emitting antenna? ••

53. For a constant current of 0.20 A, what time interval is required to deliver 1.0 MW of power to the space between the plates of a capacitor if the plates are circular and parallel, their diameter is 150 mm, and their separation distance is 0.200 mm? ••

54. Assume a 60-W incandescent light bulb radiates uniformly in all directions. At a distance of 2.0 m from the bulb, determine (a) the intensity of the electromagnetic waves, (b) the maximum electric field magnitude, and (c) the maximum magnetic field magnitude. ••

55. The emitting antenna of a 100-kW radio station radiates equally in all directions. What are the magnitudes E_{max} and B_{max} (a) 100 m from the antenna and (b) 50 km from the antenna? (c) For these two distances from the antenna, calculate the maximum potential difference caused between the ends of a receiving antenna that is 1.0 m long, assuming the antenna is aligned perfectly with the electric field of the radio wave. ••

56. A laser beam has a radius of 1.5 mm. How powerful does the laser have to be for the maximum magnitude of the magnetic field in the beam to be 5.0 μT? ••

57. Sunlight on Earth has an intensity of about $S = 1.0$ kW/m². How much power can be harvested from a solar energy panel that is 2.0 m long and 1.6 m wide if the sunlight comes in at an angle of $\theta = 20°$ with respect to the surface normal vector of the panel and the panel is 20% efficient? ••

58. You want to use your microwave oven to heat 0.20 L of water from room temperature to boiling. The water is in a cup that has a radius of 30 mm, and you want the water to reach its boiling point in 3.00 min. What are the required (a) average power, (b) average intensity, and (c) root-mean-square electric field of the microwaves? Assume all the microwaves come in from the top and are completely absorbed by the water. ••

59. The human eye can detect light intensities as small as $S_{min} = 10^{-12}$ W/m². If an incandescent 100-W light bulb is about 10% efficient, how far away could you see it under the simplest assumptions? Does your result make sense? ••

60. Similar to perceived loudness in hearing, the brightness the human eye and brain perceive for light is logarithmic rather than linear. For example, you do not perceive light that has an intensity of S as being twice as bright as light of intensity $S/2$. What happens to the perceived brightness of a light bulb if you double the distance from it? ••

61. The Poynting vector for an electromagnetic wave is given by (100 W/m²) $\sin^2[(1000 \text{ m}^{-1})z - (3.0 \times 10^{11} \text{ s}^{-1})t]\hat{k}$. What

are (a) the wave's propagation direction and (b) the time-averaged energy per unit time radiated through a 1.0-m² surface aligned with its normal parallel to the direction of propagation? (c) At an instant when the electric field is in the $+x$ direction, in what direction is the magnetic field? What are (d) the wavelength and frequency of this electromagnetic wave (you may need to review material in Chapter 16) and (e) the electric and magnetic field vectors, as a function of position and time? •••

62. A cylindrical solenoid of radius R and height h consists of N windings. There is a current through the windings, and this current increases with time as $I = \alpha t$, where α is a constant. (a) Describe the directions of the electric field, the magnetic field, and the Poynting vector. (b) Determine the magnitude of the Poynting vector at a radial distance $r = R$ from the center of the long center axis of the solenoid. (c) Use the result of part b to derive an expression for the power input to the solenoid as a function of time. (d) Using the formula for the inductance of an ideal solenoid, calculate the power from the rate of change of the stored magnetic energy. Does this answer agree with your answer in part c? •••

63. A polarizing filter is a plastic sheet that allows only certain components of the electric field in an electromagnetic wave to pass through, and a wave that has passed through such a filter is said to be *polarized*. After a wave has passed through the filter shown in Figure P30.63a, for instance, the wave's electric field contains only the vertical components of all the electric field vectors present before the wave passed through. Because the horizontal components have been blocked, the wave has lost half of its initial intensity. If this polarized wave then passes through the filter of Figure P30.63b, where the filter-polarizing direction is at an angle θ to the direction of the vertically polarized wave, the wave loses more of its intensity. If the polarized wave has an intensity $S_{before} = 200$ W/m² before passing through the filter of Figure P30.63b and $\theta = 20.0°$, what is the intensity after the wave passes through? •••

Figure P30.63

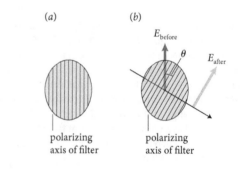

(a)   (b)

E_{before}

θ

E_{after}

polarizing axis of filter

polarizing axis of filter

Additional problems

64. Liquid argon has a dielectric constant of 1.5. What is the speed of an electromagnetic wave pulse through this medium? •

65. What needs to be the length of a half-wave antenna for a radio station that emits its signal at 90.5 MHz? •

66. Full-body scanners at airports are sometimes referred to as *millimeter-wave scanners* and sometimes as *terahertz scanners*. Does this make sense? •

67. A home microwave oven typically uses 2.45-GHz microwaves, and a microwave oven in a restaurant kitchen is more likely to run at 915 MHz. Calculate the wavelength for each frequency and the length of the emitting antenna needed in each case. •

68. A sinusoidal electromagnetic wave has a maximum electric field magnitude of $E_{max} = 500$ N/C. What is the root-mean-square value of the electric field? •

69. By focusing an ultraviolet laser pulse, you can produce an apparently hovering plasma point in midair. If it takes an electric field magnitude of 1.0×10^6 N/C to ionize air, what must the intensity of the pulse be? ••

70. For a particular electromagnetic wave, B_{rms} is 0.30×10^{-6} T. For this wave, calculate (a) E_{rms}, (b) the average energy density, and (c) the intensity. ••

71. A 500-W industrial carbon dioxide cutting laser is capable of cutting 3.0-mm thick steel at a rate of 20 mm/s. Carbon dioxide lasers operate at a wavelength of 10.6 μm. If the spot size of the cutting laser is 0.17 mm in diameter and the intensity is uniform in this spot, what are the magnitudes of the Poynting vector, the rms magnetic field, and the rms electric field for this laser? ••

72. A radio station sends out its signal via a 20-kW emitting antenna. Assuming the signal is emitted equally in all directions and no signal strength is lost, how much power per unit area remains in the signal at a location 10 km from the emitting antenna? ••

73. It takes sunlight about 8 min to travel from the Sun to Earth, where it has an average intensity of 1400 W/m². If it takes 44 min for light to travel from the Sun to Jupiter, what is the sunlight intensity there? ••

74. The intensity of sunlight striking Earth's upper atmosphere is approximately 1.35×10^3 W/m². (a) Calculate E_{max} and B_{max} at this location. (b) Given that Earth is 1.5×10^{11} m from the Sun, what is the power output of the Sun? (c) If all the sunlight that strikes the upper atmosphere reached Earth's surface, how many watts of power would reach Earth's surface?

(Hint: The Earth–Sun distance is so great that you can assume all the sunlight is perpendicular to the cross section of Earth.) ••

75. At a distance of 50 mm (about the distance from your ear to the center of your brain), the 824.6-MHz microwave radiation from a cell phone has an intensity of 35 W/m². The maximum permissible radiation leaking from a microwave oven at the same distance is 10 W/m². It occurs to you that you could estimate the average magnetic fields generated by the two devices. You also know that people concerned about the possible effects of cell phone radiation on the brain often use a Bluetooth headset, which has an intensity of 0.080 W/m² at a distance of 50 mm. But in this case the cell phone itself is probably near your waist—on a belt or in a pocket or purse. There must be an improvement in intensities and field magnitudes at the center of the brain or people would not do this. While contemplating these things, you realize that there may also be a concern that the wavelength of cell phone radiation is comparable to the size of the skull. ••• CR

76. Some people are concerned about "electromagnetic smog" and install meshes on their windows to absorb electromagnetic waves. A particular product advertises "50-dB attenuation in the range from 10 MHz to 3 GHz," with attenuation defined as

$$\text{attenuation (dB)} = 10 \log \left(\frac{\text{input intensity}}{\text{output intensity}} \right).$$

The meshes (sometimes called *Faraday cages* or *Faraday meshes*) generally work if the diameter of the holes is smaller than the wavelength of the radiation. You naturally wonder what this means in terms of reductions in the wave intensity and field strengths. However, it is also curious that the manufacturer advertises a frequency range, so you begin to think about the maximum mesh diameter allowed and whether a minimum is required. ••• CR

Answers to Review Questions

1. A changing electric field produces a magnetic field.

2. The magnetic field forms loops around the changing electric field. The direction of the magnetic field at any location can be found using the right-hand current rule by substituting the direction of $\Delta\vec{E}$ as the direction of "current."

3. Electric fields produced by charged particles are produced both by moving charged particles and by charged particles at rest; magnetic fields produced by charged particles are produced only when the particles are moving. Fields of either kind are produced by changing fields of the other kind.

4. Electric fields exert forces on charged particles, whether the particles are moving or at rest. Magnetic fields exert forces only on moving charged particles.

5. The main similarity occurs for fields whose source is a changing counterpart field: Magnetic field lines form closed loops around a changing electric field, and electric field lines form closed loops around a changing magnetic field. The main difference occurs for fields whose source is a charged particle: Magnetic field lines form closed loops around moving charged particles, but electric field lines do not; instead, electric field lines spread outward from positively charged particles and converge on negatively charged particles, whether moving or at rest.

6. The electric field is not spherically symmetrical. It is weakest along the line of the velocity and strongest in directions perpendicular to the velocity.

7. The extent of the asymmetry is determined by the particle's speed: The faster the particle moves, the more the field surrounding it deviates from spherical symmetry.

8. Kinks appear when the charged particle is accelerated. The kink in any given electric field line joins the part of the line created by the particle before acceleration began with the part of the field line created after the particle's velocity has changed.

9. An electromagnetic wave is made up of an electric field and a magnetic field.

10. The field lines near the dipole are directed from the positive pole to the negative pole and are connected to both poles. This is true in a region of space centered on the dipole and extending in all directions by the distance that changes in the electric field could have traveled since the last change in the dipole sources: $d = cT/2$, where $T/2$ is the interval from $t = T/2$ to $t = T$. The lines far from the dipole are unconnected to the dipole sources, but they reproduce the field that existed when the dipole had its original orientation. "Far from the dipole" means far enough that electric field changes could not have traveled to this region during the time interval since the first change in the dipole sources began—that is, in the interval T between $t = T$ and $t = 0$. Between these two regions the field is not that of a dipole. Rather, the field in this region must form closed loops because there are no charged sources in the region for field lines to begin or terminate on. These loops connect the "broken ends" of the dipolar fields in the near region and in the far region. This region contains a set of loops that are "disconnected" from the dipole sources. See *Principles* Figure 30.13.

11. The magnetic field is perpendicular to the electric field, and both are perpendicular to the direction in which the wave propagates.

12. *In phase* means that the two fields oscillate with the same frequency and simultaneously reach their maxima (or minima).

13. The polarization is defined to be the direction of the electric field of the wave, as seen by an observer looking along the direction of propagation.

14. An antenna is a conducting device that either emits or receives electromagnetic waves.

15. The oscillating current is created by applying across the antenna an alternating potential difference that drives charge carriers in the antenna back and forth. This oscillating motion of the carriers constitutes a current in the antenna.

16. A charging capacitor demonstrates that the Chapter 28 form of Ampère's law is incomplete. The Ampèrian path should encircle the wire leading to one of the plates, and the surface chosen to test the law should pass between the capacitor plates. The current through this surface is zero, so I_{int} for this surface is zero. There is a magnetic field between the plates, however, and so the Chapter 28 form of the law must be incomplete.

17. The generalized form of Ampère's law is $\oint \vec{B} \cdot d\vec{\ell} = \mu_0 I_{int} + \mu_0 \epsilon_0 (d\Phi_E/dt)$.

18. The term $\mu_0 I_{int}$ represents the contribution to $\oint \vec{B} \cdot d\vec{\ell}$ of any current intercepted by a surface spanning any chosen Ampèrian path. The term $\mu_0 \epsilon_0 (d\Phi_E/dt)$ represents the contribution to $\oint \vec{B} \cdot d\vec{\ell}$ of any changing electric flux through the surface.

19. Displacement current is not a current in the sense of being moving charge carriers. The name is given to the factor $\epsilon_0 (d\Phi_E/dt)$ in the generalized form of Ampère's law because this term is associated with a magnetic field in a region in which no charge carriers are moving. The name reminds us that we can use the right-hand *current* rule to determine the direction of the magnetic field associated with the changing electric field $\Delta\vec{E}$.

20. When a dielectric is present, the factor κ that represents the dielectric constant must be included in the displacement-current term: $\mu_0 \epsilon_0 \kappa (d\Phi_E/dt)$.

21. Equation 30.10, $\Phi_E = \oint \vec{E} \cdot d\vec{A} = (q_{enc}/\epsilon_0)$, is Gauss's law; Eq. 30.11, $\Phi_B = \oint \vec{B} \cdot d\vec{A} = 0$, is Gauss's law for magnetism; Eq. 30.12, $\oint \vec{E} \cdot d\vec{\ell} = -(d\Phi_B/dt)$, is a quantitative form of Faraday's law; and Eq. 30.13, $\oint \vec{B} \cdot d\vec{\ell} = \mu_0 I_{int} + \mu_0 \epsilon_0 (d\Phi_E/dt)$, is Maxwell's generalization of Ampère's law.

22. It is fitting because Maxwell was the first to recognize that—along with conservation of charge—these four expressions completely describe all electromagnetic phenomena.

23. Equation 30.10 (Gauss's law): From the experimentally determined inverse-square relationship between the electric forces two charged particles exert on each other and the distance between the particles, and from the result that in a steady state there is no surplus charge inside a hollow charged conductor. Equation 30.11 (Gauss's law for magnetism): from the observation that magnetic monopoles do not exist, an absence that guarantees zero magnetic flux through any closed surface. Equation 30.12 (Faraday's law): from experiments on electromagnetic induction. Equation 30.13 (generalized form of Ampère's law): from measurements of the force between current-carrying wires and from observations concerning electromagnetic waves.

24. Far from where the charge carrier was accelerated, the transverse part of the pulse looks like a three-dimensional slab that extends infinitely in two dimensions and has some small finite thickness in the third dimension. The slab moves away from the charge carrier along the direction corresponding to the dimension of finite thickness.

25. The ratio E/B equals the propagation speed c_0 of the pulse.

26. The ratio E/B equals the propagation speed c of the pulse, which equals the speed of light in vacuum divided by the square root of the dielectric constant.

27. In vacuum, the speed is equal to the reciprocal of the square root of these two constants: $c_0 = 1/\sqrt{\epsilon_0 \mu_0}$. In the dielectric, the speed is c_0 divided by the square root of the dielectric constant: $c = c_0/\sqrt{\kappa} = 1/\sqrt{\epsilon_0 \mu_0 \kappa}$.

28. The magnetic field, the electric field, and the velocity are perpendicular to one another. The direction of propagation is the same as the direction of $\vec{E} \times \vec{B}$.
29. No. In vacuum, electromagnetic waves of all frequencies travel at the same constant speed c_0.
30. The speed at which the wave travels is equal to the product of the wave's frequency and the wavelength, $f\lambda$.
31. From lowest to highest frequency, the names are radio waves, infrared, visible light, ultraviolet, x rays, and gamma rays.
32. The electric and magnetic energy densities are numerically equal to each other.
33. (a) $u = EB\sqrt{\epsilon_0/\mu_0}$; (b) $u = \epsilon_0 E^2$; (c) $u = B^2/\mu_0$
34. The Poynting vector is the vector product of the wave's electric field and magnetic field vectors divided by the magnetic constant. It represents the flow of energy per unit time per unit area in the wave.
35. The intensity is the magnitude of the wave's Poynting vector. For a planar electromagnetic wave, this magnitude is equal to the instantaneous electromagnetic power that crosses a unit area oriented perpendicular to the direction of $\vec{E} \times \vec{B}$.
36. The intensity of the wave equals the product of the wave's energy density and its speed: $S = uc_0$ (Eq. 30.35).

Answers to Guided Problems

Guided Problem 30.2 (a) $k = \dfrac{\omega}{c_0} = \dfrac{3.0 \times 10^9 \text{ s}^{-1}}{3.0 \times 10^8 \text{ m/s}} = 1.0 \times 10^1 \text{ m}^{-1}$;

(b) $\vec{E}(y, t) = (6.0 \times 10^3 \text{ V/m}) \cos[(1.0 \times 10^1 \text{ m}^{-1})y + (3 \times 10^9 \text{ s}^{-1})t]\hat{\imath}$

Guided Problem 30.4 $\theta = 5.4 \times 10^{-9}$ rad

Figure WGA_30.4

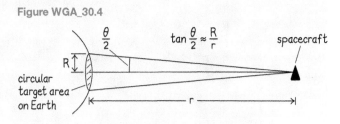

Guided Problem 30.6 $P_{max} = 15$ W

Guided Problem 30.8 $\dfrac{dU^B}{dt} = \dfrac{\mu_0 N^2}{h} b^2 t \pi a^2$; power crosses into the solenoid

31

PRACTICE
Electric Circuits

PRACTICE

Chapter Summary

The basic circuit (Section 31.1)

Concepts An **electric circuit** is an interconnection of electrical components (*circuit elements*). A **loop** is any closed conducting path through a circuit. A **power source** is any device that provides electric potential energy to an electric circuit. The potential difference across the terminals of the power source drives charge carriers through the circuit and thereby creates a current in the circuit. The **load** in an electric circuit is all the circuit elements connected to the power source. In the load, electric potential energy is converted to other forms of energy.

Quantitative Tools Standard representations of some common circuit elements used in circuit diagrams:

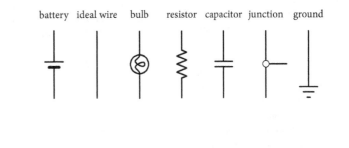

battery   ideal wire   bulb   resistor   capacitor   junction   ground

Current and resistance (Sections 31.2, 31.4, 31.5, 31.8)

Concepts A circuit is in **steady state** when the current has a constant value at all points in the circuit. The **current continuity principle** states that in steady state, the current is the same at all locations along a single-loop circuit.

The **resistance** of a circuit element is a measure of the potential difference across that element for a given current in it. The SI unit of resistance is the **ohm** Ω, where $1\,\Omega \equiv 1\ \text{V/A}$. The **conductivity** σ of a material is a measure of its ability to conduct charge carriers through the material and is measured in SI units of $\text{A}/(\text{V} \cdot \text{m})$.

When there is a current in a conductor, there must be an electric field in the conductor to cause the current. In a conductor of uniform cross section at steady state, this electric field has the same magnitude everywhere and is parallel to the walls of the conductor.

The **drift velocity** $\vec{v}_d$ of the charge carriers in a metal in which a current is present is the average velocity with which the carriers are moving.

The **current density** $\vec{J}$ in an electrical conductor is a vector whose direction is the same as the drift velocity direction when the charge carriers are positive and opposite the drift velocity direction when the charge carriers are negative.

Quantitative Tools The magnitude J of the **current density** is

$$J \equiv \frac{|I|}{A} = n|q|v_d, \tag{31.5}$$

where n is the number of charge carriers per unit volume of the conductor and v_d is the magnitude of the drift velocity of the charge carriers. If the electric field in a metal is $\vec{E}$, the **drift velocity** of the charge carriers (free electrons) is

$$\vec{v}_d = -\frac{e\vec{E}}{m_e}\tau, \tag{31.3}$$

where m_e is the mass of an electron and τ is the average time interval between collisions of the electrons with the metal ions.

The **conductivity** of a metal is

$$\sigma \equiv \frac{J}{E} = \frac{ne^2\tau}{m_e}. \tag{31.8, 31.9}$$

The **resistance** of any circuit element is

$$R \equiv \frac{V}{I}, \tag{31.10}$$

where V is the applied potential difference across the element and I is the resulting current in the element. If the curve of I versus V for a conductor is a straight line, the conductor obeys **Ohm's law** $I = V/R$ (Eq. 31.11) and we call it *ohmic*.

The resistance of a conductor of length ℓ and cross-sectional area A is

$$R = \frac{\ell}{\sigma A}. \tag{31.14}$$

The rate at which energy is dissipated in a resistor is

$$P = I^2 R. \tag{31.43}$$

The rate at which a power source delivers energy is

$$P = I\mathscr{E}, \tag{31.45}$$

where $\mathscr{E}$ is the emf of the source.

Circuit loops (Sections 31.3, 31.6, 31.7)

Concepts A **junction** is a location in a circuit where more than two wires are connected. A **branch** in a circuit is a conducting path between two junctions that is not intercepted by another junction. According to the **branch rule,** the current in a branch of a multiloop circuit is the same throughout the branch.

Two or more circuit elements are connected in *series* if there is only a single current path through them and the charge carriers flow through one element after the other. The potential difference across circuit elements connected in series is equal to the sum of the individual potential differences across each circuit element.

Two or more circuit elements are connected in *parallel* if their ends are connected to the same two junctions. The potential differences across circuit elements connected in parallel are always equal.

Quantitative Tools By the **loop rule,** the sum of the emfs and the potential differences around any loop under steady-state conditions is zero:

$$\sum \mathscr{E} + \sum V = 0. \tag{31.21}$$

For a steady-state multiloop circuit, the **junction rule** states that the sum of the charge carriers going into a junction equals the sum of the carriers coming out of that junction:

$$I_{in} = I_{out}. \tag{31.27}$$

See the Procedure boxes "Applying the loop rule in single-loop circuits" and "Analyzing multiloop circuits."

The **equivalent resistance** of resistors *in series* is given by

$$R_{eq} = R_1 + R_2 + R_3 + \cdots. \tag{31.26}$$

The **equivalent resistance** of resistors *in parallel* is given by

$$\frac{1}{R_{eq}} = \frac{1}{R_1} + \frac{1}{R_2} + \frac{1}{R_3} + \cdots. \tag{31.33}$$

Review Questions

Answers to these questions can be found at the end of this chapter.

31.1 The basic circuit

1. What is the main difference between how a direct-current electric circuit is powered and how an alternating-current electric circuit is powered?
2. What is a *loop* in an electric circuit?
3. What is the *load* in an electric circuit?
4. Are the wires in an electric circuit part of the load?
5. Describe the energy conversion that takes place in a direct-current electric circuit.

31.2 Current and resistance

6. In electric circuits, to what situation does the term *steady state* refer?
7. What is the current continuity principle?
8. What does the current continuity principle say about the accumulation or depletion of charge carriers at any location in a single-loop electric circuit?
9. When a charge carrier moves from one location in a circuit to another location, how much electric potential energy is converted to some other form of energy?
10. How are circuit elements connected in a series connection?
11. What electrical property of a circuit element determines how great a potential difference must be applied across it in order to maintain a given current in it?

31.3 Junctions and multiple loops

12. In steady state, what does the current continuity principle require for (*a*) the current in any branch of a multiloop circuit and (*b*) the current into and out of a junction?
13. What electrical quantity is the same for two light bulbs that are connected in series? For two light bulbs connected in parallel?
14. What is a short in an electric circuit, and what does it do?
15. Does the orientation of elements in a circuit diagram make any difference in whether or not the diagram correctly represents the circuit? Does the length or bending of the connecting wires make any difference?

31.4 Electric fields in conductors

16. What is the electric field like inside a conductor of uniform cross section carrying a steady current?

17. On what three factors does the resistance of an electrical conductor of uniform cross section depend?

31.5 Resistance and Ohm's law

18. Describe what a metallic electrical conductor looks like at the atomic level.
19. How does the Drude model describe the average motion of free electrons in an electrical conductor in the presence of an electric field?
20. What is the conductivity of a material, and what property of the material does conductivity measure?
21. Which properties determine the conductivity of a material?
22. How is the resistance of a circuit element defined?
23. What is an ohmic material?
24. What information about resistance can be found by plotting current as a function of applied potential difference? What does such a curve look like for a circuit element made of an ohmic material?

31.6 Single-loop circuits

25. What two conditions apply to a single-loop circuit in steady state?
26. What is the equivalent resistance of a number of resistors in series?
27. What is the internal resistance of a battery, and how is it accounted for when we analyze a circuit that contains the battery?

31.7 Multiloop circuits

28. What is the equivalent resistance of a number of resistors connected in parallel?
29. Summarize the suggested strategy for analyzing multiloop circuits.

31.8 Power in electric circuits

30. What is the general expression for the rate at which electrical energy is converted to other forms of energy in a circuit element?
31. What is the expression for the rate at which energy is dissipated in a resistor in terms of the current through it? Which type of energy conversion does this dissipation represent?

Developing a Feel

Make an order-of-magnitude estimate of each of the following quantities. Letters in parentheses refer to hints below. Use them as needed to guide your thinking.

1. The resistance of a glowing 100-W light bulb (W, E, R)
2. The resistance of a 5-W nightlight plugged into a bathroom outlet (W, E, R)
3. The height from which you must fall to gain the kinetic energy equivalent to the energy two 100-W light bulbs use in 1 h (H, A, O)
4. The length of tungsten filament in a 100-W light bulb (J, C, M)
5. The diameter of the copper wires in a 15-m heavy-duty extension cord (D, L, P, S)
6. The electric field inside the filament of a glowing 100-W light bulb (E, T)
7. The energy available for conversion in a C battery (Q, U)
8. The cost of 1 MJ (10^6 J) of C-battery energy (I, F)
9. The average rate at which electrical energy is used by the average U.S. home (N, G, V)
10. The annual cost of electricity to run the average U.S. home at $0.15/kW-h ($0.04/MJ) (K, B)

Hints

A. How do you determine your kinetic energy at the end of the fall?
B. How much energy does the home use in a year?
C. What is the diameter of the filament?
D. What potential difference is allowed for the cord?
E. What is the potential difference?
F. What is the cost of one C battery?
G. What is the rate of energy consumption when most items are in use?
H. How much energy do the bulbs use in 1 h?
I. How many C batteries are needed in order to have 1 MJ of energy?
J. What is the resistance of the filament?
K. How much power does the home use?
L. How much current can a heavy-duty cord carry?
M. What is the conductivity of tungsten at operating temperature?
N. How many lights and appliances are used in an average home?
O. What is your inertia?
P. What is the conductivity of copper?
Q. How long can a flashlight remain on before it dims dramatically?
R. If you opt to use $R = P/I^2$, how can you calculate current when you know the power and potential difference?
S. Describe the circuit you must analyze.
T. What is the length of the filament?
U. What is the power of a flashlight bulb?

V. During what fraction of the average day is home energy consumption near maximum?
W. What expression gives the resistance in a circuit element when you know the element's power rating?

Key (all values approximate)

A. all your gravitational potential energy mgh before the fall is converted to kinetic energy; B. 3×10^{10} J/y; C. 5×10^{-2} mm; D. wires should be almost ideal, so a few percent of household potential difference, or 5 V; E. 1×10^2 V, typical in household wiring; F. $1 each in bulk; G. heating/cooling dominates, so say 5 kW; H. 7×10^5 J; I. 10 batteries, see Developing a Feel question 7; J. 10^2 Ω, see Developing a Feel question 1; K. 1 kW, see Developing a Feel question 9; L. 2×10^1 A; M. 1×10^6 A/(V · m); N. a dozen lights, a refrigerator, stove, TV, computer, and heating/cooling system; O. 6×10^1 kg; P. 6×10^7 A/(V · m); Q. 5 h; R. $P = IV$; S. two 15-m wires side by side inside a sheath made of nonconducting material, an unknown circuit element (load) plugged into the female end of the cord joins the two wires into a single-loop circuit, and the house wiring at 120 V provides the power source for the circuit; T. 10^{-1} m, see Developing a Feel question 4; U. 5 W; V. 1/3; W. either $R = P/I^2$ or $R = V^2/P$

Worked and Guided Problems

Procedure: Applying the loop rule in single-loop circuits

When applying the loop rule to a single-loop circuit consisting of resistors, batteries, and capacitors, we need to make several choices in order to calculate the current or the potential difference across each circuit element.

1. Choose a reference direction for the current in the loop. (This direction is arbitrary and may or may not be the direction of current, but don't worry, things sort themselves out in step 4.) Indicate your chosen reference direction by an arrowhead, and label the arrowhead with the symbol for the current (I).
2. Choose a direction of travel around the loop. This choice is arbitrary and separate from the choice of the reference direction for the current in step 1. (You may

want to indicate the travel direction with a circular clockwise or counterclockwise arrow in the loop.)

3. Start traversing the loop in the direction chosen in step 2 from some arbitrary point on the loop. As you encounter circuit elements, each circuit element contributes a term to Eq. 31.21. Use Table 31.2 to determine the sign and value of each term. Add all terms to obtain the sum in Eq. 31.21. Make sure you traverse the loop completely.
4. Solve your expression for the desired quantity. If your solution indicates that $I < 0$, then the direction of current is opposite the reference direction you chose in step 1.

Table 31.2 Signs and values of potential differences across batteries and resistors (Figure 31.35)

Circuit element	Plus sign when traversing	Value
ideal battery	from − to +	$\mathscr{E}$
capacitor	from − to +	$q(t)/C$
resistor	opposite reference direction of current	IR

Procedure: Analyzing multiloop circuits

Here is a series of steps for calculating currents or potential differences in multiloop circuits.

1. Identify and label the junctions in the circuit.
2. Label the current in each branch of the circuit, arbitrarily assigning a direction to each current.
3. Apply the junction rule to all but one of the junctions. (The choice of which junctions to analyze is arbitrary; choose junctions that involve the quantities you are interested in calculating.)
4. Identify the loops in the circuit and apply the loop rule (see the Procedure box on page 831) enough times to obtain a suitable number of simultaneous equations relating the unknowns in the problem. The choice of loops is arbitrary, but every branch must be in at least one of the loops. Traverse each loop in whichever direction you prefer, but be sure you traverse each loop completely and stick with the

direction of travel and with the chosen directions of the currents.

There are several simplifications you can make during your analysis.

1. Multiloop circuits can sometimes be simplified by replacing parallel or series combinations of resistors by their equivalent resistances. If you can reduce the circuit to a single loop, you can solve for the current in the source. You may then need to "unsimplify" and undo the resistor simplification to calculate the current or potential difference across a particular resistor.
2. In general when solving problems, you should solve equations analytically before substituting known numerical values. When solving the simultaneous equations you obtain for multiloop circuits, however, you can often simplify the algebra if you substitute the known numerical values earlier on.

These examples involve material from this chapter but are not associated with any particular section.
Some examples are worked out in detail; others you should work out by following the guidelines provided.

Worked Problem 31.1 Battery power

A battery of emf $\mathscr{E}$ has internal resistance R_{batt}. When it is new, the battery can maintain this emf while transporting an amount of charge q between its terminals, but then further charge transport is accompanied by a rapid reduction in the value of this emf. Suppose the battery is connected to a resistive load of resistance R. (*a*) What value of R maximizes the rate at which energy is converted in the load? (*b*) Derive an expression for the maximum rate at which energy is converted in the load. (*c*) Derive an expression for the amount of electric potential energy converted to thermal energy in the load before the battery dies.

❶ GETTING STARTED We are given the emf and internal resistance for a battery in a circuit that contains a load of resistance R. The battery is capable of transporting an amount of charge q before dying. Our tasks are (*a*) to determine what value of R maximizes the rate at which energy is delivered by the battery and to express (*b*) that maximum power and (*c*) the amount of energy converted in the load in terms of the given variables. Let's first draw the circuit and show the reference direction we choose for the current and the direction in which we shall travel around the circuit as we analyze the potential differences across the various circuit elements (Figure WG31.1).

Figure WG31.1

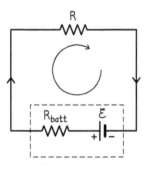

❷ DEVISE PLAN We first apply the loop rule (Eq. 31.21) to determine the current in the circuit. We then use Eq. 31.43 to obtain an expression for the power P, which is the rate at which energy is converted in the load. In order to calculate the value of R that maximizes P, we need to differentiate P with respect to R and then determine the value of R for which $dP/dR = 0$. Once we have this value of R, we can use Eq. 31.43 again to solve part *b*. For part *c*, we can use Eq. 31.41 to determine how much energy is converted in the load before the battery dies.

❸ EXECUTE PLAN (*a*) With our choices for the current reference direction and the direction in which we travel around the circuit, the loop rule takes the form

$$\mathscr{E} - IR_{\text{batt}} - IR = 0,$$

so the current is

$$I = \frac{\mathscr{E}}{R_{\text{batt}} + R}. \tag{1}$$

The rate at which energy is converted in the load is, from Eq. 31.43,

$$P = I^2 R = \left(\frac{\mathscr{E}}{R_{\text{batt}} + R} \right)^2 R.$$

Next we take the derivative of this power with respect to R and set it equal to zero:

$$\frac{dP}{dR} = \mathscr{E}^2 \left[\left(\frac{1}{R_{\text{batt}} + R} \right)^2 - 2R \left(\frac{1}{R_{\text{batt}} + R} \right)^3 \right] = 0.$$

This equation solved for R gives us

$$\left(\frac{1}{R_{\text{batt}} + R} \right)^2 = 2R \left(\frac{1}{R_{\text{batt}} + R} \right)^3$$

$$R_{\text{batt}} + R = 2R$$

$$R = R_{\text{batt}}. ✔$$

The rate at which energy is converted in the load is greatest when the load resistance is the same as the battery's internal resistance.

(*b*) Substituting R_{batt} for R in Eq. 1 gives us an expression for the current that maximizes the power:

$$I_{\text{max}} = \frac{\mathscr{E}}{R_{\text{batt}} + R} = \frac{\mathscr{E}}{2R_{\text{batt}}}.$$

Thus the maximum power is

$$P_{\text{max}} = I_{\text{max}}^2 R = \left(\frac{\mathscr{E}}{2R_{\text{batt}}} \right)^2 R_{\text{batt}} = \frac{1}{4} \frac{\mathscr{E}^2}{R_{\text{batt}}}. ✔$$

(*c*) We can now use Eq. 31.41 to obtain an expression for the energy converted in the load:

$$\Delta E = -qV_{\text{ab}} = IRq = \frac{\mathscr{E}}{2R_{\text{batt}}} R_{\text{batt}} q = \frac{\mathscr{E}q}{2}. ✔$$

❹ EVALUATE RESULT The chemical energy converted in the battery before it dies is $\Delta E = \mathscr{E}q$, so our result tells us that half of this chemical energy is converted in the load. The other half of the chemical energy must be converted in the internal resistance of the battery! All of this chemical energy is dissipated into thermal energy due to the internal resistance of the battery or the external resistance of the load. This is reasonable for a resistive load, such as a hair dryer or toaster, but it might surprise you that by maximizing the rate of energy conversion in the load we have "wasted" 50% of the chemical energy of the battery. Returning to Eq. 1, we see that if the load resistance is considerably greater than the internal resistance of the battery, the current will be much smaller. Suppose $R = 100R_{\text{batt}}$. Then the rate of energy conversion in the load is much smaller, but Eq. 31.41 allows 99% of the converted chemical energy to appear in the load, with only 1% "wasted" in the battery. By taking a much longer time to convert energy, we use the energy stored in the battery much more efficiently.

Guided Problem 31.2 Battery-powered lift

A standard D cell battery can supply 25 mA at 1.5 V for about 300 h, and its internal resistance is about 1.0 Ω. A multispeed winch powered by such a battery is 50% efficient and is being used to lift a 60-kg object that is initially on the ground. When the winch is set to a very slow speed, the load resistance is much greater than the internal resistance of the battery. The greatest speed of the winch is limited by the maximum power supplied by the battery. (*a*) In each case, how high can the winch lift the object before the battery uses all of its energy? (*b*) What are the maximum speed at which the winch lifts the object and the minimum time interval required for the lift? Assume the battery capacity (product of current and time) is independent of the discharge rate, which is not accurate for real batteries.

❶ GETTING STARTED

1. Draw a circuit diagram. Which circuit element symbol should represent the winch?
2. When the winch is run at a very slow speed, how does the amount of energy dissipated due to the battery's internal resistance compare with the amount of energy converted to mechanical potential energy of the rising object?

❷ DEVISE PLAN

3. What relationship tells you the quantity of charge the battery delivers before it dies?

4. What relationship tells you how much energy the battery delivers before it dies?
5. How can you use energy relationships to determine the height to which the object rises before the battery dies?
6. What expression allows you to compute the rate of energy transfer to the load?
7. How do you maximize the rate at which energy is delivered to the load?
8. How do you determine the greatest speed at which the winch can lift the object?

❸ EXECUTE PLAN

9. Calculate the quantity of charge delivered and the energy delivered before the battery dies.
10. Calculate how high off the ground the object is lifted at very slow speed.
11. What is the greatest speed the object attains?
12. At this greatest lift rate, what is the maximum height that the winch can lift the object before the battery dies?
13. What minimum time interval is required for the object to reach this height?

❹ EVALUATE RESULT

14. Are your results for the time interval required to raise the load to its maximum height at the greatest speed reasonable? Examine some limiting cases.

Worked Problem 31.3 Designing an ohmmeter

An ammeter that has a resistance of 20 Ω reads 50 μA when the needle on the meter scale is fully deflected. By combining the ammeter with a 1.5-V battery and resistors 1 and 2 that have resistances R_1 and R_2, you can convert it to an ohmmeter. When the leads of this ohmmeter are connected to each other (which is equivalent to connecting the leads across a circuit element of zero resistance), the needle on the meter scale is fully deflected. This full deflection represents both a current of 50 μA and a resistance of 0. In order to use the meter to measure the resistance of any circuit element, you must convert the meter-scale readings from amperes to ohms. Once you have done this calibration and connected the meter leads across a circuit element of unknown resistance R_u, the reading on your hand-calibrated scale indicates the resistance of the element. (*a*) If you want half-scale deflection to indicate 15 Ω, how should you connect the circuit elements to one another, and what values should you choose for R_1 and R_2? (*b*) When you align your ohm scale with the ampere scale on the meter, with the full-deflection reading $R = 0$ aligned with 50 μA on the ampere scale, which value on the ampere scale aligns with the 5.0-Ω position on your scale? With the 50-Ω position on your scale?

❶ GETTING STARTED We have an ammeter that has a resistance of 20 Ω, a 1.5-V battery, and resistors 1 and 2 that have resistances R_1 and R_2, and we must connect these four elements in an electric circuit in such a way that the combination acts as an ohmmeter and measures the resistance R_u of a fifth element we place in the circuit. We begin by drawing our ohmmeter as a box containing our four given elements not yet connected to one another (Figure WG31.2). We must connect the ends of our fifth element of resistance R_u to two wires that emerge from this ohmmeter "box."

Figure WG31.2

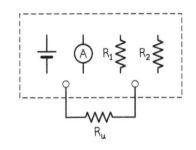

❷ DEVISE PLAN (*a*) To see why we need two resistors and how they must be connected, suppose at first that both R_1 and R_2 are very small and can be replaced by wires. Then we must connect only a battery, an ammeter, and the external resistance R_u. But if $R_u = 0$, then we obtain just a battery in series with an ammeter, and the current is $I_{\text{no resistors}} = \mathscr{E}_{\text{batt}}/R_A = 1.5 \text{ V}/20 \text{ Ω} = 75$ mA. This sounds small, but it is 1500 times the full-scale deflection current! We need a resistor to limit the current to the 50-μA scale of the meter. We can place this resistor in series with the ammeter and the battery so that the equivalent resistance of the meter + resistor combination is very great. However, we will also need to adjust the circuit so that a half-scale meter deflection corresponds to external resistance $R_u = 15$ Ω, without noticeably changing the portion of the circuit that secures the earlier value. Thus at least one more resistor connected in a parallel branch will be needed, and its value will need to be small (so as not to affect the earlier value very much). The numerical values can be computed using our knowledge of series and parallel resistances and the behavior of the current and potential difference for series and parallel connections.

(b) Having calibrated the ohmmeter, we should be able to apply the junction and loop rules to compute the scale reading for any other external resistance. If we solve for the current in the ammeter, we can determine the fraction of full-scale deflection. We can then make an appropriate mark for the corresponding scale reading in ohms.

❸ **EXECUTE PLAN** (a) We calibrate the meter scale by using the restrictions that our new "ohmmeter" requires full-scale deflection when $R_u = 0$ and half-scale deflection when $R_u = 15\ \Omega$. To satisfy the first requirement, we connect the battery, ammeter, and resistor 1 in series inside our ohmmeter "box" and place zero resistance (a wire) for R_u (Figure WG31.3). The value of R_1 must allow full-scale deflection, so

$$I_{\text{full-scale}} = \frac{\mathscr{E}_{\text{batt}}}{R_1 + R_A}$$

$$R_1 = \frac{\mathscr{E}_{\text{batt}} - R_A I_{\text{full-scale}}}{I_{\text{full-scale}}} = \frac{1.5\ \text{V} - (20\ \Omega)(50 \times 10^{-6}\ \text{A})}{50 \times 10^{-6}\ \text{A}}$$

$$= 3.0 \times 10^4\ \Omega.$$

Figure WG31.3

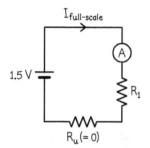

Now we add resistor 2 in a parallel branch and replace the external resistance with $R_u = 15\ \Omega$ (Figure WG31.4). We now have a two-loop circuit, and we add labels for currents and direction of travel around loops. This allows us to write the single junction equation and two loop equations:

$$I_u = I_1 + I_2 \tag{1}$$

$$+\mathscr{E}_{\text{batt}} - I_2 R_2 - I_u R_u = 0 \tag{2}$$

$$+I_2 R_2 - I_1 R_A - I_1 R_1 = 0. \tag{3}$$

Figure WG31.4

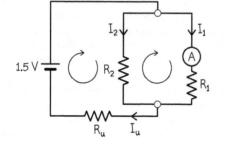

We know that the current in the ammeter for this special case is $I_1 = 0.25\ \mu\text{A}$. Thus Eq. 3 allows us to compute the potential difference across resistor 2:

$$I_2 R_2 = I_1(R_A + R_1) = (25 \times 10^{-6}\ \text{A})(20\ \Omega + 3.0 \times 10^4\ \Omega)$$

$$= 0.75\ \text{V}.$$

Next we obtain the potential difference across R_u from Eq. 2:

$$+\mathscr{E}_{\text{batt}} - I_2 R_2 - I_u R_u = 0$$

$$1.5\ \text{V} - 0.75\ \text{V} - I_u R_u = 0$$

$$I_u R_u = 0.75\ \text{V}.$$

The current in the external resistor must therefore be

$$I_u = \frac{V_u}{R_u} = \frac{0.75\ \text{V}}{15\ \Omega} = 50\ \text{mA}.$$

The current in the battery must equal the current in the external resistor because these elements are connected in series. Because the current in the ammeter is known, the current in the battery can be computed from Eq. 1:

$$I_2 = I_u - I_1 = 50\ \text{mA} - 25\ \mu\text{A} = 50\ \text{mA}.$$

Notice that the current in the ammeter is entirely negligible on the scale of the current in the battery, resistor 2, and the external resistor. In fact, these three currents are identical to two significant digits. This allows us to determine the resistance R_2:

$$R_2 = \frac{V_2}{I_2} = \frac{0.75\ \text{V}}{50 \times 10^{-3}\ \text{A}} = 15\ \Omega.$$

The design of our ohmmeter is complete. ✔

(b) The two specific cases to be solved use the same circuit shown in Figure WG31.4. Thus we can employ Eqs. 1–3, changing only the value of R_u. In each case all resistances are known, which leaves three unknown currents to be determined from our three equations. Because we wish to solve for I_1, it is convenient to use Eq. 1 to eliminate I_u from Eq. 2, leaving us with two equations in two unknowns:

$$I_2 R_2 - I_1(R_A + R_1) = 0 \tag{3}$$

$$+\mathscr{E}_{\text{batt}} - I_1 R_u - I_2(R_2 + R_u) = 0. \tag{4}$$

Next we use Eq. 3 to eliminate I_2 from Eq. 4 and solve for I_1:

$$+\mathscr{E}_{\text{batt}} - I_1 R_u - \frac{I_1(R_A + R_1)(R_2 + R_u)}{R_2} = 0$$

$$I_1 = \frac{\mathscr{E}_{\text{batt}} R_2}{R_2 R_u + (R_A + R_1)(R_2 + R_u)}. \tag{5}$$

Suppose $R_u = 5.0\ \Omega$. Then

$$I_1 = \frac{(1.5\ \text{V})(15\ \Omega)}{(15\ \Omega)(5.0\ \Omega) + (20\ \Omega + 3.0 \times 10^4\ \Omega)(15\ \Omega + 5.0\ \Omega)}$$

$$= 37\ \mu\text{A}.$$

The ammeter needle would move to 37 μA, or 75% of full-scale deflection, which is where we make the 5.0-Ω mark. ✔

Similarly, if $R_u = 50\ \Omega$, the ammeter current is

$$I_1 = \frac{(1.5\ \text{V})(15\ \Omega)}{(15\ \Omega)(50\ \Omega) + (20\ \Omega + 3.0 \times 10^4\ \Omega)(15\ \Omega + 50\ \Omega)}$$

$$= 12\ \mu\text{A}.$$

The needle is at 12 μA, or 23% of full-scale deflection, for the 50-Ω mark. ✔

④ **EVALUATE RESULT** Our circuit is a reasonable design because we can easily find resistors that have the values we need: 15 Ω and $3.0 \times 10^4\ \Omega$. An alternative design employing the first resistor in parallel with the ammeter and the second in series with that combination and the battery would produce a first resistor with an uncomfortably small resistance that would be difficult to find and small enough to call into question our assumption that the resistance of the connecting wires can be ignored. Try it!

Our assumption of zero internal resistance in the battery is the only way to proceed. The value should be small in any case, but we are not given enough information about the battery (alkaline? rechargeable? lead-acid?) to allow us to look up a reasonable value.

The expression we obtained for the ammeter current, Eq. 5, shows that the current decreases as the external resistance R_u increases. This makes sense because the resistance scale runs backward compared to the current scale. The zero of current in Eq. 5 also corresponds to an infinitely large value of R_u, which is consistent with the nonlinear resistance scale that our numerical results require.

We should examine the effect of resistor 2 on our original calculation of full-scale deflection for zero external resistance. Solving Eq. 5 for the current in the ammeter for zero external resistance gives

$$I_1 = \frac{(1.5\ \text{V})(15\ \Omega)}{(15\ \Omega)(0) + (20\ \Omega + 3.0 \times 10^4\ \Omega)(15\ \Omega + 0)}$$

$$= 50\ \mu\text{A}.$$

Thus the added small parallel resistance indeed had no effect on the full-scale deflection, at least to two significant digits.

Guided Problem 31.4 Four resistors

Resistors 1, 2, 3, and 4 are connected to a battery as shown in Figure WG31.5. Express the current through each resistor in terms of R_1 and the battery emf $\mathcal{E}$.

Figure WG31.5

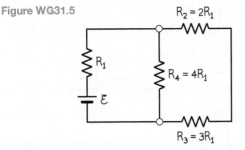

① **GETTING STARTED**
1. Apply the steps in the Procedure box "Analyzing multiloop circuits." Choose a reference direction for each current and label the currents I_1, I_2, and I_4 through the three branches. Draw curved arrows to indicate the (arbitrary) direction in which you will travel around each loop.
2. Why isn't it necessary to show current I_3 in your diagram?

② **DEVISE PLAN**
3. How many independent equations do you need to solve the problem?
4. Is there a useful simplification for this circuit?

③ **EXECUTE PLAN**
5. Compute equivalent resistances as needed.
6. What is the current through resistor 1?
7. What is the current through resistor 4?
8. What is the current through resistors 2 and 3?

④ **EVALUATE RESULT**
9. Check that the junction rule is satisfied.

Worked Problem 31.5 Resistance of a truncated cone

Consider a resistor constructed of a material of conductivity σ that has the shape of a truncated cone of length ℓ, base radius b, and top face radius a (Figure WG31.6). The base and top face are parallel to each other. Derive an expression in terms of these variables for the resistance between the base and the top face.

Figure WG31.6

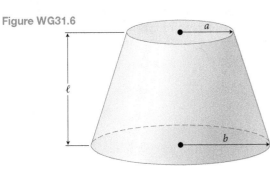

① **GETTING STARTED** We know how to compute the resistance of a conductor of uniform cross section, but the cross-sectional area of this cone varies along its length. That suggests we need to integrate. We can model the cone as a stack of thin disks, oriented parallel to the base of the cone, each disk of variable radius r and thickness dx. Because the thickness is infinitesimal, each disk is essentially of uniform cross-sectional area $A = \pi r^2$. The disks are connected in series because charge carriers must flow through each disk in the order they occur in the stack.

② **DEVISE PLAN** Figure WG31.7 shows the truncated cone in cross section, with a representative thin disk of radius r and thickness dx. We can use Eq. 31.14 to determine the resistance dR of each disk as a function of x, the distance from the base. From the geometry of the cone, we can determine how the disk radius r varies with x and therefore how the disk area A varies with x. Because the disks are connected in series, the sum of their resistances is the resistance of the cone. To determine this sum, we can integrate the resistance $dR(x)$ from $x = 0$ to $x = \ell$.

Figure WG31.7

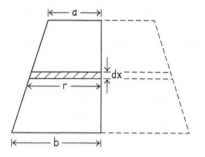

❸ **EXECUTE PLAN** We determine how the radius r of any disk and its distance x from the base are related by working with the similar triangles shown in Figure WG31.8b. Figure WG31.8a shows their origin: In the view of the cone shown in Figure WG31.7, we draw a vertical line from the left edge of the top face to the base. From the similar triangles, r and x are related by

$$\frac{b - r}{x} = \frac{b - a}{\ell}.$$

Figure WG31.8

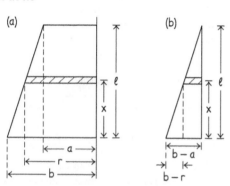

Rearranging this equation gives us an expression for $r(x)$:

$$r(x) = b + \frac{(a - b)}{\ell}x.$$

The area of the disk as a function of x is then

$$A(x) = \pi\left[b + \frac{(a - b)}{\ell}x\right]^2.$$

We now use Eq. 31.14 to obtain the resistance $dR(x)$ for any disk of thickness dx located a distance x from the base:

$$dR(x) = \frac{dx}{\sigma\pi\left[b + \dfrac{(a - b)}{\ell}x\right]^2}.$$

The resistance of the cone is therefore

$$R = \int_{x=0}^{x=\ell} \frac{dx}{\sigma\pi\left[b + \dfrac{(a - b)}{\ell}x\right]^2}.$$

Using the identity (see Appendix B)

$$\int \frac{dx}{(\alpha + \beta x)^2} = -\frac{1}{\beta(\alpha + \beta x)},$$

we have

$$R = \int_{x=0}^{x=\ell} \frac{dx}{\sigma\pi\left[b + \dfrac{(a - b)}{\ell}x\right]^2}$$

$$= -\frac{1}{\sigma\pi}\frac{1}{\left[\dfrac{(a - b)}{\ell}\right]\left[b + \dfrac{(a - b)}{\ell}x\right]}\Bigg|_{x=0}^{x=\ell}$$

$$= -\frac{1}{\sigma\pi}\left\{\frac{1}{\left[\dfrac{(a - b)}{\ell}\right](b + (a - b))} - \frac{1}{\left[\dfrac{(a - b)}{\ell}\right](b)}\right\}$$

$$= -\frac{1}{\sigma\pi}\left\{\frac{(b - a)}{\left[\dfrac{(a - b)}{\ell}\right](ab)}\right\} = \frac{\ell}{\sigma\pi ab}. \qquad \checkmark$$

② **EVALUATE RESULT** Our expression involves the dimensions of the cone in a sensible fashion; that is, the resistance increases as the cone length increases and the resistance decreases as either the base or top face increases in size. If $b = a$, the cross-sectional area of the cone is a uniform $A = \pi a^2$ and our resistance expression becomes $R = \ell/\sigma\pi a^2 = \ell/\sigma A$. That this expression is identical to Eq. 31.14, the resistance for a cylindrical or rectangular resistor, gives us confidence that our answer for the resistance of the truncated cone is correct.

Guided Problem 31.6 Conductivity of seawater

An oceanographer uses electrical conductivity to study how the ion concentration in seawater depends on depth. She does this by lowering into the ocean a device consisting of a metallic solid cylinder of radius $r_{inner} = 10.0$ mm concentric with a metallic cylindrical shell of radius $r_{outer} = 40.0$ mm (Figure WG31.9). The length of both the solid cylinder and the shell is $\ell = 400$ mm. The device is attached to the end of a cable, and the cable is lowered to a depth $D = 4000$ m, where the water temperature is 0.00 °C and the salinity is 3.50×10^4 mg per liter of solution. With the device at that depth, the oceanographer applies a potential difference $V_{outer} - V_{inner} = 0.500$ V between the solid cylinder and the cylindrical shell, producing an outward radial current $I = 2.93$ A. What is the conductivity of the seawater at that depth?

Figure WG31.9

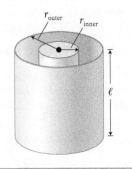

r_{outer} r_{inner}

ℓ

① GETTING STARTED

1. How can you model the seawater that fills the space between the solid cylinder and the cylindrical shell as a resistor?
2. Is your model a combination of thin shells connected in series or parallel?

② DEVISE PLAN

3. How can you calculate the resistance dR of the individual shells of seawater?
4. How can you determine the contribution of all the seawater shells to get the resistance of the seawater?
5. What expression relates resistance to potential difference and current?
6. How can you calculate the seawater conductivity?

③ EXECUTE PLAN

7. Express the resistance dR of one seawater shell in terms of the shell radius r, thickness dr, and length ℓ. (Be careful: Which dimension corresponds to the length of this shell resistor?)
8. Integrate to sum the resistances of all the seawater shells.
9. Use Eq. 31.11 to relate this expression for R to the potential difference and current.
10. Use this relationship to calculate the conductivity of the seawater.

④ EVALUATE RESULT

11. Look up the value of the conductivity of seawater. Does your answer make sense based on that value?

Worked Problem 31.7 Multiple batteries

Calculate the rate at which each of the three batteries in Figure WG31.10 either delivers or absorbs (specify which in each case) energy. Assume all the batteries have zero internal resistance, and use numerical values $R_1 = R_3 = 1.0$ Ω, $R_2 = 2.0$ Ω, $\mathscr{E}_1 = 2.0$ V, and $\mathscr{E}_2 = \mathscr{E}_3 = 4.0$ V.

Figure WG31.10

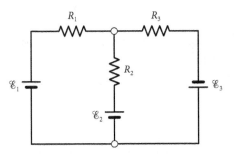

Figure WG31.11

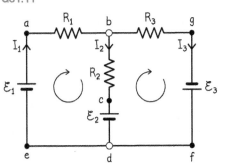

① **GETTING STARTED** We begin by observing that this is a multiloop circuit containing two junctions. We redraw the circuit diagram and label various locations along the wires to have a convenient way of identifying each loop we'll work with; our junctions are at b and d in the arbitrary lettering we use. Next we label the directions we choose for currents I_1, I_2, and I_3 through the three branches and add a clockwise arrow in the center of the left and right loops to show the direction in which we'll travel around each loop (Figure WG31.11).

② **DEVISE PLAN** To solve this problem, we must determine the value of the current in each branch and then use our current values to calculate the power for each battery. To determine the current values, we apply the junction rule (Eq. 31.27) to one of the junctions and then the loop rule (Eq. 31.21) to as many loops as necessary. Because we have three unknown currents, we need three independent equations. With only two junctions, we know that the junction rule can give us only one independent equation, and so we must use the loop rule on two loops to get our three equations. Once we have values for I_1, I_2, and I_3, we can use Eq. 31.45 to calculate the power for each battery.

③ **EXECUTE PLAN** The junction rule applied to junction b, with $I_{in} = I_1$ and $I_{out} = I_2 + I_3$, yields

$$I_1 = I_2 + I_3. \tag{1}$$

For loop abcdea, moving clockwise from a, we have

$$-I_1R_1 - I_2R_2 - \mathcal{E}_2 + \mathcal{E}_1 = 0. \qquad (2)$$

For loop bgfdcb, moving clockwise from b, we have

$$-I_3R_3 + \mathcal{E}_3 + \mathcal{E}_2 + I_2R_2 = 0. \qquad (3)$$

Now we must use these three equations to obtain expressions for I_1, I_2, and I_3. Let's begin with Eq. 2 solved for I_1:

$$I_1 = \frac{-I_2R_2 - \mathcal{E}_2 + \mathcal{E}_1}{R_1}, \qquad (4)$$

and next Eq. 3 solved for I_3:

$$I_3 = \frac{\mathcal{E}_3 + \mathcal{E}_2 + I_2R_2}{R_3}. \qquad (5)$$

We can now substitute these expressions for I_1 and I_2 into Eq. 1:

$$\frac{-I_2R_2 - \mathcal{E}_2 + \mathcal{E}_1}{R_1} = I_2 + \frac{\mathcal{E}_3 + \mathcal{E}_2 + I_2R_2}{R_3}.$$

Solving for I_2 and substituting given values yield

$$I_2 = \frac{-\mathcal{E}_2(R_3 + R_1) + \mathcal{E}_1R_3 - \mathcal{E}_3R_1}{R_1R_3 + R_1R_2 + R_2R_3}$$

$$= \frac{-(4.0\ \text{V})(1.0\ \Omega + 1.0\ \Omega) + (2.0\ \text{V})(1.0\ \Omega) - (4.0\ \text{V})(1.0\ \Omega)}{(1.0\ \Omega)(1.0\ \Omega) + (1.0\ \Omega)(2.0\ \Omega) + (2.0\ \Omega)(1.0\ \Omega)}.$$

$$= -2.0\ \text{A}.$$

The minus sign means that the direction of I_2 is the opposite of the direction we chose in Figure WG31.11. Hence battery 2 is delivering energy.

We can now calculate I_1 by substituting values in Eq. 4:

$$I_1 = \frac{-(-2.0\ \text{A})(2.0\ \Omega) - (4.0\ \text{V}) + (2.0\ \text{V})}{1.0\ \Omega} = +2.0\ \text{A}.$$

The positive result for this current indicates that battery 1 is delivering energy.

Equation 5 gives us

$$I_3 = \frac{(4.0\ \text{V}) + (4.0\ \text{V}) + (-2.0\ \text{A})(2.0\ \Omega)}{1.0\ \Omega} = +4.0\ \text{A},$$

and this positive value for I_3 tells us that battery 3 is delivering energy.

The rate at which energy is delivered to the circuit by battery 1 is, from Eq. 31.45,

$$P_1 = \mathcal{E}_1I_1 = (2.0\ \text{V})(2.0\ \text{A}) = 4.0\ \text{W}, \checkmark$$

and that rate for battery 2 is

$$P_2 = \mathcal{E}_2|I_2| = (4.0\ \text{V})(2.0\ \text{A}) = 8.0\ \text{W} \checkmark$$

Note we use the absolute value for I_2 because we have concluded that the negative value we obtained for this current meant that battery 2 is delivering energy. The power for battery 3 is

$$P_3 = \mathcal{E}_3I_3 = (4.0\ \text{V})(4.0\ \text{A}) = 16\ \text{W}. \checkmark$$

❹ EVALUATE RESULT We can check our results in two ways. First we check that our values for the current satisfy the junction rule:

$$I_{in} = I_1 = 2.0\ \text{A}$$

$$I_{out} = I_2 + I_3 = -2.0\ \text{A} + 4.0\ \text{A} = 2.0\ \text{A}.$$

Next we check that the rate at which energy is delivered by the batteries is equal to the rate at which energy is dissipated in the resistors. That rate for the batteries is $4.0\ \text{W} + 8.0\ \text{W} + 16\ \text{W} = 28\ \text{W}$, and for the resistors it is

$$P_1 = (I_1^2)(R_1) = (2.0\ \text{A})^2(1.0\ \Omega) = 4.0\ \text{W}$$

$$P_2 = (I_2^2)(R_2) = (2.0\ \text{A})^2(2.0\ \Omega) = 8.0\ \text{W}$$

$$P_3 = (I_3^2)(R_3) = (4.0\ \text{A})^2(1.0\ \Omega) = 16\ \text{W}$$

$$4.0\ \text{W} + 8.0\ \text{W} + 16\ \text{W} = 28\ \text{W}.$$

Guided Problem 31.8 Resistor network power

Consider the circuit shown in Figure WG31.12 that consists of resistors 1, 2, 3, and 4 with values $R_1 = 2.0\ \Omega$, $R_2 = 4.0\ \Omega$, $R_3 = 4.0\ \Omega$, and $R_4 = 2.0\ \Omega$, and two batteries with emfs $\mathcal{E}_1 = 50\ \text{V}$ and $\mathcal{E}_2 = 20\ \text{V}$. Calculate the rate at which energy is delivered to each resistor.

Figure WG31.12

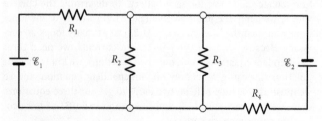

❶ GETTING STARTED

1. How can you simplify the circuit?
2. Redraw the circuit diagram, applying the steps in the "Analyzing multiloop circuits" Procedure box.

❷ DEVISE PLAN

3. How many unknown currents must you determine?
4. Use the junction and loop rules to obtain the equations you need.
5. How do you calculate the power for each resistor?

❸ EXECUTE PLAN

6. Apply the junction rule.
7. Apply the loop rule.
8. Solve your set of equations for the current in each branch.
9. What is the current through resistors 2 and 3 in the original circuit of Figure WG31.12?
10. Calculate the rate at which energy is delivered to each resistor.

❹ EVALUATE RESULT

11. Check that your current values satisfy the junction rule.
12. Check that the rate at which energy is delivered by the batteries is equal to the rate at which it is dissipated in the resistors.

Questions and Problems

For instructor-assigned homework, go to MasteringPhysics® (MP)

Dots indicate difficulty level of problems: • = easy, •• = intermediate, ••• = hard; CR = context-rich problem.

Unless instructed otherwise, assume all batteries and all wires in circuits are ideal and thus have zero (internal) resistance.

31.1 The basic circuit

1. A battery that initially contains 3.0×10^{24} electrons is used to power a light bulb for some time interval, pumping 1.1×10^{24} electrons through the bulb during that interval. How many electrons remain in the battery? •

2. How can the energy conversions in an electric circuit be represented in terms of two generalized circuit elements? •

3. A battery and four identical light bulbs are arranged in the circuit of Figure P31.3. Rank the current magnitudes at the nine lettered locations from greatest to smallest. •

Figure P31.3

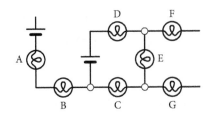

4. Which of the seven identical light bulbs in the circuit of Figure P31.4 light up? •

Figure P31.4

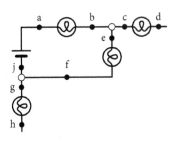

5. You have a light bulb, a battery, and one wire (which you cannot cut into two pieces). Draw the four ways of connecting these elements so that the bulb lights up. ••

6. Name any devices other than the three mentioned in Section 31.1—battery, solar cell, and electric generator—that can act as a power source in an electric circuit. ••

7. Draw a circuit diagram for a typical home hair dryer. To which form (or forms) of energy is electric potential energy converted when you use the dryer? ••

8. Figure P31.8 shows five identical light bulbs A–E connected to a battery. Initially, some of the bulbs light up because the two terminals of each bulb are connected to opposite terminals of the battery. If any wire in the circuit is cut, some bulbs may go out. Which bulbs, if any, go out when a single cut is made at (*a*) location a, (*b*) location b, (*c*) location c, and (*d*) location d? •••

Figure P31.8

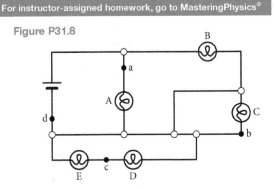

9. You and a colleague want to light a light bulb using a parallel-plate capacitor as a power source. Your colleague objects to this design, stating that the bulb cannot light up if the circuit is not continuous and the circuit is not continuous because the air gap between the capacitor plates constitutes a break in the circuit. He argues that charge carriers do not jump across the gap, so how can there be any current? What is your counterargument? •••

31.2 Current and resistance

10. Which of the light bulbs (if any) in Figure P31.10 are connected in series to each other? •

Figure P31.10

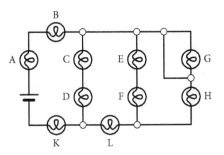

11. (*a*) In the circuit of Figure P31.11, do all four bulbs light up? (*b*) Rank the bulbs according to how brightly they light up, brightest first. • .

Figure P31.11

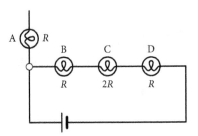

12. All the power sources (batteries or capacitors) in Figure P31.12 on the next page start with a potential difference of 9.0 V between their terminals, and all of them run down (decrease in potential difference) over time. Rank the brightness of these identical light bulbs from least bright to most bright. The *t* values in parts *d* through *g* refer to the time interval that has passed since the power source was connected to the load. ••

Figure P31.12

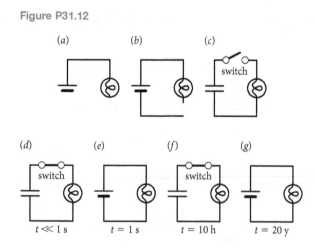

(a)   (b)   (c)

(d)   (e)   (f)   (g)

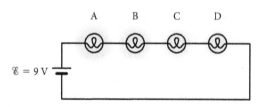

$t \ll 1$ s $t = 1$ s $t = 10$ h $t = 20$ y

13. In Figure P31.13, bulb A is brighter than bulb B, B is brighter than C, and C is brighter than D. Is it possible for the potential difference across bulb C to be (a) 3 V and (b) 2 V? ••

Figure P31.13

A   B   C   D

$\mathcal{E} = 9$ V

14. When light bulbs A and B are connected in series to a battery, A glows brightly and B glows dimly. You remove bulb B so that the circuit is just the battery and bulb A and connect bulb B to an identical battery. With the two bulbs connected to identical batteries but in separate circuits, do they glow equally brightly now? ••

15. Bulb B produces twice as much light and thermal energy as bulb A, and bulb C produces three times as much light and thermal energy as bulb A. The bulbs are connected in series to a 9.0-V battery, and the steady current through bulb A is 1.0 A. In 1.0 s, how much energy is dissipated as light and thermal energy by each bulb? •••

31.3 Junctions and multiple loops

16. Wires A, B, and C meet at a junction. The current in wire A is 3.2 mA into the junction, and the current in wire B is 4.3 mA out of the junction. What is the current in wire C, and in what direction, into or out of the junction, is this current? •

17. Which (if any) of the light bulbs in Figure P31.17 are connected to other bulbs in parallel? •

Figure P31.17

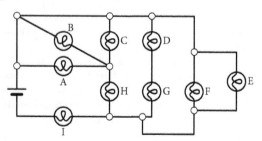

18. Which of the light bulbs in Figure P31.18 are connected to each other in series? Which are connected to each other in parallel? •

Figure P31.18

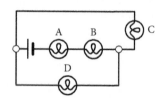

A   B   C

D

19. Draw a circuit diagram for the circuit of Figure P31.19 ••.

Figure P31.19

20. In the circuit of Figure P31.20, bulb A is bright and bulb B is dim. Which bulb (a) has the greater potential difference across it, (b) carries the greater current, and (c) has the greater resistance? ••

Figure P31.20

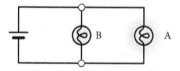

B   A

21. (a) Draw a circuit diagram for the circuit shown in Figure P31.21, which consists of a battery and four identical light bulbs. (b) Do all the bulbs light up? (c) Which bulb is brightest? Dimmest? (d) Which bulbs are connected to each other in parallel? Which are connected in series? ••

Figure P31.21

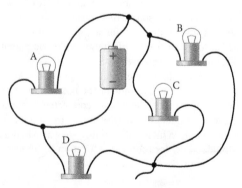

22. Decades ago, holiday lights were wired in series, so that if one bulb in a string burned out, all the lights in the string went dark because the burned-out bulb interrupted the circuit. Today's lights are wired at least partially in parallel, so that if one light goes out, many others in the string remain lit. In which circuits in Figure P31.22 does one bulb burning out leave all other bulbs lit? In which does one bulb burning out cause one or more of the other bulbs to go out? ••

Figure P31.22

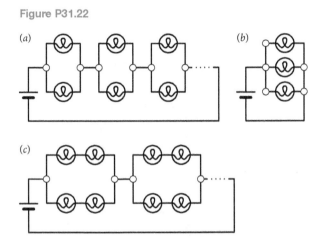

23. Are the lights in a house wired in series, in parallel, or a combination of the two? •••

31.4 Electric fields in conductors

24. In Figure P31.24, the wire connecting the positive battery terminal to the top end of the resistor is 100 mm long, and the wire connecting the negative battery terminal to the bottom end of the resistor is also 100 mm long. If the resistor is 10 mm long, what are the electric field magnitudes at locations a, b, and c? •

Figure P31.24

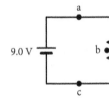

25. Once the switch in the circuit in Figure P31.25 is closed, the circuit can be used to charge the capacitor. Sketch the electric field inside wire A (a) when the switch is open, (b) at the instant just after the switch is closed, and (c) at some instant long after the switch is closed. •

Figure P31.25

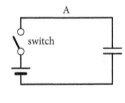

26. A cylindrical wire initially has resistance R and length ℓ. The wire is clamped in place at its midpoint, and the portion to the left of the clamp remains unchanged. The portion to the right of the clamp is stretched out to a length ℓ. Express the new resistance R' of the wire in terms of R. Assume the stretching is done uniformly and the wire remains cylindrical. ••

27. You want to use a length of insulated rigid metal rod to discharge the plates of a parallel-plate capacitor without allowing the electric field in the rod to exceed 1000 N/C. The area A of each plate is 1.00 m², the plate separation distance is $d = 100$ mm, and there is no dielectric material between the plates. Initially, each plate holds a charge of magnitude

4.51×10^{-8} C. If one end of the rod is attached to the center of one edge of plate 1, describe all the positions on plate 2 to which the other end of the rod could be attached. Illustrate your answer with a sketch. •••

31.5 Resistance and Ohm's law

28. A copper wire that is 600 mm long and has a radius of 1.0 mm is connected to the terminals of a 9.0-V battery. What is the current through the wire $[\sigma_{\text{copper}} = 5.9 \times 10^7 \, \text{A}/(\text{V} \cdot \text{m})]$? •

29. The nickel-chromium alloy nichrome is often used for heating elements. A typical household toaster heating element has a resistance of 12 Ω. If you make this element using nichrome wire 0.40 mm in diameter, how long must the wire be? How long must it be if you use copper wire of the same diameter $[\sigma_{\text{nichrome}} = 6.7 \times 10^5 \, \text{A}/(\text{V} \cdot \text{m})$, $\sigma_{\text{copper}} = 5.9 \times 10^7 \, \text{A}/(\text{V} \cdot \text{m})]$? •

30. A 6-gauge copper wire (4.115-mm diameter) carries a current of 1.20 A. What is the wire's current density? •

31. How strong must an electric field in a metal be in order for electrons in the field to have a drift speed of 10 mm/s if the time interval between electron-ion collisions is 1.0×10^{-14} s? •

32. Figure P31.32 is a graph of the current through a light-emitting diode as a function of the potential difference across the diode. What is the resistance of the diode at a potential difference of 3.0 V? ••

Figure P31.32

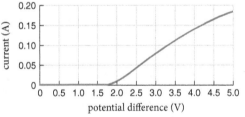

33. *Gauge* is a term used to describe the size of a wire: The greater the gauge, the smaller the wire diameter. At room temperature, 4-gauge wire has a diameter of 5.19 mm, and 22-gauge wire has a diameter of 0.64 mm. For copper, how long would a wire of each gauge need to be to have a resistance of 1.0 Ω $[\sigma_{\text{copper}} = 5.9 \times 10^7 \, \text{A}/(\text{V} \cdot \text{m})]$? ••

34. Two wires are made of the same material. If both are at the same temperature, but one has twice the diameter and three times the length of the other, which has the greater resistance, and by what factor? ••

35. When a potential difference of 1.00 V is maintained across a cube made of a metal for which the charge carrier number density is $n = 6.60 \times 10^{28}$ charge carriers/m³, the cube carries current $I = 6.10 \times 10^5$ A. What is the average time interval τ between collisions in this metal if each side of the cube is 10.0 mm long? ••

36. What is the magnitude of the applied electric field inside an aluminum wire of radius 1.0 mm that carries a 4.0-A current $[\sigma_{\text{aluminum}} = 3.6 \times 10^7 \, \text{A}/(\text{V} \cdot \text{m})]$? ••

37. For each of these changes in a metal, predict whether the average time interval between collisions of an electron with a lattice ion increases or decreases: (a) spatial density of the lattice ions is increased, (b) size of the lattice ions is decreased, (c) charge of the lattice ions is increased. ••

38. In a copper wire that has a diameter of 1.63 mm, the drift velocity is 7.08×10^{-4} m/s. If we assume one free electron per copper atom, what are (a) the current in the wire and (*b*) the current density? (*c*) This wire connects a light bulb, power source, and switch in a circuit, and the distance between the switch and bulb is 3.00 m. How long does it take for an electron initially at the switch to reach the bulb? ••

39. In a particle accelerator, the particles in a beam of protons are traveling toward a target at a speed equal to $0.100c_0$. If the beam has a radius of $0.100 \, \mu$m and carries a current of 2.00 nA, how many protons strike the target in 1.00 s? Assume the target is large enough to intercept the entire beam. •

40. When you step on the brake pedal in your car, charge carriers flow from the battery to the rear brake lights. Suppose the wire connecting the switch at the pedal to the brake lights is made of copper and has a diameter of 1.1 mm. If the current through the wire is 2.0 A, how long on average does it take an electron to travel from the switch at the pedal to one of the brake lights? The number density of free electrons in copper is $n = 8.4 \times 10^{28}$ electrons/m^3. ••

41. Even though silver is a better electrical conductor than copper, most electrical cables are made from copper. The main reason is cost: The per-kilogram price of silver is about 100 times the per-kilogram price of copper. If you want a length ℓ of wire to have a resistance R, by what factor does the cost of silver exceed that of copper? (The mass density of silver is $\rho_S = 10{,}490$ kg/m^3, and that of copper is $\rho_C = 8960$ kg/m^3.) ••

42. You have a piece of copper wire and a piece of carbon rod, each 1.5 m long and each having a cross-sectional area of 8.0×10^{-6} m^2. When you connect the copper wire to the terminals of a 9.0-V battery, the current in the wire is I. If you want to connect the carbon rod to another battery and have the same current I in the wire, what must the potential difference of the battery be [$\sigma_{copper} = 5.9 \times 10^7$ A/(V · m), $\sigma_{carbon} = 7.3 \times 10^4$ A/(V · m)]? ••

43. An electric field of magnitude 4.50×10^2 V/m is created in a wire that is 300 mm long and has a radius of 1.00 mm. The number density of the charge carriers in the wire is 1.20×10^{27} charge carriers/m^3. How much energy is gained by the lattice of metal ions in the time interval it takes for the average electron to travel the length of the wire? •••

31.6 Single-loop circuits

44. What are the magnitude and direction of the current in each circuit in Figure P31.44? •

Figure P31.44

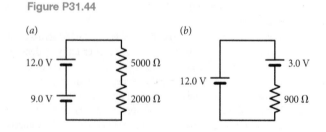

(*a*)

12.0 V   5000 Ω

9.0 V   2000 Ω

(*b*)

   3.0 V

12.0 V

   900 Ω

45. What are the magnitude and direction of the current in the circuit in Figure P31.45? •

Figure P31.45

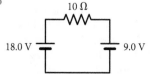

10 Ω

18.0 V   9.0 V

46. Three resistors are connected in series to a battery. If the resistances are $R_1 = 15 \, \Omega$, $R_2 = 20 \, \Omega$, and $R_3 = 25 \, \Omega$ and the current through the 15-Ω resistor is 2.3 A, what is the potential difference across the battery terminals (*a*) if the battery is ideal and (*b*) if the battery has an internal resistance of 5.0 Ω? •

47. What are the magnitude and direction of the current in each circuit in Figure P31.47? ••

Figure P31.47

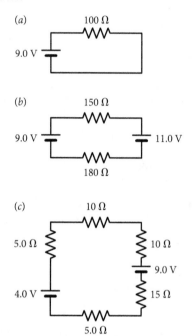

(*a*)   100 Ω

9.0 V

(*b*)   150 Ω

9.0 V   11.0 V

180 Ω

(*c*)   10 Ω

5.0 Ω   10 Ω

   9.0 V

4.0 V   15 Ω

5.0 Ω

48. When using the loop rule, what problems do you encounter with the circuit in Figure P31.48*a*? What do you expect for the current in the more realistic circuit in Figure P31.48*b*, which includes a small nonzero resistance in the wire and internal resistance in the battery? ••

Figure P31.48

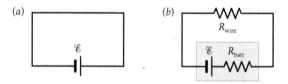

(*a*)   (*b*) R_{wire}

$\mathscr{E}$ $\mathscr{E}$ R_{batt}

49. When a nonideal battery is connected to a 2.0-Ω resistor in a circuit, the current in the circuit is 2.0 A. When the same battery is connected to a 1.0-Ω resistor in a circuit, the current in the circuit is 3.0 A. What are (*a*) the internal resistance of the battery and (*b*) its emf? ••

50. Two resistors connected in series have an equivalent resistance of 8.0 Ω. The same resistors connected in parallel have an equivalent resistance of 1.5 Ω. What is the resistance of each resistor? ••

51. The potential difference between positions a and b in Figure P31.51 is 5.5 V, and $R_1 = 5.0 \, \Omega$, $\mathscr{E}_1 = 8.0$ V, and $\mathscr{E}_2 = 4.0$ V. What is the value of the resistance R_2? ••

Figure P31.51

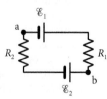

$\mathscr{E}_1$

a

R_2 R_1

b

$\mathscr{E}_2$

52. A typical car battery can be modeled as an ideal source $\mathcal{E}$ connected in series with an internal resistance R_{batt}. Using a good battery of this design to "jump start" a dead one can be dangerous if done incorrectly. (*a*) If you want to connect a good battery to a dead one in such a way that you have the smallest possible current through the dead one, should you connect them in series (+ to − and − to +) or in parallel (+ to + and − to −)? Assume you have a good battery for which $\mathcal{E}_{\text{good}} = 12.0$ V and $R_{\text{batt, good}} = 0.0200\ \Omega$ and a dead one for which $\mathcal{E}_{\text{dead}} = 11.0$ V and $R_{\text{batt, dead}} = 0.200\ \Omega$. Calculate the current through the batteries connected (*b*) in series and (*c*) in parallel. ••

53. For the circuit shown in Figure P31.53, calculate (*a*) the magnitude and direction of the current and (*b*) the potential differences V_{ab}, V_{bc}, V_{cd}, and V_{da}. Use these values: $R_1 = 5.0\ \Omega$, $R_2 = 3.0\ \Omega$, $R_3 = 6.0\ \Omega$, $\mathcal{E}_1 = 10$ V, and $\mathcal{E}_2 = 2.0$ V. ••

Figure P31.53

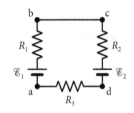

54. The internal resistance of a battery is relatively small when the battery is new but increases as the battery ages. When a new 12.0-V battery is attached to a 100-Ω load, the potential difference across the load is 11.9 V. After the circuit has operated for a while, the potential difference across the load is 11.5 V. By how much has the internal resistance of the battery changed? ••

55. (*a*) What is the equivalent resistance of the circuit in Figure P31.55? Use the values $R_1 = 200\ \Omega$, $R_2 = 900\ \Omega$, and $R_3 = 100\ \Omega$. (*b*) What is the current in the circuit? Assume $\mathcal{E} = 12$ V. (*c*) The electric potential at location d is defined to be 0, because the negative terminal of the battery is attached to ground. What is the electric potential at locations a, b, and c? ••

Figure P31.55

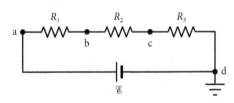

56. Resistors 1 and 2—$R_1 = 40\ \Omega$, $R_2 = 70\ \Omega$—are connected in series to a 4.5-V battery. (*a*) What is the potential difference across resistor 1? (*b*) If you decrease the value of R_1, what happens to the current in the circuit and to the potential difference across resistor 1? ••

57. A light bulb has resistance $R_{\text{bulb}} = 5.0\ \Omega$ and should be operated at a potential difference of $V_{\text{bulb}} = 3.0$ V. If you must use this bulb in a circuit powered by a battery of emf $\mathcal{E} = 9.0$ V, how much resistance must you add in series to the circuit in order to have a 3.0-V potential difference across the bulb? ••

58. You must complete the circuit of Figure P31.58 in such a way that it draws a current of 0.300 A from the battery. The battery maintains a potential difference of 10.0 V with no load, but has an internal resistance of $R_{\text{batt}} = 18.0\ \Omega$. The only material you have is 20.0 mm³ of nichrome, and you must use all of it. If your plan is to form the nichrome into a cylindrical resistor, what must the cylinder length and cross-sectional area be? [The conductivity of nichrome is 6.7×10^5 A/(V · m).] •••

Figure P31.58

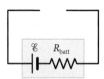

31.7 Multiloop circuits

59. What is the equivalent resistance of the circuit in Figure P31.59? Use the values $R_1 = 2.0\ \Omega$, $R_2 = 1.5\ \Omega$, $R_3 = 2.0\ \Omega$, $R_4 = 1.5\ \Omega$, $R_5 = 2.0\ \Omega$, and $R_6 = 1.5\ \Omega$. •

Figure P31.59

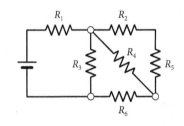

60. Figure P31.60 shows three circuits containing four identical resistors, each having resistance R. Which circuit has the smallest equivalent resistance? Which has the greatest equivalent resistance? •

Figure P31.60

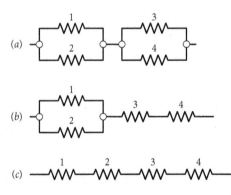

61. A nonideal ammeter that has an internal resistance of 0.503 Ω is connected in series with a 3.00-V battery and a 40.0-Ω resistor. By what percentage does the presence of the ammeter change the current measurement? •

62. In Figure P31.62 on the next page, the brightness of each bulb depends on the magnitude of the current through it. Rank these identical bulbs according to brightness, brightest first, (*a*) before the wire ab connecting the two junctions is cut and (*b*) after the wire is cut. (*c*) Does cutting the wire increase or decrease the brightness of A? Of B? Of C? ••

Figure P31.62

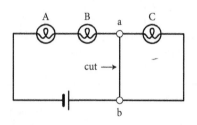

63. Using only 10.0-Ω resistors (but as many as you like), build a circuit that has a resistance of 27.5 Ω. ••
64. A copper wire has a diameter of 0.20 mm and is $\ell_{wire} = 10$ m long. (a) What is the resistance of the wire? (b) The wire is cut into N identical pieces, and the pieces are connected in parallel to form a single resistor. What is the minimum value of N that gives this resistor a resistance smaller than $R_{resistor} = 1.0$ Ω? [The conductivity of copper is 5.9×10^7 A/(V·m).] ••
65. For the circuit in Figure P31.65, assume the electric potential is zero at the negative terminal of the battery. Calculate (a) the equivalent resistance of the circuit, (b) the electric potential at position a, and (c) the magnitude and direction of the current through each resistor. ••

Figure P31.65

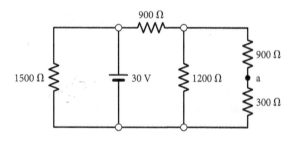

66. In Figure P31.66, determine the magnitude of current I_1. ••

Figure P31.66

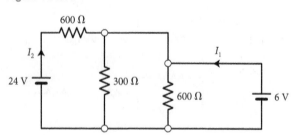

67. In Figure P31.67, calculate the magnitudes of currents I_1, I_2, and I_3. ••

Figure P31.67

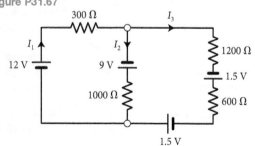

68. In Figure P31.68, the circuit has been completed for several minutes. Calculate (a) the current through each resistor and (b) the magnitude of charge on each capacitor plate. ••

Figure P31.68

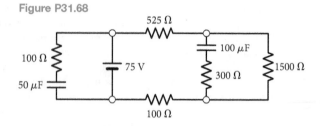

69. In Figure P31.69, calculate (a) the equivalent resistance of the circuit and (b) the magnitude of the current through each resistor. Use these values: $R_1 = 1.0$ Ω, $R_2 = 2.0$ Ω, $R_3 = 2.0$ Ω, $R_4 = 3.0$ Ω, $R_5 = 1.0$ Ω, $R_6 = 1.0$ Ω, and $\mathscr{E} = 14$ V. ••

Figure P31.69

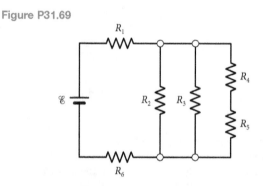

70. In Figure P31.70, determine the magnitudes of the currents I_1, I_2, and I_3 and whether the direction shown for each current is correct or should be reversed. Assume that $R_1 = 8.0$ Ω, $R_2 = 8.0$ Ω, $\mathscr{E}_1 = 6.0$ V, $\mathscr{E}_2 = 6.0$ V, and $\mathscr{E}_3 = 9.0$ V. ••

Figure P31.70

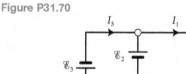

71. The eight resistors in Figure P31.71 are identical to one another, all having resistance $R = 200$ Ω. What is the magnitude of the current drawn from the battery? ••

Figure P31.71

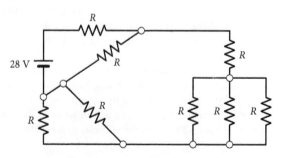

72. In Figure P31.72, $\mathcal{E}_1 = 5.0$ V, $\mathcal{E}_2 = 5.0$ V, $\mathcal{E}_3 = 1.5$ V, $R_1 = 50$ Ω, $R_2 = 50$ Ω, and $R_3 = 50$ Ω. What are (a) the current in each branch of the circuit and (b) the potential differences V_{ab}, V_{bc}, V_{cd}, V_{de}, V_{ef}, and V_{fa}? ••

Figure P31.72

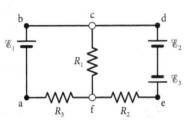

73. A string of winter holiday lights consists of N bulbs, each having resistance R_b (Figure P31.73). Wired in parallel with each bulb is a resistor of resistance R_p. What is the resistance of the string? If one of the bulbs burns out, what happens to the other N-1 bulbs? ••

Figure P31.73

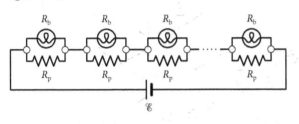

74. An ammeter that has internal resistance $R_{am} = 0.504$ Ω is designed to measure a maximum current of $I_{max} = 100$ mA. You want to use this ammeter to measure the current in a circuit that consists of a 3.00-V battery and a resistor that has a resistance of 4.00 Ω. (a) What problem do you encounter? (b) How can you overcome this problem by inserting a second resistor into the circuit and rescaling the meter readout (that is, by multiplying the readout value by some constant)? ••

75. If each resistor in Figure P31.75 has resistance $R = 5.0$ Ω, what is the equivalent resistance of the combination? ••

Figure P31.75

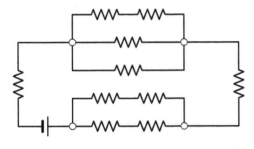

76. In Figure P31.76, $R_1 = 2.0$ Ω, $R_2 = 1.5$ Ω, $R_3 = 2.0$ Ω, $R_4 = 1.0$ Ω, $R_5 = 2.0$ Ω, $R_6 = 1.0$ Ω, $C_1 = 20$ μF, $C_2 = 40$ μF, and $\mathcal{E} = 12.0$ V. Assume that the circuit has been

connected for several minutes. (a) Calculate the current through the battery and through each resistor. (b) Compute the magnitude of charge on each plate of both capacitors. •••

Figure P31.76

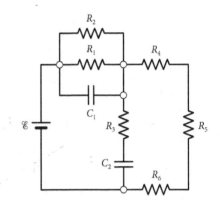

77. In Figure P31.77, each of the three batteries supplies an emf of 6.0 V and each of the four resistors has a resistance of 3.0 Ω. Calculate the magnitudes of the five currents I_1-I_5. •••

Figure P31.77

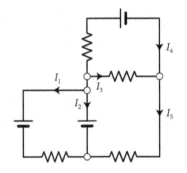

78. If the ammeter in the Wheatstone bridge of Figure P31.78 measures zero current when the resistance R_{var} of the variable resistor is set to 185 Ω, what is the current I_L through the left side of the bridge? •••

Figure P31.78

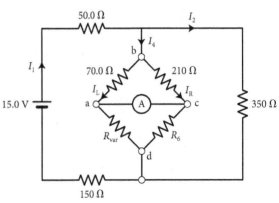

31.8 Power in electric circuits

79. If a light bulb has a resistance of 5.5 Ω and is dissipating energy at a rate of 9.0 W, what are (*a*) the current through the bulb and (*b*) the potential difference across its terminals? •

80. If the current through a 10-Ω resistor is 2.0 A, how much energy is dissipated by the resistor in 1.0 h? •

81. Two light bulbs 1 and 2 are connected in parallel to an 8.00-V battery. (*a*) If the bulb resistances are $R_1 = 4.0$ Ω and $R_2 = 6.0$ Ω, what is the rate at which each bulb consumes energy? (*b*) At what rate does the circuit consume energy? (*c*) Calculate the same three power values for the bulbs connected in series rather than in parallel. •

82. A car battery is labeled "12 V 40 Ah." You forget to switch off the light in your glove compartment, which draws 0.80 A. How long until the battery is drained? •

83. (*a*) Determine the current through and the potential difference across each resistor in Figure P31.83. Assume that $R_1 = R_2 = R_3 = R_4 = 50.0$ Ω, $\mathscr{E}_1 = 10.0$ V, and $\mathscr{E}_2 = 5.00$ V. (*b*) At what rate is energy dissipated in each resistor? (*c*) What is the power of each battery, and is energy used by or supplied by each battery? ••

Figure P31.83

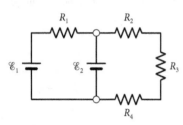

84. A 60-W light bulb has resistance $R = 10.00$ Ω when connected to a battery with emf $\mathscr{E} = 120.0$ V. What is the internal resistance R_{batt} of the battery? ••

85. Determine the current through each resistor and the magnitude of the charge on either capacitor plate after the circuit in Figure P31.85 has been connected for a few minutes. ••

Figure P31.85

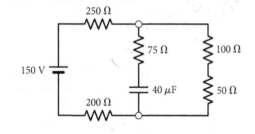

86. If the rate at which energy is dissipated by resistor 1 in Figure P31.86 is 0.75 W, and $R_1 = 12$ Ω, $\mathscr{E}_1 = 4.5$ V, and $\mathscr{E}_2 = 8.0$ V, (*a*) what is the value of R_2? (*b*) At what rate is energy dissipated in resistor 2? (*c*) Which battery supplies energy to the circuit, and at what rate does it do so? (*d*) At what rate is energy used by the other battery? ••

Figure P31.86

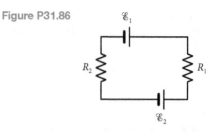

87. A copper wire of length $\ell = 1.0$ km and radius $r = 1.2$ mm carries current $I = 20$ A. At what rate is energy lost from the wire? Why do long electrical transmission lines usually work with "high voltage"? ••

88. In Figure P31.88, in which resistor is energy dissipated (*a*) at the greatest rate and (*b*) at the smallest rate? •••

Figure P31.88

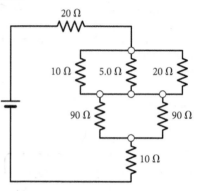

89. At what rate is energy either delivered by or delivered to each battery in Figure P31.67? At what rate is energy dissipated in each resistor? Does the power summed over all the elements make sense? •••

90. A physics student who needs a magnetic field for a project makes a solenoid coil from "magnet wire," which is copper wire coated with a very thin enamel insulation. (The insulation is so thin that you can ignore its thickness.) He chose 28-gauge wire, which is 0.321 mm in diameter, and winds a solenoid that is 50 mm in diameter and 0.20 m long. He then runs a 3.0-A current through the solenoid but is disappointed at how small the magnetic field magnitude is and horrified at how hot the magnet gets after a few minutes. Calculate the magnetic field magnitude and the rate at which energy is lost as thermal energy as the coil heats up. What would you suggest the student do to get a greater magnetic field and less thermal energy loss? •••

Additional problems

91. The filament in an incandescent light bulb is a resistor that has a resistance of 9.5 Ω at room temperature. By what factor does the resistance increase when a 100-W bulb connected to a 120-V power source is turned on and heats up? •

92. Does the light bulb in Figure P31.92 light up? Why or why not? •

Figure P31.92

93. In what type of electrical conductor could the charge on the charge carriers in a current have a magnitude other than e? •

94. The potential difference across a resistor in a circuit is 12 V when a current of 1.0 A passes through the resistor. What is the potential difference across the resistor when the current through it is 3.5 A? •

95. The battery in Figure P31.95 has internal resistance $R_{batt} = 13.0\ \Omega$ and maintains an emf $\mathcal{E} = 20.0$ V. What is the resistance R of the resistor connected in series with the battery if the current through the circuit is 0.100 A? •

Figure P31.95

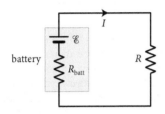

96. Calculate the values of I_1 and I_2 in the circuit shown in Figure P31.96 if all the resistors have resistance 240 Ω and $I_3 = 2.0$ A. ••

Figure P31.96

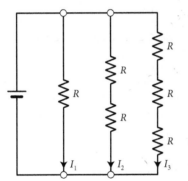

97. If each battery in Figure P31.97 has an emf of 9.0 V, what is the potential difference across the light bulb in each circuit? ••

Figure P31.97

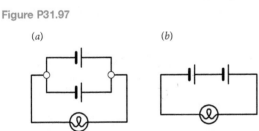

98. The two resistors in Figure P31.98 are made of the same material and are of equal length. The only difference between them is that the radius of the top one is greater than the radius of the bottom one. (a) Through which resistor is the current greater? (b) Across which resistor is the potential difference greater? (c) How does the resistance of the circuit compare with the individual resistances of the two resistors? ••

Figure P31.98

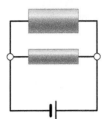

99. If you want to add a third resistor to the circuit in Figure P31.98 to reduce the circuit resistance as much as possible, should you connect it in series or in parallel? Should you add a resistor with a large cross-sectional area, like the top one in Figure P31.98, or one with a small cross-sectional area, like the bottom one? ••

100. In Figure P31.100, $\mathcal{E}_1 = 3.0$ V and $\mathcal{E}_2 = 5.0$ V. (a) What value of $\mathcal{E}_3$ causes the potential difference across resistor 1 to be zero? (b) In that situation, what is the current through resistor 2? ••

Figure P31.100

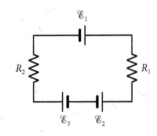

101. Your boss has given you the incomplete circuit shown in Figure P31.101 and charged you with determining the greatest and smallest currents that can be drawn from the battery using this circuit. The catch is that you must close the gap with a resistor from your laboratory. You rummage around and find a huge cabinet full of resistors ranging from very small to very large resistance. •••

Figure P31.101

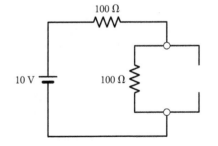

102. You illuminate a photovoltaic cell with a halogen light bulb. The cell is connected to an ammeter, a voltmeter, and a variable resistor (Figure P31.102a on the next page), and the current through and potential difference across the resistor are measured for different settings of the resistor. Figure P31.102b shows the data from these measurements, where each data point represents the potential difference and current at a particular value of R_{var}. What values of R_{var} do the data points at low and high potential differences correspond to? When is the power of the photovoltaic cell at its maximum value? ●●●

Figure P31.102

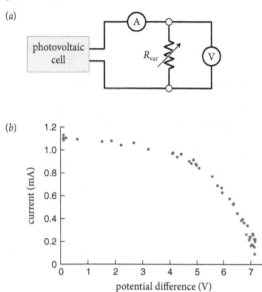

(a)

(b)

103. The circuit shown in Figure P31.103 has been connected for a few minutes. Determine the current through each resistor and the battery, and determine the magnitude of charge on either plate of each capacitor. Use resistor values $R_1 = R_2 = 5.00\ \Omega$, $R_3 = 4.00\ \Omega$, $R_4 = 6.00\ \Omega$, $R_5 = 10.0\ \Omega$, $R_6 = 0.500\ \Omega$, $R_7 = 1.00\ \Omega$, and $R_8 = 0.500\ \Omega$. ●●●

Figure P31.103

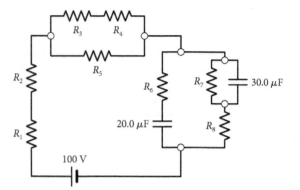

104. Three students rent a third-floor apartment. After signing the lease, they realize there's no electricity on the third floor! They run a 30.5-m, 18-gauge extension cord up from the second floor and plug everything into some power strips plugged into this cord. An electrician visiting the apartment says, "You can't do that; you'll burn the house down! Get a heavy-duty cord made with 12-gauge wire." You don't see how that could make a significant difference, so you begin to look up wire sizes in a reference table. ●●● CR

105. You need a liquid electrical conductor for a project you are working on, and as one possibility you try seawater. You know the number density of the charge carriers and the average time interval between collisions. Your preliminary calculations using *Principles* Eq. 31.9 and the mass and charge of an electron give you a theoretical conductivity, σ_{theory}. When testing the seawater, though, you obtain a conductivity less than two thousand times smaller than σ_{theory} ($\sigma_{test} < \sigma_{theory}/2000$). You struggle to understand this discrepancy. ●●● CR

Answers to Review Questions

1. In a direct-current circuit, the potential difference supplied by the power source stays constant, and in an alternating-current circuit, the potential difference of the power source changes (*alternates*) over time.
2. A loop is any closed conducting path through the circuit.
3. The load is all the circuit elements connected to the power source.
4. In a nonideal circuit, yes, because some of the potential difference of the power source is converted to other forms of energy in the wires. In this chapter, however, we consider such conversions to be negligible relative to the conversion taking place in the circuit elements, and so we do not consider the wires part of the load.
5. Electric potential energy initially in charge carriers in the power source is converted to some other form of energy in the circuit load.
6. Steady state for an electric circuit means that the current in every part of the circuit is constant over time.
7. For a single-loop electric circuit in a steady state, the current is the same at all locations in the circuit.
8. The principle states that when the circuit is in steady state, charge carriers do not accumulate at any location in the circuit. For example, every charge carrier moving from the power source into the rest of the circuit is accompanied by a charge carrier moving from the rest of the circuit into the power source.

9. The amount of electric potential energy converted is equal to the potential difference between the two locations multiplied by the charge on the carrier.
10. The elements are connected such that there is only a single current path through them, so that charge carriers must flow first through one element, then the next element, and so on.
11. The resistance of the element is the determining property.
12. (a) The current is the same everywhere in any given branch of a multiloop circuit (the branch rule). (b) The number of charge carriers going into a junction equals the number exiting the junction (junction rule).
13. The electrical quantity that is the same for the bulbs connected in series is the current through them. The quantity that is the same for the bulbs connected in parallel is the potential difference across each one.
14. A short in an electric circuit is a branch of negligible resistance connected in parallel to some other element in the circuit. Essentially all the charge carriers moving through the circuit flow through the short, and essentially none flow through the element connected in parallel.
15. No. Any orientation is allowed in a diagram as long as the connections between elements are accurately portrayed. Because the wires are treated as ideal, neither the length you draw them nor whether you show them bent or straight affects the accuracy of the diagram.

16. The electric field has the same magnitude everywhere inside the conductor, and the direction of the field is parallel to the walls of the conductor (in the direction of the current).

17. The resistance of an electrical conductor of uniform cross section depends on the material the conductor is made of and the length and cross-sectional area of the conductor. The resistance is directly proportional to the length and inversely proportional to the area.

18. A metal consists of a lattice of positive ions held in fixed positions and vibrating about those positions. The ions are metal atoms that have lost one or more of their outermost electrons, and these electrons are free to move about the lattice at very high speeds, colliding occasionally with the ions.

19. At any instant, the velocity of each electron is equal to its velocity before the last collision plus the impulse per unit of mass due to the electric force exerted on the electron. The average velocity of all the electrons is then the average velocity just after their last collision plus the average impulse per unit of mass. Because an electron can move in any direction after a collision, the average velocity of the electrons just after their last collision is zero. Therefore the average velocity of the electrons at any instant is due only to the average impulse per unit of mass due to the electric force exerted on the electrons between collisions. The average impulse per unit of mass is the product of the force and the average time interval between collisions divided by the mass of the electron. This average velocity due to the impulse is the *drift velocity* of the electrons, and its direction is opposite that of the electric field.

20. The conductivity is the proportionality factor between the current density and the electric field in any conductor made of the material. It measures how well or how poorly the material conducts an electric current.

21. The conductivity depends on the number density of the charge carriers, their charge and mass, the average time interval between collisions, and temperature.

22. The resistance is the ratio of the potential difference across the element to the current through it.

23. An ohmic material is one that obeys Ohm's law, $I = V/R$ (Eq. 31.11).

24. The slope of the curve is the reciprocal of the resistance of the element. For a circuit element made of an ohmic material, the curve is a straight line, which means that the resistance is independent of the potential difference across the element.

25. Current continuity requires that the current is the same at all locations in the circuit. Energy conservation requires that the algebraic sum of the emfs and the potential differences around the loop is zero (loop rule).

26. The equivalent resistance of resistors in series is the sum of the individual resistances.

27. A battery's internal resistance accounts for the (usually small) amount of energy dissipated inside the battery and thus not available as electric potential energy outside the battery. When we analyze the circuit, a small resistor of resistance R_{batt} is added in series with the battery of emf $\mathcal{E}$.

28. The equivalent resistance of resistors connected in parallel is the reciprocal of the sum of the reciprocals of the individual resistances.

29. Identify all junctions and label the currents in each branch. Write the junction rule for all but one junction, and write the loop rule for as many loops as necessary to obtain, along with the junction rule, as many independent equations as there are unknowns to solve for. Then perform the required algebra to solve for the unknowns.

30. The rate at which energy is converted is power, and the general expression for power in a circuit element is the product of the current through the element and the magnitude of the potential difference across it.

31. The rate of energy conversion in a resistor is equal to the current squared times the resistance and represents the conversion of electric potential energy to thermal energy (Eq. 31.43).

Answers to Guided Problems

Guided Problem 31.2 (a) $h_{slow} = \dfrac{\Delta E_{batt}}{2\,mg} = \dfrac{(4.1 \times 10^4\ \text{J})}{2(60\ \text{kg})(9.8\ \text{m/s}^2)} = 34\ \text{m}$,

$h_{max} = \dfrac{1}{4}\left(\dfrac{\Delta E_{batt}}{mg}\right) = \dfrac{1}{4}\dfrac{(4.1 \times 10^4\ \text{J})}{(60\ \text{kg})(9.8\ \text{m/s}^2)} = 17\ \text{m}$;

(b) $v_{max} = \dfrac{(\text{efficiency})(P_{max})}{mg} = 4.8 \times 10^{-4}\ \text{m/s}$,

$\Delta t_{min} = \dfrac{2R_{batt}\Delta E_{batt}}{\mathcal{E}^2} = \dfrac{(2)(1.0\ \Omega)(4.1 \times 10^4\ \text{J})}{(1.5\ \text{V})^2}$

$\qquad = 3.6 \times 10^4\ \text{s} = 10\ \text{h}$

Guided Problem 31.4 $I_1 = \dfrac{\mathcal{E}}{R_1 + R_{eq2,3,4}} = \dfrac{9}{29}\dfrac{\mathcal{E}}{R_1}$,

$I_4 = \dfrac{\mathcal{E} - I_1 R_1}{R_4} = \dfrac{5}{29}\dfrac{\mathcal{E}}{R_1}$,

$I_2 = \dfrac{\mathcal{E} - I_1 R_1}{R_{eq2,3}} = \dfrac{4}{29}\dfrac{\mathcal{E}}{R_1}$

Guided Problem 31.6 $\sigma = \dfrac{I}{\Delta V 2\pi \ell}\left(\ln \dfrac{r_{outer}}{r_{inner}}\right) = 3.23\ \text{A}/(\text{V}\cdot\text{m})$

Guided Problem 31.8 $P_{R1} = I_1^2 R_1 = 8.0 \times 10^2\ \text{W}$, $P_{R2} = 25\ \text{W}$,

$\qquad P_{R3} = 25\ \text{W}$, $P_{R4} = 4.5 \times 10^2\ \text{W}$

32

PRACTICE
Electronics

PRACTICE

Chapter Summary

AC circuits (Sections 32.1, 32.2, 32.5)

Concepts **Alternating current (AC)** is current that periodically changes direction.

In an AC circuit that contains a capacitor, the current through the capacitor leads the potential difference by 90° (one-fourth of an oscillation).

In an AC circuit that contains an inductor, the current through the inductor lags the potential difference by 90°.

In any circuit that contains a capacitor and/or an inductor, **reactance** is the proportionality constant between the potential-difference amplitude and the current amplitude.

The **phase constant** ϕ for an AC circuit, which is the phase difference between the source emf and the current, is negative when the current leads the source emf and positive when the current lags the source emf.

Quantitative Tools The instantaneous emf supplied by an AC source is

$$\mathcal{E} = \mathcal{E}_{max}\sin \omega t. \tag{32.1}$$

The instantaneous current in an AC circuit is

$$i = I \sin (\omega t - \phi), \tag{32.16}$$

where I is the amplitude (maximum value) of the current and ϕ is the **phase constant**. In an AC circuit that contains a capacitor, the *capacitive reactance* is

$$X_C \equiv \frac{1}{\omega C}, \tag{32.14}$$

and the amplitude of the potential difference across the capacitor is

$$V_C = IX_C. \tag{32.15}$$

In an AC circuit that contains an inductor, the *inductive reactance* is

$$X_L \equiv \omega L, \tag{32.26}$$

and the amplitude of the potential difference across the inductor is

$$V_L = IX_L. \tag{32.27}$$

RC and RLC series circuits (Section 32.6)

Concepts The **impedance** of a load connected to an AC source is a proportionality constant between the amplitudes of the potential difference and the current through the load.

Quantitative Tools
In an **RC series circuit,** the sum of all the instantaneous potential differences equals the emf of the source:

$$\mathcal{E} = v_R + v_C. \tag{32.28}$$

The current amplitude is

$$I = \frac{\mathcal{E}_{max}}{Z}, \tag{32.33}$$

where Z is the **impedance** of the load. For an RC series circuit, the impedance is

$$Z_{RC} \equiv \sqrt{R^2 + 1/\omega^2 C^2}. \tag{32.34}$$

The amplitudes of the potential differences are

$$V_R = IR = \frac{\mathcal{E}_{max}R}{\sqrt{R^2 + 1/\omega^2 C^2}} \tag{32.35}$$

$$V_C = IX_C = \frac{\mathcal{E}_{max}/\omega C}{\sqrt{R^2 + 1/\omega^2 C^2}}, \tag{32.36}$$

PRACTICE

and the **phase constant** for the circuit is

$$\phi = \tan^{-1}\left(-\frac{1}{\omega RC}\right).$$

(32.38)

In an **RLC series circuit,** the sum of all the instantaneous potential differences equals the emf of the source:

$$\mathcal{E} = v_R + v_L + v_C.$$

(32.39)

The **impedance** of the RLC series circuit is

$$Z_{RLC} \equiv \sqrt{R^2 + \left(\omega L - \frac{1}{\omega C}\right)^2},$$

(32.43)

and so the current amplitude is

$$I = \frac{\mathcal{E}_{max}}{Z_{RLC}} = \frac{\mathcal{E}_{max}}{\sqrt{R^2 + (\omega L - 1/\omega C)^2}}.$$

(32.42)

The **phase constant** for the circuit is given by

$$\tan\phi = \frac{\omega L - 1/\omega C}{R}.$$

(32.44)

Resonance and power in AC circuits (Sections 32.7, 32.8)

Concepts At the **resonant angular frequency,** the current in a series RLC circuit is a maximum.

The **power factor** is a measure of the efficiency with which the source in an AC circuit delivers energy to the load.

Quantitative Tools The **resonant angular frequency** is

$$\omega_0 = \frac{1}{\sqrt{LC}}.$$

(32.47)

For a sinusoidally varying current, the **root-mean-square** current is

$$I_{rms} = \frac{I}{\sqrt{2}},$$

(32.53)

and the root-mean-square potential difference is

$$V_{rms} = \frac{V}{\sqrt{2}} \qquad \mathcal{E}_{rms} = \frac{\mathcal{E}_{max}}{\sqrt{2}}.$$

(32.55)

The average power is

$$P_{av} = \mathcal{E}_{rms} I_{rms} \cos\phi,$$

(32.61)

where the cosine term is the **power factor** for the circuit:

$$\cos\phi = \frac{R}{Z}.$$

(32.62)

Semiconductor devices (Sections 32.3, 32.4)

Concepts A **semiconductor** is a material that contains a limited number of charge carriers that can move freely and that has an electrical conductivity intermediate between that of electrical conductors and that of electrical insulators.

An *intrinsic* semiconductor is made of atoms of only one element. An *extrinsic* (*doped*) semiconductor contains, interspersed among the atoms of its main element, trace amounts of atoms of other elements. These *dopant* atoms alter the number of electrons that can move freely and so change the electronic properties of the semiconductor.

A **hole** is an incomplete bond in a semiconductor that behaves like a freely moving positive charge carrier.

In a *p-type* semiconductor, holes are the free charge carriers. In an *n-type* semiconductor, electrons are the free charge carriers.

A **diode** is made by bringing a piece of *p*-type semiconductor into contact with a piece of *n*-type semiconductor. It behaves like a one-way valve for current.

The **depletion zone** in a diode is a thin insulating region at the junction between the *p*-type and *n*-type semiconductors where the positive and negative charge carriers have recombined and become immobile.

A **transistor** consists of a thin layer of one type of extrinsic semiconductor sandwiched between two layers of the opposite type of extrinsic semiconductor (such as *npn*). It behaves either like an on/off switch for current or like a current amplifier.

Review Questions

Answers to these questions can be found at the end of this chapter.

32.1 Alternating currents

1. What is an alternating current?
2. Describe how the current changes in a circuit that consists of a charged capacitor connected to an inductor.
3. What property specific to AC circuits must be considered when you apply the junction rule, the loop rule, or Ohm's law to such circuits?

32.2 AC circuits

4. What two quantities must you know in order to specify the time dependence of a sinusoidally varying function?
5. What is a phasor? Which phasor properties are used in analyzing oscillating quantities?
6. What do the descriptions *lead* and *lag* mean when applied to two oscillating quantities A and B that vary with the same angular frequency?
7. In a series AC circuit that contains a capacitor, an inductor, and a resistor, how is the current through each circuit element related to the potential difference across the element?

32.3 Semiconductors

8. What is a semiconductor?
9. What is the difference between an intrinsic semiconductor and an extrinsic semiconductor?
10. Describe how holes in an extrinsic semiconductor behave like positively charged particles.
11. How are doped silicon semiconductors classified, and what do the classifications mean?

32.4 Diodes, transistors, and logic gates

12. What are the two main components of a diode?
13. What is the depletion zone in a diode?
14. Describe how a depletion zone forms in a diode.
15. What happens when the *n* side of a diode is connected to a battery's positive terminal and the *p* side is connected to the negative terminal? What happens when the connections are *n* side to negative terminal and *p* side to positive terminal?
16. What is a bias potential difference, and what is its purpose in an *npn* transistor?
17. What two main functions can transistors perform in electric circuits?
18. Explain how a current is created in a field-effect transistor.
19. What is a logic gate?

32.5 Reactance

20. For a capacitor connected to an AC generator, compare the current through the capacitor and the potential difference across the capacitor in terms of their angular frequencies, amplitudes, and phase constants.
21. What is capacitive reactance in an AC circuit, and on what properties of the circuit does it depend?
22. For an inductor connected to an AC generator, compare the current through the inductor and the potential difference across the inductor in terms of their angular frequencies, amplitudes, and phase constants.
23. What is inductive reactance in an AC circuit? On what properties of the circuit does it depend?

32.6 *RC* and *RLC* series circuits

24. How can the sum of two or more quantities that vary sinusoidally at the same angular frequency be determined from the phasors representing the quantities?
25. How is the impedance of a load in an AC circuit defined?
26. Explain why the combination of a resistor and a capacitor connected in series to an AC source acts as a frequency filter.

32.7 Resonance

27. What does resonant angular frequency ω_0 refer to in a series *RLC* circuit, and which properties of the circuit determine its resonant angular frequency?
28. How does the amplitude of the current in a series *RLC* circuit vary with the angular frequency of the source?
29. Which properties of a series *RLC* circuit determine the maximum amplitude of the current?

32.8 Power in AC circuits

30. What is the advantage of using the root-mean-square value of the sinusoidally oscillating current or emf when analyzing power in an AC circuit?
31. What is the average power at a resistor in an AC circuit? What happens to the energy associated with this power?
32. What is the average power at a capacitor or an inductor in an AC circuit? Describe the instantaneous power at either element.
33. What is the power factor for a load connected to an AC source?

Developing a Feel

Make an order-of-magnitude estimate of each of the following quantities. Letters in parentheses refer to hints below. Use them as needed to guide your thinking.

1. The maximum displacement of an electron in the electrical wire leading to a lamp in your home (E, Q, K)
2. The reactance of a 1-μF capacitor in a 60-Hz circuit (H, A)
3. The reactance of a 1-μF capacitor in a circuit that oscillates at a typical FM radio frequency (H, O)
4. The reactance of a 5-mH inductor in a circuit that oscillates at a typical FM radio frequency (C, O)
5. The capacitance needed for a high-pass filter for the 8-Ω tweeter (high-frequency speaker) in a home stereo system (F, M)
6. The inductance needed for a low-pass filter for the 8-Ω subwoofer (very-low-frequency speaker) in a home stereo system (J, D)
7. The inductance needed for resonance in an RLC series circuit that consists of the inductor plus a 10-μF capacitor, 1-kΩ resistor, and a 60-Hz source (L)
8. The rate at which energy is consumed in a household AC circuit for a 100-W light bulb wired in series with a 5-μF capacitor (R, S, T, I, K, A, B, P)
9. The rate at which energy is consumed by a 100-W light bulb wired in series with a 10-mH inductor in an AC household circuit (R, S, T, I, K, A, B, N)
10. The inductance of the 200-W motor running a food processor in your kitchen at maximum power if the unit has a 5-μF capacitor (K, G)

Hints

A. How does angular frequency depend on frequency?
B. What is the formula for the power factor?
C. How does inductive reactance depend on angular frequency?
D. How does the cutoff angular frequency depend on inductance?
E. What is the typical drift speed of electrons in household wiring?
F. What is a typical cutoff angular frequency for a tweeter fitted with a high-pass filter?
G. What is the requirement for maximizing the power factor?
H. How does capacitive reactance depend on angular frequency?
I. What is R for the circuit?
J. What is a typical cutoff angular frequency for a subwoofer fitted with a low-pass filter?
K. What is the frequency of household AC power?
L. What is the condition for resonance?
M. How does the cutoff angular frequency depend on capacitance?
N. What is the impedance?
O. What is a typical broadcast frequency for an FM station?

P. What is the impedance?
Q. What is the maximum time interval that an electron travels in one direction?
R. How is the rate at which the bulb consumes energy determined?
S. What is $\mathscr{E}_{max}$ for household wiring?
T. What is I for the circuit?

Key (all values approximate)

A. $\omega = 2\pi f$; B. $\cos \phi = R/Z$; C. $X_L = \omega L$; D. $\omega_c = R/L$; E. 10^{-4} m/s (from *Principles* Example 31.7); F. 10^4 s^{-1}; G. the system angular frequency must be the resonant angular frequency, which happens when $\omega L = 1/\omega C$; H. $X_C = 1/\omega C$; I. that of the bulb, $R = \mathscr{E}^2_{max}/(100\ W) = 10^2\ \Omega$; J. 10^3 s^{-1}; K. 60 Hz; L. $\omega_0 = 1/\sqrt{LC}$; M. $\omega_c = 1/RC$; N. $1 \times 10^2\ \Omega$; O. 10^8 Hz; P. $5 \times 10^2\ \Omega$; Q. half the AC period; R. $P_{av} = \frac{1}{2}\mathscr{E}_{max}I \cos \phi$; S. 170 V; T. $I = \mathscr{E}_{max}/Z$

Procedure: Analyzing AC series circuits

When analyzing AC series circuits we generally know the properties of the various circuit elements (such as R, L, C, and $\mathcal{E}$), but not the potential differences across them. To determine these, follow the procedure below.

1. To develop a feel for the problem and to help you evaluate the answer, construct a phasor diagram for the circuit.

2. Determine the impedance of the load using Eq. 32.43. If there is no inductor, then ignore the term

containing L; if there is no capacitor, ignore the term containing C, and so on.

3. To determine the amplitude of the current in the circuit, you can now use Eq. 32.42; to determine the phase of the current relative to the emf, use Eq. 32.44.

4. Determine the amplitude of the potential difference across any reactive element using $V = XI$, where X is the reactance of that element. For a resistor use $V = RI$.

These examples involve material from this chapter but are not associated with any particular section.
Some examples are worked out in detail; others you should work out by following the guidelines provided.

Worked Problem 32.1 *LC* circuit

In the *LC* circuit of Figure WG32.1, $C = 80\ \mu F$. Initially, with switch S open, the capacitor is charged by an amount q_0. The switch is then closed, and 20 ms later the electric potential energy stored in the capacitor is one-fourth its initial value. What is the inductance L?

Figure WG32.1

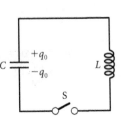

❶ GETTING STARTED The potential energy in an *LC* circuit is stored in both the inductor and the capacitor. We are told that initially the capacitor has charge q_0, and we know there is no current through the inductor because the switch is open. We are also told that 20 ms after the switch is closed, the energy stored in the capacitor is one-fourth its initial value. Our goal is to determine the inductance of the inductor.

❷ DEVISE PLAN Because the energy in an *LC* circuit is constant, the circuit behaves like a simple harmonic oscillator, with energy that oscillates back and forth between the capacitor and the inductor. The energy stored in the capacitor is proportional to the charge squared (see Eq. 26.4), and we know that the potential difference across the capacitor oscillates sinusoidally according to $v_C = V_0 \cos \omega_0 t$ (*Principles* Figure 32.4). For capacitors, we also know that $q/v_C = C$ (Eq. 26.1), so $q = Cv_C = CV_C \cos \omega_0 t$. Because the initial ($t = 0$) value of q is known to be $q(0) = q_0 = CV_C \cos(0) = CV_C$, the charge on the capacitor at any instant can be written as $q = q_0 \cos \omega_0 t$. We know that at the instant $t_1 = 20$ ms, the capacitor has only one-fourth of its initial energy. Therefore we can determine the value of ω_0 in terms of t_1. Knowing that $\omega_0 = 1/\sqrt{LC}$, we can use C and t_1 to determine the value of L.

❸ EXECUTE PLAN The electric potential energy stored in the capacitor at any instant t is given by Eq. 26.4

$$U_C^E(t) = \frac{q^2}{2C} = \frac{(q_0 \cos \omega_0 t)^2}{2C} = \frac{q_0^2}{2C} \cos^2 \omega_0 t.$$

Thus we can use the fact that at $t_1 = 20$ ms the energy in the capacitor is one-fourth the energy at $t = 0$ to say

$$\frac{U_C^E(t_1)}{U_C^E(0)} = \frac{\cos^2 \omega_0 t_1}{\cos^2(0)} = \frac{\cos^2 \omega_0 t_1}{1} = \tfrac{1}{4} \Rightarrow \cos \omega_0 t_1 = \tfrac{1}{2}.$$

Solving this cosine expression for $\omega_0 t_1$ yields

$$\omega_0 t_1 = \cos^{-1}(\tfrac{1}{2}) = \frac{\pi}{3}\,\text{rad} = 60°.$$

Therefore, with $\omega_0 = 1/\sqrt{LC}$, we obtain

$$t_1 = \frac{\pi}{3\omega_0} = \frac{\pi}{3}\sqrt{LC},$$

and the inductance is

$$L = \frac{1}{C}\left(\frac{3t_1}{\pi}\right)^2 = \frac{1}{(80 \times 10^{-6}\ \text{F})}\left[\frac{3(20 \times 10^{-3}\ \text{s})}{\pi}\right]^2$$

$$= 4.6\ \text{s}^2/\text{F} = 4.6\ \text{H}. \checkmark$$

❹ EVALUATE RESULT Our value for the inductance, $L = 4.6$ H, is not unreasonably large compared to the inductor in *Principles* Example 32.6. We can check our result by calculating the energy stored in the magnetic field of the inductor. The current in the circuit is given by

$$i = dq/dt = -\omega_0 q_0 \sin \omega_0 t.$$

The energy stored in the inductor is given by

$$U_L^B(t_1) = \tfrac{1}{2}Li^2 = \tfrac{1}{2}L\omega_0^2 q_0^2 \sin^2 \omega_0 t_1$$

$$= \tfrac{1}{2}L\frac{1}{LC}q_0^2 \sin^2 \omega_0 t_1 = \frac{q_0^2}{2C}\sin^2 \omega_0 t_1.$$

When $\omega_0 t_1 = \pi/3 \,\text{rad}$, $\sin^2 \omega_0 t_1 = \tfrac{3}{4}$. Therefore $U_L^B(t_1) = \tfrac{3}{4}q_0^2/2C$ and the energy stored in the circuit at t_1 is

$$U_L^B(t_1) + U_C^E(t_1) = \tfrac{3}{4}\frac{q_0^2}{2C} + \tfrac{1}{4}\frac{q_0^2}{2C} = \frac{q_0^2}{2C} = U_C^E(0).$$

Because there is no current through the circuit just before the switch is closed, $U_L^B(0) = 0$ and

$$U_L^B(t_1) + U_C^E(t_1) = U_C^E(0) + U_L^B(0).$$

Therefore the energy is constant, as we expect because there is no resistor in the circuit.

Guided Problem 32.2 *RLC* circuit

Consider the circuit of Figure WG32.2, consisting of an inductor of inductance $L = (8.0/\pi^2) \times 10^{-3}$ H, a resistor of resistance R, a capacitor of capacitance $C = 0.50$ nF, a battery for which $\mathscr{E} = 4.0$ V, and two switches S_1 and S_2. Initially S_1 is closed and S_2 is open. After a long time interval $\Delta t \gg RC$, S_1 is opened and S_2 is closed. What is the current in the circuit at the instant t_{equal} when the magnetic potential energy stored in the inductor is equal to the electric potential energy stored in the capacitor?

Figure WG32.2

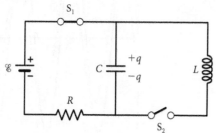

❶ GETTING STARTED

1. What happens at the capacitor while switch 1 is closed and switch 2 is open?
2. How do the capacitor potential difference and the current behave after switch 1 is opened and switch 2 is closed?

❷ DEVISE PLAN

3. How does the electric potential energy stored in the capacitor depend on the potential difference and capacitance?
4. How does the magnetic potential energy stored in the inductor depend on the current and inductance?
5. How can you use energy considerations to determine the current through the inductor at the instant t_{equal}?

❸ EXECUTE PLAN

6. What are the potential difference across the capacitor and the potential energy in the circuit at the instant switch 1 is opened and switch 2 is closed?
7. What is the stored energy in the inductor at the instant t_{equal}?
8. At that instant, what is the current amplitude in the circuit?

❹ EVALUATE RESULT

9. Is this value for the current in the range that can be easily measured with equipment from your undergraduate physics laboratory?
10. How does this value for the current magnitude I at the instant the inductor energy equals the capacitor energy compare with the maximum possible value for the current I_{max}?
11. What is I_{max}?
12. How does this value for the maximum current compare with the value you calculated?

Worked Problem 32.3 Driven *RL* circuit

Consider the *RL* circuit of Figure WG32.3, where the AC source produces a time-varying emf given by $\mathscr{E} = \mathscr{E}_{\text{max}}\sin \omega t$. The amplitude of the emf is $\mathscr{E}_{\text{max}} = 120\sqrt{2}$ V, and the angular frequency is $\omega = 120\pi \text{ s}^{-1}$. If $R = 3.0\ \Omega$ and $L = 4.0 \times 10^{-3}$ H, what is the average power delivered by the AC source?

Figure WG32.3

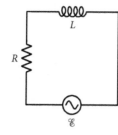

❶ GETTING STARTED We begin by drawing a phasor diagram for the circuit showing V_R, V_L, and I (Figure WG32.4). We know that V_R and I are in phase in an AC circuit, and so we show these two phasors superimposed on each other. We also know that in an AC circuit

the potential difference across the inductor leads the current by $90°$, and so we draw phasor V_L at a right angle to our other two phasors. Our goal is to calculate the average power delivered by the source, which is the average rate at which the source delivers energy.

Figure WG32.4

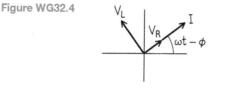

❷ DEVISE PLAN We can use Eq. 32.60, $P_{\text{av}} = \tfrac{1}{2}\mathscr{E}_{\text{max}} I \cos \phi$, to calculate the average power delivered by the AC source, which means we must know $\mathscr{E}_{\text{max}}$, I, and $\cos \phi$. We are given the value for $\mathscr{E}_{\text{max}}$ but must determine I and $\cos \phi$. We can use Eq. 32.42 without the capacitance term (because our circuit contains no capacitors) for I, and for the power factor $\cos \phi$ we have Eq. 32.62. In order to use this relationship, however, we must know the circuit impedance Z, and we are given all the values needed to determine Z from Eq. 32.43.

…UTE PLAN From Eq. 32.42, the current amplitude expressed …rms of values we know is

$$I = \frac{\mathcal{E}_{max}}{\sqrt{R^2 + (\omega L)^2}}.$$

The impedance of the circuit is, from Eq. 32.43,

$$Z = \sqrt{R^2 + (\omega L)^2},$$

and substituting this expression for Z in Eq. 32.62 gives us the power factor $\cos\phi$:

$$\cos\phi = \frac{R}{Z} = \frac{R}{\sqrt{R^2 + (\omega L)^2}}.$$

Therefore the average power delivered by the AC source is, from Eq. 32.60,

$$P_{av} = \tfrac{1}{2}\mathcal{E}_{max}I \cos\phi = \tfrac{1}{2}\frac{\mathcal{E}_{max}^2 R}{[R^2 + (\omega L)^2]}$$

$$= \tfrac{1}{2}\frac{(120\sqrt{2}\ V)^2(3.0\ \Omega)}{[(3.0\ \Omega)^2 + (120\pi\ s^{-1})^2(4.0 \times 10^{-3}\ H)^2]}$$

$$= 3.8 \times 10^3\ W \qquad \checkmark$$

④ EVALUATE RESULT With this large value for the average power, we expect the current amplitude to be large, so we can check that value:

$$I = \frac{\mathcal{E}_{max}}{\sqrt{R^2 + (\omega L)^2}}$$

$$= \frac{120\sqrt{2}\ V}{\sqrt{(3.0\ \Omega)^2 + (120\pi\ s^{-1})^2(4.0 \times 10^{-3}\ H)^2}}$$

$$= 5.1 \times 10^1\ A.$$

This relatively large value for I gives us confidence that our power calculation is the right order of magnitude.

Another check for evaluating our result is to look at the phase difference, which we expect to satisfy the condition $0 < \phi < \pi/2$. From Eq. 32.44,

$$\phi = \tan^{-1}\frac{\omega L}{R}$$

$$= \tan^{-1}\frac{(120\pi\ s^{-1})(4.0 \times 10^{-3}\ H)}{3.0\ \Omega} = 0.47\ rad,$$

again giving us confidence in our result.

As a third check, we can plot on the same graph the AC source potential difference as a function of time and the current as a function of time (Figure WG32.5). The potential difference leads the current, as we expect.

Figure WG32.5

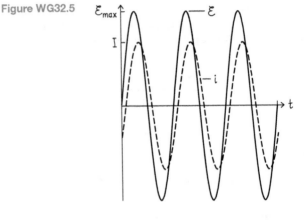

Guided Problem 32.4 Driven RC circuit

In the RC circuit of Figure WG32.6, the emf of the AC source is given by $\mathcal{E} = \mathcal{E}_{max}\sin\omega_1 t$. The emf amplitude is $\mathcal{E}_{max} = 10$ V, and the angular frequency is $\omega_1 = 100\ s^{-1}$. When the angular frequency is changed to a new value ω_2, the time average of the power delivered by the source decreases by a factor of 2. If $R = 3.0\ \Omega$ and $C = 5.0 \times 10^{-2}$ F, what is the value of ω_2?

Figure WG32.6

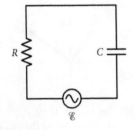

① GETTING STARTED

1. Draw a phasor diagram for the circuit, showing V_R, V_C, and I.

② DEVISE PLAN

2. What is the current amplitude as a function of ω?
3. What is the phase difference as a function of ω?
4. What is the time average of the power delivered by the AC source as a function of ω?
5. Write an expression showing the ratio of the average power when $\omega = \omega_1$ and the average power when $\omega = \omega_2$.
6. Solve this expression for ω_2.

③ EXECUTE PLAN

7. Determine ω_2 from the given values.

④ EVALUATE RESULT

8. Knowing that the average power decreases when the angular frequency changes from ω_1 to ω_2, do you expect the amplitude of the current to increase or decrease?
9. Does the average power vary as you expect as a function of ω?
10. Does your answer for ω_2 agree with what you expect?

Worked Problem 32.5 Unknown circuit element I

Figure WG32.7 shows a circuit containing an AC source for which the emf varies with time as $\mathscr{E} = \mathscr{E}_{max} \sin \omega t$ and a resistor of resistance R. The square with the question mark represents either an inductor or a capacitor (but not both). The amplitude of the emf is $\mathscr{E}_{max} = 100\sqrt{2}$ V, and the angular frequency is $\omega = 10$ s^{-1}. The time-dependent current is given by $i = (10$ A$)\sin(\omega t + \pi/4)$. Is the unknown element a capacitor or an inductor? What is the value of R? What is the value of the capacitance or of the inductance of the unknown element?

Figure WG32.7

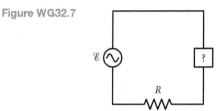

❶ GETTING STARTED We know from the current expression $i = (10$ A$) \sin(\omega t + \pi/4)$ that the phase difference between the AC source emf and the current is $\phi = -\pi/4$. The minus sign tells us that the current leads the AC source emf. Therefore the unknown element must be a capacitor, and we have the answer to the first question this problem asks. ✔

With this information, we can draw a phasor diagram for the circuit showing V_R, V_C, and I (Figure WG32.8).

Figure WG32.8

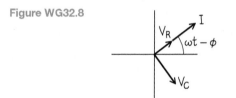

❷ DEVISE PLAN We have two unknowns, R and C, so our plan should be to obtain two independent equations containing these unknowns. We know that the unknown element is a capacitor, and we know the phase constant ϕ. Thus we can use Eq. 32.44 without the inductance term as one equation containing C and R. The current equation given in the problem statement shows the amplitude of current $I = 10$ A, and we are told the value of $\mathscr{E}_{max}$. Therefore we can use Eq. 32.42 without the inductance term as our second equation containing C and R.

❸ EXECUTE PLAN We know that $\phi = -\pi/4$ and $\tan(-\pi/4) = -1$. Thus Eq. 32.44 yields

$$-1 = \frac{-1/\omega C}{R}$$

$$\frac{1}{\omega C} = R. \qquad (1)$$

With this result, we can eliminate $1/\omega C$ from Eq. 32.42, solve that equation for R, and use our numerical values:

$$I = \frac{\mathscr{E}_{max}}{\sqrt{R^2 + (1/\omega C)^2}} = \frac{\mathscr{E}_{max}}{\sqrt{R^2 + R^2}} = \frac{\mathscr{E}_{max}}{\sqrt{2}R}$$

$$R = \frac{\mathscr{E}_{max}}{\sqrt{2}I} = \frac{100\sqrt{2} \text{ V}}{\sqrt{2}(10 \text{ A})} = 10 \text{ V/A} = 10 \text{ }\Omega. ✔$$

Now that we know R, we solve Eq. 1 for the capacitance:

$$C = \frac{1}{\omega R} = \frac{1}{(10 \text{ s}^{-1})(10 \text{ }\Omega)} = 1.0 \times 10^{-2} \text{ F.} ✔$$

❹ EVALUATE RESULT Our value for the capacitance is somewhat large, and our value for the resistance is small but reasonable. Because $\phi = -\pi/4$, the reactance of the capacitor is equal to the resistance, the impedance of the circuit is $Z = \sqrt{R^2 + X_C^2} = \sqrt{2}R$, and therefore the amplitude of current

$$I = \frac{\mathscr{E}_{max}}{\sqrt{2}R} = \frac{100\sqrt{2} \text{ V}}{\sqrt{2}(10 \text{ }\Omega)} = 10 \text{ A.}$$

This agrees with our result above, which gives us confidence in our calculation.

We can also check our result by comparing the average power delivered by the AC source—the average rate at which the source delivers energy to the resistor—and the power at the resistor—the average rate at which that energy is dissipated by the resistor. We know that $\cos\phi = \cos(-\pi/4) = 1/\sqrt{2}$. Hence the average power delivered by the source is, from Eq. 32.60,

$$P_{av} = \tfrac{1}{2}\mathscr{E}_{max}\frac{\mathscr{E}_{max}}{\sqrt{2}R}\frac{1}{\sqrt{2}} = \tfrac{1}{4}\frac{\mathscr{E}_{max}^2}{R}.$$

The average rate at which energy is dissipated in the resistor is, from Eq. 32.52,

$$P_{av} = \tfrac{1}{2}I^2 R = \tfrac{1}{2}\left(\frac{\mathscr{E}_{max}}{\sqrt{2}R}\right)^2 R = \tfrac{1}{4}\frac{\mathscr{E}_{max}^2}{R}.$$

We see that these two are equal, which is what we expect because the phasors V_C and I are 90° out of phase, and so no energy is dissipated in the capacitor.

Guided Problem 32.6 Unknown circuit element II

Figure WG32.9 on the next page shows a circuit containing an AC source for which the emf varies with time as $\mathscr{E} = \mathscr{E}_{max}\sin\omega t$. The emf amplitude is $\mathscr{E}_{max} = 6.0$ V, and the resistor is rated at $R = 3.0$ Ω. The square with the question mark represents an inductor, a capacitor, or both. When the angular frequency is

$\omega_1 = 1.0$ s^{-1}, the current is in phase with the source emf. When the angular frequency is $\omega_2 = 2.0$ s^{-1}, the current is out of phase with the emf by $|\pi/4|$ rad. What is the average rate at which energy is dissipated in this circuit when the angular frequency is ω_1? Repeat for angular frequency ω_2.

WG32.9

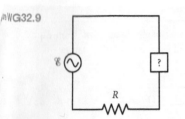

① GETTING STARTED

1. Does the square represent an inductor, a capacitor, or both?
2. When the angular frequency is $\omega_2 = 2.0 \text{ s}^{-1}$, what reactance(s) must be accounted for?
3. Draw a phasor diagram for the circuit.

② DEVISE PLAN

4. What's the appropriate expression relating angular frequency to the inductance and/or capacitance?
5. How can you determine whether the source emf leads or lags the current at angular frequency ω_2?

6. How can you determine the values of L and/or C?
7. How can you determine the current amplitude when the angular frequency is ω_1? ω_2?
8. How can you determine the average rate at which energy is dissipated in the resistor?
9. Is there any energy dissipated in the inductor and/or capacitor?

③ EXECUTE PLAN

10. Write the expressions relating L and/or C at both given frequencies.
11. Calculate values for L and/or C.
12. Calculate the current amplitude at ω_1 and ω_2.
13. Determine the average rate at which energy is dissipated at ω_1 and ω_2.

④ EVALUATE RESULT

14. What is the average power delivered by the AC source at angular frequency ω_1? Did you expect that result?

Worked Problem 32.7 FM radio tuner

Suppose you want a series RLC circuit to tune to a radio station that broadcasts at a frequency of 89.7 MHz, but you do not want to pick up the signal from a station that broadcasts at 89.5 MHz. To achieve this, for a given input signal from your antenna, you want your resonance curve to be narrow enough to make the current in the circuit at 89.5 MHz be 100 times smaller than the current in the circuit at 89.7 MHz. You cannot avoid having a resistance of $R = 0.100 \ \Omega$, and practical considerations also dictate that you use the smallest possible value for L. What values of L and C must you use?

① **GETTING STARTED** We begin by drawing a phasor diagram showing V_R, V_C V_L, and I (Figure WG32.10). We first draw phasors V_R and I in phase, and then draw V_L leading I by 90° and V_C lagging I by 90°. We model the time-dependent input signal by the sinusoidal function $\mathcal{E} = \mathcal{E}_{\max}\sin\omega t$ and the time-dependent current in the circuit by $i = I\sin(\omega t - \phi)$. We want resonance to occur at $\omega_{89.7} = (2\pi)(89.7 \times 10^6 \text{ Hz})$. We also require that the current amplitude $I(\omega_{89.5})$ at $\omega_{89.5} = (2\pi)(89.5 \times 10^6 \text{ Hz})$ be one-hundredth the maximum current at resonance $I(\omega_{89.7})$: $I(\omega_{89.5}) = 0.0100I(\omega_{89.7})$. We are given that $R = 0.100 \ \Omega$.

Figure WG32.10

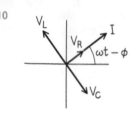

② **DEVISE PLAN** The current amplitude I is a function of ω (Eq. 32.42). We also use the resonance condition Eq. 32.47 to simplify the expression for $I(\omega_{89.7})$. We have two expressions, one for $I(\omega_{89.7})$ and one for $I(\omega_{89.5})$, and the condition that $I(\omega_{89.5}) = 0.0100I(\omega_{89.7})$. We can thus obtain a relationship between L and C. We again use the resonance condition Eq. 32.47, which gives a second condition for L and C. We now solve our system of equations for the values of L and C.

③ **EXECUTE PLAN** Equation 32.42 gives the current amplitude as a function of ω:

$$I = \frac{\mathcal{E}_{\max}}{\sqrt{R^2 + (\omega L - 1/\omega C)^2}}. \tag{1}$$

We know from Eq. 32.46 that at resonance, $\omega L = 1/\omega C$, which means that at our resonant angular frequency $\omega_{89.7}$, Eq. 1 reduces to

$$I(\omega_{89.7}) = \frac{\mathcal{E}_{\max}}{R}. \tag{2}$$

Once we set $\omega = \omega_{89.5}$ in Eq. 1:

$$I(\omega_{89.5}) = \frac{\mathcal{E}_{\max}}{\sqrt{R^2 + (\omega_{89.5}L - 1/\omega_{89.5}C)^2}}, \tag{3}$$

we are ready to determine values for L and C. To keep the notation simple, let's for now use h to represent the factor by which the two current amplitudes must differ: $h = 0.0100$. Thus

$$I(\omega_{89.5}) = hI(\omega_{89.7}),$$

and from Eqs. 2 and 3 we have

$$\frac{\mathcal{E}_{\max}}{\sqrt{R^2 + (\omega_{89.5}L - 1/\omega_{89.5}C)^2}} = h\frac{\mathcal{E}_{\max}}{R}.$$

Squaring both sides and eliminating $\mathcal{E}_{\max}$ yield

$$\frac{1}{R^2 + (\omega_{89.5}L - 1/\omega_{89.5}C)^2} = h^2\frac{1}{R^2}. \tag{4}$$

A little algebraic manipulation yields the condition that

$$\frac{R^2}{R^2 + (\omega_{89.5}L - 1/\omega_{89.5}C)^2} = h^2$$

$$\Rightarrow (\omega_{89.5}L - 1/\omega_{89.5}C)^2$$

$$= \left(\frac{1}{h^2} - 1\right)R^2.$$

PRACTICE

Taking square roots, we have

$$\omega_{89.5}L - \frac{1}{\omega_{89.5}C} = -\sqrt{\frac{1}{h^2} - 1}\, R.$$

We show a minus sign on the term on the right because the circuit is below resonance, which means that $(\omega_{89.5}L - 1/\omega_{89.5}C) < 0$. Using Eq. 32.47 in the form $C = 1/L\omega_{89.7}^2$, where $\omega_{89.7}$ is the resonant angular frequency, we obtain

$$\omega_{89.5}L\left[1 - \left(\frac{\omega_{89.7}}{\omega_{89.5}}\right)^2\right] = -\sqrt{\frac{1}{h^2} - 1}\, R,$$

which yields

$$L = \frac{\sqrt{\left(\frac{1}{h^2} - 1\right)}\, R}{\omega_{89.5}\left[(\omega_{89.7}/\omega_{89.5})^2 - 1\right]}$$

$$= \frac{\sqrt{(1.00 \times 10^4 - 1)}(0.100\ \Omega)}{(5.62 \times 10^8\ \text{s}^{-1})\left[(89.7/89.5)^2 - 1\right]} = 3.97 \times 10^{-6}\ \text{H.} \checkmark$$

The capacitance is therefore

$$C = \frac{1}{L\omega_{89.7}^2} = \frac{1}{(3.97 \times 10^{-6}\ \text{H})(5.63 \times 10^8\ \text{s}^{-1})^2}$$

$$= 7.92 \times 10^{-13}\ \text{F.} \checkmark$$

4 EVALUATE RESULT Suppose the antenna produces a maximum signal $\mathcal{E}_{max} = 100\ \mu\text{V}$. Then at resonance, where $\phi = 0$, the time average of the signal's power is, from Eq. 32.60,

$$P_{av}(\omega_{89.7}) = \tfrac{1}{2}\mathcal{E}_{max}I(\omega_{89.7}) = \tfrac{1}{2}\frac{\mathcal{E}_{max}^2}{R}$$

$$= \frac{(1.00 \times 10^{-4}\ \text{V})^2}{2(0.100\ \Omega)} = 5.00 \times 10^{-8}\ \text{W}, \qquad (5)$$

where we have substituted from Eq. 2 for $I(\omega_{89.7})$. The signal's average power at $\omega = \omega_{89.5}$ is

$$P_{av}(\omega_{89.5}) = \tfrac{1}{2}\mathcal{E}_{max}I(\omega_{89.5})\cos\phi.$$

The power factor at 89.5 MHz is given by Eq. 32.62:

$$\cos\phi = \frac{R}{Z} = \frac{R}{\sqrt{R^2 + (\omega_{89.5}L - 1/\omega_{89.5}C)^2}}.$$

Therefore the average power at 89.5 MHz, when we substitute this expression for $\cos\phi$ and the expression for $I(\omega_{89.5})$ using Eq. 1, is

$$P_{av}(\omega_{89.5}) = \tfrac{1}{2}\frac{\mathcal{E}_{max}^2 R}{R^2 + (\omega_{89.5}L - 1/\omega_{89.5}C)^2}.$$

We can use Eqs. 4 and 5 to write this as

$$P_{av}(\omega_{89.5}) = \tfrac{1}{2}\frac{\mathcal{E}_{max}^2}{R}h^2 = P_{av}(\omega_{89.7})h^2$$

$$= (5.00 \times 10^{-8}\ \text{W})(1.00 \times 10^{-4}) = 5.00 \times 10^{-12}\ \text{W}.$$

So the current at 89.5 MHz is 100 times smaller than the peak current $I(\omega_0)$ at resonance, and the time average of the power of the input signal at 89.5 MHz is down by a factor of 10^4, which is a very small power value compared to the signal we want.

Guided Problem 32.8 *RLC* circuit

A series *RLC* circuit with $R = 10.0\ \Omega$, $L = 400\ \text{mH}$, and $C = 2.0\ \mu\text{F}$ is connected to an AC source of emf $\mathcal{E} = \mathcal{E}_{max}\sin\omega t$, which has amplitude $\mathcal{E}_{max} = 100\ \text{V}$. The angular frequency is $\omega = 4000\ \text{s}^{-1}$, and the time-dependent current is given by $i = I\sin(\omega t - \phi)$.

(a) Calculate the amplitude I of the current and the phase constant ϕ that represents the phase difference between the current and the source emf.

(b) What is the ratio of the potential-difference amplitude V_L across the inductor to the potential-difference amplitude V_C across the capacitor?

1 GETTING STARTED
1. Draw a phasor diagram for the circuit.

2 DEVISE PLAN
2. What quantities must you know in order to calculate the current amplitude?
3. What quantities must you know in order to calculate the phase constant?

4. How can you determine the values of the amplitudes V_C and V_L?
5. How can you determine the value of X_C you need for Eq. 32.15 and the value of X_L you need for Eq. 32.27?

3 EXECUTE PLAN
6. You have all the data you need to obtain a value for I from Eq. 32.42. However, you have surely noticed by now that many circuit problems require you to calculate ωL and $1/\omega C$, so it is usually most efficient to begin by calculating these two values and then the impedance.
7. Calculate the current amplitude.
8. Calculate the phase constant.
9. Calculate the ratio V_L/V_C.

4 EVALUATE RESULT
10. Compute the resonant angular frequency ω_0.
11. When $\omega = 4000\ \text{s}^{-1}$, is the circuit being driven at an angular frequency greater than or less than the resonant angular frequency?
12. What does this tell you about the expected current? About the expected ratio V_L to V_C?

PRACTICE

ots indicate difficulty level of problems: • = *easy,* •• = *intermediate,*
••• = *hard;* CR = *context-rich problem.*

32.1 Alternating currents

1. A fully charged parallel-plate capacitor is connected to an
inductor as shown in Figure P32.1. What is the time average of the magnitude of the magnetic field produced in the
inductor? •

Figure P32.1

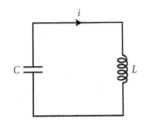

2. (a) If each vertical gray line in *Principles* Figure 32.4b
represents 0.020 s, what is the frequency of the oscillation?
(b) What is the average potential difference across the capacitor in one cycle? •

3. For the circuit shown in *Principles* Figure 32.4a, let the
period T of the oscillation be 1.0 s. Identify the instant(s) at
which the energy stored in the inductor reaches a maximum. •

4. (a) For the circuit shown in Figure P32.4a, draw (qualitative) curves showing the current as a function of time and
the potential difference across the parallel-plate capacitor as a
function of time. Assume that the capacitor is fully charged at
$t = 0$ and that the potential is positive when the upper plate
is positively charged, and use the current reference direction
shown. (b) Repeat for the circuit in Figure P32.4b. ••

Figure P32.4   (a)   (b)

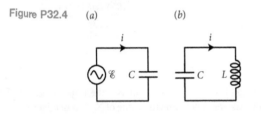

5. Two circuits X and Y each contain a parallel-plate capacitor
and may contain other elements as well. The capacitors are
identical, and the potential difference across each is shown in
Figure P32.5. Which circuit—X, Y, or both—could contain a
resistor, and under what circumstances could it/they contain
a resistor? ••

Figure P32.5

circuit X   circuit Y

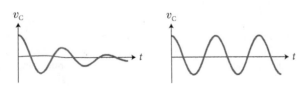

6. In an LC circuit like the one shown in Figure P32.1, which of
these quantities simultaneously reach their maximum values:
$|v_C|$, $|q_C|$, $|i|$, $|B|$, $|U^E|$, $|U^B|$? ••

7. A parallel-plate capacitor is fully charged and connected to an
inductor. The capacitor initially stores charge q and electric
potential energy U^E. Once the circuit is closed, charge carriers flow from the capacitor, producing a current in the circuit.
When the charge on the capacitor has been reduced to $q/2$,
what is the magnetic potential energy U^B stored in the inductor? Report your answer in terms of U^E. ••

8. If the circuit in Figure P32.8 operates at 60 Hz with
$\mathscr{E}_{max} = 170$ V and $R = 9.0\ \Omega$, how much energy is dissipated in the resistor in 0.75 s? ••

Figure P32.8

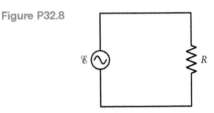

9. A circuit consists of a parallel-plate capacitor, an inductor,
and a switch, which is initially open. The capacitor plates
have an area of $1.00 \times 10^{-4}\ m^2$ and are held 0.100 mm apart
by a thin layer of barium titanate. The capacitor is charged to
a potential difference of 10 V, and then the switch is closed.
How much charge remains on the capacitor at the instant
the energy stored in the inductor has increased to 85% of its
maximum? •••

10. In an LC circuit, there is always some energy dissipation as
electrical energy is converted to thermal energy. (a) What
property of the circuit is responsible for electrical energy
being converted to thermal energy? (b) Describe the shape of
a graph showing the charge on one capacitor plate as a function of time. (c) What sort of function would describe the rate
at which energy is converted? [Hint: See the discussion of
damped mechanical oscillators in Chapter 15.] •••

32.2 AC circuits

11. Draw a phasor diagram at instant t_0 for the circuit element
whose instantaneous current and instantaneous potential
difference are shown in Figure P32.11. •

Figure P32.11

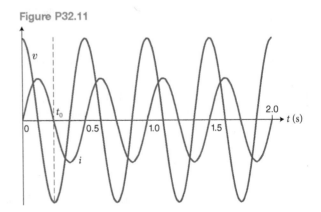

12. Draw a phasor diagram for the current and potential difference represented in Figure P32.12 at the instant $t = T$. Be
sure to note which way it is rotating. •

Figure P32.12

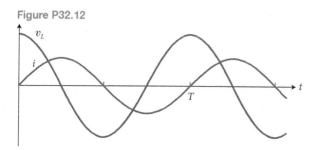

13. In a circuit consisting of an inductor connected to a nonsi-nusoidal AC source, the current varies as a function of time as shown in Figure P32.13. Sketch the potential difference across the inductor as a function of time. ••

Figure P32.13   *i*

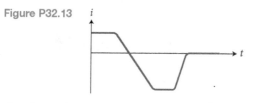

14. The phasor diagram in Figure P32.14 shows the potential difference across a circuit element and the current through the element at $t = 0$. (*a*) Is the element a resistor, capacitor, or inductor? (*b*) On a single graph, sketch a curve showing v as a function of time and a curve showing i as a function of time. ••

Figure P32.14

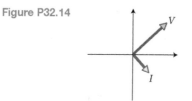

15. Figure P32.15 shows, for an AC circuit, the current phasor and a potential difference phasor at $t = 0$ and at $t = 1.0$ s. In each case, assume phasor magnitudes $I = 1.0$ A and $V = 9.0$ V. Give as many details about this circuit as you can. ••

Figure P32.15

t = 0   t = 1.0 s

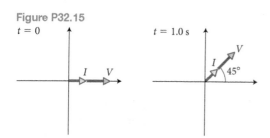

16. Figure P32.16 shows, for a circuit consisting of one element and an AC source, the current through the element as a function of time and the potential difference across the element. Is the element an inductor, a capacitor, or a resistor? ••

Figure P32.16

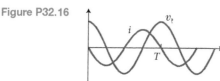

17. In a circuit consisting of a nonsinusoidal AC source plus one additional element, the instantaneous current varies as shown in Figure P32.17. Sketch the potential difference across the additional element as a function of time if that element is (*a*) a capacitor and (*b*) an inductor. •••

Figure P32.17   *i*

18. A friend has built an AC circuit for you to analyze. You know the circuit contains a resistor, but it also contains another element. Because you know the circuit components available to your friend, you know that the unknown element must be a 0.32-F capacitor, a 0.32-mF capacitor, a 6.28-mH inductor, or a 62.8-mH inductor. Figure P32.18 shows curves for the current through the unknown element and the potential difference across it. The maximum current is 1.00 mA, and the maximum potential difference is 1.00 V. Which of the four available elements did your friend use, and how do you know? •••

Figure P32.18

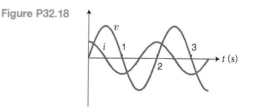

32.3 Semiconductors

19. A sample contains 3.0×10^{22} Si atoms and nothing else. (*a*) How many valence electrons does the sample contain? (*b*) How many of the valence electrons in the sample can conduct electricity? •

20. Silicon is doped with the following elements. In each case, is the resultant extrinsic semiconductor *n*-type or *p*-type: indium, gallium, phosphorus, boron, arsenic, aluminum, antimony? •

21. Conduction in a semiconductor can be greatly enhanced by the addition of very small quantities of dopant atoms, even in the parts-per-million range. Explain how the addition of such a tiny percentage of dopant atoms can increase the conduction by a significant factor. •

22. Unlike electrons, the holes in a semiconductor do not leave the semiconductor in which they are formed. Yet, holes can be thought of as positive charge carriers. When a hole has traveled to the edge of the semiconductor and reaches an electrical lead, where does it go? ••

23. You have an intrinsic semiconductor, a *p*-type semiconductor, and an *n*-type semiconductor. The doped samples each contain the same number density of dopant atoms. Which of the three semiconductors do you expect to have (*a*) the greatest ability to carry current when the three are connected to identical batteries, (*b*) the greatest number of electrons, and (*c*) the greatest number of holes entering the battery as they leave the semiconductor? ••

24. You have ordered a 10.00 mm × 10.00 mm × 2.000 mm sheet of pure silicon from a laboratory supply company, but the sheet the company sends has a mass of 463.05 mg. You know that the company also produces silicon doped with

...on, and you wonder if there may have been some contamination. The mass densities are $\rho_{Si} = 2329.6 \text{ kg/m}^3$ and
$\rho_B = 2340 \text{ kg/m}^3$, and the atomic weights are B = 10.81
atomic units, Si = 28.085 atomic units. Determine as much
information as possible about the contamination of your
sheet. If you need pure silicon for its conduction properties, is
this sheet likely to meet your needs? •••

32.4 Diodes, transistors, and logic gates

25. Which circuit in Figure P32.25 produces the greatest current
in the emitter? •

Figure P32.25

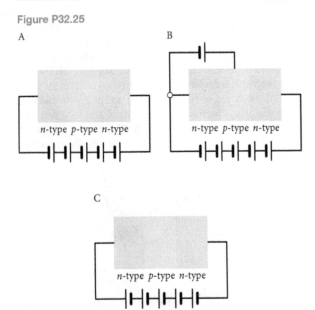

A

B

n-type p-type n-type

n-type p-type n-type

C

n-type p-type n-type

26. The two transistors in Figure P32.26 are connected to each
other by wires and also connected to input wires at terminals A
and B. The output of this combination depends on the inputs at
A and B. In terms of this circuit's reaction to input at A and B,
which type of logical operation is performed? •

Figure P32.26

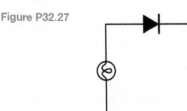

+5 V
n-type
p-type
n-type
n-type
p-type
n-type
A
B
output

27. Is the light bulb in Figure P32.27 lit? •

Figure P32.27

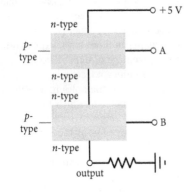

28. The rectifier shown in Figure P32.28 converts the alternating emf from an AC source to a positive-only potential difference from a to b. Sketch graphs showing (a) the source
emf as a function of time and (b) the potential difference
from a to b as a function of time. (c) If diode 1 is blown out
and acts as an open circuit, what is the output potential difference from a to b? (d) What happens to the potential
difference from a to b if diode 1 operates normally but diode 2
is blown out? ••

Figure P32.28

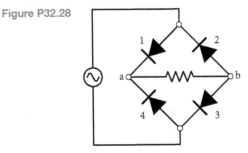

29. The circuit diagram for a rectifier is typically drawn with a
resistor in the center. Would the rectifier function if this resistor were replaced by a capacitor? ••

30. The logic gate in Figure P32.30 contains four field-effect transistors. Each of the gates A–D of the transistors may be positively
biased (Y in the table) or not (N in the table). Depending on
the various bias combi-
nations, charge carriers
may or may not flow
through the circuit. Fill
in the output column of
the table. ••

Figure P32.30

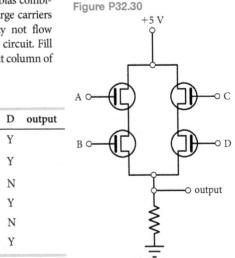

+5 V
A
C
B
D
output

A	B	C	D	output
Y	Y	Y	Y	
Y	N	Y	Y	
Y	Y	Y	N	
N	N	Y	Y	
N	Y	Y	N	
N	N	N	Y	

31. You have two regions, A and B, of differently doped silicon, with
the regions joined together to make a continuous silicon wafer.
When the positive terminal of a battery is connected to region A
and the negative terminal is connected to region B, no charge
carriers flow. When the terminal connections are switched,
charge carriers flow. (a) When there is a current, in which
direction—A to B or B to A—do the positive charge carriers
move? (b) In which direction do the electrons move? (c) Which
region is p-type and which is n-type? (d) Which region may
contain boron, and which may contain phosphorus? ••

32. Suppose a transistor consists of a very narrow p-type material
sandwiched between two very wide regions of n-type material. (a) Is the charge on the p-type region positive or negative, and why? (b) Is the charge on the n-type region positive
or negative, and why? ••

33. In Figure P32.33, what combinations of positive bias (input signals) A, B, C, D allow the light bulb to light up? ••

Figure P32.33

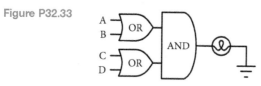

34. If in Figure P32.33 the two gates on the left were both AND and the gate on the right was OR, what combinations of positive bias (input signals) A, B, C, D would allow the light bulb to light up? ••

35. You are using the logic gate of Figure P32.35 to test some transistors and emf sources. The output produced by the logic gate depends on the potential relative to ground at inputs A and B. The only emf sources available to you are AC sources, but using one of them to bias either input A or input B results in an oscillating input potential. Consider how using an AC source affects the potential relative to ground at either A or B. Describe how using an AC source differs from using a DC source, both in general and in the specific function of this circuit. Could any modifications or additions be made to the circuit so that the way it functions with an AC source more closely resembles the way it would function with a DC source? Draw a circuit diagram of any useful modifications. •••

Figure P32.35

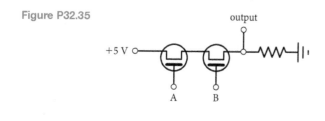

32.5 Reactance

36. What is the reactance of a 50.0-mH inductor when connected to an AC current source that has a frequency of 120 Hz? ••

37. The reactance of a 30.0-μF capacitor is $X_C = 1.0 \times 10^4\ \Omega$. What is the angular frequency of the current through the capacitor? •

38. For the circuit shown in Figure P32.38, what must the frequency f of the AC source be in order for the amplitude V_C of the potential difference across the capacitor to equal the amplitude V_R of the potential difference across the resistor? •

Figure P32.38

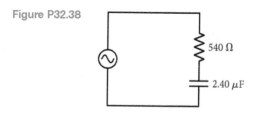

540 Ω

2.40 μF

39. A capacitor for which $C = 10$ mF is connected to an AC source. The source emf is given by $\mathscr{E} = \mathscr{E}_{max} \sin \omega t$, with $\mathscr{E}_{max} = 5.0$ V and $\omega = 20\ s^{-1}$. (a) What is the amplitude of the current

through the capacitor? (b) How does the current amplitude change as you increase the source angular frequency? ••

40. An inductor for which $L = 10$ mH is connected to an AC source. The source emf is given by $\mathscr{E} = \mathscr{E}_{max} \sin \omega t$, with $\mathscr{E}_{max} = 5.0$ V and $\omega = 200\ s^{-1}$. (a) What is the amplitude of the current through the inductor? (b) How does the current amplitude change as you lower the source angular frequency? As you lower the inductance? ••

41. Figure P32.41 shows resistors $R_1 = 30.0\ \Omega$ and $R_2 = 10.0\ \Omega$ connected in parallel to an AC source. (a) If the maximum current in the circuit is 2.03 A, what is the amplitude $\mathscr{E}_{max}$ of the AC source? (b) If the source emf peaks at $t = 0$, and the frequency is 60.0 Hz, what is the potential difference across each resistor at $t = 20.2$ ms? ••

Figure P32.41

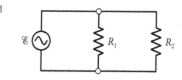

42. You must use a resistor, a capacitor, or an inductor to fill a gap in a circuit. You want to have as much current as possible through this circuit element to ensure that it can be easily detected. Which element should you use if the current through it is (a) very high frequency (VHF), (b) very low frequency (VLF), (c) DC, (d) time-varying so that it is sometimes VHF and other times VLF? ••

43. A device is connected to a 60.0-Hz AC source for which the emf is given by $\mathscr{E} = \mathscr{E}_{max} \sin(\omega t)$. If after 5.00 ms the current is 30.9% of its maximum value, is the current leading or lagging the source emf? ••

44. A resistor for which $R = 60.0\ \Omega$ is connected to an AC source. The source emf is given by $\mathscr{E} = \mathscr{E}_{max} \sin(\omega t + \phi_i)$, where $\mathscr{E}_{max} = 5.00$ V, $\omega = 2\pi(30\ Hz)$, and $\phi_i = \pi/4$. At what instants is there no current in the circuit? If you replace the resistor with a capacitor for which $C = 200$ mF, at what instants is there no current in the circuit? ••

45. In the parallel circuit of Figure P32.45, the current amplitude is the same through the inductor branch, the capacitor branch, and the resistor branch. If $L = 20.0$ mH and $C = 10.0$ mF, what are the source angular frequency and the resistance R? •••

Figure P32.45

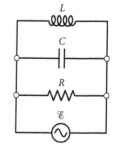

32.6 RC and RLC series circuits

46. A circuit contains a 1.00×10^3-Ω resistor and a 5.00×10^2-mH inductor in series. What is the impedance of the circuit when a 1.00-kHz AC source is used? ••

RLC series circuit driven by an AC source, the amplitude of the potential difference across the inductor is 29.0 V and that across the capacitor is 13.0 V. If the amplitude of the current through the 900-Ω resistor is 5.00 mA, what is the amplitude of the source emf? •

48. An RC series circuit consists of an AC source, a 6.00-mF capacitor, and a 20.0-Ω resistor. If the source emf is given by $\mathcal{E} = \mathcal{E}_{max}\sin(\omega t)$, where $\mathcal{E}_{max} = 5.00$ V and $\omega = 10.0$ s^{-1}, what is the current amplitude? •

49. A circuit consists of an AC source wired in series to a 1000-Ω resistor and a 1.00-μF capacitor. For a source emf amplitude $\mathcal{E}_{max} = 35.0$ V, calculate the phase constant ϕ and the amplitudes V_C and V_R if the source frequency is (a) 60 Hz and (b) 2100 Hz. ••

50. A circuit consists of an AC source, for which $\mathcal{E}_{max} = 18$ V, in series with a 1200-Ω resistor and a capacitor. If the amplitude of the potential difference across the resistor is $V_R = 9.0$ V when the source operates at 1500 Hz, what is the capacitance of the capacitor? ••

51. A 120-V AC source has a frequency of 60.0 Hz and produces the same maximum current in two series circuits. Each circuit contains a 100-Ω resistor. Circuit 1 contains a 4.50-mF capacitor, and circuit 2 contains an inductor. What is the inductance in circuit 2? ••

52. You need a filter circuit to eliminate a 60-Hz signal and lower frequencies. The load you are trying to drive has a resistance of 50 Ω. You decide to design a low-pass filter that has a cutoff frequency of 200 Hz. If you use the circuit shown in Figure P32.52, what capacitance C should you use? What fraction of any 60-Hz signal potential difference passes through this circuit? ••

Figure P32.52

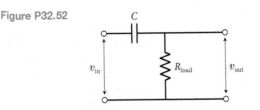

53. (a) Construct a phasor diagram for the circuit shown in Figure P32.53. (b) What is the phase constant if $C_1 = 1.00$ μF, $C_2 = 3.00$ μF, $R_1 = 200$ Ω, $R_2 = 400$ Ω, and $\omega = 4000$ s^{-1}? ••

Figure P32.53

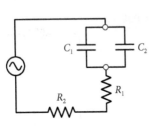

54. A loudspeaker has a resistance of 8.00 Ω. If you connect it in series with a 10.0-mH inductor, what percentage of the original maximum current are you going to get for a sound that has a pure frequency of 1000 Hz? ••

55. In the circuit shown in Figure P32.55, the current amplitude through the RL branch is the same as that through the RC branch. If $R = 10.0$ Ω and $C = 50.0$ μF, and the source operates at $\omega = 80.0$ s^{-1}, what is the inductance L? ••

Figure P32.55

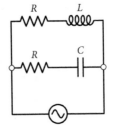

56. In an RC series circuit consisting of a 20.0-Ω resistor, a 300-μF capacitor, and an AC source, the source frequency is 150 s^{-1}. If the current has its maximum value at $t = 0$, at what later instant is the source emf at its maximum value? ••

57. A 200-Hz power source in a series RLC circuit applies an AC potential difference that has an amplitude of 60 V. The current amplitude is 1.0 A, and the phasor diagram for the circuit is shown in Figure P32.57. What is the resistance of the circuit? ••

Figure P32.57

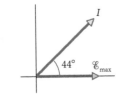

58. (a) What can you say, at all instants, about v_R, v_C, and v_L in the parallel circuit of Figure P32.58? (b) Construct a phasor diagram for V_R, V_C, V_L, and $\mathcal{E}$ and a phasor diagram for i_R, i_C, and i_L. (c) What is the current in the source? (d) Show that the current is a minimum at the frequency $\omega = \sqrt{1/LC}$. •••

Figure P32.58

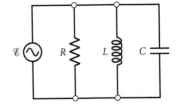

59. Two AC potential differences $v_1 = V_1\sin(\omega t + \phi_1)$ and $v_2 = V_2\sin(\omega t + \phi_2)$ are added according to

$$v_{sum} = V\sin(\omega t + \phi) = v_1 + v_2$$
$$= V_1\sin(\omega t + \phi_1) + V_2\sin(\omega t + \phi_2),$$

with $\omega = 10.0$ s^{-1}, $V_1 = 5.00$ V, and $V_2 = 8.00$ V. At $t = 0$, $v_1(t = 0) = 4.50$ V and $v_2(t = 0) = 3.70$ V. (a) Use phasors to determine values for V and ϕ in the expression $v_{sum} = V\sin(\omega t + \phi)$ and a value for $v(t = 0.0500$ s$)$. (b) Repeat using trigonometry, and then compare your results from the two methods. •••

60. In the circuit shown in Figure P32.60, $\mathcal{E} = \mathcal{E}_{max}\sin \omega t$ and $\omega = 100$ s^{-1}. If $R = 20.0$ Ω, $R_C = 18.0$ Ω, and $R_L = 15.0$ Ω, what must the values of L and C be in order for the current amplitude I to be the same in branches 1, 2, and 3? •••

Figure P32.60

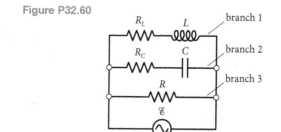

32.7 Resonance

61. An *RLC* circuit consists of a 20-μF capacitor, a 300-Ω resistor, and a 50-mH inductor connected in series with an AC source. What is the resonant angular frequency for this circuit? •

62. A 6.00-mH solenoid is connected in series with a 1.0-μF capacitor and an AC source. The solenoid has internal resistance 3.0 Ω, which can be treated as a series resistor in the circuit. (*a*) What is the resonant angular frequency? (*b*) If the source emf amplitude is $\mathcal{E}_{max}$ = 15 V, what is the current amplitude at the resonant angular frequency? •

63. A circuit contains an electromagnet that can be modeled as an inductor of inductance 0.80 H in series with a resistance of 0.50 Ω. If you want to add a capacitor in series with the electromagnet to make the circuit resonate at 380 s^{-1}, what value of *C* must you use? •

64. A series *RLC* circuit is driven by an AC source at resonance. The resistor has a resistance of R = 10 Ω, and the AC source has an emf amplitude of $\mathcal{E}_{max}$ = 12 V. What is the current amplitude? •

65. An *RLC* series circuit initially has resonant angular frequency ω_{0i}. Circuit elements are then changed such that, for any fixed operating angular frequency, both the capacitive reactance and the inductive reactance are twice their initial values. What is the resonant angular frequency ω_{0f} after the changes are made? ••

66. An *RLC* series circuit has $X_C = X_L = R$. When the circuit is operating at resonance, the current amplitude is 1.0 A. When the angular frequency of the current is doubled, what is the new current amplitude? ••

67. An inductor resonates at 4.08×10^4 s^{-1} when placed in series with a 2.00-μF capacitor. When driven at that resonant angular frequency, an AC source for which $\mathcal{E}_{max}$ = 5.00 V produces a 0.400-A current in the circuit. What is the inductance? What is the resistance in the circuit? ••

68. In Figure P32.68, C_1 = 1.00 μF, C_2 = 2.00 μF, and L = 47.0 mH. Which circuit has the lower resonant angular frequency, and what is that resonant angular frequency? ••

Figure P32.68

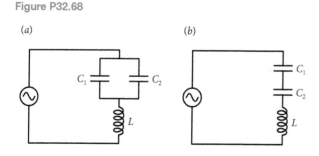

(*a*)   (*b*)

69. An *RLC* series circuit contains an AC source of emf for which $\mathcal{E}_{max}$ = 30.0 V, a 5.00-Ω resistor, a 4.00-mH inductor, and an 8.00-μF capacitor. What are (*a*) the resonant angular frequency and (*b*) the current amplitude if it is driven at the resonant angular frequency? (*c*) If a 1.00-kHz, 30.0-V source is used, what is the current amplitude? ••

70. An *RLC* series circuit has a 350-mH inductor and a 25.0-Ω resistor connected to a 50.0-Hz AC power source, and a variable capacitor. (*a*) To what capacitance value must it be set in order to have the circuit be at resonance? (*b*) If the source produces $\mathcal{E}_{rms}$ = 120 V, what is the maximum potential difference across the inductor and the capacitor at resonance? ••

71. You want to build an AM radio that uses an *RLC* circuit for tuning. The circuit consists of a 30.0-Ω resistor, a 15.0-μH inductor, and an adjustable capacitor. At what capacitance should the capacitor be set in order to receive the signal from a station that broadcasts at 870 kHz? How would you make the tuning more selective? ••

72. The resonant angular frequency is ω_0 in two identical *RLC* circuits 1 and 2. After determining that the power delivered by the source at resonance is too high, you reduce the angular frequency of the source of circuit 1 to $\omega_1 = \omega_0/2$. To what value $\omega_2 \neq \omega_1$ must you change the angular frequency of the source of circuit 2 in order to have the power delivered by the source of circuit 1 equal that of circuit 2? •••

32.8 Power in AC circuits

73. An *RLC* circuit consists of a 200-Ω resistor, a 300-μF capacitor, and a 3.00-H inductor. The circuit is connected to a power outlet that has a peak emf of 170 V and oscillates at 400 Hz. What is the average rate at which energy is dissipated in this circuit? •

74. A toaster oven has a resistive heating element. The average rate at which it dissipates energy as thermal energy is 1.00 kW. In the United States, emf amplitude in household circuits is $\mathcal{E}_{max}$ = 170 V and the AC oscillation rate is 60 Hz. What is the root-mean-square current through the heating element? •

75. An AC power line has a current amplitude of 4.00 A and a resistance of 0.500 Ω. At what average rate is energy lost from the line? •

76. For household electrical outlets in the United States, the root-mean-square value of the source emf is 120 V. (*a*) For a hair dryer rated at 1875 W, what are the root-mean-square current and the current amplitude? Ignore any capacitive and inductive reactance in the hair dryer circuit. (*b*) If an equally powerful hair dryer is to be sold in Germany, where household outlets have $\mathcal{E}_{rms}$ = 220 V, what are I_{rms} and I? ••

77. In the first 100.0 ms after the switch on an *RLC* circuit is closed, the resistor dissipates 5.005 J of energy. In the first 200.0 ms, the resistor dissipates 10.03 J of energy. If the circuit contains a 70.0-mH inductor, what is the smallest possible inductive reactance of the circuit? ••

78. For the circuit of Problem 69, what is the average rate at which energy is delivered by the source when the circuit is operated at the resonant frequency? When it is operated at 1.00 kHz? What is the power factor in each case? ••

79. An *RLC* series circuit containing a 6.00-mH inductor, a 100-Ω resistor, a 4.00-μF capacitor, and an AC source for which $\mathcal{E}_{max}$ = 30.0 V is operated at an angular frequency of 5000 s^{-1}. Determine the phase constant, the power factor, the impedance, the rms emf for the source, the rms current, and the average rate at which energy is delivered by the source. ••

ₒ0-V AC circuit has a 20.0-Ω resistor connected in series to a capacitor for which the capacitive reactance is $X_C = 35.0\ \Omega$. (a) What is the phase constant? (b) What is the average rate at which energy is dissipated in the circuit? (c) If the resistance in the circuit is 25.0 Ω, what would the capacitive reactance have to be in order for the power factor to be 0.25? ••

81. An *RLC* series circuit containing a 5.0-Ω resistor, a 15-mH inductor, and a 10-mF capacitor is driven at a frequency of 8.0 Hz by an AC source for which $\mathscr{E}_{max} = 8.0$ V. At what average rate is energy dissipated? What is the average dissipation rate at resonance? ••

82. You need to design a power cable to connect an energy-storage facility located at the ocean shore to a wind turbine farm 2 km offshore (Figure P32.82). The farm can deliver energy at an average rate of 45 MW, and you need to run a single cable to deliver energy at this rate (the turbines and the storage facility share a common ground). The cable has a resistance *R*, leading to a loss of energy during transmission. Assume that all other loads on the circuit (electrical appliances in all the buildings serviced by this facility) have no capacitive or inductive reactance. Using different transformers at either end, you can change the value of $\mathscr{E}_{max}$ and *I* while maintaining the same rate at which electrical energy is delivered to the cable. Should you choose a high or a low value for $\mathscr{E}_{max}$? •••

Figure P32.82

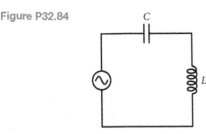

83. An *RLC* series circuit consists of a 450-Ω resistor, a 3.00-mF capacitor, and a 1.00-H inductor. The circuit is driven by a power source that oscillates at 20.0 Hz and has an $\mathscr{E}_{rms}$ value of 60.0 V. The power source is switched on at $t = 0$, and at that instant the emf is at its maximum value. Calculate the power supplied at (a) $t = 0.0200$ s, (b) $t = 0.0375$ s, and (c) $t = 0.500$ s. •••

Additional problems

84. Sketch the phasor diagram for v_C, v_L, and the instantaneous current for the circuit shown in Figure P32.84 at an arbitrary instant $t \neq 0$. If the potential difference across the capacitor is a maximum at $t = 0$, what are the initial phases of v_C, v_L, and *i*? •

Figure P32.84

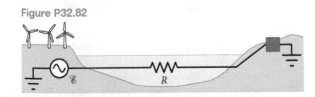

85. A capacitor is connected to an AC source. Sketch a graph showing how the current amplitude changes as you increase the AC angular frequency. •

86. Can a diode control anything other than the direction of current? ••

87. (a) What are the four possible combinations for input at A and B in an AND logic gate? What is the output for each combination? (b) What are the four possible combinations for input at A and B in an OR logic gate? What is the output for each combination? ••

88. A solenoid can be treated as a series *RL* circuit. If such a solenoid driven by a 60-Hz, 15-V AC source has an inductance of 6.0 mH and a resistance of 3.0 Ω, what are the phase constant and the current amplitude? ••

89. A circuit consisting of an AC source, a 100-Ω resistor, and a 1.00-μF capacitor has an impedance of 1330 Ω. (a) What is the source frequency? (b) What is the phase difference between the current and the source emf? ••

90. An *RLC* series circuit containing a 20.0-Ω resistor, a 30.0-mH inductor, and a 300-μF capacitor is driven by an AC source at a very high frequency. If the source amplitude is $\mathscr{E}_{max} = 12.0$ V, what can you say about the current in the circuit? ••

91. In the circuit shown in Figure P32.91, the AC source oscillates at 60 Hz and its emf is given by $\mathscr{E} = \mathscr{E}_{max} \sin(2\pi ft)$, where $\mathscr{E}_{max} = 15$ V and $R = 150\ \Omega$. The voltage source is operating at 60 Hz. Sketch, as functions of time, the current, the potential difference, and the power to the resistor. ••

Figure P32.91

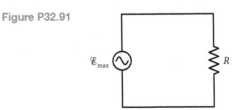

92. What happens with the light bulb shown in Figure P32.92 as you increase the frequency of the AC source? ••

Figure P32.92

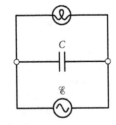

93. A diode *clipper* is a circuit used to eliminate extremes in input potential. If the graph in Figure P32.93 represents input potential as a function of time for the circuit shown, sketch a graph showing the output potential as a function of time. ••

Figure P32.93

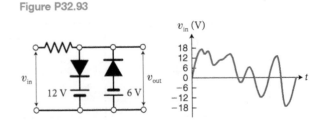

94. Figure P32.94 shows, for an AC circuit, the instantaneous current through a circuit element and the potential difference across the element. What can you determine about the element? ●●●

Figure P32.94

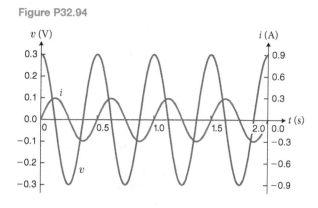

95. Your boss has purchased a new AC power source to run a high-voltage, low-current display, but it is not working. While he is fuming, you look at the owner's manual and discover that this power source produces only half the peak potential difference needed to operate the display. Because you are pretty sure you have a transformer on your workbench that will solve the problem, you tell your boss that you can fix it. When you return to your workbench, you are horrified to discover that the other members of your team have scavenged not only the transformer but most of your other supplies as well! Ignoring hookup wire and solder, you have only two identical capacitors and two identical diodes at your disposal. You collapse onto your lab stool and start thinking about how to word your apology to the boss, when suddenly you realize you can solve the problem after all! ●●● CR

96. The circuit in Figure P32.96 represents your planned design for a wall power supply that will run a radio that usually runs on a 9-V battery. The power supply uses a transformer (not shown) to convert the 110-V AC household emf of the wall outlet to a 9-V AC emf. If you do not add any additional components to this circuit, the potential difference over time is as shown in graph *a*, a typical sinusoidally varying $v(t)$ curve. Batteries supply direct current, however, and a radio designed to run on batteries cannot run on alternating current. If you address this problem by adding a rectifier to your circuit, the potential difference over time is as shown in graph *b*. The radio still will not run properly, though, because the 120-Hz

cycle would either render the radio dysfunctional or result in an annoying 120-Hz buzz. By adding a large capacitor in parallel with the rectifier, you can smooth out the potential difference as the capacitor charges and discharges over the course of a cycle. Still, there is going to be a residual 120-Hz "wiggle" on top of the DC signal, as shown in graph *c*. You can filter out this wiggle by using an inductor as a low-pass filter. If the radio has an internal resistance of $R = 20.0\ \Omega$, what inductance value do you need in order to reduce the wiggle by a factor of 2? ●●●

Figure P32.96

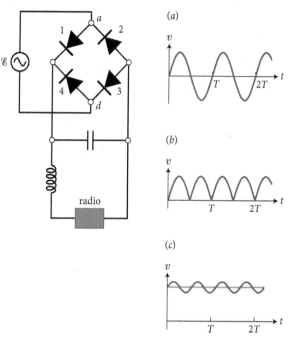

97. The research laboratory you work in is less than a block away from the transmitting antenna of a radio station that broadcasts at 1100 kHz. You notice that every piece of equipment in the lab has 1100-kHz noise in addition to the signals you want, which are in the range from 2 kHz to 5 kHz. You wonder if there is some sort of simple circuit you could add to the lab equipment that would allow your desired frequencies to pass through without much loss, while reducing the 1100-kHz signal by at least a factor of ten. ●●● CR

.swers to Review Questions

1. An alternating current is a time-dependent electric current that periodically changes direction.

2. The current varies sinusoidally. Before the capacitor begins to discharge, the current is zero. As the capacitor discharges, the current increases to its maximum magnitude in one direction, then returns to zero, then increases to its maximum magnitude in the opposite direction, and then returns to zero again to end one cycle. In any nonideal circuit, the amplitude of the current oscillations decays because there is resistance in the circuit.

3. The property is that the potential differences and currents in AC circuits are time-dependent rather than constant.

4. The phase of a sinusoidal function describes how the function depends on time. The two quantities necessary to specify the phase at any instant t are ω, the angular frequency, and ϕ_i, the value of the phase at the instant $t = 0$. Then the phase at any instant t is given by $\omega t + \phi_i$.

5. A phasor is a rotating arrow whose component on a vertical axis can be used to represent oscillating quantities. The vertical component of the phasor represents the value of the oscillating quantity, the phasor length represents the quantity's amplitude, and the angle of the phasor measured counterclockwise from the horizontal axis of the reference circle at any instant represents the quantity's phase $\omega t + \phi_i$ at that instant.

6. Quantity A is said to *lead* quantity B when the maximum value of A during one oscillation cycle occurs before the maximum value of B occurs. Quantity A is said to *lag* quantity B when the maximum value of A during one cycle occurs after the maximum value of B occurs.

7. The current leads the potential difference across the capacitor by 90°, lags the potential difference across the inductor by 90°, and is in phase with the potential difference across the resistor.

8. A semiconductor is a material that has a limited supply of free charge carriers, so that its electrical conductivity is intermediate between that of conductors and that of insulators.

9. An intrinsic semiconductor is chemically pure and its conductivity too small for many practical applications (except as an electrical insulator). An extrinsic semiconductor (also called a doped semiconductor) has a precisely controlled level of impurity atoms (called dopants) introduced so that the conductivity can be adjusted to suit specific applications.

10. In a *p*-type semiconductor, dopant atoms have fewer valence electrons than the host lattice atoms, creating a deficit of one electron—a hole—in the surrounding covalent bonds. An electron from another covalent bond can move into the hole, as if the hole "attracted" the electron. The hole has now moved to the site previously occupied by the electron, and the process can be repeated. Because the hole moves in a direction opposite the moving electrons, the hole behaves like a positively charged particle moving between lattice sites.

11. Doped silicon semiconductors are classified as *p*-type (*p* for *positive*) or *n*-type (*n* for *negative*). A *p*-type semiconductor contains dopant atoms that have fewer valence electrons than the host lattice atoms and thus create holes in the semiconductor lattice; the holes behave like free positive-charge carriers. An *n*-type semiconductor contains dopant atoms that have more valence electrons than the host lattice atoms, providing free negative-charge carriers.

12. A diode is made up of a *p*-type silicon semiconductor and an *n*-type silicon semiconductor in contact with each other.

13. The depletion zone is a thin region containing no free charge carriers that develops at the junction between the *n*-type and *p*-type sides of the diode.

14. The depletion zone forms as electrons from the *n*-type side cross into the *p* side and fill up holes there, while holes from the *p*-type side cross into the *n* side and combine with electrons there. These electron-hole recombinations result in the accumulation of negative charge on the *p*-type side of the depletion zone and accumulation of positive charge on the *n*-type side of the zone, with the resulting electric field directed from the *n* side to the *p* side.

15. Connecting the *n* side to the positive terminal and the *p* side to the negative terminal creates an electric field across the depletion zone directed from *n* to *p*; this external field broadens the depletion zone and maintains the condition of no charge carriers able to flow in the diode. Connecting the *n* side to the negative terminal and the *p* side to the positive terminal creates an electric field across the zone directed from *p* to *n*; when sufficiently strong, this external field shrinks and then eliminates the depletion zone with the result that charge carriers can flow through the diode. Thus, a diode allows electric current in one direction only.

16. It is a potential difference between emitter and base that shrinks the base-collector depletion zone enough to allow electrons to move from emitter to collector, thus creating a current through the transistor.

17. Transistors can function as switches or as current amplifiers.

18. First, two *n*-type wells are created in a layer of *p*-type material, then an insulating layer and a metal gate are added above the *p*-type region. Depletion zones form between the *n*- and *p*-type regions, preventing the flow of charge carriers between regions. When the gate receives a small positive charge, holes are driven from the *p*-type material beneath the gate, and the depletion zones at the boundaries of the two regions of *n*-type material become joined. A greater positive charge on the gate causes the depletion zone beneath it to be pushed away, creating an *n*-type channel connecting the two *n*-type wells and allowing conduction through the *n*-type materials.

19. A logic gate is a device that accepts two input signals, performs a logical operation on them, and emits the result as an output signal. In integrated circuits such as computer chips, logic gates are often implemented with field-effect transistors.

20. The current and the potential difference oscillate at the same angular frequency. The current amplitude I is directly proportional to the potential-difference amplitude V_C according to $I = \omega C V_C$. The current leads the potential difference by 90°, and so the phase constant of the current is $\phi = -\pi/2$ relative to $\phi = 0$ for the generator.

21. For a circuit containing a capacitor, the amplitude of the potential difference across the capacitor is proportional to the amplitude of the current through the capacitor, and the proportionality constant is the capacitive reactance of the circuit. Capacitive reactance depends on the angular frequency of the oscillation and on the capacitance: $X_C = 1/\omega C$.

22. The current and the potential difference oscillate at the same angular frequency. The current amplitude I is directly proportional to the potential-difference amplitude V_L according to $I = V_L/\omega L$. The current lags the potential difference by 90°, and so the phase constant of the current is $\phi = +\pi/2$ relative to $\phi = 0$ for the generator.

23. For a circuit containing an inductor, the amplitude of the potential difference across the inductor is proportional to the amplitude of the current through the inductor, and the proportionality constant is the inductive reactance of the circuit. Inductive reactance depends on the angular frequency of the oscillation and on the inductance: $X_L = \omega L$.

24. The sum at any given instant is determined by adding up the vertical components of the phasors of all the quantities. The result of this addition is the vertical component of the phasor of the sum, which equals the vector sum of the phasors.

25. The impedance is the ratio of the amplitude of the source emf to the amplitude of the current through the load: $Z = \mathscr{E}_{max}/I$.

26. Equation 32.34 shows that the impedance of a load consisting of a resistor and a capacitor connected in series is very great at low angular frequencies and nearly equal to the resistance at high angular frequencies. Therefore the amplitude of the potential difference across the resistor (the output) is very small if the angular frequency of the source (the input) is low but is nearly equal to the amplitude $\mathscr{E}_{max}$ of the source emf if the source angular frequency is high. This difference

in impedance allows high-frequency signals to pass through the circuit but weakens low-frequency signals so that they cannot pass through the circuit—the low-frequency signals are filtered out.

27. The resonant angular frequency is the source angular frequency that results in the greatest current amplitude. This occurs when ωL is equal to $1/\omega C$, which means $\omega_0 = 1/\sqrt{LC}$. Inductance and capacitance are the circuit properties that determine the value of ω_0.

28. The current amplitude has its maximum value when the source angular frequency ω equals the circuit's resonant angular frequency ω_0 and decreases both as ω gets smaller than ω_0 and as ω gets greater than ω_0.

29. The maximum current amplitude depends on the resistance in the circuit and on the amplitude of the source emf.

30. The time average of any sinusoidally oscillating quantity is zero, and $I_{av} = 0$ and $\mathcal{E}_{av} = 0$ give no insight into how these quantities change over time. The root-mean-square value of a sinusoidally oscillating quantity is nonzero, however, and so is a more meaningful measure of the quantity.

31. The average power at a resistor is $P_{av} = I_{rms}^2 R = \frac{1}{2}I^2 R$. The energy is dissipated as thermal energy.

32. The average power at a capacitor or an inductor is zero because the potential difference across either of these circuit elements is 90° out of phase with the current through the element (i leads v_C by 90°, i lags v_L by 90°). In those parts of the oscillation cycle where i and either v_C or v_L have the same sign, the instantaneous power

to the element is positive (energy is added to the element by the source); in those parts of the cycle where i and v have opposite signs, the instantaneous power is negative (energy is removed from the element by the source).

33. The power factor is the cosine of the phase difference between the source emf and the current. Because the average power to a load is $P_{av} = \frac{1}{2}\mathcal{E}_{max} I \cos \phi$, the power factor is a measure of the efficiency with which the source delivers energy to the load.

Answers to Guided Problems

Guided Problem 32.2 $I = \sqrt{\dfrac{C}{2L}}\,\mathcal{E} = 2.2 \times 10^{-3}$ A

Guided Problem 32.4 $\omega_2 = \sqrt{\dfrac{1}{C^2R^2 + 2/\omega_1^2}} = 6.6\ \text{s}^{-1}$

Guided Problem 32.6 The box contains a capacitor and an inductor in series, and $P_{av} = \frac{1}{2}I^2 R = 6.0$ W at ω_1 and $P_{av} = 3.0$ W at ω_2.

Guided Problem 32.8 (a) $I = \dfrac{\mathcal{E}_{max}}{\sqrt{R^2 + (\omega L - 1/\omega C)^2}} = 6.8 \times 10^{-2}$ A

and $\phi = \tan^{-1}\dfrac{\omega L - 1/\omega C}{R} = 1.6$ rad. (b) $\dfrac{V_L}{V_C} = \dfrac{X_L}{X_C} = 13$

33

PRACTICE
Ray Optics

PRACTICE

Chapter Summary

Rays (Sections 33.1, 33.2, 33.3, 33.5)

Concepts A **ray** is a line that represents the direction in which light travels.

For **reflected light,** the **angle of incidence** θ_i is the angle between the incident ray and the normal to the reflecting surface, and the **angle of reflection** θ_r is the angle between the reflected ray and the normal to the surface. The **law of reflection** says that when a ray strikes a smooth surface, $\theta_r = \theta_i$ and the two angles are in the same plane.

Refraction is the bending of light when it travels from one medium to another. The **angle of refraction** is the angle between the refracted ray and the normal to the surface at the interface between the materials.

Light passing from a high-density medium into a lower-density medium is bent away from the normal to the surface at the interface between the media. The **critical angle** θ_c is the angle of incidence for which the angle of refraction is 90°, which means the refracted rays emerge along the interface. If the angle of incidence is greater than θ_c, the light is all reflected back into the denser medium (**total internal reflection**).

An **image** is formed when light rays emanating from an object either intersect or appear to intersect at some location in space. The image is *real* when the rays actually do intersect at the location of the image and *virtual* when the rays do not pass through the location of the image.

Dispersion is the spatial separation of waves of different wavelengths in a light ray. When caused by refraction, the separation occurs because the speed at which each wave in the ray moves through a medium depends on the frequency of the wave.

Fermat's principle states that the path taken by a light ray between any two locations is the path for which the time interval needed for the ray to travel between those locations is a minimum.

Quantitative Tools The **index of refraction** n of a medium is

$$n \equiv \frac{c_0}{c},\tag{33.1}$$

where c_0 is the speed of light in vacuum and c is the speed of light in the medium.

If light has wavelength λ in vacuum, its wavelength λ_1 in a medium having index of refraction n_1 is

$$\lambda_1 = \frac{\lambda}{n_1}.\tag{33.3}$$

Snel's law: When light passes from a medium having index of refraction n_1 into a medium having index of refraction n_2, the angles and indices satisfy the relationship

$$n_1 \sin \theta_1 = n_2 \sin \theta_2,\tag{33.7}$$

where θ_1 is the angle of incidence and θ_2 is the angle of refraction.

For light traveling from a high-density medium having index of refraction n_2 to a lower-density medium having index of refraction $n_1 < n_2$, the **critical angle** is

$$\theta_c = \sin^{-1}\left(\frac{n_1}{n_2}\right).\tag{33.9}$$

Forming images using thin lenses (Sections 33.4, 33.5, 33.6, 33.8)

Concepts A **lens** is an optical element that redirects light rays by refraction such that they form images. The *axis* of a lens is a line that passes through the lens center and is perpendicular to the lens surface. Rays that run close to the lens axis are called *paraxial* rays. They can be either parallel to the lens axis or at a small angle to it.

Quantitative Tools The **lens equation** is

$$\frac{1}{f} = \frac{1}{o} + \frac{1}{i},\tag{33.16}$$

where f is the **focal length** of the thin lens, o is the *object distance*, and i is the *image distance*. The sign possibilities for f, o, and i are given in Table 33.2 on the next page.

nat are parallel to and close to s of a thin *converging* (*convex*) lens verge to a point called the **focal point** (or **focus**) of the lens. For a thin *diverging* (*concave*) lens, rays entering the lens from the left parallel to and close to the axis diverge as though they came from a single point to the left of the lens, called the **focal point.**

The **focal length** of a lens is the distance from the focal point to the center of the lens.

To determine the location and orientation of an image formed by a lens, make a ray diagram using the **principal rays.** See the accompanying Procedure boxes.

The **magnification** of a lens is

$$M \equiv \frac{h'}{h} = -\frac{i}{o},$$ (33.17)

where h' is the image height and h is the object height. The image is upright if M is positive and inverted if M is negative.

Lensmaker's formula: The focal length of a lens made of material of index of refraction n, having radii of curvature R_1 and R_2, and surrounded by air is given by

$$\frac{1}{f} = (n - 1)\left(\frac{1}{R_1} + \frac{1}{R_2}\right).$$ (33.36)

The radii are positive for convex surfaces, negative for concave surfaces, and infinity for planar surfaces.

Table 33.2 Sign conventions for f, i, and o (positive = real; negative = virtual)

Sign	Lens	Mirror
$f > 0$	converging lens	converging mirror
$f < 0$	diverging lens	diverging mirror
$o > 0$	object in front[b] of lens	object in front of mirror
$o < 0$[a]	object behind lens	object behind mirror
$i > 0$	image behind lens	image in front of mirror
$i < 0$	image in front of lens	image behind mirror
$h_i > 0$	image upright	image upright
$h_i < 0$	image inverted	image inverted
$|M| > 1$	image larger than object	image larger than object
$|M| < 1$	image smaller than object	image smaller than object

[a] Encountered only with lens or mirror combinations.
[b] For both lenses and mirrors, *in front* means *on the side where the rays originate*; *behind* refers to the opposite side.

Optical instruments (Section 33.6)

Concepts The lens of the eye forms an image on the retina. The *near point* is the closest object distance at which the eye can focus comfortably, about 0.25 m from the eye for an adult.

A compound microscope uses two converging lenses to form its image. The image formed by the first lens (the *objective* lens) serves as the object for the second lens (the *eyepiece* lens).

A refracting telescope uses two converging lenses to form its image. They are positioned so that the objective lens forms a real image of a distant object and the eyepiece lens forms, at infinity, a virtual image of this real image.

Quantitative Tools The **angular magnification** M_θ of a lens is

$$M_\theta = \left|\frac{\theta_i}{\theta_o}\right|,$$ (33.18)

where θ_i is the angle subtended by the image and θ_o is the angle subtended by the object.

For small angles, the angular magnification of a converging lens placed between an object and the eye is

$$M_\theta \approx \frac{0.25 \text{ m}}{f}.$$ (33.21)

The *strength d* of a lens measured in diopters is

$$d \equiv \frac{1 \text{ m}}{f}.$$ (33.22)

The magnification M of a compound microscope is

$$M = M_1 M_{\theta 2} = \frac{-0.25 \text{ m}}{f_2\left(\dfrac{o_1}{f_1} - 1\right)},$$

where M_1 is the magnification of the objective lens, $M_{\theta 2}$ is the angular magnification of the eyepiece lens, o_1 is the distance from the object to the objective lens, f_1 is the focal length of the objective lens, and f_2 is the focal length of the eyepiece lens.

The angular magnification M_θ of a refracting telescope is

$$M_\theta = \left|\frac{\theta_i}{\theta_o}\right| \approx \left|\frac{f_1}{f_2}\right|,$$

where f_1 is the focal length of the objective lens and f_2 is the focal length of the eyepiece lens.

Mirrors (Sections 33.2, 33.7)

Concepts A flat mirror forms a virtual image of an object. The image is just as far behind the mirror as the object is in front of the mirror.

A *concave* spherical mirror focuses incident rays that are parallel to and close to the axis of the mirror to a point in front of the mirror (the **focal point**), corresponding to a real focus. A *convex* spherical mirror disperses the parallel incident rays such that they appear to come from a point behind the mirror (the **focal point**), corresponding to a virtual focus.

To determine the location and orientation of an image formed by a mirror, make a ray diagram showing the three **principal rays**. See the accompanying Procedure boxes.

Quantitative Tools The focal length of a spherical mirror is one-half its *radius of curvature*:

$$f = \frac{R}{2}. \tag{33.23}$$

For a spherical mirror, the relationship of focal length f, object distance o, and image distance i is given by the lens equation:

$$\frac{1}{f} = \frac{1}{o} + \frac{1}{i}. \tag{33.24}$$

The sign possibilities for f, o, and i are given in Table 33.2.

PRACTICE

w Questions

swers to these questions can be found at the end of this chapter.

33.1 Rays

1. What has to happen in order for you to see an object?
2. What is a light ray? What is the relationship between a light ray and a light beam?
3. What is a shadow?

33.2 Absorption, transmission, and reflection

4. Describe the three possibilities for what happens to light that falls on an object.
5. What happens to most of the light that strikes an opaque object? To most of the light that strikes a translucent object?
6. State the law of reflection.
7. What is the difference between specular reflection and diffuse reflection?
8. If every ray that strikes a rough surface obeys the law of reflection, why is no image formed?
9. What is an image?
10. What is the difference between a real image and a virtual image?
11. Explain what it means to form an image of an object—for example, in a mirror. Why does an observer see the image of an object placed in front of a mirror as being located behind the mirror?
12. What do the colors of visible light correspond to?
13. How are the wavefronts and rays that represent the propagation of light drawn relative to the direction of propagation and relative to each other?

33.3 Refraction and dispersion

14. What is refraction, and why does it occur?
15. Does the wavelength change when light passes from a medium that has a high mass density into one that has a lower mass density, and if so, how?
16. For a refracting light ray, what are the names of the two angles associated with the bending, and how are their relative sizes related to the relative densities of the media?
17. What is the definition of *critical angle* for light rays undergoing refraction as they move from one medium into another?
18. Describe how total internal reflection occurs.
19. What is Fermat's principle?
20. What is dispersion, and why does it occur?

33.4 Forming images

21. A light ray traveling along a path in medium A is refracted when it enters medium B. If the ray's direction of travel is then reversed, how does its path change as the ray moves through medium B and back into medium A?

22. What are paraxial light rays?
23. For light moving from left to right through a lens, describe the paths of the three principal rays used to locate the image formed by the lens.
24. Describe the difference between the shapes of converging and diverging lens surfaces and the difference in what happens to light rays passing through them.

33.5 Snel's law

25. What is the definition of the index of refraction of a material through which light can pass?
26. How does the wavelength of light traveling in a transparent material depend on the material's index of refraction?
27. What is Snel's law?
28. How does the critical angle for total internal reflection at the boundary between two media with different mass densities depend on the indices of refraction of the media?

33.6 Thin lenses and optical instruments

29. What is the lens equation? What are the sign conventions for the distances f, o, and i in it?
30. What is the expression for determining the magnification of an image? What does the sign of the magnification tell you?
31. What is the near point of the human eye?
32. How is the angular magnification of an image formed by a lens defined?
33. What is a diopter?

33.7 Spherical mirrors

34. How does the focal length of a spherical mirror depend on the radius of curvature of the mirror?
35. Can the lens equation, $1/f = 1/o + 1/i$, be used for analyzing the image formed by a spherical mirror? If so, what are the sign conventions for the three variables?
36. What determines whether the image formed by a converging mirror is real or virtual?

33.8 Lensmaker's formula

37. What restrictions apply to the lensmaker's formula?
38. What is the sign convention for the radii of curvature in the lensmaker's formula?

Developing a Feel

Make an order-of-magnitude estimate of each of the following quantities. Letters in parentheses refer to hints below. Use them as needed to guide your thinking.

1. The thickness of glass needed to delay light by 1 μs compared to an equal thickness of vacuum (H, A, L)
2. The thickness of air (at STP) needed to delay light by 1 μs compared to an equal thickness of vacuum (H, D, L)
3. The vertical displacement of a horizontal light ray passing through a car windshield (I, A, M, Y)
4. The angular range in water through which you can see objects in the air when looking up from underwater (J, V)
5. The angular displacement of the Sun by the atmosphere when sunlight is tangent to Earth's surface (D, Q, K, I, X)
6. The time interval during which you can see the Sun after it has dropped below the horizon (F, R)
7. The change in the eye's average focal length needed to make either distant or nearby objects visible (G, S, Z, N)
8. The radius of curvature of a funhouse mirror that makes you look very fat (U, B, O, W)
9. The radius of curvature of one side of a +5-diopter glass lens if the other side is flat (A, P, E, AA)
10. The altitude at which a large airplane casts no shadow on the ground (C, T)

Hints

A. What is the index of refraction of glass?
B. What is the object distance?
C. How large is an airplane?
D. By how much does the index of refraction of air at standard temperature and pressure exceed the index of refraction of vacuum?
E. What is the lensmaker's formula?
F. By what angle is the Sun displaced by the atmosphere when sunlight is tangent to Earth's surface?
G. What is the lens equation?
H. For any material, how are distance traveled, speed, and travel time interval related?
I. At an interface between medium 1 and medium 2, how are the incident and refracted angles related?
J. What is the critical angle?
K. If you model the atmosphere as a spherical shell of uniform mass density (hence, uniform index of refraction), what is its effective height?
L. For any material, how are the speed of light and the index of refraction related?
M. What is the windshield thickness?
N. What is the distance from the eye's lens to the image?
O. What is the relationship between magnification and o, i, and f?
P. What is the relationship between diopters and focal length?
Q. Does the index of refraction of air vary in the atmosphere?
R. How fast does Earth rotate on its axis?
S. What is the minimum distance from an object that can be clearly seen to the eye's lens?
T. What is the angular size of the Sun?
U. By how much must your image be magnified horizontally to make you look very fat?

V. What is the index of refraction of water?
W. What is the relationship between focal length and radius of curvature?
X. How can you determine the angle of refraction?
Y. What is the angle of incidence for light entering the windshield?
Z. What is the maximum distance from an object to the eye's lens?
AA. What is the radius of curvature for a flat surface?

Key (all values approximate)

A. $n = \frac{3}{2}$; B. 1 m; C. about 50 m (either length or wingspan); D. 3×10^{-4}; E. $1/f = (n-1)(1/R_1 + 1/R_2)$; F. 10^{-2} rad (see Developing a Feel 5); G. $1/f = 1/o + 1/i$; H. $d_{mat} = c_{mat}\Delta t_{mat}$; I. $n_1 \sin\theta_1 = n_2 \sin\theta_2$; J. $\theta_c = \sin^{-1}(n_1/n_2)$; K. to produce atmospheric pressure, a spherical shell of uniform mass density (1 kg/m^3) must have height $h = P_0/\rho g = 1 \times 10^4$ m; L. $c_{mat} = (3 \times 10^8 \text{ m/s})/n_{mat}$; M. 5 mm; N. diameter of the eyeball, 25 mm; O. $M = -i/o$ and $1/f = 1/o + 1/i$; P. $d = (1 \text{ m})/f$; Q. yes, the index decreases as the mass density of the atmosphere decreases nonlinearly from sea level to vacuum; R. $\omega = 2\pi/\text{day} = 7 \times 10^{-5} \text{ s}^{-1}$; S. about 0.25 m; T. about the same angular size as a finger held at arm's length: $\theta = 0.01 \text{ m}/1 \text{ m} = 0.01$ rad; U. by a factor of 3; V. $n = \frac{4}{3}$; W. $f = R/2$; X. sketch Earth with a refracted ray tangent to the surface, and the angle of refraction appears in a right triangle in which two of the sides are Earth's radius $(R_E = 6 \times 10^6 \text{ m})$ and the radius to the top of the atmosphere $(R_E + h)$; Y. 50°; Z. infinity; AA. $R = \infty$

and Guided Problems

Procedure: Simplified ray diagrams for lenses

To determine the location and orientation of an image formed by a lens, follow this procedure.

1. Draw a horizontal line representing the lens axis (the line perpendicular to the lens through its center). In the center of the diagram, draw a vertical line representing the lens. Put a + above the line to represent a converging lens or a – to represent a diverging lens.
2. Put two dots on the axis on either side of the lens to represent the foci of the lens. The dots should be equidistant from the lens.
3. Represent the object by drawing an upward pointing arrow from the axis at the appropriate relative distance to the lens. For example, if the distance from the object to the lens is twice the focal length of the lens, put the arrow twice as far from the lens as the dot you drew in step 2. The top of the arrow should be at about half the height of the lens.

4. From the top of the arrow representing the object draw two or three of the three *principal rays* listed in the following Procedure Box Principal rays for lenses.
5. The top of the image is at the point where the rays *that exit the lens* intersect (if they diverge, trace them backward to determine the point of intersection). If the intersection is on the opposite side of the lens from the object, the image is real; if it is on the same side, the image is virtual. Draw an arrow pointing from the axis to the intersection to represent the image (use a dashed arrow for a virtual image).

In general it is sufficient to draw two principal rays, but depending on the situation, some rays may be easier to draw than others. You can also use a third ray to verify that it, too, goes through the intersection. (If it doesn't, you have made a mistake.)

Procedure: Principal rays for lenses

The propagations of principal rays for converging and diverging lenses are very similar. The description below holds for rays that travel from left to right.

Converging lens

1. A ray that travels parallel to the lens axis before entering the lens goes through the right focus after exiting the lens.
2. A ray that passes through the center of the lens continues undeflected.
3. A ray that passes through the left focus travels parallel to the lens axis after exiting the lens. If the object is between the focus and the lens, this ray doesn't pass through the focus but lies on the line from the focus to the point where the ray originates.

Diverging lens

1. A ray that travels parallel to the lens axis before entering the lens continues along the line from the left focus to the point where the ray enters the lens.
2. A ray that passes through the center of the lens continues undeflected.
3. A ray that travels toward the right focus travels parallel to the lens axis after exiting the lens.

Procedure: Ray diagrams for spherical mirrors

Ray diagrams for spherical mirrors are very similar to those for lenses. The procedure below is for rays traveling from the left to the right.

1. Draw a horizontal line representing the mirror axis. In the center of the diagram, draw a circular arc representing the mirror. A converging mirror curves toward the left; a diverging mirror curves toward the right.
2. Put a dot on the axis at the center of the circular arc and label it C. Add another dot on the axis, halfway between C and the mirror. This point is the focus. Label it f.
3. Represent the object by drawing an upward pointing arrow from the axis at the appropriate relative distance to the left of the mirror. For example, if the distance

from the object to a converging mirror is one-third the radius of curvature of the mirror, put the arrow a bit to the right of the focus The top of the arrow should be at about half the height of the mirror.
4. From the top of the arrow representing the object draw two or three of the following three so-called *principal rays* listed in the Procedure Box Principal rays for spherical mirrors on page 619.
5. The top of the image is at the point where the rays that are reflected by the mirror intersect. If the intersection is on the left side of the lens, the image is real; if it is on the right, the image is virtual. Draw an arrow pointing from the axis to the intersection to represent the image (use a dashed arrow for a virtual image).

Procedure: Principal rays for spherical mirrors

The description below holds for rays that travel from left to right.

Converging mirror

1. A ray that travels parallel to the mirror axis before reaching the mirror goes through the focus after being reflected.
2. A ray that passes through the center of the sphere on which the mirror surface lies is reflected back onto itself. If the object is between the center and the mirror, this ray doesn't pass through the center but lies on the line from the center to the point at which the ray originates.
3. A ray that passes through the focus is reflected parallel to the axis. If the object is between the focus and the mirror, this ray doesn't pass through the focus but lies

on the line from the focus to the point at which the ray originates.

Diverging mirror

1. A ray that travels parallel to the mirror axis before reaching the mirror is reflected along the line that goes through the focus and the point where the ray strikes the surface.
2. A ray that passes through the center of the sphere on which the mirror surface lies is reflected back onto itself.
3. A ray whose extension passes through the focus is reflected parallel to the axis.

For both converging and diverging mirrors a ray that hits the mirror on the axis is reflected back symmetrically about the axis.

These examples involve material from this chapter but are not associated with any particular section. Some examples are worked out in detail; others you should work out by following the guidelines provided.

Worked Problem 33.1 Aquarium beams

You shine a laser pointer into a filled aquarium tank from above. The laser beam strikes the water surface at 40.0° from the normal and then travels to one of the glass sidewalls of the tank. Does the beam pass through that wall into the air, and if so, at what angle of refraction?

❶ **GETTING STARTED** This problem involves a sequence of encounters of a laser beam with interfaces between materials that have different indices of refraction. Our goal is to determine whether the beam passes through a sidewall of the tank and enters the air and, if so, at what angle of refraction. The question we must answer is: At each interface—(1) air–water, (2) water–glass, (3) glass–air—is the beam totally reflected, or does it enter the second material and become refracted? Consequently, we need to work out the change of direction of the beam at each interface.

To visualize the situation, we arbitrarily choose the right sidewall of the tank and make a sketch showing that wall, the water surface, and the laser beam (Figure WG33.1). If the beam is to pass all the way through and end up back in the air, it travels first through the air to the water surface, then through the water to the left surface of the right sidewall, and then through the glass to the right surface of this wall. To keep the diagram simple, we omit any reflected rays. We number the three interfaces and show the beam bending toward the normal to interfaces 1 and 2 as it crosses those interfaces (moving in each case from the lower-density material to the higher-density material) and bending away from the normal as it crosses interface 3 because now it moves from higher density to lower density. We label the six angles the beam makes to the interface normals θ_{a1}, θ_{w1}, θ_{w2}, θ_{g2}, θ_{g3}, and θ_{a3}.

Figure WG33.1

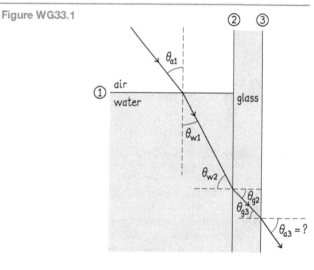

❷ **DEVISE PLAN** We know from *Principles* Table 33.1 that the index of refraction of air is smaller than that of water, which is smaller than that of glass. Thus total internal reflection—if it happens—can happen only at the glass–air interface because this is the only place the beam might move from a material of greater n value to a material of smaller n value. If total internal reflection occurs, Snel's law applied to the glass–air interface cannot be satisfied, and so the value of the critical angle is exceeded. We then obtain the indices of refraction we need in *Principles* Table 33.1. Two types of glass are listed, and we arbitrarily assume the aquarium is made of flint glass.

.1 Indices of refraction for common transparent materials

Material	n (for λ = 589 nm)
Air (at standard temperature and pressure)	1.00029
Liquid water	1.33
Sugar solution (30%)	1.38
Sugar solution (80%)	1.49
Microscope cover slip glass	1.52
Sodium chloride (table salt)	1.54
Flint glass	1.65
Diamond	2.42

We repeatedly apply Snel's law, along with some trigonometry, to determine the angles and thereby determine whether the Snel's law condition at interface 3 can be met. If no value of θ_{a3} exists, total internal reflection occurs and the beam does not pass from glass to air; if a value exists, θ_{a3} is the exit angle.

❸ EXECUTE PLAN We apply Snel's law at each interface in numerical order, beginning with interface 1: the air–water interface.

$$n_{air} \sin \theta_{a1} = n_{water} \sin \theta_{w1}.$$

We are given $\theta_{a1} = 40.0°$, and from *Principles* Table 33.1 we see that $n_{air} = 1.00029$ and $n_{water} = 1.33$. Thus

$$\theta_{w1} = \sin^{-1}\left(\frac{n_a \sin \theta_{a1}}{n_w}\right) = \sin^{-1}\left(\frac{1.00029 \sin 40.0°}{1.33}\right) = 28.9°.$$

Next we note that the normals to interfaces 1 and 2 form a right triangle that has the in-water portion of the beam as its hypotenuse.

Therefore $\theta_{w1} + \theta_{w2} = 90°$ and

$$\theta_{w2} = 90.0° - 28.9° = 61.1°.$$

Now we apply Eq. 33.7 to interface 2:

$$n_w \sin \theta_{w2} = n_g \sin \theta_{g2}$$

$$\theta_{g2} = \sin^{-1}\left(\frac{n_w \sin \theta_{w2}}{n_g}\right) = \sin^{-1}\left(\frac{1.33 \sin 61.1°}{1.65}\right) = 44.9°.$$

Interfaces 2 and 3 are parallel, which means $\theta_{g2} = \theta_{g3}$, allowing us to calculate θ_{a3}:

$$n_g \sin \theta_{g3} = n_a \sin \theta_{a3}$$

$$\theta_{a3} = \sin^{-1}\left(\frac{n_g \sin \theta_{g3}}{n_a}\right) = \sin^{-1}\left(\frac{1.65 \sin 44.9°}{1.00029}\right) = \sin^{-1}(1.16).$$

Because the argument of the inverse sine function exceeds 1, no angle exists that can satisfy this condition. This tells us that θ_{g3} exceeds the critical angle for the glass–air interface. The beam must undergo total internal reflection at interface 3 and thus does not exit the tank. ✔

❹ EVALUATE RESULT We know that total internal reflection can happen only to light traveling from a medium with a higher index of refraction into a medium with a lower index of refraction, and this is the case here, as the beam moves from glass ($n_g = 1.65$) to air ($n_a = 1.00029$). For total internal reflection to occur, $\theta_{g3} = \theta_{g2} = 44.9°$ must exceed the critical angle θ_c for the glass–air interface. To see whether or not $\theta_{g3} > \theta_c$, we can use Eq. 33.9 with glass for medium 2 and air for medium 1:

$$\sin \theta_c = \frac{n_a}{n_g} = \frac{1.00029}{1.65} = 0.606; \quad \theta_c = \sin^{-1}\left(\frac{n_a}{n_g}\right) = 37.3°.$$

Thus $\theta_{g3} > \theta_c$, consistent with total internal reflection at interface 3 (the glass–air interface).

Guided Problem 33.2 Prism in air or liquid

A beam of light enters a flint-glass prism as shown in Figure WG33.2, entering normal to face AB. When the prism is surrounded by air, the beam is totally internally reflected at face AC. When the prism is immersed in a clear liquid, the beam exits the prism through face AC. What minimum value of the index of refraction of the liquid permits the beam to exit?

❶ GETTING STARTED

1. In Figure WG33.2, draw the path the beam follows when the prism is surrounded by air, and label the angles.
2. What principle determines the beam's path?
3. Does the beam change direction on entering the prism?

❷ DEVISE PLAN

4. How does the path of the beam *in the prism* depend on whether the prism is surrounded by air or by liquid?
5. Draw a diagram showing the beam's path when the prism is surrounded by liquid.
6. What determines the angle at which the beam strikes face AC?
7. How can you use the angle from question 6 and total internal reflection to determine the minimum index of refraction of the liquid?
8. What value do you need to look up to calculate the liquid's index of refraction?

❸ EXECUTE PLAN

❹ EVALUATE RESULT

9. Is your result plausible, and why?

Figure WG33.2

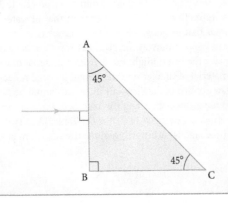

Worked Problem 33.3 Magnified insect

Using a magnifying lens outdoors to examine an insect, you notice that when you hold a piece of paper underneath the lens and let sunlight fall on the lens, the smallest bright spot forms when the paper is 150 mm from the lens. Where should you hold the lens to form an image of the insect that is upright and three times larger than the insect?

1 GETTING STARTED This is a problem about image formation with a magnifying lens. We need to determine the lens–object distance that produces an upright image three times larger than the object. We know that magnifying lenses are converging lenses. Because the smallest bright spot of sunlight is formed when the lens is 150 mm from the paper, we know that the sunlight is focused there, and thus the focal length f of the lens is $+0.150$ m (positive because the lens is converging). We start by drawing a simplified ray diagram (Figure WG33.3). Because our image must be upright, we position our object closer to the lens than the focal point.

Figure WG33.3

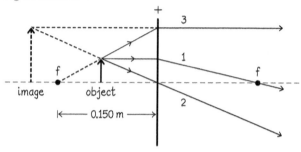

2 DEVISE PLAN We can use Eq. 33.17 to determine the image distance i in terms of the object distance o. Then we can use the lens equation (Eq. 33.16) together with our known value of f to determine o. Figure WG33.3 shows that the image is on the same side of the lens as the object and therefore the image distance i is negative. The image is upright, and therefore the image height and magnification are positive.

3 EXECUTE PLAN Equation 33.17 gives us $i = -Mo$. This result substituted in Eq. 33.16 yields

$$\frac{1}{f} = \frac{1}{i} + \frac{1}{o} = -\frac{1}{Mo} + \frac{1}{o} = \left(\frac{M-1}{M}\right)\frac{1}{o}.$$

Solving this expression for o yields

$$o = \left(\frac{M-1}{M}\right)f = \left(\frac{3-1}{3}\right)(0.150 \text{ m}) = 0.100 \text{ m}. ✔$$

4 EVALUATE RESULT From our simplified ray diagram, we expect to obtain $o < f$, and we do. An object distance of 0.100 m is fairly short, but it is reasonable because we know from experience that we hold a magnifying glass close to the object we are viewing.

Guided Problem 33.4 Image on paper

Your friend holds a lens and a sheet of paper near a flower so that an image of the flower appears on the paper. The flower is 0.10 m away from the lens, and the image is four times the size of the flower. Which lens did your friend borrow from the physics lab to produce this image?

1 GETTING STARTED

1. What quantity (value and sign) can you use to identify a lens? What algebraic symbol is used to denote this quantity?
2. Which type of lens—converging or diverging—can produce an image on a sheet of paper, or can both types of lens do so?
3. Draw a simplified ray diagram showing an enlarged image that can appear on a sheet of paper, using the type of lens you identified in question 2, and label the relevant distances. If you identified more than one type of lens, draw a simplified ray diagram for each type and identify which can produce an enlarged image.

2 DEVISE PLAN

4. What equations relate image size and object size to image distance and object distance?
5. What equation relates image distance, object distance, and focal length?

3 EXECUTE PLAN

4 EVALUATE RESULT

6. Is your answer plausible?

Worked Problem 33.5 Corrective lenses

Your friend's eyeglass lenses, made of a material for which the index of refraction is 1.498, have one convex surface and one concave surface. The concave surface is on the side nearer to the eye and has a radius of curvature of magnitude 71.3 mm, and the convex surface has a radius of curvature of 125 mm. If your friend looks at her computer screen at a distance of 500 mm, how far from her eyes is the image of the screen formed? Is she near-sighted (has difficulty seeing distant objects) or far-sighted (has difficulty seeing nearby objects)?

1 GETTING STARTED We need to determine the image distance for eyeglass lenses used to view a computer screen (the object) at an object distance of 500 mm. We are given the index of refraction for the lens material ($n = 1.498$), the radii of curvature for the two surfaces of each lens—$R_{convex} = 125$ mm and $R_{concave} = -71.3$ mm—and the object distance $o = 500$ mm.

To determine whether your friend is near-sighted or far-sighted, we must identify the overall effect of each lens as being converging or diverging. We also need this information to draw a ray diagram. That the convex surface has a greater magnitude of radius of curvature than the concave surface means that the convex surface is flatter than the concave surface. Thus the concave surface refracts light and the lens overall is a diverging lens. We indicate this ...wing a minus sign above the lens in our simplified ray dia-...m (Figure WG33.4). As this illustration shows, it doesn't matter, with a diverging lens, whether the object is farther or closer than the focal point. Either way, the image is virtual and appears between the lens and the object.

Figure WG33.4

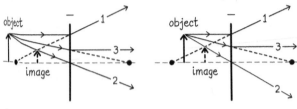

object distance greater than focal length

object distance smaller than focal length

② **DEVISE PLAN** We can use the lens equation (Eq. 33.16) to obtain i in terms of f and o. First, though, we must calculate f, which we can do by using the lensmaker's formula (Eq. 33.36).

③ **EXECUTE PLAN** In Eq. 33.36, a convex radius of curvature is positive and a concave radius of curvature is negative. Substituting the values provided in this equation gives us

$$\frac{1}{f} = (1.498 - 1)\left(\frac{1}{125 \times 10^{-3}\,\text{m}} + \frac{1}{-71.3 \times 10^{-3}\,\text{m}}\right) = -3.00/\text{m}.$$

Now we solve Eq. 33.16 for i and calculate its value using this value for $1/f$ and our known value for o:

$$\frac{1}{f} = \frac{1}{i} + \frac{1}{o}$$

$$i = \frac{1}{\dfrac{1}{f} - \dfrac{1}{o}} = \frac{1}{-3.00/\text{m} - \dfrac{1}{0.500\,\text{m}}} = -0.200\,\text{m}.$$

A negative image distance means the image is on the same side of the lens as the object, so the image appears to be between the computer screen and your friend's eyes, 0.200 m from her eyes. ✔

From the fact that the image distance is shorter than the object distance, we infer that your friend is near-sighted, meaning she sees near objects well. She thus needs her contact lenses to bring the image of a faraway object closer to her eyes, so that the image appears where her eyes can focus on it. ✔

④ **EVALUATE RESULT** The relative radii of curvature told us that the lens is overall diverging, which means the image distance must be negative, as our result is. According to the ray diagram, the image distance should be shorter than the object distance, giving us added support for the reasonableness of our result.

Guided Problem 33.6 Correcting near-sightedness

A near-sighted person's eyes cannot create focused images of distant objects on the retina because the retina is too far from the eye's lens. Near-sighted individuals see nearby objects clearly because images of closer objects form farther from the eye's lens and can reach the retina. Therefore corrective lenses for near-sightedness are designed to form images of distant objects at the person's "far point" (the farthest distance at which a person can see clearly). If a person has an eyeglass prescription of -3.00 diopters but is not wearing his glasses, what is the far point?

❶ **GETTING STARTED**

1. Is a -3.00-diopter lens converging or diverging? How do you know?
2. Where does this lens form an image of a distant object?

3. Draw a ray diagram showing the image of a distant object formed by this lens.
4. What quantity must you determine? How does it relate to your ray diagram?

❷ **DEVISE PLAN**

5. What distance in your ray diagram can you determine from the lens strength?
6. What equation can you use to relate the distances in your ray diagram?

❸ **EXECUTE PLAN**

❹ **EVALUATE RESULT**

7. Is your answer plausible?

Worked Problem 33.7 Mirror image

You are looking at your face in a spherical mirror and see an upright image that is enlarged 1.50 times.

(a) Is the mirror diverging or converging? (b) Is the distance from you to the mirror surface longer or shorter than the mirror's focal length? (c) If the absolute value of the radius of curvature of the mirror is 0.96 m, where is the image?

❶ **GETTING STARTED** We are told that a spherical mirror produces an upright image that is 1.50 times larger than the object and asked whether the mirror is converging or diverging and where the object is located relative to the mirror's focal point. We are also given the absolute value of the mirror's radius of curvature and asked to determine the image distance.

❷ **DEVISE PLAN** We know that all diverging spherical mirrors form images that are smaller than the objects, so the mirror in this problem must be a converging mirror. For part b, we know that a spherical converging mirror forms an upright image only when the object distance is shorter than the mirror's focal length. To determine the image distance, we have Eq. 33.24 relating focal length f, object distance o, and image distance i. To obtain i from this relationship, however, we must know f and o. The magnification, which we know, relates o to i through Eq. 33.17, and so we have a way of expressing o in terms of i:

$$M = 1.50 = \frac{-i}{o}.$$

For f, we know that in spherical mirrors, $|f| = R/2$.

③ EXECUTE PLAN

(a) This is a converging mirror, indicated by the enlarged image. ✔

(b) The fact that the image is upright tells us that the distance from the object (your face) to the mirror must be shorter than the focal length. ✔

(c) The focal length of a converging mirror is positive. Thus, for this mirror, $f = 0.96 \, \text{m}/2 = +0.48 \, \text{m}$. Equation 33.17 lets us express o in terms of i:

$$M = -\frac{i}{o}$$

$$o = -\frac{i}{1.50}.$$

We now have what we need to determine i:

$$\frac{1}{f} = \frac{1}{i} + \frac{1}{o} = \frac{1}{i} + \left(\frac{-1.50}{i}\right) = \frac{-0.50}{i}$$

$$i = -0.50 f = -0.50(+0.48 \, \text{m}) = -0.24 \, \text{m}.$$

The image of your face is 0.24 m behind the mirror surface. ✔

④ EVALUATE RESULT We can use a ray diagram to check that our result is reasonable (Figure WG33.5). The figure shows that we have a virtual image, and so we expect to obtain a negative value for i. The image seems to be about 1.5 times larger than the object. Although we haven't calculated o, we can confirm that $o < f$ is correct by this reasoning: $|i| = 0.24 \, \text{m}$ is less than $f = 0.48 \, \text{m}$. When an image is larger than its object, the object–mirror distance is shorter than the image–mirror distance. Thus, because $|i| < f$ and $o < |i|$, we know that $o < f$.

Figure WG33.5

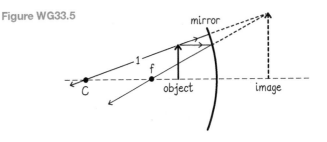

Guided Problem 33.8 Reflecting flames

You want to use a spherical mirror to cast an image of a candle flame on a sheet of paper.

(a) Should you use a diverging mirror or a converging mirror?
(b) If the absolute value of the radius of curvature of the mirror you use is 300 mm and you position the candle 360 mm in front of the mirror, do you see the image of the flame on the paper? If so, at what distance from the mirror must you hold the paper, and how big is the image?

❶ GETTING STARTED

1. Which type of image can be viewed on a sheet of paper: real or virtual?
2. Which type of image is created by a converging mirror? By a diverging mirror?
3. Combine your answers to questions 1 and 2 to answer part *a*.

❷ DEVISE PLAN

4. Draw a ray diagram showing the candle, the mirror, and two principal rays that allow you to locate the image. Check that you obtain the correct type of image.
5. How does the shape of the mirror determine the sign of the focal length?
6. How can you use the mirror radius of curvature and the object–mirror distance to determine where to hold the paper?

❸ EXECUTE PLAN

❹ EVALUATE RESULT

7. Is the paper–mirror distance you calculated consistent with your answer to question 1? Is this distance reasonable?
8. Is your result for image size plausible?

Worked Problem 33.9 Reflecting telescope

A *Cassegrain telescope* (Figure WG33.6) uses a large converging spherical mirror, the *primary*, to collect light from distant stars and a small diverging spherical mirror, the *secondary*, to send the light through a gap in the primary to a detector located outside the telescope. If the primary has a focal length of 1.00 m, the secondary is mounted 0.85 m from the surface of the primary, and the final real image forms 0.12 m behind the surface of the primary, what is the focal length of the secondary?

Figure WG33.6

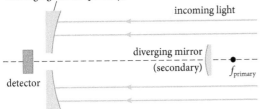

converging mirror (primary)

❶ GETTING STARTED This is a problem about image formation by two mirrors, so we apply the principle that the image formed by the first mirror (the primary) serves as the object for the second mirror (the secondary). Because a telescope is used to observe distant objects, light from the objects enters the telescope as parallel rays. We start by drawing a ray diagram for the primary, showing these parallel rays reflected from this mirror (Figure WG33.7a on the next page). Parallel rays converge in the primary's focal plane, which means that the distance $i_{primary}$ from the primary to the image it forms is equal to the focal length $f_{primary}$.

Next we draw a diagram showing both mirrors (Figure WG33.7b). It is difficult to draw principal rays showing how light reflects from the secondary. However, the problem tells us the location of the final image—0.12 m behind the primary—and so in this diagram we show the rays reflected from the secondary as meeting at this location. We also label the other distances specified in the problem. Our task is to calculate the focal length of the secondary $f_{secondary}$, that places the final image at the proper location.

Figure WG33.7

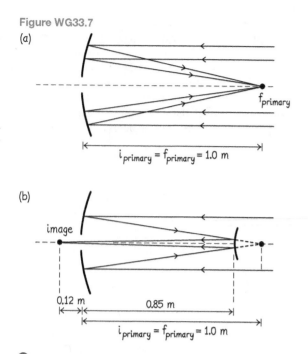

(a)

$i_{primary} = f_{primary} = 1.0 \text{ m}$

(b)

image

0.12 m

0.85 m

$i_{primary} = f_{primary} = 1.0 \text{ m}$

❷ **DEVISE PLAN** The image formed by the primary is *behind* the secondary. Light does not actually reach that location, however, because the secondary is in the way. Therefore the object distance for

the secondary, $o_{secondary}$, is negative. The image distance, $i_{secondary}$, is positive because the image is real. We can use the distance between the two mirrors and the distance from the final image to the primary, along with $f_{primary} = 1.00 \text{ m}$, to obtain values for $o_{secondary}$ and $i_{secondary}$, and then use these distances in Eq. 33.24 to determine $f_{secondary}$.

❸ **EXECUTE PLAN** The distance from the primary to $f_{primary}$ is 1.00 m, and the distance between the mirrors is 0.85 m. Because the object for the secondary is the image formed by the primary, we have $|o_{secondary}| = 1.00 \text{ m} - 0.85 \text{ m} = 0.15 \text{ m}, o_{secondary} = -0.15 \text{ m}$. Also, $i_{secondary} = 0.85 \text{ m} + 0.12 \text{ m} = 0.97 \text{ m}$. These two values in Eq. 33.24 yield

$$f_{secondary} = \left(\frac{1}{o_{secondary}} + \frac{1}{i_{secondary}}\right)^{-1}$$

$$= \left(\frac{1}{-0.15 \text{ m}} + \frac{1}{0.97 \text{ m}}\right)^{-1} = -0.18 \text{ m}. ✔$$

❹ **EVALUATE RESULT** We expect $f_{secondary}$ to be negative because the secondary is a diverging mirror. Because $|i_{secondary}| \gg |o_{secondary}|$, and thus $|1/i_{secondary}| \ll |1/o_{secondary}|$, we expect $f_{secondary}$ to be comparable to $o_{secondary}$. Our result agrees with both expectations and so seems reasonable.

Guided Problem 33.10 Double lens

You have a camera in which the lens is a combination of a diverging lens of focal length −120 mm and a converging lens of focal length 42 mm. The two are mounted 60 mm apart, and the converging lens is the one closer to the camera body. To focus the image produced on the sensor in the camera body, you move the pair of lenses closer to or farther from the sensor, keeping the distance between the lenses fixed at 60 mm. Suppose you are photographing a plant that is 400 mm tall and is located 500 mm in front of the diverging lens. When you have this object in focus, how far is the converging lens from the sensor?

❶ **GETTING STARTED**

1. What principle determines how the image forms after the light from the object passes through both lenses?
2. Draw a diagram showing the object, the two lenses, and the camera sensor. Label the important distances. If a distance is not known, label it with an appropriate symbol.
3. What quantity must you determine? How is this quantity related to the image distance for the converging lens?

❷ **DEVISE PLAN**

4. What ray diagrams should you draw?
5. What equation can you use to calculate the distance from the converging lens to the sensor?

❸ **EXECUTE PLAN**

6. Draw a diagram showing the rays for the image formed by the diverging lens.
7. Draw a ray diagram showing both lenses and the rays for the image formed by the converging lens. Remember that for a combination of two lenses, the principal rays for the second lens are not necessarily the continuation of the rays from the first lens.
8. Calculate the image distance for the converging lens.

❹ **EVALUATE RESULT**

9. Is your answer for the distance between the converging lens and the sensor plausible?

Questions and Problems

For instructor-assigned homework, go to MasteringPhysics® (MP)

33.1 Rays

1. Figure P33.1 shows eight point sources of light, a–h, and two detectors, A and B. The point sources are evenly spaced, with 0.10 m between adjacent sources, and detector A shields part of detector B from the point sources. If no light is reflected from any nearby objects, how many of the point sources illuminate any part of (*a*) detector A and (*b*) detector B? •

Figure P33.1

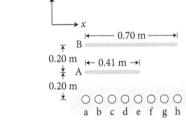

2. A point source is fixed 1.0 m away from a large screen. Call the line normal to the screen surface and passing through the center of the point source the *z* axis. When a sheet of cardboard in which a square hole 0.040 m on a side has been cut is placed between the point source and the screen, 0.50 m from the point source with the hole centered on the *z* axis, a bright square shows up on the screen. If, instead, a second sheet of cardboard with a similar square hole is placed between the point source and screen, 0.25 m from the point source with the hole centered on the *z* axis, the bright square it casts on the screen is identical to the bright square from the first sheet. What are the dimensions of the hole in this sheet? •

3. A thin, flat object in which a square hole 30.0 mm on a side has been cut is illuminated with a point source. Light that passes through the hole strikes a screen 300 mm behind the object. Call the direction normal to the screen the *z* direction. The point source is shifted away from the center of the hole by 150 mm in the positive *x* direction. The point source is centered on the hole in the *y* direction and is 300 mm in front of the object in the *z* direction. What are (*a*) the dimensions of the bright region on the screen and (*b*) the *x* and *y* coordinates of the perimeter of the bright region? ••

4. Sunlight that reaches Earth is blocked by Earth from traveling any farther, so that the region on the side of Earth facing away from the Sun is in shadow. The portion of this region in complete shadow is the *umbra*, and the portion in partial shadow is the *penumbra*. The Sun's radius is 7.0×10^5 km, Earth's radius is 6.4×10^3 km, and the Sun–Earth distance is 1.5×10^8 km. (*a*) What is the shape of the umbra? Of the penumbra? (*b*) Consider an observer in space on the side of Earth facing away from the Sun—that is, in the shadow region. Does this observer see the Sun when he is in the umbra? When he is in the penumbra? ••

5. Two models of light emitted from a light bulb are illustrated in Figure P33.5. (*a*) Describe the difference in the behavior of light in each model. (*b*) Describe an experiment that can determine which model of light is more accurate. ••

Figure P33.5   model A   model B

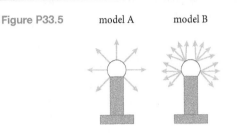

6. An aquarium light bulb has a long, straight glowing filament surrounded by a tubular, clear glass bulb. This lighted bulb, with its filament oriented vertically, is placed 1.0 m from a screen in an otherwise dark room. A thin sheet of cardboard is placed halfway between the filament and the screen so that no light can reach the screen. If a small hole, shaped like an equilateral triangle, is cut through the center of the cardboard sheet, describe the pattern of light that appears on the screen. •••

7. A burning candle is placed in front of a screen, and a sheet of cardboard with a small round hole in it is inserted between the candle and the screen as shown in Figure P33.7. Describe the pattern of light that appears on the screen. •••

Figure P33.7

33.2 Absorption, transmission, and reflection

8. Figure P33.8 shows light rays reflected from a smooth surface. Draw three wavefronts along the rays that have not yet struck the surface and three wavefronts along the reflected rays. •

Figure P33.8

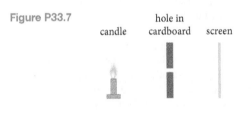

9. Where in the room shown in Figure P33.9 should a mirror be mounted so that a person sitting in the chair has a full view of the gate in the fence outside? •

Figure P33.9

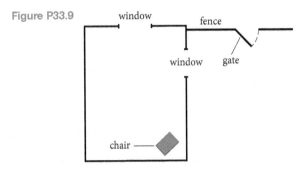

10. A classmate exclaims about the professor's bright blue shirt, "Wow, that shirt has a lot of blue in it!" Evaluate your classmate's statement. •

11. A flat mirror oriented perpendicular to the y axis of a Cartesian coordinate system extends along the x axis from $x = 0$ to $x = 4.0$ m. An object is located in the xy plane at the point (1.0 m, 2.0 m). With your eye in the xy plane in the range $y < 0$ and x equal to any value, you cannot see the image of this object in the mirror. For what range of x and y in the xy plane can you see the image in the mirror? ••

12. The bottom edge of a wall-mounted mirror aligns with your waist, and the top edge aligns with a point somewhere above your head. Draw a diagram that illustrates, when you stand in front of this mirror, the portion of your whole body that you can see in the image. ••

13. The minimum height for a wall mirror in which you can view your entire body is half your height, with the distance from the floor to the bottom of the mirror equal to half the distance between your eyes and feet. This relationship between object height and mirror height/position does not hold for distant objects, however. How large (height, width, or both) a reflecting surface is needed in order for you to see the entire image of a large distant object—a tree, say? (Hint: What quantity is different when you view your own image as opposed to when you view the image of a distant object?) ••

14. Standing 1.0 m away from a large mirror, you see an image of a flashlight in the mirror. If the image appears to be 2.0 m behind the mirror, 1.0 m vertically above your eyes, and 3.0 m to your right (your actual right, not your reflection's right), what is the flashlight's location relative to you? ••

15. A classmate believes that the image you see in a mirror is on the mirror surface rather than behind the mirror. What is something you can do to convince your classmate he is incorrect? ••

16. A woman holds a mirror stationary and perfectly vertical as a boy runs toward it at a speed of 1.0 m/s. (a) In her reference frame, what does the woman observe for the speed at which the boy and his reflection move toward the mirror? (b) In the reference frame of the boy, what does he observe for the speed at which the woman and his reflection move toward him? ••

17. Consider this statement: Think of the reflection of the Moon on a cloudless night: Look in the ocean, you see a large moon. Look in a pond; the same moon is there. In a puddle, in a teacup—everywhere, diminished somewhat in size, but all the features are there. (a) What physical attribute (referred to only indirectly in the statement) is it that differs in size for the ocean, pond, puddle, and cup? (b) What other quantities determine this attribute? Draw a diagram showing how the image of the Moon forms and relating all the quantities you've identified to one another. •••

18. You want to see how your new belt buckle matches your new hat. Your eyes are 110 mm below the top of the hat and 800 mm above the buckle. You walk up to your mirror and notice that the mirror is exactly large enough and exactly in the right position for you see both the top of the hat and the buckle. (a) What is the position of the top edge of the mirror relative to your eyes? (b) How tall is the mirror? •••

33.3 Refraction and dispersion

19. The light bulb in a bathroom ceiling is directly over a toy boat floating in a bathtub filled with water to a depth x. How does the shadow the boat casts on the bottom of the tub compare with the shadow it casts when the water is drained out and the boat is held the same distance x above the tub bottom? Treat the bulb as a point source. •

20. While scuba diving, you have injured yourself and must signal the boat on the surface for help. You have five laser pointers, each emitting light of a different color: red, orange, yellow, green, and blue. When you shine the yellow light up toward the boat, the beam makes such a small angle with the surface that all the light is reflected back into the water. (a) If you are not able to move closer to the boat, which color or colors of light might you try? (b) Are these other lights likely to be successful in penetrating the surface at that point? •

21. The observer in Figure P33.21 is looking at a coin near the edge of a pool filled with water. To this observer, does the water appear to be shallower or deeper than it really is? •

Figure P33.21

22. In Figure P33.22, a straight plank of lumber enters a pool of water at an angle. What does the plank look like to the observer? ••

Figure P33.22
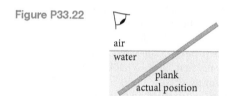

23. Figure P33.23 shows incident and all reflected or refracted light rays in three cases, A, B, and C. For each case, state (a) in which material, 1 or 2, the light travels faster and (b) in which material, 1 or 2, the ray originates. ••

Figure P33.23
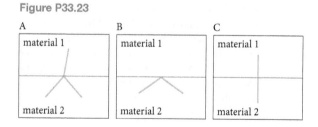

24. Parallel red and green laser rays are incident on a glass slab as shown in Figure P33.24. Sketch the rays as they pass through the slab and after they have entered the air to the right of the slab. Are the rays parallel after they exit the slab? Is the distance between the rays after they exit the slab equal to the distance between them before they entered? ••

Figure P33.24

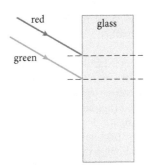

red
green
glass

25. A thick layer of transparent oil floats on top of water. Sketch what happens to a ray of light coming in at a 30° angle away from the normal to the surface. ••

26. Suppose a small flashlight bulb is on the bottom of the bathtub of Problem 19, directly under the toy boat. When this bulb is lit and the ceiling light is turned off, how does the size of the shadow cast by the boat on the ceiling change when the water in the tub is replaced by a liquid in which the speed of light is (a) faster than the speed of light in water and (b) slower than the speed of light in water? ••

27. Suppose the prism in Figure WG33.2 is immersed in a liquid in which the speed of light is lower than the speed of light in glass. Describe what happens to the light shown entering at normal incidence in the figure. ••

28. Driving down a long straight highway, you see a reflection of the sky in the road ahead. It disappears before you get to it but reappears down the road continually. Because there is nothing different about the road from one location to another, explain what is happening in terms of refraction. ••

29. White light passing through a prism is dispersed into its constituent colors. Describe how this rainbow of colors can be changed back to white light. •••

30. A glass cylinder is placed inside a large beaker, and corn oil is poured into the combination until the beaker is full. If the glass cylinder is now invisible inside the oil, what must you conclude about how light interacts with the oil and the glass? •••

33.4 Forming images

31. (a) Draw a simplified ray diagram showing the three principal rays for an object located outside the focal length of a converging lens. (b) Is the image real or virtual? (c) Is it upright or inverted? (d) What happens to the image as the object is moved farther from the lens? •

32. (a) Draw a simplified ray diagram showing the three principal rays for an object located outside the focal length of a diverging lens. (b) Is the image real or virtual? (c) Is it upright or inverted? (d) What happens to the image as the object is moved farther from the lens? •

33. The lens in a magnifying glass is a converging lens, but parallel light rays that pass through a converging lens must converge to a point. This being true, how can a magnifying glass form an image that is larger than the object? Why isn't the image reduced to a point? •

34. A lens has a radius of curvature of magnitude R on its left surface and a radius of curvature of magnitude $2R$ on its right surface. Parallel rays entering the lens from the left are focused to a point 100 mm to the right of the right surface. At what distance from the lens is the point at which parallel rays entering from the right are focused? •

35. Looking at an object through a thin lens, you see a virtual image. Which side of the lens is the image on, or does it appear to be inside the lens? What property of this image tells you whether the lens is converging or diverging? ••

36. (a) Draw a simplified ray diagram showing the three principal rays for an object located inside the focal length of a diverging lens. (b) Is the image real or virtual? (c) Is it upright or inverted? (d) What happens to the image as the object is moved toward the focal point? ••

37. (a) Draw a simplified ray diagram showing the three principal rays for an object located inside the focal length of a converging lens, closer to the lens than to the focal point. (b) Is the image real or virtual? (c) Is it upright or inverted? (d) What happens to the image as the object is moved closer to the focal point? ••

38. An object 20 mm tall is placed 70 mm to the left of a converging lens that has a focal length of 100 mm. (a) Draw a scale diagram showing the three principal rays, and use them to locate the image. Is the image (b) real or virtual, (c) inverted or upright, (d) larger or smaller than the object? ••

39. An object is placed 80 mm to the left of a diverging lens for which the focus is 100 mm from the lens. (a) Draw a scale diagram showing the three principal rays, and use them to locate the image. Is the image (b) real or virtual, (c) inverted or upright, (d) larger or smaller than the object? ••

40. Complete the table below for a converging lens. ••

| Object Location | Image Location | Image | | |
		Real or virtual?	Upright or inverted?	Larger or smaller than the object?
Between lens and focus	Between positive infinity and lens (same side)	Virtual	Upright	Larger
At focus				
Between focus and twice the focal length				
At twice the focal length				
Beyond twice the focal length				
At infinity				

41. Figure P33.41 shows light passing first through a diverging lens and then through a converging lens placed 100 mm to the right of the diverging lens. The rays emerge from the converging lens parallel to one another. Calculate the distance from each lens to its focus. ••

Figure P33.41

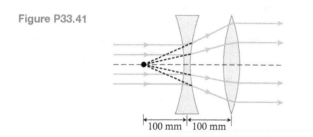

100 mm   100 mm

42. Two identical converging lenses of focal length 100 mm are placed 400 mm apart, and an object 40 mm tall is placed 230 mm to the left of the left lens. (a) Draw a scale diagram showing the three principal rays for the left lens, and use them to locate the image formed by this lens. (b) Draw the principal rays for the right lens, and use them to locate the image formed by this lens. Is the image formed by the right lens (c) real or virtual, (d) inverted or upright, (e) larger or smaller than the object? •••

33.5 Snel's law

43. Light is traveling at a speed of 1.24×10^8 m/s through a certain material. Determine what material it is likely traveling through. •

44. What is the index of refraction of a material in which the speed of light is 7.50% slower than the speed of light in vacuum? •

45. Green light has a wavelength of 530 nm in air. What are the frequency and wavelength of this light in flint glass (index of refraction $n = 1.65$)? •

46. A light ray traveling through medium 1, index of refraction $n_1 = 1.45$, reaches the interface between medium 1 and medium 2, index of refraction $n_2 = 1.24$. (a) At what minimum angle with respect to the normal must the ray be incident on the interface in order to be totally internally reflected? (b) How would the situation change if the ray were traveling in medium 2 when it reached the interface? •

47. A light ray travels up from the bottom of a tank containing mineral water (index of refraction $n = 1.37$). Assuming that the water surface is smooth, at what angle from the normal to that surface would the light ray have to strike the surface in order to reflect back into the tank and not escape? •

48. You shine a laser pointer at an angle of 30° from the normal onto the surface of a thick block of glass for which the index of refraction is $n = 1.5$. (a) What is the angle of refraction of the laser beam? (b) Draw a diagram showing the normal, the surface of the block, and the incident and refracted wavefronts and rays. (c) How would the angles in parts a and b change if the incident angle were 45°? ••

49. In vacuum, the wavelength of the light in your laser pointer is 538 nm. Standing at the shore of a calm pond, you shine the laser beam onto the water surface at an angle of 60° from the normal to the surface. If the index of refraction for the water is $n = 1.333$, how do each of the following properties of the light change as the light enters the water: (a) wavelength, (b) frequency, (c) speed, and (d) direction of propagation?

(e) If you shine the beam directly onto the surface (along the normal), do any of your answers change, and if so, how? ••

50. A light ray is incident on a layer of oil floating on water. The index of refraction of oil is greater than that of water, which is greater than that of air. Call the angle of incidence in air θ_a, the angle of refraction in oil θ_o, and the angle of refraction in water θ_w. (a) Draw a diagram showing all three layers and all angles. (b) Show that $n_a \sin \theta_a = n_w \sin \theta_w$. (c) The result in part b implies that in calculating the final direction (θ_w) of a light ray passing from medium 1 into medium 2 and then into medium 3, all having different n values, we can ignore the presence of medium 2. Can you also ignore medium 2 if what you are calculating is the *location* where the ray strikes the bottom of the container of water? ••

51. The index of refraction in flint glass is 1.66 for blue light and 1.61 for red light, with the values for other colors between these limits. A ray of white light traveling from left to right through a slab of flint glass undergoes dispersion as it exits the slab and enters the air. If the exiting ray strikes the right surface of the slab at an angle of 30.0° from the normal to the surface, what is the angle of refraction (a) for the blue light and (b) for the red light? (c) A flat opaque screen is placed in the path of the refracted rays such that the red ray strikes perpendicular to the screen. If the distance along the refracted red ray from slab to screen is 0.50 m, what is the distance between the point of red light and the point of blue light in the rainbow produced on the screen? (Use the small-angle approximation.) ••

52. What is the critical angle for total internal reflection for an optical fiber cable surrounded by air if the index of refraction is (a) 1.4 and (b) 1.8? (c) Which fiber could have a sharper bend (smaller radius of curvature) and still be capable of total internal reflection? ••

53. Show that the ray exiting the block in Figure P33.53 is parallel to the ray entering the block. ••

Figure P33.53

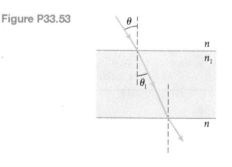

54. Red light for which the wavelength in air is 700 nm strikes a diamond ($n_{diamond} = 2.42$) at an angle of 40.0° from the normal to the air–diamond interface. Calculate (a) the wavelength and frequency of the light inside the diamond and (b) the angle of refraction. ••

55. A light ray travels through medium 1, index of refraction $n_1 = 1.1$, into medium 2, index of refraction $n_2 = 1.5$ (Figure P33.55). At what angle with respect to the normal to the interface between the media does the light need to strike the interface so that the reflected and the refracted rays are at right angles to each other? ••

Figure P33.55

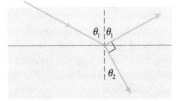

56. A researcher stands at the end of a lakeside pier, 4.0 m above the water surface and 6.0 m away from a buoy floating on the lake (Figure P33.56). A rope hangs from the bottom of the buoy down into the water, with a light attached to its end. When the researcher looks at the light from a position at which his line of sight intersects the water surface exactly halfway between the pier and the buoy, the light appears to be 4.0 m below the water surface. How far under the surface is the light? ●●

Figure P33.56

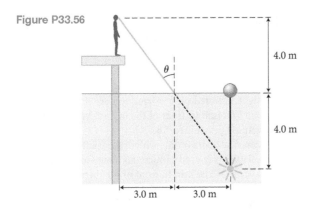

4.0 m

4.0 m

3.0 m   3.0 m

57. Figure P33.57 depicts a light ray entering an optical fiber from air and being transmitted through the fiber by total internal reflection. (a) If the index of refraction of the fiber is n, what is the maximum value of θ, the angle the entering ray makes with the normal to the flat end of the fiber, for which total internal reflection occurs? (b) When n is greater than a certain value n_0, the light ray can enter the fiber at any angle θ between 0 and 90° and total internal reflection still occurs inside the fiber. What is n_0? ●●●

Figure P33.57

58. A ray traveling through a large vat filled with medium 1, index of refraction $n_1 = 1.3$, is incident on a flat layer (thickness $d = 12$ mm) of medium 2, index of refraction $n_2 = 1.6$. If the light enters medium 2 at an angle $\theta_1 = 40°$ with respect to the normal to the interface between the media, how far is it shifted from its original path once it exits medium 2? ●●●

59. A child's toy sits on the bottom of a swimming pool in which the water depth is $d = 1.8$ m (Figure P33.59). To a child standing at the pool edge and a distance $h = 3.5$ m above the pool bottom, the toy appears to be a horizontal distance $y = 4.2$ m away from the sidewall. At what horizontal distance from the sidewall is the toy located? ●●●

Figure P33.59

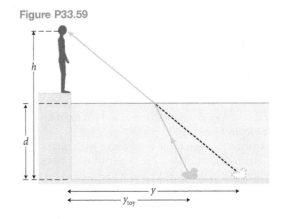

33.6 Thin lenses and optical instruments

60. What is the lens strength of a diverging lens that has a focal length of magnitude 400 mm? ●

61. Mathematically, why can't a single diverging lens produce a real image? ●

62. What is the focal length of eyeglasses that have a lens strength of +1.5 diopters? ●

63. Using a converging lens that has focal length $f = 100$ mm, how far behind the lens do you expect to see a sharp image of an object located 2.00 m in front of the lens? ●

64. A cheap cell phone camera uses a single lens to form an image on a sensor that is 10 mm high and 5.8 mm behind the lens. How far do you need to be away from the Eiffel Tower (height 324 m) to get its whole length in a photograph? Ignore the tilting that occurs as you take the photo from the ground. ●

65. The objective lens in a telescope that produces a 40-fold angular magnification has a focal length of 2.0 m. What is the focal length of the eyepiece lens? ●

66. An object is placed 800 mm away from a thin converging lens that has a focal length of 500 mm. What are (a) the image distance and (b) the magnification? (c) Draw a simplified ray diagram for this case. ●●

67. An object is placed 150 mm away from a converging thin lens that has a focal length of 400 mm. What are (a) the image distance and (b) the magnification? (c) Draw a simplified ray diagram for this case. ●●

68. An object is placed 600 mm away from a diverging thin lens for which the focal length is –300 mm. What are (a) the image distance and (b) the magnification of the image? ●●

69. An object is placed 200 mm from a diverging thin lens that has a focal length of −500 mm. What are (a) the image distance and (b) the magnification? (c) Draw a simplified ray diagram for this case. ●●

70. A bug is 30 mm away from a lens. As you look through the lens, the bug appears to be just at your near point (0.250 m in front of your eyes). If the actual distance between your eyes and the bug is 130 mm, what is the lens focal length? ●●

71. A woman is not able to focus on objects that are closer to her eyes than 400 mm unless she wears eyeglasses. Her glasses enable her to clearly see objects at the near point of an average human (and no closer). What is the strength of the lenses in her glasses? ●●

72. Two converging lenses are placed facing each other and 600 mm apart, with lens 1 to the left of lens 2. An object is placed 400 mm to the left of lens 1, which has a focal length

of 150 mm. (*a*) If the focal length of lens 2 is 200 mm, where is the image located? (*b*) What is the overall magnification of the image? (*c*) Is the image upright or inverted? ••

73. An astronomical telescope of angular magnification M_θ consists of an objective lens and an eyepiece lens separated by a distance d, such that the focal points of the lenses coincide inside the telescope. In terms of M_θ and d, what are (*a*) the focal length of the objective lens and (*b*) the focal length of the eyepiece lens? ••

74. A schematic diagram of a refractive microscope is shown in Figure P33.74. The focal length of the objective lens is 25 mm, that of the eyepiece lens is 63 mm, and the two lenses are 200 mm apart. If the object is 30 mm away from the objective lens, what are (*a*) the distance between the eyepiece lens and the image produced by that lens and (*b*) the overall magnification of this image? ••

Figure P33.74

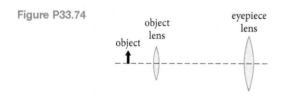

75. Two converging lenses, 1 and 2, are positioned facing each other, with lens 1 on the left. The focal length of lens 1 is 100 mm, that of lens 2 is 180 mm, and the two lenses are 150 mm apart. If an object is 50 mm to the left of lens 1, (*a*) at what distance from lens 2 should a screen be placed if the object's image is to be focused on the screen? (*b*) What is the overall magnification of the image? (*c*) Is the image upright or inverted? ••

76. Two lenses with focal lengths $f_1 = 100$ mm and $f_2 = 200$ mm are placed facing each other a distance $d = 550$ mm apart, with lens 1 to the left of lens 2. What is the location of the image formed of an object placed 150 mm to the left of lens 1? ••

77. The focal points of the two converging lenses shown in Figure P33.77 are denoted by solid dots for the left lens and open dots for the right lens. Describe the final image. ••

Figure P33.77

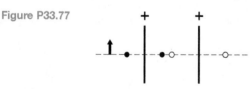

78. In Figure P33.78, a converging lens 1, of focal length 100 mm, and a diverging lens 2, of focal length –80.0 mm, are 160 mm apart. If the object is 180 mm away from lens 1, what are (*a*) the distance between lens 2 and the image produced by that lens and (*b*) the overall magnification of this image? •••

Figure P33.78

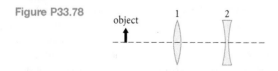

79. Problem 42 describes a setup of two identical converging lenses spaced 400 mm apart. Each lens has a focal length of 100 mm, and a 40-mm-tall object stands 230 mm to the left of the left lens. (*a*) Use an analytical approach to determine

the position of the final image. Based on your calculation, is the final image (*b*) inverted or upright and (*c*) real or virtual? (*d*) Calculate the overall magnification. •••

80. You need to design a magnification system that provides a magnification of 3.00 and creates a real, upright image located 300 mm from the surface of the final lens in the system. The only lenses you have to work with are two converging lenses, each having a focal length of 100 mm. How should you place them with respect to the object, as well as with respect to each other, so as to achieve your goals? •••

81. You are trying to look at a geosynchronous communications satellite that is 5.500 m long. A typical human eye can resolve objects that are 0.1000 mm wide when the objects are at the person's near point, and the same angular size applies to objects farther away than the near point. Suppose the telescope you are using is 1.000 m long from one lens to the other. Describe what must be true of the lenses in order for you to be able to look at the satellite. Assume the satellite is exactly resolvable when viewed through your telescope. Is your result reasonable? What modifications could you make to the telescope in order to make it easier to see the satellite? •••

33.7 Spherical mirrors

82. Sunlight reflected off a mirror you are holding is focused at a point 160 mm in front of the mirror. What is the radius of curvature of the mirror? •

83. A spherical mirror for which the radius of curvature is $R = 250$ mm is used to form an image of an object placed a distance $d = 200$ mm in front of the mirror. Where does the image appear? •

84. A bathroom shaving mirror has radius of curvature $R = 400$ mm. Describe the image of your face formed when you stand (*a*) a distance $d_{close} = 100$ mm from the mirror and (*b*) a distance $d_{far} = 1.20$ m from the mirror. •

85. Passenger-side car mirrors often carry the warning "Objects in mirror are closer than they appear." If the mirror on your car has radius of curvature $R = -800$ mm and the car behind you and one lane to the right is a distance $o = 20.0$ m away, how far away does it appear? •

86. An object is placed 60 mm in front of a converging spherical mirror for which the radius of curvature is 200 mm. What are (*a*) the image distance and (*b*) the magnification of the image? (*c*) Is the image real or virtual? (*d*) Is it upright or inverted? (*e*) Draw a ray diagram illustrating this situation and including the three principal rays. ••

87. A converging mirror that has a radius of curvature of 70.0 mm forms an image of an object that is 20.0 mm tall and 150 mm in front of the mirror. (*a*) What is the image height? (*b*) Is the image real or virtual? (*c*) Is it upright or inverted? (*d*) Draw a ray diagram illustrating this situation and including the principal rays. ••

88. You stand 0.50 m in front of a diverging mirror for which the radius of curvature is −3.5 m. (*a*) Is your image real or virtual? (*b*) Is it upright or inverted? (*c*) How far away from the mirror surface is it located? (*d*) What is its magnification? ••

89. When you look at yourself in a converging mirror, you appear to be one-fourth your actual size. If you are standing 1.0 m in front of the mirror, what is the mirror's radius of curvature? ••

90. You wish to use a converging mirror to form an image that is N times larger than the object. In terms of N and R, the radius

of curvature of the mirror, at what distance *o* from the mirror should you place the object? ••

91. A spherical mirror produces a real image of your face that is twice as large as your face. If your face is 750 mm from the mirror, what is the radius of curvature of the mirror? ••

92. A converging mirror has a focal length of 300 mm. Calculate the image distance and magnification for an object located (*a*) halfway between the focal point and the mirror, (*b*) at the focal point, (*c*) halfway between the focal point and the center of curvature, (*d*) at the center of curvature, (*e*) a distance *f* beyond the center of curvature, and (*f*) at infinity. ••

93. Repeat Problem 92 for a diverging mirror. Comment on any similarities or differences with the two types of mirrors. ••

94. A security mirror in a shop is designed to give a wide-angle view, but as a result the images it forms are much smaller than their objects. If you want an image that appears 10.0 m behind the mirror to have a magnification of 10.0%, what radius of curvature must the mirror have? ••

95. The optical system of Figure P33.95 consists of a converging lens and a converging mirror. The focal points of the lens are marked by open dots and the center of curvature of the mirror by a solid dot. Draw a simplified ray diagram, and describe the final image. •••

Figure P33.95

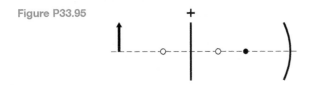

96. The kind of image a spherical mirror produces for a real object depends on where the object is located relative to the focal point of the mirror. There are three types of spherical mirrors—converging, diverging, and flat—if you consider a flat mirror as being one portion of a curved surface for which the radius of curvature is infinitely large. For a real object placed in front of each type of mirror, characterize the image as real or virtual; upright or inverted; in front of or behind the mirror; and enlarged, shrunken, or the same size as the object. •••

97. You position an object in front of a spherical mirror for which the magnitude of the radius of curvature is R_1. The image formed is real, inverted, and twice as large as the object. You then replace this spherical mirror with one that has a radius of curvature of magnitude R_2 (keeping the object distance unchanged). The image formed by this mirror is virtual, upright, and twice as large as the object. Calculate a value for the ratio R_2/R_1. •••

33.8 Lensmaker's formula

98. All the lenses in Figure P33.98 are surrounded by air. Which of the lenses are converging, and which are diverging? •

Figure P33.98

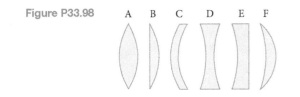

99. You have a thin lens that is convex on both surfaces. The material of which the lens is made has index of refraction $n = 1.40$, and the radii of curvature are $|R_1| = 300$ mm and $|R_2| = 500$ mm. What is the lens focal length in air? •

100. To correct the vision of a near-sighted patient, an optician needs to make a pair of eyeglasses using –3.0-diopter lenses. The lenses are plano-concave, and the front surface (that is, the surface farthest from the eye) is the flat surface. If the glass used for the lenses has an index of refraction of 1.5, what radius of curvature must the remaining surface have? •

101. A plano-convex lens has a focal length of 170 mm, and the material of which the lens is made has an index of refraction of 1.6. What is the radius of curvature of the convex surface? •

102. The radius of curvature of one surface of a glass lens ($n = 1.45$) is 1.50 m. If sunlight is focused at a point 0.300 m away from the lens, what is the radius of curvature of the other surface? ••

103. The two surfaces of a double convex, thin lens made of plastic each have an absolute value of radius of curvature of 1.8 mm. If the focal length of the lens is 4.5 mm, what is the index of refraction of the plastic? ••

104. A lens has an index of refraction of 1.50. Its left side curves outward with an absolute value of radius of curvature of 0.15 m, and its right side curves inward with an absolute value of radius of curvature of 0.25 m. What is its focal length if you look through it (*a*) from the left side and (*b*) from the right side? ••

105. A thin lens is made of material that has an index of refraction of 1.50. When an object 10 mm tall is placed 500 mm away from the lens, an upright image 21.5 mm tall is formed. One surface of the lens is concave, with an absolute value of radius of curvature of 350 mm. What is the radius of curvature of the other surface? ••

106. A lens made of glass for which the index of refraction is 1.55 has a focal length of 0.500 m in air. What is its focal length when this lens is submerged in water? ••

107. The convex surface of a plano-convex lens has an absolute value of radius of curvature of 40 mm. The index of refraction for the glass of which the lens is made is 1.5. (*a*) What is the focal length of the lens? (*b*) You take some measurements and determine that the 40-mm radius of curvature is correct but the focal length is 100 mm instead of the value calculated in part *a*. What must the index of refraction for the glass be? ••

108. A thin lens of focal length f_A is made of a material for which the index of refraction is $n_A = 1.1$. If you make a lens B that is identical to lens A in every way except that the index of refraction of the material used to make B is $n_B = 2n_A$, how does the focal length f_B for this lens compare with f_A? ••

109. The thin lens in air of Figure P33.109 is drawn showing $|R_1| < |R_2|$. (*a*) Is this lens converging or diverging? (*b*) If the lens were drawn showing $|R_1| = |R_2|$, would it be converging or diverging? (*c*) If it were drawn showing $|R_1| > |R_2|$, would it be converging or diverging? ••

Figure P33.109

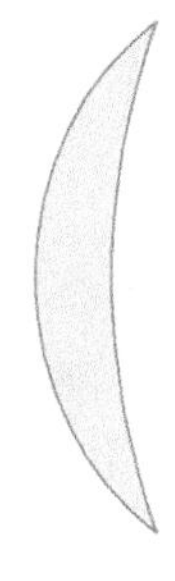

110. The two surfaces of a lens made of an unknown material have the same magnitude of radius of curvature $|R|$. When an object is placed a distance R away from the lens, the image formed is real and twice as large as the object. What is the index of refraction of the material of which the lens is made? ●●●

Additional problems

111. When you shine a laser-beam pointer at a wall, why do you see a dot on the wall but not the beam running from pointer to wall? ●

112. A man spearfishing from a dock sees a fish in the water. In order to hit the fish, should he aim the speargun above, below, or directly at the image he sees? ●

113. Traveling through an optical cable for which the index of refraction is 1.6, how long does it take a light signal to travel from New York to Los Angeles, a distance of 4.0×10^3 km? ●

114. In about the years 214–212 BC, the Greek philosopher and scientist Archimedes is said to have repelled a Roman attack with a "death-ray" converging mirror, using sunlight to set the approaching fleet on fire. Assume an early morning attack from the east, with the Sun directly behind the ships. If the approaching fleet is 100 m away from the mirror, what would the mirror's radius of curvature have to be in order to achieve the maximum effect? ●

115. What is an application of a converging lens for these situations: (a) object is at twice the focal length, (b) object is at the focal length, and (c) object is at infinity? ●●

116. An object that is 40 mm tall is placed 60 mm in front of a converging thin lens. If the image is inverted and 80 mm tall, what are (a) the distance from the image to the lens and (b) the focal length of the lens? ●●

117. A converging lens for which $f = 50$ mm forms an image that is three times larger than the object. How far from the lens is the object? ●●

118. In vacuum, the wavelength of a certain light wave is 550 nm. (a) What is the wavelength in a medium where the wave speed is 2.4×10^8 m/s? What is the frequency of this light (b) in vacuum and (c) in the medium? ●●

119. The focal length of a lens can be different for different colors of light. (a) What optical principle causes this problem? (b) Can the problem be corrected? (c) Does the same problem affect mirrors? ●●

120. When an object is placed 1.2 m in front of a diverging mirror, an image of the object is formed 0.75 m away from the mirror. (a) Is the image real or virtual? (b) Is it upright or inverted? (c) What is the mirror's radius of curvature? ●●

121. The focal points of the two converging lenses shown in Figure P33.121 are denoted by solid dots for the left lens and open dots for the right lens. Draw a simplified ray diagram to locate the final image. ●●

Figure P33.121

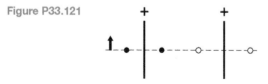

122. Using a camera fitted with a lens for which $f = 50$ mm, you take a photograph of a person who is 1.7 m tall and is standing 29 m away from you. What is the height of the person's image on the film? ●●

123. A piece of electronic circuitry embedded in a layer of diamond ($n_{diamond} = 2.42$) emits light. The diamond is covered by a coating of flint glass ($n_{flint} = 1.65$). The interface between the two materials is flat, as is the interface between the flint glass and the surrounding air. The two interfaces are parallel. Relative to the direction normal to both interfaces, what are (a) the greatest angle at which light emitted in the diamond layer can enter the flint glass and (b) the greatest angle at which light emitted in the diamond layer travels through the flint glass and enters the surrounding air? ●●●

124. You and a friend are scuba diving on a calm day when you decide it would be neat to estimate the critical angle for light going from water into air. Your friend is underwater and has a laser pointer and a waterproof earpiece so that he can hear your instructions. He also has a floating marker attached to him that remains on the surface directly above him. Sitting in a small motorboat on the surface, you have a variety of tools for measuring distances (tape measures, fishing line that could be let out and later accurately measured, and so on). You think for a moment and decide on a course of action. ●●● CR

125. You are in charge of the projector in a movie theater. The film passes through a holder, and light from a bright bulb passes first through the film and then through a lens. You have several additional lenses that can be swapped out, and the position of the lens holder is easily adjustable, but moving the film holder seems more troublesome. A single film frame is 20.00 mm tall. You notice that when the lens is placed 100.0 mm from the film, a sharp image 1450 mm tall is formed on the movie screen on the other side of the lens. This image is far too small, filling less than one-third of the screen. If the patrons do not see a much larger, well-focused image, you may be returned to your previous job making popcorn. ●●● CR

126. For a lens in air, you have learned the conditions on its radii of curvature to make the lens converging or diverging. You have done some diving, and you realize that a lens has a different focal length underwater than it does in air. That starts you thinking about what would happen if a lens is placed in a medium with an index of refraction greater than that of the material of which the lens is made, but you are not even sure that it is possible to form images under such conditions. Lost in your thoughts, you drift off into dreamland. ●●● CR

Answers to Review Questions

1. The object has to either emit light or redirect light from a source, and this light must enter your eye and be formed into an image of the object.

2. A light ray is a line drawn in a diagram to represent the direction in which light from a source travels. A ray corresponds to a very thin beam of light emitted by the source.

3. A shadow is the dark region behind an object that is facing a light source, formed because the object blocks some of the light emitted by the source, preventing it from reaching the shadow region.

4. The light can be absorbed, which means it enters the object and does not come out; transmitted, which means it passes through the object; or reflected, which means it bounces off the object surface and is redirected away from the surface.

5. Most of the light striking an opaque object is absorbed by the object, which means that light goes into the object and does not come out. Most of the light striking a translucent object is transmitted diffusely through the object, meaning the rays are redirected randomly as they pass through the object.

6. For a ray striking a smooth surface, the angle of reflection is equal to the angle of incidence, and the two angles are in the same plane.

7. Specular reflection is reflection from a smooth surface (which is a surface for which the direction of the surface normal doesn't change on the scale of the wavelength of the light). Diffuse reflection is reflection from an irregular surface in which the irregularities are comparable in size to the wavelength of the light. Because the normal to an irregular surface varies randomly, the light is reflected in all directions.

8. No image is formed because different portions of the rough surface have randomly different normal directions, so that incoming rays are randomly scattered even though, for each ray, the angle of incidence and reflection are equal.

9. An image is an optical reproduction of an object formed by light rays that travel from the object.

10. Any rays that travel from a selected point on the object and reach the image must intersect or appear to intersect at a common point on the image. A real image is formed by light rays that intersect at a point on the image. A virtual image is formed by rays that do not intersect at a point on the image, but only appear to do so when traced backward.

11. The object either emits or reflects light rays in all directions, and some of those that reach the mirror surface are reflected to the observer's eye. When the observer traces these rays backward from his eye, they appear to pass through the mirror and intersect (hence apparently originate) at a location behind the mirror, causing the image to be located there.

12. The colors correspond to the different frequencies of the waves in the visible region of the electromagnetic spectrum.

13. Wavefronts are drawn perpendicular to the direction of propagation, and rays are drawn in the direction of propagation. Thus, rays and wavefronts representing the same light are drawn perpendicular to each other.

14. Refraction is the bending of light rays as they move from a medium A into a medium B when the media have different mass densities. The rays bend because as each wavefront crosses from A into B, the speed of that portion of the wavefront that has entered B is different from the speed of the portion still in A.

15. Yes. Because $\lambda = c/f$ and frequency does not change at a boundary, wavelength λ must change as wave speed c changes. Passing into a medium of lower mass density causes c to increase, and so λ also increases.

16. The angle the unrefracted ray forms with the normal to the interface between the media is the angle of incidence; the angle the refracted ray makes with the normal to the interface is the angle of refraction. When the ray moves from a high-density medium into a low-density medium, the angle of incidence is smaller than the angle of refraction because the refracted ray bends away from the normal to the interface. When the ray moves from a low-density medium into a high-density medium, the angle of incidence is greater than the angle of refraction because the refracted ray bends toward the normal.

17. The critical angle is the angle of incidence that causes the angle of refraction to be 90°, so that the refracted rays travel along the interface between the two media.

18. When light travels from a high-density medium into a low-density medium, the angle of refraction is greater than the angle of incidence. When the angle of incidence is greater than the critical angle, the light cannot be refracted because the angle of refraction cannot exceed 90° (if it did exceed 90°, the ray would no longer be in the low-density medium). With no refraction, the interface reflects all the light back into the high-density medium.

19. The path a light ray takes in moving from one location to another is that path for which the time interval needed for the trip is a minimum.

20. In a light beam consisting of rays of different frequencies, dispersion is the spreading out of the beam as the light is refracted. The speed of light in most materials depends slightly on the frequency of the light, so the amount by which each ray in the beam is refracted depends on the ray's frequency.

21. The ray's path is not changed when the travel direction is reversed, so the ray travels along its original path back through B to the interface and then into A.

22. Paraxial light rays are rays that enter a lens near its central axis and are either parallel to that axis or oriented at a small angle to it.

23. (1) A ray that is parallel to the lens axis before entering the lens on the left is refracted to pass through the focal point on the right side of the lens, (2) a ray that passes through the lens center continues on its original path, and (3) a ray that passes through the focal point on the left side of the lens is refracted to a path parallel to the lens axis on the right. Where these three rays intersect (or appear to intersect) is the location of the image.

24. A converging lens surface curves the way the outside of a sphere curves and causes parallel light rays passing through the lens to converge at a point after they leave the lens. A diverging lens surface curves the way the inside of a sphere curves and causes parallel rays passing through the lens to diverge from one another after they leave the lens, as if they had originated from a common point on the opposite side of the lens.

25. The index of refraction is the ratio of the speed of light in vacuum to the speed of light in the material: $n_{material} = c_0/c_{material}$ (Eq. 33.1).

26. The wavelength in the material is equal to the wavelength in vacuum divided by the material's index of refraction: $\lambda_{material} = \lambda_{vac}/n_{material}$ (Eq. 33.3).

27. Snel's law describes the relationship between the angles of incidence and refraction when light traveling in a medium 1 enters a medium 2 and is refracted: The product of the sine of the angle of refraction and the index of refraction of the refractive medium 2 equals the product of the sine of the angle of incidence and the index of refraction of the incident medium 1: $n_1 \sin \theta_1 = n_2 \sin \theta_2$ (Eq. 33.7).

28. The sine of the critical angle is equal to the index of refraction of the lower-density medium divided by the index of refraction of the higher-density medium: $\sin \theta_c = n_{lower\ density}/n_{higher\ density}$ (from Eq. 33.9).

29. The lens equation relates, for any image formed by the lens, the lens focal length f to the object distance o and image distance i: $1/f = 1/o + 1/i$ (Eq. 33.16). Focal length is positive for converging lenses and negative for diverging lenses. Image distance is positive if the object and image are on opposite sides of the lens and negative if they are on the same side of the lens. Object distance is positive if the object is in front of the lens and negative if it is behind the lens, where *front* means the side on which the rays forming the image originate.

30. Magnification is the ratio of image height to object height: $M = -i/o$ (Eq. 33.17). A positive value of M indicates an upright image; a negative value of M indicates an inverted image.
31. The near point is the closest distance at which the eye can see an object in sharp focus.
32. Angular magnification is the absolute value of the ratio of the angle subtended by the image to the angle subtended by the object: $M_\theta = |\theta_i/\theta_o|$ (Eq. 33.18).
33. The diopter is the unit in which the strength of eyeglass lenses is measured. The lens strength d is given by Eq. 33.22: $d = (1\text{ m})/f$, where f is the lens focal length.
34. The focal length is half the radius of curvature: $f = R/2$ (Eq. 33.23).
35. Yes. Focal length is positive for converging mirrors and negative for diverging mirrors. Image distance is positive if the object and image are on the same side of the mirror and negative if they are on opposite sides of the mirror. Object distance is positive if the object is in front of the mirror and negative if it is behind the mirror.
36. Whether the image is real or virtual depends on where the object is located. When the object is between the focus and the mirror surface, the image forms behind the mirror and so is virtual because the rays cannot enter the space behind the mirror. When the object–mirror distance is greater than the focus–mirror distance, the image forms in front of the mirror and so is real because the rays pass through the image location.
37. The formula applies only to thin lenses and only when the rays used to calculate the radii of curvature are paraxial so that the small-angle approximation can be used.
38. The radii are positive for convex surfaces, negative for concave surfaces, and infinite for flat surfaces.

Answers to Guided Problems

Guided Problem 33.2 $n_{liq} = 1.17$
Guided Problem 33.4 A lens of focal length $f = 80$ mm
Guided Problem 33.6 0.333 m
Guided Problem 33.8 (a) Converging. (b) Yes. With the candle upright and its base on the mirror axis, place the paper 257 mm in front of the mirror and below the axis to capture the image, which is 71.4% the size of the candle.
Guided Problem 33.10 57 mm

34

PRACTICE

Wave and Particle Optics

PRACTICE

Chapter Summary

Diffraction (Sections 34.1–34.3, 34.6)

Concepts Light is diffracted as it passes through an opening only when the width of the opening is either comparable to or smaller than the wavelength of the light.

Interference fringes are a pattern of alternating bright and dark bands (called *fringes*) cast on a screen by coherent light passing through two or more slits. **Fringe order** is the numerical ordering of bright and dark fringes. The central bright fringe is the *zeroth-order bright fringe*, the bright fringes to the left and right of it are the first-order bright fringes, the next bright fringes to the left and right are the second-order bright fringes, and so on. The two dark fringes bordering the central bright fringe are the first-order dark fringes, and so on.

When the light passes through two slits, the interference pattern formed on a screen behind the slits consists of alternating bright and dark fringes. When light passes through three or more slits, each dark fringe contains one or more regions that are not as bright as the bright fringes but not completely dark. In these patterns, the brightest fringes are *principal maxima*, and the fainter bright regions are *secondary maxima*.

A **diffraction grating** is a barrier containing a large number of equally spaced slits or grooves. A transmissive diffraction grating contains slits that transmit light, and a reflective diffraction grating contains grooves that reflect light.

The **Bragg condition** states that a crystal reflects x rays of wavelength λ only at angles of incidence relative to the crystal plane given by $2d \cos \theta = m\lambda$, where m is an integer and d is the distance between adjacent crystal planes.

Quantitative Tools When light of wavelength λ passes through two slits a distance d apart, the bright fringes occur at angles given by

$$\sin \theta_m = \pm \frac{m\lambda}{d}, m = 0, 1, 2, 3, \ldots, \quad (34.5)$$

and the dark fringes occur when

$$\sin \theta_n = \pm \frac{(n - \frac{1}{2})}{d}\lambda, n = 1, 2, 3, \ldots. \quad (34.7)$$

The integers m and n give the **fringe order.**

For light passing through N slits, the *principal maxima* occur when

$$d \sin \theta_m = \pm m\lambda, m = 0, 1, 2, 3, \ldots, \quad (34.16)$$

and the dark fringes occur when

$$d \sin \theta_{\min} = \pm \frac{k}{N}\lambda, \quad (34.17)$$

where k is an integer that is not an integer multiple of N.

Thin-film interference (Section 34.7)

Concepts Thin-film interference occurs in transparent materials whose thickness is comparable to one of the wavelengths of visible light. Light reflecting from the front surface of the material interferes with light reflecting from the back surface.

Quantitative Tools Light reflects from a thin film of thickness t and index of refraction n_b. At normal incidence of the light, the phase difference ϕ between the light rays reflected from the front and back surfaces of the film is

$$\phi = \frac{4\pi n_b t}{\lambda} + \phi_{r2} - \phi_{r1}, \quad (34.23)$$

where the phase shifts ϕ_{r1} and ϕ_{r2} are due to reflection at the front and back surfaces. Each phase shift must be either 0 or π, depending on the indices of refraction of the media in front of and behind the film.

Diffraction by single slits and circular apertures (Sections 34.8, 34.9)

Concepts Light passing through a circular aperture is diffracted, and the interference fringes are circular. The central bright fringe is called the *Airy disk*.

Quantitative Tools When light is diffracted by a thin slit of thickness a, the dark fringes occur when

$$\sin \theta_n = \pm n\frac{\lambda}{a}, n = 1, 2, 3, \ldots. \tag{34.26}$$

When light is diffracted by a small circular aperture of diameter d, the first dark fringe occurs when

$$\sin \theta_1 = 1.22\frac{\lambda}{d}. \tag{34.29}$$

Rayleigh's criterion: The minimum angular separation θ_r for which two light sources can be *resolved* by a lens of diameter d is

$$\theta_r \approx 1.22\frac{\lambda}{d}. \tag{34.30}$$

Matter waves and photons (Sections 34.4, 34.5, 34.10)

Concepts **Wave-particle duality** says that particles and light have both wave and particle properties.

The **de Broglie wavelength** expresses the wavelength of a particle.

A **photon** is the "particle" of light. It is an indivisible, discrete unit of light.

Photoelectric effect: When photons of light of sufficiently high frequency shine on a metal, electrons are ejected from the metal. The *stopping potential difference* is the potential needed to stop the ejected electrons. The **work function** E_0 of a metal is the minimum energy needed to free an electron from the metal surface.

Quantitative Tools **Planck's constant** is

$$h = 6.626 \times 10^{-34} \, \text{J} \cdot \text{s}.$$

The **de Broglie wavelength** of a particle having momentum p is

$$\lambda = h/p.$$

In the **photoelectric effect,**

$$E_{\text{photon}} = hf = K_{\max} + E_0, \tag{34.35}$$

where f is the frequency of the light hitting the metal, $K_{\max}$ is the maximum kinetic energy of the ejected electron, and E_0 is the work function of the metal.

The energy of a photon is

$$E_{\text{photon}} = hf_{\text{photon}}, \tag{34.39}$$

and its momentum is

$$p_{\text{photon}} = \frac{hf_{\text{photon}}}{c_0}. \tag{34.40}$$

Review Questions

Answers to these questions can be found at the end of this chapter.

34.1 Diffraction of light

1. What is diffraction?
2. For a beam of planar waves passing through a narrow gap in a barrier located in the path of the beam, what relationship between wavelength and wavefront width determines whether the beam undergoes diffraction?

34.2 Diffraction gratings

3. What are interference fringes?
4. What does the order of an interference fringe designate?
5. When a light beam passes through two slits in a barrier, what condition determines where on a screen placed behind the barrier the bright interference fringes fall? What condition determines where on the screen the dark fringes fall?
6. Is the condition for constructive interference in light passing through a barrier containing many equally spaced slits the same as or different from the condition for constructive interference in light passing through a two-slit barrier? Is the condition for destructive interference the same or different in the two cases?
7. What is the distinction between principal and secondary maxima in an interference pattern created by light passing through a many-slit barrier?
8. What is a diffraction grating? What are the two types?

34.3 X-ray diffraction

9. What property of a crystal lattice allows the lattice to act as a diffraction grating for x rays?
10. What information does the Bragg condition convey?

34.4 Matter waves

11. What happens to a beam of electrons passing through a crystal? What does this suggest about how electrons behave?
12. What quantity measures the wave nature of a particle?
13. Why isn't it possible to observe wave behavior in macroscopic objects?

34.5 Photons

14. What is a photon, and what determines its energy?
15. The pattern on adjacent detecting screens when very-low-intensity light travels directly from a source to the screens is different from the pattern when the light passes through adjacent slits before reaching a detecting screen. Describe how this difference supports the model of light as a stream of particles.

34.6 Multiple-slit interference

16. Given that the waves leaving two slits correspond to waves from in-phase point sources, why are the waves out of phase when they arrive at a given location on a detecting screen?
17. When planar light waves pass through two side-by-side slits and then travel to a detecting screen, how does the maximum intensity in the interference pattern on the screen compare with the sum of the intensities of the waves incident on the slits?

18. What is the limiting condition for resolving two wavelengths, λ_1 and $\lambda_2 < \lambda_1$, in the dispersed spectrum formed by a diffraction grating?

34.7 Thin-film interference

19. How does thin-film interference occur?
20. When visible light passes through a transparent material, what limit on the thickness of the material determines whether or not interference occurs?
21. In thin-film interference, what two factors determine the phase difference between a light beam reflected from the front film surface and a beam reflected from the back surface?
22. Consider a ray of light traveling from medium 1 with index of refraction n_1 to medium 2 with index of refraction n_2. Describe the phase shift undergone upon reflection of the beam at the interface between media 1 and 2.

34.8 Diffraction at a single-slit barrier

23. By dividing a planar wavefront passing through a slit into suitable pairs of point sources, what feature of the interference pattern can be determined?
24. What is the expression for determining the directions to minima in the interference pattern created by light passing through a single slit?
25. What does the interference pattern created by light waves passing through a single slit look like if the slit width is smaller than the wavelength of the waves?

34.9 Circular apertures and limits of resolution

26. What does the interference pattern created by light passing through a circular aperture look like?
27. What is an Airy disk?
28. What is Rayleigh's criterion?
29. What is a diffraction limit, and how is it defined by the Airy disk of an interference pattern?

34.10 Photon energy and momentum

30. What is the photoelectric effect?
31. In an electric circuit in which the current is due to the photoelectric effect, what is the stopping potential difference, and on what property of the incident light does it depend?
32. What is the relationship between the stopping potential difference in a photoelectric circuit and the kinetic energy of the electrons ejected from the target?
33. How does the fact that the stopping potential difference for a photoelectric circuit depends on the frequency of the incident light rather than on the light intensity support a particle interpretation of light over a wave interpretation?
34. In a photoelectric circuit, what is the relationship between the current and the intensity of the incident light?
35. What is the work function of a metal?

Developing a Feel

Make an order-of-magnitude estimate of each of the following quantities. Letters in parentheses refer to hints below. Use them as needed to guide your thinking.

1. The distance between the first and second maxima 20 km away from two AM radio towers separated by 3 km, if they were to emit at the same frequency (E, L, P)
2. The angular location of the first "dark" fringe (*dark* in this case indicating no sound rather than no light) in the diffraction pattern when the sound wave created by striking the middle C key on a piano passes through a garage door (D, I, V)
3. The angular location of the first dark fringe in the diffraction pattern when a microwave signal passes through a metal doorway set in a metal wall (W, J)
4. The diameter of the image formed on the back of your eye by a point source of bright light (A, Q, U)
5. The number of photons per second emitted by a 5-mW green laser pointer (X, T)
6. The force exerted on a sheet of aluminum by the beam from a 5-mW green laser pointer (K, B)
7. The number of photons per second entering your eye from a 5-W LED lamp located 2 m away (S, F, O)
8. The wavelength of a neutron traveling at 300 m/s (M, C)
9. The minimum thickness of an oil slick lying on a puddle of water that appears red (R, H)
10. The electron speed needed in order for an electron beam to image a single virus (N, G)

Hints

A. What is the average wavelength of visible light?
B. How much momentum is carried by the laser beam in 1 s?
C. What is the neutron's momentum?
D. What is the frequency of the middle C sound wave?
E. What is the average frequency of AM radio waves?
F. What is the surface area of your pupil?
G. What wavelength must the electrons have in order to image this virus?
H. What is the index of refraction of oil?
I. What is the wavelength of this sound wave?
J. What is a typical width for a doorway?
K. How much energy is carried by the laser beam in 1 s?
L. What is the average wavelength of AM radio waves?
M. What is the neutron's mass?
N. What is a typical diameter for a virus?
O. What is the surface area of a sphere that has a radius of 2 m?
P. What is the angular separation of the two maxima?

Q. What is the focal length of the eye?
R. What is the wavelength of red light?
S. How many photons per second are emitted by the lamp?
T. What is the energy of a green photon?
U. What is the diameter of the pupil of the eye in bright light?
V. What is a typical width for a garage door?
W. What is the average wavelength of microwaves?
X. What is the wavelength of green light?

Key (all values approximate)

A. 5×10^{-7} m; **B.** 2×10^{-11} kg·m/s; **C.** 6×10^{-25} kg·m/s; **D.** 262 Hz; **E.** 1 MHz; **F.** 10^{-5} m^2; **G.** 10 nm; **H.** $n = 1.5$; **I.** 1 m; **J.** 1 m; **K.** 5 mJ; **L.** 300 m; **M.** 2×10^{-27} kg; **N.** 100 nm; **O.** 50 m^2; **P.** 0.1 rad; **Q.** 3×10^{-2} m; **R.** 7×10^{-7} m; **S.** 10^{19}; **T.** 4×10^{-19} J; **U.** 3×10^{-3} m; **V.** 3 m; **W.** 0.1 m; **X.** 5×10^{-7} m

Worked and Guided Problems

These examples involve material from this chapter, but they are not associated with any particular section. Some examples are worked out in detail; others you should work out by following the guidelines provided.

Worked Problem 34.1 Distinguishing headlights

You are driving east on a straight highway at night, with the pupils of your eyes dilated to a diameter of 6.0 mm. Far down the road, you spot a lone car traveling west toward you, and the headlights on this car are 1.5 m apart. Assuming diffraction is the only factor limiting your vision, how far away is the approaching car when you start seeing its headlights as two separate objects?

❶ GETTING STARTED This is a problem about distinguishing two adjacent point sources of light in the image formed by the lens in each of your eyes. We can consider just one eye, however, because the situation is the same for both eyes. To visualize the situation, we sketch it, defining L to be the distance from your eye to the headlights of the approaching car and θ the angle subtended at your eye by those headlights (Figure WG34.1).

Figure WG34.1

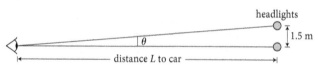

❷ DEVISE PLAN Figure WG34.1 shows that $\tan \theta = (1.5 \text{ m})/L$, which means we can obtain L once we know θ. Because L is the distance at which the two headlights cease to be separate images, θ has to be the angle that satisfies Rayleigh's criterion. Equation 34.30 shows that this criterion depends on the diameter of the lens through which the light passes and on the wavelength of that light. In the eye, the pupil lies in front of the lens, which means the pupil diameter determines how much light passes through the lens. Thus we use the pupil diameter as the lens diameter. For wavelength, we choose a value near the center of the visible spectrum—$\lambda = 550$ nm—because the headlights emit visible light.

❸ EXECUTE PLAN Using y to represent the distance between the headlights, we have from Figure WG34.1 and the small-angle approximation

$$\theta \approx \tan \theta = \frac{y}{L}$$

Equation 34.30 says that the angle by which two objects must be separated if they are to satisfy Rayleigh's criterion is

$$\theta_r \approx \frac{y}{L} = \frac{1.22\lambda}{d}$$

and so—if diffraction is the only factor determining what you see— the distance at which you start to see the two headlights emerging from a single bright glow is

$$L = \frac{yd}{1.22\lambda} = \frac{(1.5 \text{ m})(6.0 \times 10^{-3} \text{ m})}{1.22(550 \times 10^{-9} \text{ m})} = 1.3 \times 10^4 \text{ m}. ✔$$

❹ EVALUATE RESULT You know that this distance, 8 miles, is much greater than the distance at which normally you can see an approaching car. (Of course, it's rare that you have a straight highway that is empty of cars over such a long distance!) In this case, the unreasonably large result suggests that diffraction is only one of the many phenomena limiting your vision. However, we can still tell that most likely the calculation is correct because the distance is on a reasonable scale—neither vastly too short (100 m or less) nor vastly too long (100 km or more).

We also notice that although we had to assume a wavelength for the light emitted by the headlights, L is inversely proportional to that wavelength. Because the range of the visible spectrum runs from 700 nm to 400 nm, the value of L we would get by choosing a different wavelength would change by at most 40%, not changing the order of magnitude of the result.

Guided Problem 34.2 Geosynchronous satellites

Television satellite dishes are approximately spherical mirrors that collect 12-GHz electromagnetic signals emitted by satellites in orbit around Earth. Each mirror serves as a circular aperture just as a lens does. How many satellites can be placed in geosynchronous orbit above the equator, at a height of 36,000 km above Earth's surface, if all of them are to send signals that can be distinguished by a satellite dish having a diameter of 0.45 m?

❶ GETTING STARTED

1. Draw a diagram showing two sources and the dish receiving their signals, labeling the relevant distances.
2. What condition determines whether the signals from two adjacent satellites are distinguishable? What distances does this condition depend on?

❷ DEVISE PLAN

3. What quantity must you determine to solve this problem? How does this quantity relate to the distance between adjacent distinguishable satellites?
4. What information do you need to look up to work this problem?
5. How can you determine the wavelength of the electromagnetic waves broadcast by the satellites?

❸ EXECUTE PLAN

❹ EVALUATE RESULT

6. Is the number of satellites you obtain plausibly large enough to satisfy telecommunications needs? Small enough to be consistent with any experience you have observing satellites in the night sky?

Worked Problem 34.3 Measuring the index of refraction of air

An *interferometer* (Figure WG34.2) exploits two-source interference to measure either very short distances or differences in indices of refraction. In the device, a laser beam is directed to a

beam splitter, which reflects half of the light in the beam to adjustable mirror M_1, which can be moved closer to or farther from the beam splitter, and transmits the other half to stationary mirror M_2.

The two beams follow the paths shown in Figure WG34.2, each traveling to its mirror M_1 or M_2, back to the beam splitter, and then to a detector that measures the intensity of the combined beams. For this problem, the laser has a wavelength in vacuum of 488 nm.

A sealed cylindrical chamber that is 50.0 mm long and has glass windows at both ends is initially filled with air. The chamber is placed so that the beam traveling to M_2 passes through it, and the position of adjustable mirror M_1 is set so that the intensity at the detector is a maximum. Then the air is gradually pumped out of the chamber. While the air is being pumped out, the intensity at the detector goes to a minimum and then returns to a maximum 60.0 times. Calculate the index of refraction of air.

Figure WG34.2

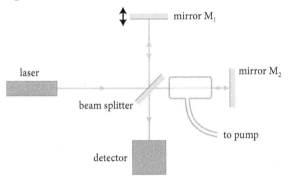

laser

mirror M_1

mirror M_2

beam splitter

to pump

detector

❶ GETTING STARTED This problem involves interference between light beams from two sources, M_1 and M_2. The amount of interference varies as the index of refraction of the contents of the chamber decreases as the air is pumped out. Changing the index of refraction changes the wavelength of the beam inside the chamber and thus changes the number of wavelengths along the path the beam travels from the splitter to M_2 and then back to the splitter.

Initially, when the chamber is filled with air, the combined intensity of the two beams at the detector is a maximum. This means that initially the beam passing through the chamber is in phase with the beam from M_1 when the two arrive at the detector. Then each intensity cycle down to a minimum and back to a maximum corresponds to decreasing the number of wavelengths in the chamber by 1 as the index of refraction decreases and consequently the wavelength gets longer. In the time interval during which the chamber goes from filled to evacuated, the minimum/maximum cycle occurs

60.0 times. We thus need to identify the index of refraction of air that causes the number of wavelengths to decrease by 60.0 as the index of refraction decreases to $n_{vacuum} = 1$.

❷ DEVISE PLAN The beam traveling to M_2 passes through the chamber twice, so the distance it travels through the chamber is $2L$, where L is the chamber length. We can express the number of wavelengths N_{air} in the air-filled chamber in terms of L, the beam wavelength in vacuum λ, and the index of refraction n_{air}. Likewise, we can express the number of wavelengths N_{vacuum} in the evacuated chamber in terms of L and λ. Then we can equate the difference $N_{air} - N_{vacuum}$ to 60.0 and solve for n_{air}.

❸ EXECUTE PLAN When the chamber is filled with air, the number of wavelengths in the chamber is

$$N_{air} = \frac{2L}{\lambda_{air}} = \frac{2L}{(\lambda/n_{air})} = \frac{2Ln_{air}}{\lambda},$$

and the number of wavelengths in the evacuated chamber is

$$N_{vacuum} = \frac{2L}{\lambda}.$$

Therefore

$$N_{air} - N_{vacuum} = \frac{2Ln_{air}}{\lambda} - \frac{2L}{\lambda} = \frac{2L}{\lambda}(n_{air} - 1)$$

$$n_{air} = \frac{\lambda(N_{air} - N_{vacuum})}{2L} + 1$$

$$= \frac{(488 \times 10^{-9}\,\text{m})(60.0)}{2(5.00 \times 10^{-2}\,\text{m})} + 1$$

$$= 2.93 \times 10^{-4} + 1 = 1.000293. ✔$$

Because the 1 in this calculation is an exact number and thus has an infinite number of significant digits, the number of significant digits in our value for n_{air} is determined by keeping all of the significant digits in the 2.93×10^{-4} value.

❹ EVALUATE RESULT This value is plausible because it is very close to but greater than 1, as it must be, and significantly smaller than the index of refraction for water (1.33) or other transparent materials. It also matches the value given in *Principles* Table 33.1.

Guided Problem 34.4 Colorful soap film

As a film of soap and water evaporates and thins, the dominant reflected color changes and eventually the film disappears. (*a*) What is the last color you see as the film thins? (*b*) How thick is the film just as the last vestige of color vanishes?

❶ GETTING STARTED

1. What principle determines the color reflected from the film? Based on this principle, what properties of the film affect the color?
2. As the film gets thinner, does the dominant reflected wavelength increase or decrease?
3. What reasonable assumption can you make about the angle at which you view the film?
4. Draw a sketch showing the film and the paths taken by reflected light.

❷ DEVISE PLAN

5. How can you use what you know about interference to determine the relationship between the film thickness and the dominant color reflected at that thickness?
6. At which film surface or surfaces is there a phase shift when the light is reflected?

❸ EXECUTE PLAN

7. What value is reasonable for the index of refraction of the film?

❹ EVALUATE RESULT

8. How does your result compare with the thickness of a piece of paper? Is the ratio of the two thicknesses reasonable?
9. To evaluate the reasonableness of your result another way, estimate the volume of soap solution a child might use to blow a single bubble and the size of the resulting bubble.

Worked Problem 34.5 Overlapping rainbows

White light (400–700 nm) is incident on a diffraction grating that has 300 lines/mm. As noted in *Principles* Section 34.2, the interference pattern in this case is not simply alternating bright and dark fringes but rather a sequence of red-to-violet rainbows located symmetrically to the left and right of a central white fringe. Which wavelengths in either third-order rainbow overlap the adjacent fourth-order rainbow?

❶ GETTING STARTED This is a problem about white light incident on a diffraction grating. To visualize the situation, we start with the interference pattern that results when monochromatic light strikes a grating (Figure WG34.3). Each wavelength produces an interference pattern consisting of narrow bright fringes separated by relatively wide dark fringes. The light in this problem is not monochromatic, however. It contains all visible wavelengths, so the interference pattern is a bright white spot at the center (where all colors undergo constructive interference) surrounded by a series of rainbows, each oriented with its violet end toward the center white spot. The orientation is this way because fringe position depends directly on wavelength. The shorter the wavelength, the closer to

Figure WG34.3

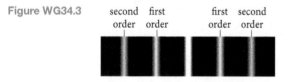

second   first   first   second
order   order   order   order

the midline of the interference pattern the fringe is. Because the wavelength of violet light is shorter than the wavelength of red light, in any rainbow in the interference pattern, the violet end of the rainbow is the end closer to the center. The rainbows overlap, and Figure WG34.4 shows this overlap for the first-order and second-order rainbows on either side of the central white spot.

Figure WG34.4

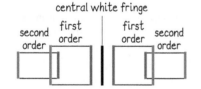

central white fringe

second   first   first   second
order   order   order   order

(only red and violet ends of each rainbow shown)

To solve this problem, we need to find the range of angular positions of the third- and fourth-order rainbows, and identify which wavelengths fall in the same angular range.

❷ DEVISE PLAN Figure WG34.4 shows that the longest wavelengths (those toward the red end) in the first-order rainbow overlap the shortest wavelengths (those toward the violet end) in the

second-order rainbow. The same is true for all other orders, and Figure WG34.5 shows the overlap for the third- and fourth-order rainbows to the right of the central white spot. To determine the wavelength ranges that overlap, we calculate the angular position at which the fourth-order rainbow in Figure WG34.5 begins, which is the angular position of the violet end ($\lambda_{\text{short}} = 400$ nm). Next we calculate the wavelength in the third-order rainbow that falls at that same angular position, calling this wavelength $\lambda_{3,\text{overlap}}$. The third-order rainbow ends at its red end ($\lambda_{\text{long}} = 700$ nm), so the overlap extends from $\lambda_{3,\text{overlap}}$ to λ_{long}. For all these calculations, we use the Eq. 34.16 relationship between wavelength and angular position.

Figure WG34.5   third and fourth order:

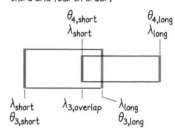

❸ EXECUTE PLAN The angular position of the violet end of the fourth-order rainbow is given by

$$d \sin \theta_{4,\text{short}} = 4\lambda_{\text{short}}, \tag{1}$$

where d is the grating spacing. Applying Eq. 34.16 to the wavelength $\lambda_{3,\text{overlap}}$ in the third-order rainbow where overlap begins gives us

$$d \sin \theta_{3,\text{overlap}} = 3\lambda_{3,\text{overlap}}. \tag{2}$$

Because the beginning of the overlap region and the violet end of the fourth-order rainbow occur at the same angular position, we can rewrite Eq. 2 as

$$d \sin \theta_{4,\text{short}} = 3\lambda_{3,\text{overlap}}. \tag{3}$$

Comparing Eqs. 1 and 3 tells us that $4\lambda_{\text{short}} = 3\lambda_{3,\text{overlap}}$, so

$$\lambda_{3,\text{overlap}} = \tfrac{4}{3}\lambda_{\text{short}} = \tfrac{4}{3}(400 \times 10^{-9}\ \text{m}) = 533 \times 10^{-9}\ \text{m}.$$

So, in the third-order rainbow, the wavelengths from 533 nm to 700 nm overlap with the fourth-order rainbow. ✔

❹ EVALUATE RESULT The wavelength in the third-order rainbow where overlap begins, 533 nm, is in the visible region of the electromagnetic spectrum, so our result is reasonable.

Guided Problem 34.6 Two colors

Light from a red laser ($\lambda_r = 633$ nm) passes through a narrow slit located 2.00 m from a screen and creates an interference pattern on the screen. When this laser is removed and light from a blue laser ($\lambda_b = 488$ nm) passes through the slit, the $n = 1$ minima of the interference pattern move by 3.00 mm. (*a*) In which direction do the minima move: toward the center of the interference pattern or away from the center? (*b*) What is the slit width?

❶ GETTING STARTED

1. How do the angular positions of the $n = 1$ minima depend on wavelength?
2. Draw a sketch showing the pattern formed by the red light and the pattern formed by the blue light.

DEVISE PLAN

3. For a single-slit interference pattern, what equation relates the angular position of the minima to the wavelength of the light and the slit width?
4. What quantity do you need to determine in order to solve this problem?
5. Does the distance by which the $n = 1$ minima move depend on only one wavelength or on both wavelengths? How can you relate this distance to the wavelength(s) and the slit width?

EXECUTE PLAN

EVALUATE RESULT

6. How does the slit width compare with the wavelengths of the red and blue light? To the thickness of a piece of paper?

Worked Problem 34.7 Electron and neutron diffraction

Electrons moving at 2.0×10^6 m/s pass through a double-slit apparatus, producing an interference pattern in which adjacent bright fringes are separated by 1.5 mm. (*a*) What is the bright-fringe spacing when the electrons are replaced by neutrons moving at the same speed? (*b*) Can visible light be used with this apparatus to produce the same interference pattern as the electrons or neutrons?

① GETTING STARTED This is a problem about the interference pattern created on a screen by particles passing through a double-slit. In this case, electrons and neutrons rather than electromagnetic waves (photons) are interfering.

② DEVISE PLAN For any kind of waves, the bright-fringe separation distance y is determined by the center-to-center distance d between the slits, the normal distance L from the slits to the screen, and the wavelength λ of the interfering waves: $y = L\lambda/d$ (Eq. 34.15). The same apparatus is used for the electrons and neutrons, and so d and L remain unchanged.

To solve part *a*, we use Eq. 34.15 to express the bright-fringe spacing y_n obtained with neutrons in terms of the bright-fringe spacing y_e obtained with electrons and the electron and neutron wavelengths λ_e and λ_n. We can then use the de Broglie relationship, $\lambda = h/mv$ (Section 34.4), to substitute for λ_e and λ_n and obtain a value for y_n. For part *b*, we can compare the electron and neutron wavelengths with wavelengths in the visible region of the electromagnetic spectrum.

③ EXECUTE PLAN (*a*) Equation 34.15 gives the relationship for y_n, y_e, and the electron and neutron wavelengths:

$$y_n = \frac{L\lambda_n}{d} \qquad \frac{y_n}{\lambda_n} = \frac{L}{d}$$

$$y_e = \frac{L\lambda_e}{d} \qquad \frac{y_e}{\lambda_e} = \frac{L}{d}$$

$$\frac{y_n}{\lambda_n} = \frac{y_e}{\lambda_e}.$$

We solve this expression for y_n, substitute the de Broglie relationship for the wavelengths, and substitute values:

$$y_n = y_e \frac{\lambda_n}{\lambda_e} = y_e \frac{h/m_n v_n}{h/m_e v_e} = y_e \frac{m_e}{m_n}$$

$$= (1.5 \times 10^{-3} \text{ m}) \left(\frac{9.11 \times 10^{-31} \text{ kg}}{1.67 \times 10^{-27} \text{ kg}} \right)$$

$$= 8.2 \times 10^{-7} \text{ m} = 0.82 \text{ } \mu\text{m.} \checkmark$$

(*b*) The electron and neutron wavelengths are

$$\lambda_e = \frac{h}{mv} = \frac{6.626 \times 10^{-34} \text{ J} \cdot \text{s}}{(9.11 \times 10^{-31} \text{ kg})(2.0 \times 10^6 \text{ m/s})}$$

$$= 3.6 \times 10^{-10} \text{ m} = 0.36 \text{ nm}$$

$$\lambda_n = \frac{h}{mv} = \frac{6.626 \times 10^{-34} \text{ J} \cdot \text{s}}{(1.67 \times 10^{-27} \text{ kg})(2.0 \times 10^6 \text{ m/s})}$$

$$= 2.0 \times 10^{-13} \text{ m} = 2.0 \times 10^{-4} \text{ nm.}$$

The electron wavelength is in the x-ray region of the electromagnetic spectrum, and the neutron wavelength is in the gamma-ray region. The visible spectrum extends roughly from 400 nm to 700 nm, meaning it is not possible for visible light to duplicate the interference pattern created by passing electrons or neutrons through a double slit. $\checkmark$

④ EVALUATE RESULT Neutrons passing through a double slit at a given speed produce a much smaller bright-fringe spacing (by more than three orders of magnitude) than electrons passing through at the same speed. This makes sense because, with both having the same speed, the greater mass of the neutrons gives these particles greater momentum and hence shorter wavelength. Shorter wavelength results in closer bright-fringe spacing.

Because the speed in this problem is very large, the very small values we obtained for λ_e and λ_n are reasonable.

Guided Problem 34.8 Photoelectric effect with two light sources

For an experiment involving the photoelectric effect, you have two lasers for illuminating the target, and you can vary the potential difference between the target and the collector. With zero potential difference, the greatest value you measure for the kinetic energy of the electrons ejected from the target is 2.8 eV with laser 1 and 1.1 eV with laser 2. The wavelength of the light emitted by laser 2 is 50% greater than the wavelength of the light emitted by laser 1. What is the work function of the material of which the target is made?

① GETTING STARTED

1. Which conservation principle applies to this situation?
2. How is the work function related to the measured kinetic energies?

② DEVISE PLAN

3. With zero potential difference between target and collector, how is the maximum kinetic energy of the electrons measured at the collector related to the energy of the laser photons?
4. How can you relate the photon wavelength to photon energy?
5. What quantity do you need to determine in order to solve the problem?

③ EXECUTE PLAN

④ EVALUATE RESULT

6. Is the magnitude of your answer reasonable given the parameter values specified in the problem?

Questions and Problems

For instructor-assigned homework, go to MasteringPhysics® (MP)

Dots indicate difficulty level of problems: • = easy, •• = intermediate, ••• = hard; CR = context-rich problem.

34.1 Diffraction of light

1. Name some materials that allow you to observe light diffraction. •
2. Which wavelength of electromagnetic radiation do you expect to be diffracted by a window screen? What is the frequency of this radiation? •
3. Planar waves from a monochromatic light source are normally incident on a circular obstacle, which casts a shadow on a screen positioned behind the obstacle. What do the wave properties of light predict about how dark the center of the shadow is? ••
4. Light of wavelength λ is incident on an aperture of width a, producing diffraction. Describe the change(s) in the diffracted waves (a) when the aperture width is doubled and (b) when the wavelength is doubled. ••
5. A friend is standing behind a large tree and yelling. You can hear him, but not see him. Why? ••

34.2 Diffraction gratings

6. Coherent green light of wavelength 530 nm passes through two narrow slits for which the center-to-center separation distance is 100 μm. What is the difference in phase between the waves from the two slits for those that arrive at a distant screen at an angular position θ of (a) 15.4° and (b) 20.7°? •
7. A diffraction grating has adjacent slits separated by 4.00 μm. When yellow light ($\lambda = 589$ nm) is incident on the grating, what is the angular position of the second-order bright fringes? •
8. You shine a red laser beam on a diffraction grating and then shine a green laser beam on the grating. Is the spacing of the bright fringes for the red beam greater than, smaller than, or equal to the spacing of the bright fringes for the green beam? •
9. A reflection diffraction grating of width w has N grooves and is illuminated by normally incident monochromatic light. What condition determines how many orders of constructive interference can be seen in the interference pattern? ••
10. Violet light ($\lambda = 400$ nm) passing through a diffraction grating for which the slit spacing is 6.0 μm forms a pattern on a screen 1.0 m away from the grating. Is the fringe located at a linear distance $y = 394$ mm to the left of the central bright fringe a bright fringe, a dark fringe, or something in between? What is the order of this fringe? ••
11. Light passing through a two-slit grating makes a pattern on a screen located 500 mm away. In this pattern, the fifth-order dark fringe is 45.0 mm from the central bright fringe. How far from the central bright fringe is the third-order bright fringe? ••
12. A diffraction grating casts a pattern on a screen located a distance L from the grating. The central bright fringe falls directly in the center of the screen. For the highest-order bright fringe that hits the screen, $m = x$, and this fringe hits exactly on the screen edge. This means that $2x + 1$ bright fringes are visible on the screen. What happens to the number of bright fringes on the screen (a) if the wavelength of the light passing through the grating is doubled and (b) if the spacing d between adjacent slits is doubled? •••

13. (a) For the two-slit barrier shown in Figure P34.13, calculate the angle θ_1 for the first-order bright fringe if the slit separation distance is $d_{\text{orig}} = 1.0$ μm and the wavelength of the light passing through the slits is 546 nm. (b) Now consider a barrier in which one of the slits oscillates vertically and as a result the slit separation distance varies with time according to $d(t) = d_{\text{orig}} + A \sin \omega t$. Calculate θ_1 for the first-order bright fringe as a function of time for $A = 0.25$ μm and $\omega = 100$ s^{-1}. (c) At what instant after $t = 0$ does θ_1 have its maximum value for the first time? What is this maximum value? (d) At what instant after $t = 0$ does θ_1 have its minimum value for the first time? What is this minimum value? (e) Which of the parameters A, ω, λ, d_{orig} affect the values of these angles?

Figure P34.13

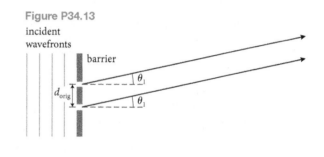

34.3 X-ray diffraction

14. Why are x rays rather than visible light used to determine structure in crystals? •
15. Do the bright spots in an x-ray diffraction pattern get closer together or farther apart when the energy of the x rays is doubled? •
16. A monochromatic x-ray beam that has a wavelength of 1.000×10^{-10} m strikes a sodium chloride crystal that has a lattice spacing of 2.815×10^{-10} m. What are (a) the $m = 1$ Bragg angle and (b) the highest-order Bragg angle? •
17. In an x-ray diffraction experiment on a crystal that has a cubic lattice, the greatest Bragg angle at which you see a peak in the intensity of diffracted x rays is 35.00°. If the x-ray wavelength is 1.000 nm, what is the atomic spacing in the crystal? Assume that only first-order fringes are visible in the diffraction pattern. ••
18. You are doing x-ray diffraction on a crystal that has a cubic structure, using 0.500-nm x rays. If the lattice spacing is $d = 6.70 \times 10^{-10}$ m, what are the two greatest Bragg angles at which you observe peaks in the intensity of the diffracted rays? ••

34.4 Matter waves

19. What is the order of magnitude of the de Broglie wavelength of a person walking down the street? •
20. How fast must a proton move in order to have the same de Broglie wavelength as the electron in Example 34.4, 1.5×10^{-10} m? •
21. A narrow solid obstacle is placed in the path of the electron in Figure P34.21. Does the electron have a chance of reaching the detector? •

Figure P34.21

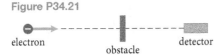

electron · · · · · · · · · · · detector
obstacle

22. What is the de Broglie wavelength of a 0.17-kg hockey puck moving at 45 m/s? •

23. An alpha particle, which consists of two neutrons and two protons, has a mass of 6.645×10^{-27} kg and a charge of $2e$. What is the de Broglie wavelength of an alpha particle of kinetic energy 7.48×10^{-13} J? ••

24. Rank the following radiation and particles in order of increasing spacing between bright fringes in their diffraction patterns: yellow light, blue light, electrons moving at 1.04×10^3 m/s, protons moving at 1.04×10^3 m/s, and neutrons moving at 1.04×10^3 m/s. ••

25. You are accelerating electrons toward a diffraction grating to produce a diffraction pattern. If you want the pattern to contain 101 bright fringes and the spacing between slits in the grating is 7.00 μm, what speed must the electrons have? •••

34.5 Photons

26. Which photons contain more energy: those of blue light or those of red light? •

27. In a region of Earth's surface where the average amount of solar energy striking a square meter of ground each second is 200 J, how many photons strike each square meter each second? Use 580 nm for the average wavelength of this solar radiation. •

28. What is the smallest amount of (a) momentum and (b) energy that can be delivered using red light for which $\lambda = 700$ nm? •

29. At what rate do photons emitted by a green-light laser ($\lambda = 532$ nm) hit a wall 2.00 m from the laser if the power rating is 5.00 mW? What assumption must you make to solve this problem? ••

30. The sun has a power output of 3.83×10^{26} W. (a) How many photons does the Sun emit each second? What assumption(s) must you make to answer this question? (b) Installed on your roof is a solar panel that has a surface area of 1.00 m². How many photons from the Sun reach the panel? What assumption(s) must you make to answer this question? ••

31. (a) What is the energy of a 633-nm photon? (b) Two helium-neon lasers both emit 633-nm photons. Laser A has a power rating of 1.0 mW, but laser B has a power rating of only 0.25 mW. Why do the power ratings differ when the lasers emit the same wavelength of light? ••

34.6 Multiple-slit interference

32. Near the center of a diffraction pattern, adjacent maxima are separated by a distance of 20 mm. The diffraction grating is 0.200 m from the screen and has a slit spacing of 4.5 μm. What is the wavelength of light being used? •

33. A red laser beam ($\lambda = 650$ nm) is sent through a double slit to a screen that is 400 mm wide and 1.00 m away from the slits. (a) If the separation distance between the slits is 4000 nm, how many bright fringes appear on the screen? (b) Verify your answer to part a by calculating the distance between adjacent bright fringes. •

34. Laser light passes through a double-slit barrier with slit separation $d = 0.150$ mm onto a screen a distance $L = 5.00$ m

away. The distance between the central and first-order bright fringes is $y = 23.0$ mm. What is the wavelength of the light? •

35. Using a diffraction grating with 200 slits/mm to create a diffraction pattern on a screen 2.00 m away from the grating, you see bright fringes 170 mm apart. What is the wavelength of the light? •

36. Green light ($\lambda = 510$ nm) shines through two slits separated by 2.30×10^{-6} m. The resulting diffraction pattern is cast on a screen 450 mm away. How far from the central bright fringe is the time-averaged intensity reduced to 12% of its maximum? ••

37. The radiation emitted by mercury vapor lamps includes green 546.1-nm light and blue 435.8-nm light. If this radiation passes through a transmission grating that has 600 slits/mm to form a diffraction pattern on a screen 0.500 m from the grating, what are the positions of the first-order and second-order bright fringes for each wavelength? Report your answers in terms of the linear distance y from the central bright fringe. ••

38. Cell phone radiation has a wavelength of about 300 mm. You are in the lobby of an office building in which the façade is a series of large, multistory panes of glass separated by vertical aluminum beams installed every 500 mm across the width of the building. Aluminum shields electromagnetic radiation. You are 10 m from the glass trying to make a phone call, but you don't get any reception. Could this have to do with interference? ••

39. You pass 589.0-nm radiation and 589.6-nm radiation through a diffraction grating that has 500.0 slits/mm. (a) In the diffraction pattern, what is the angular separation between the $m = 3$ peak for the 589.0-nm radiation and the $m = 3$ peak for the 589.6-nm radiation? (b) Are there fourth-order fringes in the diffraction pattern? ••

40. A beam of 550-nm light illuminates six parallel slits spaced 0.125 mm apart, and the resulting pattern is viewed on a screen. (a) What are the angular positions of the first-order and second-order principal maxima? (b) What are the angular positions of all the dark fringes between the central maximum and the first-order principal maximum? Between the central maximum and the first-order principal maximum, (c) how many dark fringes (minima) are there and (d) how many secondary maxima? ••

41. You shine a red ($\lambda = 650$ nm) laser beam and a green ($\lambda = 532$ nm) laser beam at a diffraction grating that has 400 slits/mm to create an interference pattern on a wall 3.00 m from the grating. If the two lasers are directly on top of each other, how far apart are the two $m = 1$ bright fringes from each other? Report your answer as a linear distance. ••

42. Is it possible to shine two laser beams of visible light into the same diffraction grating so that the dark fringes created by one beam overlay the bright fringes created by the other beam for all values of m? ••

43. Light of wavelength 570 nm passes through a pair of parallel slits that are 0.115 mm apart. It then falls on a screen that is 45.0 mm from the slits and centered directly opposite them. What must the minimum screen width be in order to have all the bright fringes fall on it? ••

44. A beam of light containing all the visible wavelengths from 400 nm to 700 nm passes through a pair of parallel slits that are 2.50 μm apart. These slits spread the beam into a series of full-color spectra. How many complete full-color spectra are formed? ••

45. You are designing a diffraction grating that, for 566.0-nm light, will produce second-order bright fringes that are an angular distance of 22.00° from the central bright fringe. How many equally spaced slits should this grating contain across its width if it is 24.00 mm wide? ••

46. You want to use a diffraction grating to resolve a beam of visible light into its component wavelengths, from 390 nm to 750 nm. Do the spectra from different orders overlap; that is, does a color from one order overlap with a different color from another order? If so, for which orders? ••

47. The spectrum of the radiation emitted by hydrogen atoms has a peak at $\lambda_r = 656.3$ nm (red) and a peak at $\lambda_b = 486.1$ nm (blue-green). (a) If this radiation is passed through a double-slit apparatus in which the slit separation is $d = 0.100$ mm and is then incident on a screen placed a distance $L = 2.10$ m from the slits, how far apart are the $m = 1$ maxima for the two wavelengths? Can these two maxima be resolved? (b) If, instead, a grating with 600 slits/mm is used, how far are the maxima be apart? •••

48. How many slits are needed in a diffraction grating that must resolve the $m = 1$ maxima of two spectral lines at $\lambda_s = 610$ nm and $\lambda_l = 615$ nm? •••

34.7 Thin-film interference

49. A 0.500-μm-thick flake of glass ($n_{glass} = 1.52$) from a broken cover slip is floating on water ($n_{water} = 1.33$). If white light initially traveling in the air ($n_{air} = 1.00$) is incident normal to the surface of the glass, what wavelengths in the visible spectrum undergo constructive interference as the white light is reflected from the top and bottom surfaces of the glass? •

50. You are designing a thin transparent reflective coating for the front surface of a sheet of glass. The index of refraction of the glass is 1.52, and when it is in use the coated glass has air on both sides. Because the coating is expensive, you want to use a layer that has the minimum thickness possible, which you determine to be 104 nm. What should the index of refraction of the coating be if it must cancel 550-nm light that hits the coated surface at normal incidence? ••

51. A sheet of glass ($n_{glass} = 1.5$) is coated with a 90.6-nm-thick layer of magnesium fluoride ($n_{coating} = 1.38$) to prevent reflection in the visible spectrum. What is the longest wavelength of light strongly reflected from this coated surface? Assume the incoming light is normal to the surface. ••

52. The thin film that forms a soap bubble has an index of refraction of 1.42. When white light strikes the outer surface of the film at normal incidence, 625-nm reflected light is especially bright. Derive an expression for the possible thicknesses of the film. ••

53. You are working with the mineral fluorite (CaF$_2$, $n_{fluorite} = 1.43$) and have a sample that is coated with a layer of liquid 158 nm thick. For various wavelengths of visible light incident normal to the surface of the liquid, you observe very strong reflection for green light ($\lambda = 510$ nm), essentially zero reflection for red light ($\lambda = 750$ nm), and intermediate levels of reflection for all wavelengths between the red and green extremes. What is the index of refraction of the liquid? •••

54. A thin film that is 175 nm thick and has an index of refraction smaller than 1.56 covers the front surface of a vertical sheet of glass that has an index of refraction of 1.56. The back surface of the glass interfaces with air, as does the front surface of the film. When a beam of light of variable wavelength is normally incident on the front surface of the film, we observe that, as the wavelength of the light is varied, 473-nm light reflects strongly from the front film surface. We also determine that if the film is any thinner than 175 nm, no constructive interference occurs. When the beam direction is changed so that the angle of incidence at which the light strikes the air–film interface is 51.0°, what is the angle of refraction for the beam in the film? •••

34.8 Diffraction at a single-slit barrier

55. When 633-nm light shines on a fracture-line crack in a thin piece of metal, a diffraction pattern is observed on a screen located $L = 0.90$ m from the metal. If the width of the central bright fringe is $w = 12$ mm, what is the width of the crack in the metal? •

56. How wide does a single slit have to be so that 650-nm light passing through the slit has its first dark fringe 30.0° from the center of the interference pattern? •

57. You send 400-nm violet light through a slit that is 0.500 mm wide. How far from the slit must you place a screen so that the distance between the $n = 1$ fringes is 10.0 mm? •

58. Red laser light ($\lambda = 656.5$ nm) passes through a slit of width $a = 0.100$ mm. On a screen a distance $L = 2.000$ m from the slit, what is the linear distance between the central bright fringe and either first-order dark fringe? •

59. Monochromatic 545-nm light is incident on a 15-μm-wide slit. If the diffraction pattern is cast on a screen 710 mm from the slit, what is the linear distance from the center of the pattern to the $n = 4$ dark fringe? •

60. A student makes the following claim: For radiation of any wavelength passing through a single slit, the separation distance between any two adjacent dark fringes is twice the source–screen distance when the slit width equals the wavelength. Evaluate this claim. ••

61. At sunset, red light travels horizontally through the doorway in the western wall of your beach cabin, and you observe the light on the eastern wall. What is the size of the interference pattern created by the doorway "slit"? ••

62. An experimental setup consists of a 550-nm laser, a screen at a distance of 0.50 m, and an adjustable-width single slit. At what slit width is the width of the central maximum of the interference pattern the same as that of the bright spot it would make in the absence of diffraction? In other words, for what slit width are the effects of wave optics and geometric optics comparable? ••

63. When 440-nm light is incident on a slit that is 75 μm wide, the diffraction pattern is cast on a screen 0.450 m from the slit. How wide is the central bright fringe? ••

64. A slit 0.002470 mm wide is used to study a light ray made up of two wavelengths, 482.0 nm and 517.3 nm, and the diffraction pattern is viewed on a screen 0.220 m from the slit. In the pattern, what is the distance between the $n = 2$ dark fringe for the 482.0-nm light and the $n = 2$ dark fringe for the 517.3-nm light? (Take both dark fringes to be on the same side of the central maximum.) ••

65. A 485-nm light beam passes through a slit and forms a diffraction pattern on a screen 0.320 m from the slit. The $n = 1$ and $n = 1$ dark fringes are 22.4 mm apart on the screen. (a) How wide is the slit? (b) What is the greatest angle from the original beam direction at which a dark fringe occurs? ••

66. Two extremely narrow, parallel slits are cut in a sheet of cardboard, with the width a of each slit very much smaller than

the distance d between them. When the slits are illuminated by a coherent beam of 620-nm light, the angular position of the two third-order bright fringes is $\pm 4.27°$. The cardboard between the slits is then cut out so that the sheet contains only a single opening. When this opening is illuminated by the 620-nm light, what are the angular positions of the $n = 1$, 2, 3 dark fringes? ••

67. In the interference pattern created by 800-nm radiation passing through a single slit 45 μm wide, what is the angular separation between the $n = 3$ and $n = 5$ dark fringes on the same side of the central maximum? ••

68. In the interference pattern created by light diffracted from a single slit, which are wider: the first-order bright fringes or the third-order bright fringes? (Hint: Plot or plug in typical numerical values for the slit width and wavelengths to make an educated guess.) •••

69. A laser beam passes through a slit that is 1500 nm wide. In the interference pattern created on a distant screen, the angular position of the two first-order dark fringes is 25.0°. The beam then is shone on a soap film ($n_{film} = 1.40$) floating on water ($n_{water} = 1.33$). What is the minimum film thickness that causes light reflected at normal incidence from the air–film interface to cancel light reflected at normal incidence from the film–water interface? •••

34.9 Circular apertures and limits of resolution

70. A pinhole of diameter 0.20 mm is illuminated with 550-nm light. What is the width of the Airy disk on a screen 1.5 m away? •

71. The human eye is most sensitive to green light at 550 nm, which is why this wavelength is most frequently used when calculating the resolution limits of telescopes. A telescope for amateur astronomers has a focal length of 1200 mm and an aperture diameter of 200 mm. What is the radius of the Airy disk? •

72. You wish to use a lens to focus a beam of light that has a diameter of 40.0 mm. Which lens focuses the beam to the smallest point: lens A, 10.0-mm diameter, 25.0-mm focal length; lens B, 150-mm diameter, 50.0-mm focal length; or lens C, 30.0-mm diameter, 30.0-mm focal length? •

73. The Spitzer Space Telescope, launched in 2003, has a mirror that is 0.85 m in diameter and detects infrared light with wavelengths from 3.00 μm to 180 μm. If the instrument is used to study a pair of stars, what are the resolvable angular separations of the stars for the minimum and maximum wavelengths? •

74. For an eye in which the pupil has a radius of 3.0 mm, what is the smallest angular separation that can be resolved (a) when two violet ($\lambda = 400$ nm) objects are placed side by side and (b) when two red ($\lambda = 650$ nm) objects are placed side by side? When the objects are 100 m away from this eye, what minimum linear separation distance is needed for resolution (c) of the two violet objects and (d) of the two red objects? ••

75. A 530-nm laser beam passes through a circular aperture that has diameter 0.400 mm. What is the diameter of the first dark fringe on a screen 800 mm away from the aperture? ••

76. The pupil of the human eye can vary in diameter from 2.00 mm in bright light to 8.00 mm in dim light. The eye has a focal length of about 25 mm, and the visible spectrum extends from 390 nm (violet) to 750 nm (red). What range of Airy disk radii is possible for the eye? (Note that the light-sensitive cells on the retina have radii ranging from 0.75 μm to 3.0 μm.) ••

77. In vacuum, the Airy disk generated by a pinhole in a metal sheet has radius $y_{r,vac}$. How does the disk radius change when the sheet is submerged in water ($n = 1.33$)? ••

78. When 500-nm light is incident on a circular aperture that has diameter $d = 30.0$ μm, a diffraction pattern forms on a screen 350 mm from the aperture. Calculate the area of the central bright fringe. ••

79. Two objects emitting 550-nm light are placed side by side 30.0 mm apart. For an eye in which the pupil has a diameter of 6.00 mm, what is the minimum eye–objects distance L at which the objects are not resolvable? ••

80. You are using your telescope to view stars by observing the visible light they emit. If the diameter of the lens is 60.0 mm, what must the minimum angular separation of two stars be in order for you to resolve them? ••

81. A satellite studying Earth's surface uses a telescope mirror 2.75 m in diameter to focus light of wavelength 525 nm. If the satellite orbits at an altitude of 25,000 km and points the mirror straight downward, what is the diameter of the smallest surface feature it can resolve? ••

82. A beam of 650-nm light passes through a small round hole and falls on a screen 350 mm past the hole. If the diameter of the Airy disk on the screen is 139 mm, what is the diameter of the hole? ••

83. The red brake lights of a car are 2.00 m apart. Standing 300 m away from the rear of the car, you use a $f = 50$ mm lens with an aperture of diameter $d = 4.00$ mm to photograph the illuminated brake lights. Are the lights likely to be resolved in the photograph, or will they blur together? •••

84. You are building a pinhole camera, which uses a small hole instead of a lens to produce an image (Figure P34.84. (a) If the distance between the hole and the film is 100 mm and the hole diameter is 0.300 mm, what is the smallest resolved image point you can have on the film for light ranging from 390 nm to 750 nm? Consider both geometric optics (simply considering the shadow) and wave optics. (b) How can you determine the optimum pinhole size for a given wavelength of light? •••

Figure P34.84

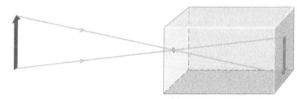

34.10 Photon energy and momentum

85. What happens to (a) the kinetic energy of a marble when its speed is reduced to half its initial speed and (b) the energy of a photon when its speed is reduced to half its initial speed (as, for instance, when the photon travels from a medium with an index of refraction of 1 into a medium with an index of refraction of 2)? •

86. What is the energy of (a) a 400-nm photon and (b) a 700-nm photon? •

87. What is the wavelength of a gamma-ray photon that has energy of 8.0×10^{-14} J? •

88. What is the momentum of a photon that has energy of 8.0×10^{-14} J? •

...m has a work function of $E_0 = 6.54 \times 10^{-19}$ J. What ...e maximum wavelength of light that can free electrons .rom the surface? •

90. If the work function of a material is such that red light of wavelength 700 nm just barely initiates the photoelectric effect, what must the maximum kinetic energy of ejected electrons be when violet light of wavelength 400 nm illuminates the material? ••

91. When 410-nm light is incident on a sheet of metal, the maximum kinetic energy of electrons ejected from the metal surface is measured to be $K_{max} = 3.5 \times 10^{-20}$ J. What is the work function of the metal? ••

92. When three metals, 1, 2, and 3, are illuminated with light of frequency f in a photoelectric-effect experiment, the relationship of the stopping potential differences is found to be $V_{stop,1} > V_{stop,2} > V_{stop,3}$. Which material has (a) the lowest frequency below which no electrons are ejected and (b) the highest frequency below which the effect does not happen? ••

93. In a photoelectric-effect experiment, the stopping potential difference is found to be 3.4 V when 140-nm light is used. What is the work function of the metal? ••

94. A metal alloy has a work function of $E_0 = 4.6 \times 10^{-19}$ J. It is irradiated with light of different wavelengths, and the maximum kinetic energy of ejected electrons is measured. What are the maximum kinetic energy and the maximum electron speed (a) when 390-nm light is used and (b) when 750-nm light is used? ••

95. You determine that light of minimum-frequency 7.20×10^{14} Hz is needed to eject electrons from the surface of a certain metal. What frequency should the light have in order for the ejected electrons to have a maximum speed of 8.50×10^5 m/s? ••

96. A helium-neon laser that has a power rating of 0.250 mW operates at a wavelength of 633 nm and a beam diameter of 2.00 mm. Calculate (a) the energy per photon, (b) the number of photons emitted per second, (c) the momentum per photon, and (d) the pressure exerted on an absorber on which the beam is incident. ••

97. (a) If the kinetic energy of an electron and the energy of a photon are both 2.00×10^{-18} J, calculate the ratio of the de Broglie wavelength of the electron to the wavelength of the photon. Which particle has the shorter wavelength? (b) If the wavelength of a photon and the de Broglie wavelength of an electron are both 250 nm, calculate the ratio of the energy of the photon to the kinetic energy of the electron. Which particle has greater energy? ••

98. A 3.50-W beam of 216-nm laser light shines on the surface of a metal for which the work function is 2.00×10^{-19} J. What is the maximum number of electrons per second the beam can cause to be ejected from the metal? ••

99. A laser beam with an intensity of 60 W/m² shines on a black object of mass 2.3 mg. The beam hits an area of 4.5 mm² head-on (that is, the beam is perpendicular to the surface). Assuming a totally inelastic collision (meaning the incident photons are absorbed by the black object) and ignoring friction, what is the resulting acceleration of the object? •••

100. In the vacuum tube of Figure P34.98, the lower metal plate, the target, is irradiated with 400-nm light of intensity 5.50 W/m². The frequency of the light is great enough to cause electrons to be ejected from the target and travel to the upper metal plate, the collector. What is the maximum possible current in the circuit if the area of the target is 600 mm²? •••

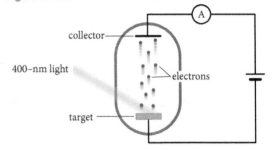

101. When 550-nm light passes through a thin slit and then travels to a screen, the first-order dark fringe in the interference pattern is at 32.5° from the center of the screen. When a beam of electrons, each having kinetic energy equal to the energy of the photons in the 550-nm beam, passes through the slit and travels to the screen, what is the smallest angle from the screen center at which no electrons are found? •••

102. A uniform film of a material that has index of refraction 1.30 covers the front surface of a pane made of glass with index of refraction 1.55. When a beam of monochromatic light initially traveling in air strikes the film at normal incidence, the minimum film thickness for which the light reflected from the air–film interface and the light reflected from the film–glass interface cancel is 123 nm. What is the energy of each photon in the light beam? •••

Additional problems

103. Monochromatic light of which wavelength diffracts the most through a 3.0-μm aperture: 400 nm, 500 nm, or 600 nm? •

104. A double-slit barrier with slit separation distance d is a distance L from a screen, with $L \gg d$. When green laser light ($\lambda_g = 532$ nm) passes through the barrier, the bright fringes on the screen are a distance y_g apart. When red laser light ($\lambda_r = 650$ nm) passes through the barrier, the bright fringes on the screen are a distance y_r apart. What is y_r expressed in terms of y_g? •

105. On a screen 2.5 m from a slit 0.0500 mm wide, you measure a separation distance of 31 mm between adjacent $n = 1$ and $n = 2$ dark fringes of a laser interference pattern. What is the wavelength of the laser radiation? The screen is far enough away and the fringes close enough together to justify the small-angle approximation. •

106. NASA plans to use x-ray diffraction to identify minerals on the surface of Mars. If the wavelength of the x rays is 0.155 nm, what is the lattice spacing in a crystalline sample if the crystal strongly reflects x rays at an incident angle of 51.7° in the first order? •

107. Babinet's principle states that, except for differences in intensity, the interference pattern created by light passing around an opaque object is the same as the pattern created by the same light passing through a hole of the same size and shape as the object. You shine a 690-nm laser beam on a human hair and observe an interference pattern on a screen 1.2 m from the hair. If each first-order dark fringe is 16 mm from the center of the pattern, what is the diameter of the hair? ••

108. Many hundreds of planets beyond our solar system have been discovered in recent years, but they have all been too far away to be resolved by present-day optical telescopes. Using light of wavelength 525 nm, what must the minimum mirror

diameter of a space telescope be in order to resolve an Earth-sized planet at a distance of 10 light years? Are our present space telescopes nearing this size? The diameter of Earth is 1.27×10^7 m. ••

109. You shine light of frequency f_i on a diffraction grating and create a diffraction pattern on a screen made up of tiny photon detectors. (*a*) How does the pattern change if you increase the frequency of the light? (*b*) How does the pattern change if you replace the initial light source with one that emits brighter light of the same frequency f_i? (*c*) Is the number of photons detected at the screen smaller than, equal to, or greater than the number detected with the initial source? ••

110. A layer of oil ($n_{oil} = 1.48$) 0.0100 mm thick is resting on a puddle of water ($n_{water} = 1.33$). If white light is incident on the oil, what is the smallest angle from normal at which green light ($\lambda = 510$ nm) is strongly reflected? ••

111. When a monochromatic beam of light passes through a thin slit, the $n = 9$ dark fringe is $10°$ beyond the adjacent $n = 8$ dark fringe. What is the ratio of the wavelength of the light to the width of the slit? ••

112. In a double-slit interference pattern, it is the amplitudes of the light waves from each slit that add, not the light intensities. Usually, in the analysis of interference patterns, the radiation intensity (or amplitude) is assumed to be exactly the same for both slits. Because of inaccurate optical alignment, however, the illumination is often not the same for the two slits. If the intensity of light going through one slit is 0.010 mW/mm^2 while the intensity going through the second slit is 0.030 mW/mm^2, what is the intensity at an interference maximum and at an interference minimum? ••

113. Electrons are accelerated from rest through a 2.0-kV potential difference. What are (*a*) their speed after this acceleration and (*b*) their wavelength? (*c*) If the accelerated electrons are incident on a graphite crystal that has a lattice spacing of 0.123 nm, do you expect to observe diffraction? ••

114. You are designing a diffraction grating that will disperse white light into its spectrum (400-nm violet to 700-nm red). In the first-order spectrum, you want the angular separation between the shortest and longest wavelengths to be $12.0°$. (*a*) How many slits per millimeter should the grating have? (*b*) How many complete full-color spectra will the grating produce, not counting the central bright fringe? ••

115. Monochromatic light passes through a small round hole 1.36 μm in radius. The light then strikes a detector 120 mm away from the hole and is absorbed by the detector surface. If the radius of the Airy disk on the detector is 33.3 mm, how much energy and momentum does each photon transfer to the detector? •••

116. A young adult with good vision is reading a document placed at her near point. She is using ordinary reading light of wavelength 500 nm, and the diameter of her pupil is 3.0 mm. Under these conditions, what is the height of the smallest letter she can resolve on the document? •••

117. In experiment 1, a laser beam of 750-nm light is passed through a double-slit barrier and creates a diffraction pattern on a screen. In experiment 2, one slit is covered with a semi-cylindrical piece of material that has an index of refraction of $n = 1.001$, as shown in Figure P34.117, and the 750-nm beam again passes through and creates a diffraction pattern on the screen. If the distance between the slits is $d = 1.2$ mm, what is the smallest radius of the semicylindrical piece that results in the screen locations that were bright fringes in experiment 1 being dark fringes in experiment 2, and the screen locations that were dark fringes in experiment 1 being bright fringes in experiment 2? •••

Figure P34.117

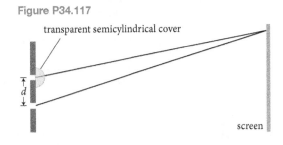

118. You have an unlabeled container in the laboratory that contains the solid lithium fluoride (LiF) and an identical unlabeled container that contains the solid sodium chloride (NaCl). You know that both materials crystallize in a cubic structure, with alternating Na and Cl ions in the NaCl lattice and alternating Li and F ions in the LiF lattice. The only testing instrument available is a diffraction apparatus that uses monochromatic 0.154-nm x rays. After reading in the literature that the lattice spacing is 0.202 nm for LiF and 0.283 nm for NaCl, you test one of the samples in the apparatus and observe the first intensity peak at a Bragg angle of $22.4°$. ••• CR

119. As a mission engineer for NASA, you are working on a mission to map the surface of Mars. Your boss asks you to design the optical system for a satellite that can resolve surface features as small as 2.00 m across in the visible part of the electromagnetic spectrum. He tells you the instrument has to fit in a cubic bay of 1.0-m width. You know that to get sharp pictures, the satellite must take at least 17 hours to orbit the planet. Luckily you remember your physics classes on gravity, so you sit down to evaluate whether the job is feasible. ••• CR

Answers to Review Questions

1. Diffraction is the spreading out of a wave in the direction of wave propagation after the wave passes either through a small aperture or past the edge of a smooth barrier, such as a razor blade.

2. If the wavelength is comparable to the wavefront width, the beam diffracts after passing through the gap. If the wavefront width is much greater than the wavelength, there is no diffraction.

3. Interference fringes are the bright and dark bands formed on a screen when light passes through adjacent narrow slits in a barrier. As they travel to the screen, the beams emerging from the slits interfere with each other both constructively, producing bright fringes, and destructively, producing dark fringes.

4. The order refers to the numbering of fringes on either side of the central bright fringe, for which the order is zero. The symbol m is used for bright-fringe orders, and n is used for dark-fringe orders.

5. Bright fringes appear at any location on the screen where the difference in the slit-to-screen distance for the two slits is equal to a whole-number multiple of the wavelength. Dark fringes appear at any screen location where the difference in the slit-to-screen distance is equal to an odd multiple of $\lambda/2$.

6. The condition for constructive interference is the same in the two cases: If the path difference between adjacent slits is an integer number of wavelengths, constructive interference given by $d \sin \theta_m = \pm m\lambda$ results for N slits as for two slits. For destructive interference, the condition is not the same in the two cases. Rather than the alternating bright-dark sequence created by a two-slit barrier, the pattern created by a many-slit barrier has both strongly bright fringes called *principal maxima* and fainter bright fringes called *secondary maxima*. For a barrier containing N slits, there are $N - 1$ dark fringes between each pair of adjacent principal maxima and $N - 2$ secondary maxima between each pair of principal maxima. If N is large, the principal maxima are bright and narrow, and the minima and secondary maxima are essentially dark.

7. The principal maxima are the brightest fringes in the pattern, corresponding to constructive interference by *all* the beams created by the slits. The secondary maxima are weak bright fringes that break up the dark fringe between any two adjacent principal maxima. The secondary maxima are regions where the interference of all the beams is neither completely constructive nor completely destructive.

8. A diffraction grating is a barrier that consists of a large number of equally spaced slits or grooves. A barrier containing slits is called a transmission diffraction grating because the diffraction occurs after light passes—is transmitted—through the slits. A barrier containing grooves is called a reflective diffraction grating because the diffraction occurs after light reflects from the grooved surface of the barrier.

9. The atom-to-atom spacing in the lattice is generally of the same order of magnitude as x-ray wavelengths, so that adjacent planes of atoms act as a grating from which the x rays are diffracted.

10. For x rays diffracted by a crystal lattice, the Bragg condition defines the incidence angles θ that result in constructive interference of the rays reflected by the crystal. These angles are given by $2d \cos \theta_m = \pm m\lambda$, where d is the distance between planes in the lattice, m is any integer, and λ is the wavelength of the incident x rays.

11. The electrons are diffracted. Because diffraction is a wave phenomenon, this suggests that electrons exhibit wavelike behavior.

12. The wave nature of a particle is determined by its de Broglie wavelength $\lambda = h/p$, where $h = 6.626 \times 10^{-34}$ J·s is Planck's constant and p is the particle's momentum.

13. Observing macroscopic objects behaving like waves is not possible because the de Broglie wavelength of any macroscopic object is many orders of magnitude smaller than any length that can be measured.

14. A photon is a particle of light. The energy of a photon is proportional to the frequency of the light, with the proportionality constant being Planck's constant: $E = hf$.

15. Very-low-intensity light behaves like a beam of particles. When it is made to strike two small detecting screens placed close together, each particle of light in the beam strikes one screen or the other, and no matter for how long the experiment is run, the screens always record individual particle impacts. An interference pattern, which is characteristic of waves but not of particles, never builds up on the screens.

16. The waves are out of phase when they reach the screen because of the different distance each wave travels from its slit to the screen.

17. The maximum intensity in the interference pattern is four times the intensity of the waves incident on the slits because the intensity is proportional to the square of the electric field and the electric field is the sum of the fields of the waves from the two slits.

18. The wavelengths can be distinguished if, in the spectrum, the angular position of the mth-order principal maximum of λ_1 is greater than or equal to the angular position of the minimum adjacent to the mth-order principal maximum of λ_2.

19. Thin-film interference occurs when light reflected from the front surface of a thin film interferes with light reflected from the back surface of the film.

20. Interference occurs only if the thickness of the material is comparable to the wavelength of the light.

21. The phase difference is determined by the difference in path length of the two beams (the path of a beam reflected from the back surface is longer than the path of a beam reflected from the front surface) and by whether or not reflection from either surface inverts the wave.

22. There is a phase shift of π if the wave is inverted by the reflection, which happens when $n_2 > n_1$, and no phase shift if the wave is not inverted by the reflection, which happens when $n_1 > n_2$.

23. The directions to the dark fringes of the interference pattern can be determined.

24. The expression is $\sin \theta_n = n\lambda/a$, where θ is the angle between the direction to the minima and the original propagation direction of the light, n is any integer except zero, λ is the wavelength of the light, and a is the slit width.

25. The waves spread out in all directions once they pass through the slit, so there is no discernible interference pattern.

26. The interference pattern is a circular central maximum surrounded by alternating concentric dark fringes and secondary bright fringes.

27. An Airy disk is the circular central maximum in the interference pattern created by light passing through a circular aperture.

28. Rayleigh's criterion is a description of how close together two objects being viewed through a circular lens can be and still be distinguished from each other. The objects can be distinguished only if the distance between the centers of the two interference patterns is equal to or greater than the position of the first minimum of either pattern; this minimum separation occurs when the angular separation between the objects is at least $\theta = 1.22\lambda/d$, where d is the lens diameter.

29. A diffraction limit is a limit on how small the image of any object viewed through a lens can be; even if the object is a point, which has zero width, the image has some finite width because the light from the point diffracts as it passes through the lens. This smallest size is equal to the radius of the Airy disk.

30. The photoelectric effect is the emission of electrons from matter as a consequence of their absorption of energy from incident light with a photon energy greater than a certain minimum energy called the work function.

31. The stopping potential difference is the greatest positive value of the potential difference V_{CT} between the target and collector at which electrons ejected from the target can travel to the collector. It depends on the frequency of the incident light.

32. The stopping potential difference is proportional to the maximum kinetic energy the electrons can have: $K_{max} = eV_{stop}$ (Eq. 34.34).

33. In order to leave the target, an electron must acquire from the incident light a certain minimum amount of energy, proportional to the stopping potential difference, $K = eV_{stop}$. Because V_{stop} depends on the light's frequency rather than on its intensity, the energy delivered by the light must depend on frequency and not on intensity. In the wave model of light, the light energy is a function of intensity, and so this model does not work as an explanation of the photoelectric effect. In the particle model of light, the light consists of photons, with the energy in each photon proportional to the light frequency, agreeing with what is seen in the photoelectric effect.

34. The current is proportional to the intensity if the frequency of the light is great enough that a photon has enough energy to eject an electron from the metal surface. If the frequency of the light is too small, then there is no current, no matter how intense the incident light.

35. The work function is the minimum amount of energy necessary to free an electron from the surface of the metal.

Answers to Guided Problems

Guided Problem 34.2 110 satellites

Guided Problem 34.4 (*a*) The last color seen is violet, the color of visible light that has the shortest wavelength. (*b*) Assuming 400 nm is the shortest visible wavelength and the index of refraction of the soap film is that of water, the film thickness is 75 nm just before it becomes invisible.

Guided Problem 34.6 (*a*) The minima move toward the center of the pattern. (*b*) The slit is 0.097 mm wide.

Guided Problem 34.8 2.3 eV

Appendix A

Notation

Notation used in this text, listed alphabetically, Greek letters first.
For information concerning superscripts and subscripts, see the explanation at the end of this table.

Symbol	Name of Quantity	Definition	Where Defined	SI units
α (alpha)	polarizability	scalar measure of amount of charge separation occurring in material due to external electric field	Eq. 23.24	$C^2 \cdot m/N$
α	Bragg angle	in x-ray diffraction, angle between incident x rays and sample surface	Section 34.3	degree, radian, or revolution
α_ϑ	(ϑ component of) rotational acceleration	rate at which rotational velocity ω_ϑ increases	Eq. 11.12	s^{-2}
β (beta)	sound intensity level	logarithmic scale for sound intensity, proportional to $\log(I/I_{th})$	Eq. 17.5	dB (not an SI unit)
γ (gamma)	Lorentz factor	factor indicating how much relativistic values deviate from nonrelativistic ones	Eq. 14.6	unitless
γ	surface tension	force per unit length exerted parallel to surface of liquid; energy per unit area required to increase surface area of liquid	Eq. 18.48	N/m
γ	heat capacity ratio	ratio of heat capacity at constant pressure to heat capacity at constant volume	Eq. 20.26	unitless
Δ	delta	change in	Eq. 2.4	
$\Delta \vec{r}$	displacement	vector from object's initial to final position	Eq. 2.8	m
$\Delta \vec{r}_F, \Delta x_F$	force displacement	displacement of point of application of a force	Eq. 9.7	m
Δt	interval of time	difference between final and initial instants	Table 2.2	s
Δt_{proper}	proper time interval	time interval between two events occurring at same position	Section 14.1	s
Δt_v	interval of time	time interval measured by observer moving at speed v with respect to events	Eq. 14.13	s
Δx	x component of displacement	difference between final and initial positions along x axis	Eq. 2.4	m
δ (delta)	delta	infinitesimally small amount of	Eq. 3.24	
ϵ_0 (epsilon)	electric constant	constant relating units of electrical charge to mechanical units	Eq. 24.7	$C^2/(N \cdot m^2)$
η (eta)	viscosity	measure of fluid's resistance to shear deformation	Eq. 18.38	Pa $\cdot$ s
η	efficiency	ratio of work done by heat engine to thermal input of energy	Eq. 21.21	unitless
θ (theta)	angular coordinate	polar coordinate measuring angle between position vector and x axis	Eq. 10.2	degree, radian, or revolution
θ_c	contact angle	angle between solid surface and tangent to liquid surface at meeting point measured within liquid	Section 18.4	degree, radian, or revolution
θ_c	critical angle	angle of incidence greater than which total internal reflection occurs	Eq. 33.9	degree, radian, or revolution
θ_i	angle of incidence	angle between incident ray of light and normal to surface	Section 33.1	degree, radian, or revolution

Symbol	Name of Quantity	Definition	Where Defined	SI units
θ_i	angle subtended by image	angle subtended by image	Section 33.6	degree, radian, or revolution
θ_o	angle subtended by object	angle subtended by object	Section 33.6	degree, radian, or revolution
θ_r	angle of reflection	angle between reflected ray of light and normal to surface	Section 33.1	degree, radian, or revolution
θ_r	minimum resolving angle	smallest angular separation between objects that can be resolved by optical instrument with given aperture	Eq. 34.30	degree, radian, or revolution
ϑ (script theta)	rotational coordinate	for object traveling along circular path, arc length traveled divided by circle radius	Eq. 11.1	unitless
κ (kappa)	torsional constant	ratio of torque required to twist object to rotational displacement	Eq. 15.25	$N \cdot m$
κ	dielectric constant	factor by which potential difference across isolated capacitor is reduced by insertion of dielectric	Eq. 26.9	unitless
λ (lambda)	inertia per unit length	for uniform one-dimensional object, amount of inertia in a given length	Eq. 11.44	kg/m
λ	wavelength	minimum distance over which periodic wave repeats itself	Eq. 16.9	m
λ	linear charge density	amount of charge per unit length	Eq. 23.16	C/m
μ (mu)	reduced mass	product of two interacting objects' inertias divided by their sum	Eq. 6.39	kg
μ	linear mass density	mass per unit length	Eq. 16.25	kg/m
$\vec{\mu}$	magnetic dipole moment	vector pointing along direction of magnetic field of current loop, with magnitude equal to current times area of loop	Section 28.3	$A \cdot m^2$
μ_0	magnetic constant	constant relating units of electric current to mechanical units	Eq. 28.1	$T \cdot m/A$
μ_k	coefficient of kinetic friction	proportionality constant relating magnitudes of force of kinetic friction and normal force between two surfaces	Eq. 10.55	unitless
μ_s	coefficient of static friction	proportionality constant relating magnitudes of force of static friction and normal force between two surfaces	Eq. 10.46	unitless
ρ (rho)	mass density	amount of mass per unit volume	Eq. 1.4	kg/m^3
ρ	inertia per unit volume	for uniform three-dimensional object, amount of inertia in a given volume divided by that volume	Eq. 11.46	kg/m^3
ρ	(volume) charge density	amount of charge per unit volume	Eq. 23.18	C/m^3
σ (sigma)	inertia per unit area	for uniform two-dimensional object, inertia divided by area	Eq. 11.45	kg/m^2
σ	surface charge density	amount of charge per unit area	Eq. 23.17	C/m^2
σ	conductivity	ratio of current density to applied electric field	Eq. 31.8	$A/(V \cdot m)$
τ (tau)	torque	magnitude of axial vector describing ability of forces to change objects' rotational motion	Eq. 12.1	$N \cdot m$
τ	time constant	for damped oscillation, time for energy of oscillator to decrease by factor e^{-1}	Eq. 15.39	s
τ_ϑ	(ϑ component of) torque	ϑ component of axial vector describing ability of forces to change objects' rotational motion	Eq. 12.3	$N \cdot m$
Φ_E (phi, upper case)	electric flux	scalar product of electric field and area through which it passes	Eq. 24.1	$N \cdot m^2/C$

Symbol	Name of Quantity	Definition	Where Defined	SI units
Φ_B	magnetic flux	scalar product of magnetic field and area through which it passes	Eq. 27.10	Wb
ϕ (phi)	phase constant	phase difference between source emf and current in circuit	Eq. 32.16	unitless
$\phi(t)$	phase	time-dependent argument of sine function describing simple harmonic motion	Eq. 15.5	unitless
Ω (omega, upper case)	number of basic states	number of basic states corresponding to macrostate	Section 19.4, Eq. 19.1	unitless
ω (omega)	rotational speed	magnitude of rotational velocity	Eq. 11.7	s^{-1}
ω	angular frequency	for oscillation with period T, $2\pi/T$	Eq. 15.4	s^{-1}
ω_0	resonant angular frequency	angular frequency at which current in circuit is maximal	Eq. 32.47	s^{-1}
ω_ϑ	(ϑ component of) rotational velocity	rate at which rotational coordinate ϑ changes	Eq. 11.6	s^{-1}
A	area	length $\times$ width	Eq. 11.45	m^2
A	amplitude	magnitude of maximum displacement of oscillating object from equilibrium position	Eq. 15.6	m (for linear mechanical oscillation; unitless for rotational oscillation; various units for nonmechanical oscillation)
$\vec{A}$	area vector	vector with magnitude equal to area and direction normal to plane of area	Section 24.6	m^2
$\vec{a}$	acceleration	time rate of change in velocity	Section 3.1	m/s^2
$\vec{a}_{Ao}$	relative acceleration	value observer in reference frame A records for acceleration of object o in reference frame A	Eq. 6.11	m/s^2
a_c	magnitude of centripetal acceleration	acceleration required to make object follow circular trajectory	Eq. 11.15	m/s^2
a_r	radial component of acceleration	component of acceleration in radial direction	Eq. 11.16	m/s^2
a_t	tangential component of acceleration	component of acceleration tangent to trajectory; for circular motion at constant speed $a_t = 0$	Eq. 11.17	m/s^2
a_x	x component of acceleration	component of acceleration directed along x axis	Eq. 3.21	m/s^2
$\vec{B}$	magnetic field	vector field providing measure of magnetic interactions	Eq. 27.5	T
$\vec{B}_{ind}$	induced magnetic field	magnetic field produced by induced current	Section 29.4	T
b	damping coefficient	ratio of drag force on moving object to its speed	Eq. 15.34	kg/s
C	heat capacity per particle	ratio of energy transferred thermally per particle to change in temperature	Section 20.3	J/K
C	capacitance	ratio of magnitude of charge on one of a pair of oppositely charged conductors to magnitude of potential difference between them	Eq. 26.1	F
C_P	heat capacity per particle at constant pressure	ratio of energy transferred thermally per particle to change in temperature, while holding pressure constant	Eq. 20.20	J/K
C_V	heat capacity per particle at constant volume	ratio of energy transferred thermally per particle to change in temperature, while holding volume constant	Eq. 20.13	J/K
$COP_{cooling}$	coefficient of performance of cooling	ratio of thermal input of energy to work done on a heat pump	Eq. 21.27	unitless

Symbol	Name of Quantity	Definition	Where Defined	SI units
$COP_{heating}$	coefficient of performance of heating	ratio of thermal output of energy to work done on a heat pump	Eq. 21.25	unitless
c	shape factor	ratio of object's rotational inertia to mR^2; function of distribution of inertia within object	Table 11.3, Eq. 12.25	unitless
c	wave speed	speed at which mechanical wave travels through medium	Eq. 16.3	m/s
c	specific heat capacity	ratio of energy transferred thermally per unit mass to change in temperature	Section 20.3	$J/(K \cdot kg)$
c_0	speed of light in vacuum	speed of light in vacuum	Section 14.2	m/s
c_V	specific heat capacity at constant volume	ratio of energy transferred thermally per unit mass to change in temperature, while holding volume constant	Eq. 20.48	$J/(K \cdot kg)$
$\vec{D}$	displacement (of particle in wave)	displacement of particle from its equilibrium position	Eq. 16.1	m
d	diameter	diameter	Section 1.9	m
d	distance	distance between two locations	Eq. 2.5	m
d	degrees of freedom	number of ways particle can store thermal energy	Eq. 20.4	unitless
d	lens strength	1 m divided by focal length	Eq. 33.22	diopters
E	energy of system	sum of kinetic and internal energies of system	Table 1.1, Eq. 5.21	J
$\vec{E}$	electric field	vector field representing electric force per unit charge	Eq. 23.1	N/C
E_0	work function	minimum energy required to free electron from surface of metal	Eq. 34.35	J
E_{chem}	chemical energy	internal energy associated with object's chemical state	Eq. 5.27	J
E_{int}	internal energy of system	energy associated with an object's state	Eqs. 5.20, 14.54	J
E_{mech}	mechanical energy	sum of system's kinetic and potential energies	Eq. 7.9	J
E_s	source energy	incoherent energy used to produce other forms of energy	Eq. 7.7	J
E_{th}	thermal energy	internal energy associated with object's temperature	Eq. 5.27	J
$\mathcal{E}$	emf	in charge-separating device, nonelectrostatic work per unit charge done in separating positive and negative charge carriers	Eq. 26.7	V
$\mathcal{E}_{ind}$	induced emf	emf resulting from changing magnetic flux	Eqs. 29.3, 29.8	V
$\mathcal{E}_{max}$	amplitude of emf	amplitude of time-dependent emf produced by AC source	Section 32.1, Eq. 32.1	V
$\mathcal{E}_{rms}$	rms emf	root-mean-square emf	Eq. 32.55	V
e	coefficient of restitution	measure of amount of initial relative speed recovered after collision	Eq. 5.18	unitless
e	eccentricity	measure of deviation of conic section from circular	Section 13.7	unitless
e	elementary charge	magnitude of charge on electron	Eq. 22.3	C
$\vec{F}$	force	time rate of change of object's momentum	Eq. 8.2	N
$\vec{F}^B$	magnetic force	force exerted on electric current or moving charged particle by magnetic field	Eqs. 27.8, 27.19	N
$\vec{F}^b$	buoyant force	upward force exerted by fluid on submerged object	Eq. 18.12	N
$\vec{F}^c$	contact force	force between objects in physical contact	Section 8.5	N

Symbol	Name of Quantity	Definition	Where Defined	SI units
$\vec{F}^d$	drag force	force exerted by medium on object moving through medium	Eq. 15.34	N
$\vec{F}^E$	electric force	force exerted between electrically charged objects or on electrically charged objects by electric field	Eq. 22.1	N
$\vec{F}^{EB}$	electromagnetic force	force exerted on electrically charged objects by electric and magnetic fields	Eq. 27.20	N
$\vec{F}^f$	frictional force	force exerted on object due to friction between it and a second object or surface	Eq. 9.26	N
$\vec{F}^G$	gravitational force	force exerted by Earth or any object having mass on any other object having mass	Eqs. 8.16, 13.1	N
$\vec{F}^k$	force of kinetic friction	frictional force between two objects in relative motion	Section 10.4, Eq. 10.55	N
$\vec{F}^n$	normal force	force directed perpendicular to a surface	Section 10.4, Eq. 10.46	N
$\vec{F}^s$	force of static friction	frictional force between two objects not in relative motion	Section 10.4, Eq. 10.46	N
f	frequency	number of cycles per second of periodic motion	Eq. 15.2	Hz
f	focal length	distance from center of lens to focus	Section 33.4, Eq. 33.16	m
f_{beat}	beat frequency	frequency at which beats occur when waves of different frequency interfere	Eq. 17.8	Hz
G	gravitational constant	proportionality constant relating gravitational force between two objects to their masses and separation	Eq. 13.1	$\text{N} \cdot \text{m}^2/\text{kg}^2$
g	magnitude of acceleration due to gravity	magnitude of acceleration of object in free fall near Earth's surface	Eq. 3.14	m/s^2
h	height	vertical distance	Eq. 10.26	m
h	Planck's constant	constant describing scale of quantum mechanics; relates photon energy to frequency and de Broglie wavelength to momentum of particle	Eq. 34.35	$\text{J} \cdot \text{s}$
I	rotational inertia	measure of object's resistance to change in its rotational velocity	Eq. 11.30	$\text{kg} \cdot \text{m}^2$
I	intensity	energy delivered by wave per unit time per unit area normal to direction of propagation	Eq. 17.1	W/m^2
I	(electric) current	rate at which charged particles cross a section of a conductor in a given direction	Eq. 27.2	A
I	amplitude of oscillating current	maximum value of oscillating current in circuit	Section 32.1, Eq. 32.5	A
I_{cm}	rotational inertia about center of mass	object's rotational inertia about an axis through its center of mass	Eq. 11.48	$\text{kg} \cdot \text{m}^2$
I_{disp}	displacement current	current-like quantity in Ampère's law caused by changing electric flux	Eq. 30.7	A
I_{enc}	enclosed current	current enclosed by Ampèrian path	Eq. 28.1	A
I_{ind}	induced current	current in loop caused by changing magnetic flux through loop	Eq. 29.4	A
I_{int}	intercepted current	current intercepted by surface spanning Ampèrian path	Eq. 30.6	A
I_{rms}	rms current	root-mean-square current	Eq. 32.53	A
I_{th}	intensity at threshold of hearing	minimum intensity audible to human ear	Eq. 17.4	W/m^2
i	time-dependent current	time-dependent current through circuit; $I(t)$	Section 32.1, Eq. 32.5	A
i	image distance	distance from lens to image	Section 33.6, Eq. 33.16	m

Symbol	Name of Quantity	Definition	Where Defined	SI units
$\hat{\imath}$	unit vector ("i hat")	vector for defining direction of x axis	Eq. 2.1	unitless
$\vec{J}$	impulse	amount of momentum transferred from environment to system	Eq. 4.18	$kg \cdot m/s$
$\vec{J}$	current density	current per unit area	Eq. 31.6	A/m^2
J_ϑ	rotational impulse	amount of angular momentum transferred from environment to system	Eq. 12.15	$kg \cdot m^2/s$
$\hat{\jmath}$	unit vector	vector for defining direction of y axis	Eq. 10.4	unitless
K	kinetic energy	energy object has because of its translational motion	Eqs. 5.12, 14.51	J
K	surface current density	current per unit of sheet width	Section 28.5	A/m
K_{cm}	translational kinetic energy	kinetic energy associated with motion of center of mass of system	Eq. 6.32	J
K_{conv}	convertible kinetic energy	kinetic energy that can be converted to internal energy without changing system's momentum	Eq. 6.33	J
K_{rot}	rotational kinetic energy	energy object has due to its rotational motion	Eq. 11.31	J
k	spring constant	ratio of force exerted on spring to displacement of free end of spring	Eq. 8.18	N/m
k	wave number	number of wavelengths in 2π units of distance; for wave with wavelength λ, $2\pi/\lambda$	Eqs. 16.7, 16.11	m^{-1}
k	Coulomb's law constant	constant relating electrostatic force to charges and their separation distance	Eq. 22.5	$N \cdot m^2/C^2$
k_B	Boltzmann constant	constant relating thermal energy to absolute temperature	Eq. 19.39	J/K
L	inductance	negative of ratio of induced emf around loop to rate of change of current in loop	Eq. 29.19	H
L_ϑ	(ϑ component of) angular momentum	capacity of object to make other objects rotate	Eq. 11.34	$kg \cdot m^2/s$
L_m	specific transformation energy for melting	energy transferred thermally per unit mass required to melt substance	Eq. 20.55	J/kg
L_v	specific transformation energy for vaporization	energy transferred thermally per unit mass required to vaporize substance	Eq. 20.55	J/kg
ℓ	length	distance or extent in space	Table 1.1	m
ℓ_{proper}	proper length	length measured by observer at rest relative to object	Section 14.3	m
ℓ_v	length	measured length of object moving at speed v relative to observer	Eq. 14.28	m
M	magnification	ratio of signed image height to object height	Eq. 33.17	unitless
M_θ	angular magnification	ratio of angle subtended by image to angle subtended by object	Eq. 33.18	unitless
m	mass	amount of substance	Table 1.1, Eq. 13.1	kg
m	inertia	measure of object's resistance to change in its velocity	Eq. 4.2	kg
m	fringe order	number indexing bright interference fringes, counting from central, zeroth-order bright fringe	Section 34.2, Eq. 34.5	unitless
m_v	inertia	inertia of object moving at speed v relative to observer	Eq. 14.41	kg
N	number of objects	number of objects in sample	Eq. 1.3	unitless
N_A	Avogadro's number	number of particles in 1 mol of a substance	Eq. 1.2	unitless
n	number density	number of objects per unit volume	Eq. 1.3	m^{-3}

Symbol	Name of Quantity	Definition	Where Defined	SI units
n	windings per unit length	in a solenoid, number of windings per unit length	Eq. 28.4	unitless
n	index of refraction	ratio of speed of light in vacuum to speed of light in a medium	Eq. 33.1	unitless
n	fringe order	number indexing dark interference fringes, counting from central, zeroth-order bright fringe	Section 34.2, Eq. 34.7	unitless
O	origin	origin of coordinate system	Section 10.2	
o	object distance	distance from lens to object	Section 33.6, Eq. 33.16	m
P	power	time rate at which energy is transferred or converted	Eq. 9.30	W
P	pressure	force per unit area exerted by fluid	Eq. 18.1	Pa
P_{atm}	atmospheric pressure	average pressure in Earth's atmosphere at sea level	Eq. 18.3	Pa
P_{gauge}	gauge pressure	pressure measured as difference between absolute pressure and atmospheric pressure	Eq. 18.16	Pa
p	time-dependent power	time-dependent rate at which source delivers energy to load; $P(t)$	Eq. 32.49	W
$\vec{p}$	momentum	vector that is product of an object's inertia and velocity	Eq. 4.6	$kg \cdot m/s$
$\vec{p}$	(electric) dipole moment	vector representing magnitude and direction of electric dipole, equal amounts of positive and negative charge separated by small distance	Eq. 23.9	$C \cdot m$
$\vec{p}_{ind}$	induced dipole moment	dipole moment induced in material by external electric field	Eq. 23.24	$C \cdot m$
p_x	x component of momentum	x component of momentum	Eq. 4.7	$kg \cdot m/s$
Q	quality factor	for damped oscillation, number of cycles for energy of oscillator to decrease by factor $e^{-2\pi}$	Eq. 15.41	unitless
Q	volume flow rate	rate at which volume of fluid crosses section of tube	Eq. 18.25	m^3/s
Q	energy transferred thermally	energy transferred into system by thermal interactions	Eq. 20.1	J
Q_{in}	thermal input of energy	positive amount of energy transferred into system by thermal interactions	Sections 21.1, 21.5	J
Q_{out}	thermal output of energy	positive amount of energy transferred out of system by thermal interactions	Sections 21.1, 21.5	J
q	electrical charge	attribute responsible for electromagnetic interactions	Eq. 22.1	C
q_{enc}	enclosed charge	sum of all charge within a closed surface	Eq. 24.8	C
q_p	dipole charge	charge of positively charged pole of dipole	Section 23.6	C
R	radius	radius of an object	Eq. 11.47	m
R	resistance	ratio of applied potential difference to resulting current	Eqs. 29.4, 31.10	Ω
R_{eq}	equivalent resistance	resistance that could be used to replace combination of circuit elements	Eqs. 31.26, 31.33	Ω
r	radial coordinate	polar coordinate measuring distance from origin of coordinate system	Eq. 10.1	m
$\vec{r}$	position	vector for determining position	Eqs. 2.9, 10.4	m
$\hat{r}_{12}$	unit vector ("r hat")	unit vector pointing from tip of $\vec{r}_1$ to tip of $\vec{r}_2$	Eq. 22.6	unitless
$\vec{r}_{AB}$	relative position	position of observer B in reference frame of observer A	Eq. 6.3	m
$\vec{r}_{Ae}$	relative position	value observer in reference frame A records for position at which event e occurs	Eq. 6.3	m

Symbol	Name of Quantity	Definition	Where Defined	SI units
$\vec{r}_{cm}$	position of a system's center of mass	a fixed position in a system that is independent of choice of reference frame	Eq. 6.24	m
$\vec{r}_{p}$	dipole separation	position of positively charged particle relative to negatively charged particle in dipole	Section 23.6	m
$r_{\perp}$	lever arm distance *or* lever arm	perpendicular distance between rotation axis and line of action of a vector	Eq. 11.36	m
$\Delta\vec{r}$	displacement	vector from object's initial to final position	Eq. 2.8	m
$\Delta\vec{r}_{F}$	force displacement	displacement of point of application of a force	Eq. 9.7	m
S	entropy	logarithm of number of basic states	Eq. 19.4	unitless
S	intensity	intensity of electromagnetic wave	Eq. 30.36	W/m^2
$\vec{S}$	Poynting vector	vector representing flow of energy in combined electric and magnetic fields	Eq. 30.37	W/m^2
s	arc length	distance along circular path	Eq. 11.1	m
s^2	space-time interval	invariant measure of separation of events in space-time	Eq. 14.18	m^2
T	period	time interval needed for object in circular motion to complete one revolution	Eq. 11.20	s
T	absolute temperature	quantity related to rate of change of entropy with respect to thermal energy	Eq. 19.38	K
$\mathcal{T}$	tension	stress in object subject to opposing forces stretching the object	Section 8.6	N
t	instant in time	physical quantity that allows us to determine the sequence of related events	Table 1.1	s
t_{Ae}	instant in time	value observer A measures for instant at which event e occurs	Eq. 6.1	s
Δt	interval of time	difference between final and initial instants	Table 2.2	s
Δt_{proper}	proper time interval	time interval between two events occurring at same position	Section 14.1	s
Δt_{v}	interval of time	time interval between two events measured by observer moving at speed v relative to an observer for whom the events occur at the same position	Eq. 14.13	s
U	potential energy	energy stored in reversible changes to system's configuration state	Eq. 7.7	J
U^{B}	magnetic potential energy	potential energy stored in magnetic field	Eqs. 29.25, 29.30	J
U^{E}	electric potential energy	potential energy due to relative position of charged objects	Eq. 25.8	J
U^{G}	gravitational potential energy	potential energy due to relative position of gravitationally interacting objects	Eqs. 7.13, 13.14	J
u_{B}	energy density of magnetic field	energy per unit volume stored in magnetic field	Eq. 29.29	J/m^3
u_{E}	energy density of electric field	energy per unit volume stored in electric field	Eq. 26.6	J/m^3
V	volume	amount of space occupied by an object	Table 1.1	m^3
V_{AB}	potential difference	negative of electrostatic work per unit charge done on charged particle as it is moved from point A to point B	Eq. 25.15	V
V_{batt}	battery potential difference	magnitude of potential difference between terminals of battery	Eq. 25.19	V
V_{C}	amplitude of oscillating potential	maximum magnitude of potential across circuit element C	Section 32.1, Eq. 32.8	V
V_{disp}	displaced volume	volume of fluid displaced by submerged object	Eq. 18.12	m^3

Symbol	Name of Quantity	Definition	Where Defined	SI units
V_P	(electrostatic) potential	potential difference between conveniently chosen reference point of potential zero and point P	Eq. 25.30	V
V_{rms}	rms potential	root-mean-square potential difference	Eq. 32.55	V
V_{stop}	stopping potential	minimum potential difference required to stop flow of electrons from photoelectric effect	Eq. 34.34	V
$\mathcal{V}$	"volume" in velocity space	measure of range of velocities in three dimensions	Eq. 19.20	$(m/s)^3$
v	speed	magnitude of velocity	Table 1.1	m/s
$\vec{v}$	velocity	time rate of change in position	Eq. 2.23	m/s
$\vec{v}_{12}$	relative velocity	velocity of object 2 relative to object 1	Eq. 5.1	m/s
$\vec{v}_{AB}$	relative velocity	velocity of observer B in reference frame of observer A	Eq. 6.3	m/s
v_C	time-dependent potential	time-dependent potential across circuit element C; $V_C(t)$	Section 32.1, Eq. 32.8	V
$\vec{v}_{cm}$	velocity, center of mass	velocity of the center of mass of a system, equal to the velocity of the zero-momentum reference frame of the system	Eq. 6.26	m/s
$\vec{v}_d$	drift velocity	average velocity of electrons in conductor in presence of electric field	Eq. 31.3	m/s
v_{esc}	escape speed	minimum launch speed required for object to reach infinity	Eq. 13.23	m/s
v_r	radial component of velocity	for object moving along circular path, always zero	Eq. 11.18	m/s
v_{rms}	root-mean-square speed	square root of average of square of speed	Eq. 19.21	m/s
v_t	tangential component of velocity	for object in circular motion, rate at which arc length is swept out	Eq. 11.9	m/s
v_x	x component of velocity	component of velocity directed along x axis	Eq. 2.21	m/s
W	work	change in system's energy due to external forces exerted on system	Eqs. 9.1, 10.35	J
$W_{P \to Q}$	work	work done along path from P to Q	Eq. 13.12	J
W_{in}	mechanical input of energy	positive amount of mechanical work done on system	Section 21.1	J
W_{out}	mechanical output of energy	positive amount of mechanical work done by system	Section 21.1	J
W_q	electrostatic work	work done by electrostatic field on charged particle moving through field	Section 25.2, Eq. 25.17	J
X_C	capacitive reactance	ratio of potential difference amplitude to current amplitude for capacitor	Eq. 32.14	Ω
X_L	inductive reactance	ratio of potential difference amplitude to current amplitude for inductor	Eq. 32.26	Ω
x	position	position along x axis	Eq. 2.4	m
$x(t)$	position as function of time	position x at instant t	Section 2.3	m
Δx	x component of displacement	difference between final and initial positions along x axis	Eq. 2.4	m
Δx_F	force displacement	displacement of point of application of a force	Eq. 9.7	m
Z	impedance	(frequency-dependent) ratio of potential difference to current through circuit	Eq. 32.33	Ω
z	zero-momentum reference frame	reference frame in which system of interest has zero momentum	Eq. 6.23	

Math notation

Math notation	Name	Where introduced
$\equiv$	defined as	Eq. 1.3
$\approx$	approximately equal to	Section 1.9
Σ (sigma, upper case)	sum of	Eq. 3.25
$\int$	integral of	Eq. 3.27
$\parallel$	parallel	Section 10.2
$\perp$	perpendicular	Section 10.2
$\propto$	proportional to	Section 13.1
$\cdot$	scalar product of two vectors	Eq. 10.33
$\times$	vector product of two vectors	Eq. 12.35
$\dfrac{\partial f}{\partial x}$	partial derivative of f with respect to x	Eq. 16.47
$\vec{b}$	vector b	Eq. 2.2
$\lvert \vec{b} \rvert$ or b	magnitude of $\vec{b}$	Eq. 2.3
b_x	x component of $\vec{b}$	Eq. 2.2
$\vec{b}_x$	x component vector of $\vec{b}$	Eq. 10.5
$\hat{i}$	unit vector ("i hat")	Eq. 2.1
$\hat{r}_{12}$	unit vector ("r hat")	Eq. 22.6

Note concerning superscripts and subscripts

Superscripts are appended to forces and potential energies to indicate the type of force or energy. They may be found in the main list under F, for forces, and U, for potential energies. Uppercase superscripts are used for fundamental interactions.

Subscripts are used on many symbols to identify objects, reference frames, types (for example, of energy), and processes. Object identifiers may be numbers, letters, or groups of letters. Reference frames are indicated by capital letters. Object identifiers and reference frames can occur in pairs, indicating relative quantities. In this case, the main symbol describes a property of whatever is identified by the second subscript relative to that of the first. In the case of forces, the first subscript identifies the object that causes the force and the second identifies the object on which the force is exerted. Types and processes are identified in various ways; many are given in the main list. Here are some examples:

m_1	inertia of object 1
m_{ball}	inertia of ball
$\vec{v}_{\text{cm}}$	velocity of center of mass of system

$\vec{r}_{12}$	position of object 2 relative to object 1; $\vec{r}_{12} = \vec{r}_2 - \vec{r}_1$
$\vec{p}_1$	momentum of object 1
$\vec{p}_{Z2}$	momentum of object 2 as measured in zero-momentum reference frame
$\vec{v}_{AB}$	velocity of observer B as measured in reference frame of observer A
$\vec{v}_{Ao}$	velocity of object o as measured in reference frame A
$\vec{r}_{Ee}$	position of event e as measured in Earth reference frame
$\vec{F}^{c}_{pw}$	contact force exerted by person on wall
$\vec{F}^{G}_{Eb}$	gravitational force exerted by Earth on ball
E_{th}	thermal energy
K_{conv}	convertible kinetic energy
P_{av}	average power
a_{c}	centripetal acceleration
$W_{P \to Q}$	work done along path from P to Q

Initial and final conditions are identified by subscripts i and f, following other identifiers. For example:

$\vec{p}_{1i}$	initial momentum of object 1
$\vec{p}_{Z\text{ball},f}$	final momentum of ball as measured in zero-momentum reference frame

Italic subscripts are used to identify components of vectors. These include x, y, z, r (radial), t (tangential), and ϑ (angular, with respect to given axis). They are also used to enumerate collections, for example, as indices of summation, and to indicate that a subscript refers to another variable. Here are some examples:

r_x	x component of position
a_t	tangential component of acceleration
L_ϑ	ϑ component of angular momentum
$p_{Z\text{ball}\,y,f}$	final y component of momentum of ball as measured in zero-momentum reference frame
$\delta m_n r_n^2$	contribution to rotational inertia of extended object of small segment n, with inertia δm_n at position r_n
c_P	specific heat capacity at constant pressure
W_q	electrostatic work

Appendix B

Mathematics Review

1 Algebra

Factors

$$ax + bx + cx = (a + b + c)x$$
$$(a + b)^2 = a^2 + 2ab + b^2$$
$$(a - b)^2 = a^2 - 2ab + b^2$$
$$(a + b)(a - b) = a^2 - b^2$$

Fractions

$$\left(\frac{a}{b}\right)\left(\frac{c}{d}\right) = \frac{ac}{bd}$$

$$\left(\frac{a/b}{c/d}\right) = \frac{a}{b} \div \frac{c}{d} = \frac{a}{b} \cdot \frac{d}{c} = \frac{ad}{bc}$$

$$\left(\frac{1}{1/a}\right) = a$$

Exponents

$$a^n = \underbrace{a \times a \times a \times \cdots \times a}_{n \text{ factors}}$$

Any real number can be used as an exponent:

$$a^{-x} = \frac{1}{a^x}$$

$$a^0 = 1$$

$$a^1 = a$$

$$a^{1/2} = \sqrt{a}$$

$$a^{1/n} = \sqrt[n]{a}$$

$$a^x a^y = a^{x+y}$$

$$\frac{a^x}{a^y} = a^{x-y}$$

$$(a^x)^y = a^{x \cdot y}$$

$$a^x b^x = (ab)^x$$

$$\frac{a^x}{b^x} = \left(\frac{a}{b}\right)^x$$

Logarithms

Logarithm is the inverse function of the exponential function:

$$y = a^x \Leftrightarrow \log_a y = \log_a a^x = x \quad \text{and} \quad x = \log_a(a^x) = a^{\log_a x}$$

The two most common values for the base a are 10 (the common logarithm base) and e (the natural logarithm base).

$$y = e^x \Leftrightarrow \log_e y = \ln y = \ln e^x = x \quad \text{and} \quad x = \ln e^x = e^{\ln x}$$

Logarithm rules (valid for any base):

$$\ln(ab) = \ln(a) + \ln(b)$$

$$\ln\left(\frac{a}{b}\right) = \ln(a) - \ln(b)$$

$$\ln(a^n) = n\ln(a)$$

$$\ln 1 = 0$$

The expression $\ln(a + b)$ cannot be simplified.

Linear equations

A linear equation has the form $y = ax + b$, where a and b are constants. A graph of y versus x is a straight line. The value of a equals the slope of the line, and the value of b equals the value of y when x equals zero.

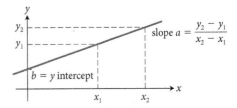

If $a = 0$, the line is horizontal. If $a > 0$, the line rises as x increases. If $a < 0$, the line falls as x increases. For any two values of x, say x_1 and x_2, the slope a can be calculated as

$$a = \frac{y_2 - y_1}{x_2 - x_1}$$

where y_1 and y_2 correspond to x_1 and x_2 (that is to say, $y_1 = ax_1 + b$ and $y_2 = ax_2 + b$).

Proportionality

If y is proportional to x (written $y \propto x$), then $y = ax$, where a is a constant. Proportionality is a subset of linearity. Because $y/x = a = $ constant for any corresponding x and y,

$$\frac{y_1}{x_1} = \frac{y_2}{x_2} \Leftrightarrow \frac{y_1}{y_2} = \frac{x_1}{x_2}.$$

Quadratic equation

The equation $ax^2 + bx + c = 0$ (the quadratic equation) has two solutions (called *roots*) for x:

$$x = \frac{-b \pm \sqrt{b^2 - 4ac}}{2a}$$

If $b^2 \geq 4ac$, the solutions are real numbers.

2 Geometry

Area and circumference for two-dimensional shapes

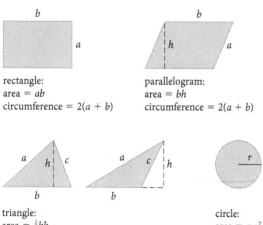

rectangle:
area = ab
circumference = $2(a + b)$

parallelogram:
area = bh
circumference = $2(a + b)$

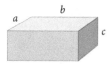

triangle:
area = $\frac{1}{2}bh$
circumference = $a + b + c$

circle:
area = πr^2
circumference = $2\pi r$

Volume and area for three-dimensional shapes

rectangular box:
volume = abc
area = $2(a^2 + b^2 + c^2)$

sphere:
volume = $\frac{4}{3}\pi r^3$
area = $4\pi r^2$

right circular cylinder:
volume = $\pi r^2 \ell$
area = $2\pi r \ell + 2\pi r^2$

right circular cone:
volume = $\frac{1}{3}\pi r^2 h$
area = $\pi r^2 + \pi r \sqrt{r^2 + h^2}$

3 Trigonometry

Angle and arc length

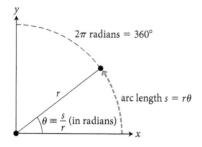

2π radians = $360°$

arc length $s = r\theta$

$\theta \equiv \dfrac{s}{r}$ (in radians)

Right triangles

A right triangle is a triangle in which one of the angles is a right angle:

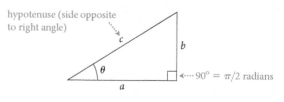

hypotenuse (side opposite to right angle)

$90° = \pi/2$ radians

Pythagorean theorem: $a^2 + b^2 = c^2 \Leftrightarrow c = \sqrt{a^2 + b^2}$

Trigonometric functions:

$$\sin\theta = \frac{b}{c} = \frac{\text{opposite side}}{\text{hypotenuse}}, \quad \theta = \sin^{-1}\left(\frac{b}{c}\right) = \arcsin\left(\frac{b}{c}\right)$$

$$\cos\theta = \frac{a}{c} = \frac{\text{adjacent side}}{\text{hypotenuse}}, \quad \theta = \cos^{-1}\left(\frac{a}{c}\right) = \arccos\left(\frac{a}{c}\right)$$

$$\tan\theta = \frac{b}{a} = \frac{\text{opposite side}}{\text{adjacent side}}, \quad \theta = \tan^{-1}\left(\frac{b}{a}\right) = \arctan\left(\frac{b}{a}\right)$$

General triangles

For any triangle, the following relationships hold:

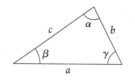

$$\alpha + \beta + \gamma = 180° = \pi \text{ rad}$$

Sine law: $\dfrac{\sin\alpha}{a} = \dfrac{\sin\beta}{b} = \dfrac{\sin\gamma}{c}$

Cosine law: $c^2 = a^2 + b^2 - 2ab\cos\gamma$

Identities

$$\tan\theta = \frac{\sin\theta}{\cos\theta}$$

$$\cot\theta = \frac{1}{\tan\theta} = \frac{\cos\theta}{\sin\theta}$$

$$\csc\theta = \frac{1}{\sin\theta}$$

$$\sec\theta = \frac{1}{\cos\theta}$$

Periodicity

$$\cos(\alpha + 2\pi) = \cos\alpha$$

$$\tan(\alpha + \pi) = \tan\alpha$$

Angle addition

$$\sin(\alpha \pm \beta) = \sin\alpha\cos\beta \pm \cos\alpha\sin\beta$$

$$\cos(\alpha \pm \beta) = \cos\alpha\cos\beta \mp \sin\alpha\sin\beta$$

Double angles

$$\sin(2\alpha) = 2\sin\alpha\cos\alpha$$

$$\cos(2\alpha) = \cos^2\alpha - \sin^2\alpha = 1 - 2\sin^2\alpha = 2\cos^2\alpha - 1$$

Other relations

$$\sin^2\alpha + \cos^2\alpha = 1$$

$$\sin(-\alpha) = -\sin\alpha$$

$$\cos(-\alpha) = \cos\alpha$$

$$\sin(\alpha \pm \pi) = -\sin\alpha$$

$$\cos(\alpha \pm \pi) = -\cos\alpha$$

$$\sin(\alpha \pm \pi/2) = \pm\cos\alpha$$

$$\cos(\alpha \pm \pi/2) = \mp\sin\alpha$$

The following graphs show $\sin\theta$, $\cos\theta$, and $\tan\theta$ as functions of θ:

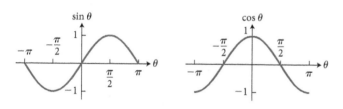

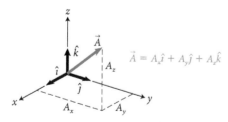

4 Vector algebra

A vector $\vec{A}$ in three-dimensional space can be written in terms of magnitudes A_x, A_y, and A_z of unit vectors $\hat{\imath}$, $\hat{\jmath}$, and $\hat{k}$, which have length 1 and lie along the x, y, and z axes:

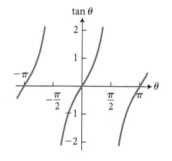

$$\vec{A} = A_x\hat{\imath} + A_y\hat{\jmath} + A_z\hat{k}$$

Dot products between vectors produce scalars:

$$\vec{A} \cdot \vec{B} = A_xB_x + A_yB_y + A_zB_z = |A||B|\cos\theta$$
$$(\theta \text{ is the angle between vectors } \vec{A} \text{ and } \vec{B})$$

Cross products between vectors produce vectors:

$$\vec{A} \times \vec{B} = (A_yB_z - A_zB_y)\hat{\imath} + (A_zB_x - A_xB_z)\hat{\jmath} + (A_xB_y - A_yB_x)\hat{k}$$

$$|\vec{A} \times \vec{B}| = |\vec{A}||\vec{B}|\sin\theta \ (\theta \text{ is the angle between vectors } \vec{A} \text{ and } \vec{B})$$

The direction of $\vec{A} \times \vec{B}$ is given by the right-hand rule (see Figure 12.44).

5 Calculus

In this section, x is a variable, and a and n are constants.

Derivatives

Geometrically, the derivative of a function $f(x)$ at $x = x_1$ is the slope of $f(x)$ at x_1:

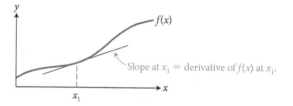

Slope at x_1 = derivative of $f(x)$ at x_1.

Derivatives of common functions

$$\frac{d}{dx}a = 0$$

$$\frac{d}{dx}x^n = nx^{n-1} \ (n \text{ need not be an integer})$$

$$\frac{d}{dx}\sin x = \cos x$$

$$\frac{d}{dx}\cos x = -\sin x$$

$$\frac{d}{dx}\tan x = \frac{1}{\cos^2 x}$$

$$\frac{d}{dx}e^{ax} = ae^{ax}$$

$$\frac{d}{dx}\ln(ax) = \frac{1}{x}$$

$$\frac{d}{dx}a^x = a^x\ln a$$

Derivatives of sums, products, and functions of functions

Constant times a function: $\dfrac{d}{dx}[a \cdot f(x)] = a \cdot \dfrac{d}{dx}f(x)$

Sum of functions: $\dfrac{d}{dx}[f(x) + g(x)] = \dfrac{d}{dx}f(x) + \dfrac{d}{dx}g(x)$

Product of functions:

$$\frac{d}{dx}[f(x) \cdot g(x)] = g(x)\frac{d}{dx}f(x) + f(x)\frac{d}{dx}g(x)$$

Quotient of functions: $\dfrac{d}{dx}\left[\dfrac{f(x)}{g(x)}\right] = \dfrac{g(x)\dfrac{d}{dx}f(x) - f(x)\dfrac{d}{dx}g(x)}{[g(x)]^2}$

Functions of functions (the chain rule): If f is a function of u, and u is a function of x, then

$$\frac{d[f(u)]}{du} \cdot \frac{d[u(x)]}{dx} = \frac{d[f(x)]}{dx}$$

Second and higher derivatives The second derivative of a function f with respect to x is the derivative of the derivative:

$$\frac{d^2 f(x)}{dx^2} = \frac{d}{dx}\left(\frac{d}{dx}f(x)\right)$$

Higher derivatives are defined similarly:

$$\frac{d^n f(x)}{dx^n} = \underbrace{\cdots\frac{d}{dx}\left(\frac{d}{dx}\left(\frac{d}{dx}f(x)\right)\right)}_{n \text{ uses of } \frac{d}{dx}} \quad \text{(where } n \text{ is a positive integer).}$$

Partial derivatives For functions of more than one variable, the partial derivative, written $\frac{\partial}{\partial x}$, is the derivative with respect to one variable; all other variables are treated as constants.

Integrals

Indefinite integrals Integration is the reverse of differentiation. An indefinite integral $\int f(x)dx$ is a function whose derivative is $f(x)$.

That is to say, $\frac{d}{dx}\left[\int f(x)dx\right] = f(x)$.

If $A(x)$ is an indefinite integral of $f(x)$, then so is $A(x) + C$, where C is any constant. Thus, it is customary when evaluating indefinite integrals to add a "constant of integration" C.

Definite integrals The definite integral of $f(x)$, written as $\int_{x1}^{x2} f(x)dx$, represents the sum of the area of contiguous rectangles that each intersect $f(x)$ at some point along one base and that each have another base coincident with the x axis over some part of the range between x_1 and x_2; the indefinite integral evaluates the sum in the limit of arbitrarily small rectangle bases. In other words, the indefinite integral gives the net area that lies under $f(x)$ but above the x axis between the boundaries x_1 and x_2.

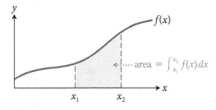

If $A(x)$ is any indefinite integral of $f(x)$, then the definite integral is given by $\int_{x1}^{x2} f(x)dx = A(x_2) - A(x_1) \equiv A(x)|_{x_1}^{x_2}$. The constant of integration C does not affect the value of definite integrals and thus can be ignored (i.e., set to zero) during evaluation.

Integration by parts $\int_a^b u\,dv$ is the area under the curve of $u(v)$. If $\int_a^b u\,dv$ is difficult to evaluate directly, it is sometimes easier to express the area under the curve as the area within part of a rectangle minus the area under the curve of $v(u)$. In other words:

$$\int_a^b u\,dv = uv|_a^b - \int_a^b v\,du.$$

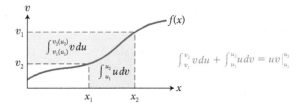

By choosing u and dv appropriately (both can be functions of x), this approach, called "integration by parts", can transform difficult integrals into easier ones.

Table of integrals In the following expressions, a and b are constants. An arbitrary constant of integration C can be added to the right-hand side.

$$\int x^n dx = \frac{1}{n+1}x^{n+1} \text{ (for } n \neq -1)$$

$$\int x^{-1}dx = \ln|x|$$

$$\int \frac{1}{a^2 + x^2}dx = \frac{1}{a}\tan^{-1}\frac{x}{a}$$

$$\int \frac{1}{(a^2 + x^2)^2}dx = \frac{1}{2a^3}\tan^{-1}\frac{x}{a} + \frac{x}{2a^2(x^2 + a^2)}$$

$$\int \frac{1}{\sqrt{\pm a^2 + x^2}}dx = \ln|x + \sqrt{\pm a^2 + x^2}|$$

$$\int \frac{1}{\sqrt{a^2 - x^2}}dx = \sin^{-1}\frac{x}{|a|} = \tan^{-1}\frac{x}{\sqrt{a^2 - x^2}}$$

$$\int \frac{x}{\sqrt{\pm a^2 - x^2}}dx = -\sqrt{\pm a^2 - x^2}$$

$$\int \frac{x}{\sqrt{\pm a^2 + x^2}}dx = \sqrt{\pm a^2 + x^2}$$

$$\int \frac{1}{(\pm a^2 + x^2)^{3/2}}dx = \frac{\pm x}{a^2\sqrt{\pm a^2 + x^2}}$$

$$\int \frac{x}{(a^2 + x^2)^{3/2}}dx = -\frac{1}{\sqrt{a^2 + x^2}}$$

$$\int \frac{1}{a + bx}dx = \frac{1}{b}\ln(a + bx)$$

$$\int \frac{1}{(a + bx)^2}dx = -\frac{1}{b(a + bx)}$$

$$\int \sin(ax)dx = -\frac{1}{a}\cos(ax)$$

$$\int \cos(ax)dx = \frac{1}{a}\sin(ax)$$

$$\int \tan(ax)dx = -\frac{1}{a}\ln(\cos ax)$$

$$\int \sin^2(ax)dx = \frac{x}{2} - \frac{\sin 2ax}{4a}$$

$$\int \cos^2(ax)dx = \frac{x}{2} + \frac{\sin 2ax}{4a}$$

$$\int x\sin(ax)dx = \frac{1}{a^2}\sin ax - \frac{1}{a}x\cos ax$$

$$\int x\cos(ax)dx = \frac{1}{a^2}\cos ax + \frac{1}{a}x\sin ax$$

$$\int e^{ax}dx = \frac{1}{a}e^{ax}$$

$$\int xe^{ax}dx = \frac{e^{ax}}{a^2}(ax - 1)$$

$$\int x^2 e^{ax}dx = \frac{x^2 e^{ax}}{a} - \frac{2}{a}\left[\frac{e^{ax}}{a^2}(ax - 1)\right]$$

$$\int \ln ax\,dx = x\ln(ax) - x$$

$$\int_0^\infty x^n e^{-ax}dx = \frac{n!}{a^{n+1}}$$

$$\int_0^\infty e^{-ax^2}dx = \frac{1}{2}\sqrt{\frac{\pi}{a}}$$

Line integrals. A *line integral* is an integral of a function that needs to be evaluated over a path (that is, a curve connecting two points in space). Consider, for example, the two-dimensional path C from point A to point B in the figure below. (The procedure described below is equally applicable in three dimensions.)

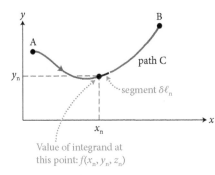

The path from A to B is *directed*: At any point the direction along the path away from A and toward B is forward (positive). Suppose we have a function $f(x, y, z)$ defined everywhere along the path. The function can be either a scalar or a vector; we will first discuss line integrals of scalar functions. We divide the path between A and B into small segments of length $\delta\ell_n$, each segment small enough that we can consider it essentially straight and small enough that the value of the function $f(x, y, z)$ can be considered constant over that segment. We then calculate the product $f(x_n, y_n, z_n)\delta\ell_n$ for each segment. The line integral of the function $f(x, y, z)$ along path C is then given by the sum of all those products along the path in the limit of infinitesimally small segments:

$$\int_C f(x, y, z)d\ell = \lim_{\delta\ell \to \infty} \sum_n f(x_n, y_n, z_n)\delta\ell_n.$$

To evaluate the integral on the right, we need to know the path C. Usually the path is specified in terms of the length parameter ℓ: $x = x(\ell)$, $y = y(\ell)$, $z = z(\ell)$. The line integral can then be written as an ordinary definite integral:

$$\int_C f(x, y, z)d\ell = \int_A^B f[x(\ell), y(\ell), z(\ell)]d\ell.$$

Next we consider the line integral of a vector function. We consider the same path C from A to B, but now we consider a vector function $\vec{F}(x, y, z)$. Instead of taking infinitesimally small scalar segments $d\ell_n$ along the path, we take small vector segments $d\vec{\ell}_n$ along the path, of length $d\ell_n$ and whose direction is tangent to the path in the direction of the path from A to B:

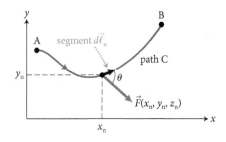

At each point we calculate the scalar product $\vec{F}(x_n, y_n, z_n) \cdot d\vec{\ell}_n$ and then sum these products over path C to obtain the line integral.

$$\int_C \vec{F}(x, y, z) \cdot d\vec{\ell}.$$

By writing out the scalar product, $\vec{F}(x, y, z) \cdot d\vec{\ell} = F(x, y, z)\cos\theta\,d\ell$, we can reduce the line integral of a vector function to that of a scalar function:

$$\int_C \vec{F}(x, y, z) \cdot d\vec{\ell} = \int_C F(x, y, z)\cos\theta\,d\ell.$$

In other words, we need to compute the line integral of the component of the vector $\vec{F}(x, y, z)$ along the tangent to the path.

If the path is closed—that is, the path returns to the starting point—we indicate that by putting a circle through the integration sign:

$$\oint_C \vec{F}(x, y, z) \cdot d\vec{\ell}.$$

Surface integrals. A *surface integral* is an integral of a function that needs to be evaluated over a surface. As with line integrals, the integrand of a surface integral can be a scalar or a vector function. We will only discuss the more general case of a vector function here.

The surface over which the integration is to be taken can be either *closed* or *open*. A closed surface, such as the surface of a sphere, divides space into two parts—an inside and an outside—and to get from one part to the other one has to go through the surface. An open surface does not have this property: For the surface S shown in the figure below, for example, one can go from one side of the surface to the other without passing through it.

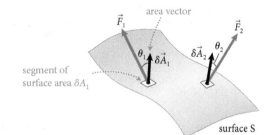

area vector

$\vec{F}_1$

$\vec{F}_2$

θ_1 $\delta\vec{A}_1$ $\delta\vec{A}_2$ θ_2

segment of
surface area δA_1

surface S

Consider a vector function $\vec{F}(x, y, z)$. To calculate the surface integral of this function over surface S, we begin by dividing the surface into small segments of surface area δA_n, each segment being small enough that we can consider it to be essentially flat and small enough so that the function $\vec{F}(x, y, z)$ can be considered constant over the segment. We then define an *area vector* $\delta\vec{A}_n$ whose magnitude is equal to the surface area δA_n of the segment and whose direction is normal to that segment. For each segment we then calculate the scalar product of the area vector and the value $\vec{F}_n$ of the vector function at that location: $\vec{F}_n(x_n, y_n, z_n) \cdot \delta\vec{A}_n$. The surface integral of the vector function over the surface S is then given by the sum of all those products for all the segments that make up the surface:

$$\int_S \vec{F}(x, y, z) \cdot d\vec{A} = \lim_{\delta\vec{A}_n \to \infty} \sum_n \vec{F}_n(x_n, y_n, z_n) \cdot \delta\vec{A}_n.$$

If the surface is closed, we indicate that by putting a circle through the integration sign:

$$\oint_S \vec{F}(x, y, z) \cdot d\vec{A}$$

6 Complex numbers

A complex number $z = x + iy$ is defined in terms of its real part x and its imaginary part y. Both x and y are real numbers. i is Euler's constant, defined by the property $i^2 = -1$.

Each complex number z has a "complex conjugate" z^* which has the same real part but an imaginary part with opposite sign: $z = x + iy \Leftrightarrow z^* = x - iy$.

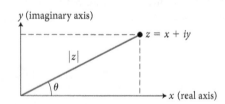

y (imaginary axis)

$z = x + iy$

$|z|$

θ

x (real axis)

The real and imaginary parts can be expressed in terms of the complex number and its conjugate:

$$x = \tfrac{1}{2}(z + z^*)$$

$$y = \tfrac{1}{2i}(z - z^*)$$

A complex number is like a two-dimensional vector in a plane with a real axis and an imaginary axis. Thus, z can be described by a magnitude or length $|z|$ and an angle θ formed with the real axis (called the "phase angle"):

$$z = |z|(\cos\theta + i\sin\theta), \text{ where } |z| = \sqrt{zz^*} \text{ and}$$

$$\theta = \tan^{-1}\frac{y}{x} = \tan^{-1}\frac{(z - z^*)}{i(z + z^*)}.$$

Euler's formula says that $e^{i\theta} = \cos\theta + i\sin\theta$, allowing complex numbers to be written in the form $z = |z|e^{i\theta}$. This is a convenient form for expressing complex numbers. For example, it is easy to raise a complex number z to a power n: $z^n = |z|^n e^{in\theta}$.

7 Useful approximations

Binomial expansion

$$(1 + x)^n = 1 + nx + \frac{n(n-1)}{2}x^2 + \cdots$$

If $x \ll 1$, then $(1 + x)^n \approx 1 + nx$

Trigonometric expansions

$$\sin\alpha = \alpha - \frac{\alpha^3}{3!} + \frac{\alpha^5}{5!} - \frac{\alpha^7}{7!} + \cdots \ (\alpha \text{ in rad})$$

$$\cos\alpha = 1 - \frac{\alpha^2}{2!} + \frac{\alpha^4}{4!} - \frac{\alpha^6}{6!} + \cdots \ (\alpha \text{ in rad})$$

$$\tan\alpha = \alpha + \frac{1}{3}\alpha^3 + \frac{2}{15}\alpha^5 + \frac{17}{315}\alpha^7 + \cdots \ (\alpha \text{ in rad})$$

If $\alpha \ll 1$ rad, then $\sin\alpha \approx \alpha$, $\cos\alpha \approx 1$, and $\tan\alpha \approx \alpha$.

Other useful expansions

$$\frac{1}{1 - x} = 1 + x + x^2 + x^3 + \cdots \text{ for } -1 < x < 1$$

$$e^x = 1 + x + \frac{1}{2}x^2 + \frac{1}{6}x^3 + \frac{1}{24}x^4 + \cdots$$

$$\ln(1 + x) = x - \frac{1}{2}x^2 + \frac{1}{3}x^3 - \frac{1}{4}x^4 + \cdots \quad \text{for } -1 < x < 1$$

$$\ln\left(\frac{1 + x}{1 + x}\right) = 2x + \frac{2}{3}x^3 + \frac{2}{5}x^5 - \frac{2}{7}x^7 + \cdots \quad \text{for } -1 < x < 1$$

Appendix C

SI Units, Useful Data, and Unit Conversion Factors

The seven base SI units

Unit	Abbreviation	Physical quantity
meter	m	length
kilogram	kg	mass
second	s	time
ampere	A	electric current
kelvin	K	thermodynamic temperature
mole	mol	amount of substance
candela	cd	luminous intensity

Some derived SI units

Unit	Abbreviation	Physical quantity	In terms of base units
newton	N	force	$kg \cdot m/s^2$
joule	J	energy	$kg \cdot m^2/s^2$
watt	W	power	$kg \cdot m^2/s^3$
pascal	Pa	pressure	$kg/m \cdot s^2$
hertz	Hz	frequency	s^{-1}
coulomb	C	electric charge	$A \cdot s$
volt	V	electric potential	$kg \cdot m^2/(A \cdot s^3)$
ohm	Ω	electric resistance	$kg \cdot m^2/(A^2 \cdot s^3)$
farad	F	capacitance	$A^2 \cdot s^4/(kg \cdot m^2)$
tesla	T	magnetic field	$kg/(A \cdot s^2)$
weber	Wb	magnetic flux	$kg \cdot m^2/(A \cdot s^2)$
henry	H	inductance	$kg \cdot m^2/(A^2 \cdot s^2)$

SI Prefixes

10^n	Prefix	Abbreviation	10^n	Prefix	Abbreviation
10^0	—	—			
10^3	kilo-	k	10^{-3}	milli-	m
10^6	mega-	M	10^{-6}	micro-	μ
10^9	giga-	G	10^{-9}	nano-	n
10^{12}	tera-	T	10^{-12}	pico-	p
10^{15}	peta-	P	10^{-15}	femto-	f
10^{18}	exa-	E	10^{-18}	atto-	a
10^{21}	zetta-	Z	10^{-21}	zepto-	z
10^{24}	yotta-	Y	10^{-24}	yocto-	y

Values of fundamental constants

Quantity	Symbol	Value
Speed of light in vacuum	c_0	3.00×10^8 m/s
Gravitational constant	G	6.6738×10^{-11} N $\cdot$ m^2/kg^2
Avogadro's number	N_A	6.0221413×10^{23}
Boltzmann's constant	k_B	1.381×10^{-23} J/K
Charge on electron	e	1.60×10^{-19} C
Electric constant	ϵ_0	$8.85418782 \times 10^{-12}$ C^2/(N $\cdot$ m^2)
Magnetic constant	μ_0	$4\pi \times 10^{-7}$ T $\cdot$ m/A
Planck's constant	h	6.626×10^{-34} J $\cdot$ s
Electron mass	m_e	9.11×10^{-31} kg
Proton mass	m_p	1.6726×10^{-27} kg
Neutron mass	m_n	1.6749×10^{-27} kg
Atomic mass unit	amu	1.6605×10^{-27} kg

Other useful numbers

Number or quantity	Value
π	3.1415927
e	2.7182818
1 radian	57.2957795°
Absolute zero ($T = 0$)	-273.15 °C
Average acceleration g due to gravity near Earth's surface	9.8 m/s^2
Speed of sound in air at 20 °C	343 m/s
Density of dry air at atmospheric pressure and 20 °C	1.29 kg/m^3
Earth's mass	5.97×10^{24} kg
Earth's radius (mean)	6.38×10^6 m
Earth–Moon distance (mean)	3.84×10^8 m

Unit conversion factors

Length

1 in. = 2.54 cm (defined)

1 cm = 0.3937 in.

1 ft = 30.48 cm

1 m = 39.37 in. = 3.281 ft

1 mi = 5280 ft = 1.609 km

1 km = 0.6214 mi

1 nautical mile (U.S.) = 1.151 mi = 6076 ft = 1.852 km

1 fermi = 1 femtometer (fm) = 10^{-15} m

1 angstrom (Å) = 10^{-10} m = 0.1 nm

1 light − year (ly) = 9.461×10^{15} m

1 parsec = 3.26 ly = 3.09×10^{16} m

Volume

1 liter (L) = 1000 mL = 1000 cm^3 = 1.0×10^{-3} m^3
     = 1.057 qt (U.S.) = 61.02 $in.^3$

1 gal (U.S.) = 4 qt (U.S.) = 231 $in.^3$ = 3.785 L = 0.8327 gal (British)

1 quart (U.S.) = 2 pints (U.S.) = 946 mL

1 pint (British) = 1.20 pints (U.S.) = 568 mL

1 m^3 = 35.31 ft^3

Speed

1 mi/h = 1.4667 ft/s = 1.6093 km/h = 0.4470 m/s

1 km/h = 0.2778 m/s = 0.6214 mi/h

1 ft/s = 0.3048 m/s = 0.6818 mi/h = 1.0973 km/h

1 m/s = 3.281 ft/s = 3.600 km/h = 2.237 mi/h

1 knot = 1.151 mi/h = 0.5144 m/s

Angle

1 radian (rad) = 57.30° = 57°18'

1° = 0.01745 rad

1 rev/min (rpm) = 0.1047 rad/s

Time

1 day = 8.640×10^4 s

1 year = 365.242 days = 3.156×10^7 s

Mass

1 atomic mass unit (u) = 1.6605×10^{-27} kg

1 kg = 0.06852 slug

1 metric ton = 1000 kg

1 long ton = 2240 lbs = 1016 kg

1 short ton = 2000 lbs = 909.1 kg

1 kg has a weight of 2.20 lb where g = 9.80 m/s^2

Force

1 lb = 4.44822 N

1 N = 10^5 dyne = 0.2248 lb

Energy and work

1 J = 10^7 ergs = 0.7376 ft · lb

1 ft · lb = 1.356 J = 1.29×10^{-3} Btu = 3.24×10^{-4} kcal

1 kcal = 4.19×10^3 J = 3.97 Btu

1 eV = 1.6022×10^{-19} J

1 kWh = 3.600×10^6 J = 860 kcal

1 Btu = 1.056×10^3 J

Power

1 W = 1 J/s = 0.7376 ft · lb/s = 3.41 Btu/h

1 hp = 550 ft · lb/s = 746 W

1 kWh/day = 41.667 W

Pressure

1 atm = 1.01325 bar = 1.01325×10^5 N/m^2 = 14.7 $lb/in.^2$ = 760 torr

1 $lb/in.^2$ = 6.895×10^3 N/m^2

1 Pa = 1 N/m^2 = 1.450×10^{-4} $lb/in.^2$

Periodic Table of the Elements

Group	1	2	3	4	5	6	7	8	9	10	11	12	13	14	15	16	17	18
Period 1	1 **H** 1.008																	2 **He** 4.003
Period 2	3 **Li** 6.941	4 **Be** 9.012											5 **B** 10.811	6 **C** 12.011	7 **N** 14.007	8 **O** 15.999	9 **F** 18.998	10 **Ne** 20.180
Period 3	11 **Na** 22.990	12 **Mg** 24.305											13 **Al** 26.982	14 **Si** 28.086	15 **P** 30.974	16 **S** 32.065	17 **Cl** 35.453	18 **Ar** 39.948
Period 4	19 **K** 39.098	20 **Ca** 40.078	21 **Sc** 44.956	22 **Ti** 47.867	23 **V** 50.942	24 **Cr** 51.996	25 **Mn** 54.938	26 **Fe** 55.845	27 **Co** 58.933	28 **Ni** 58.693	29 **Cu** 63.546	30 **Zn** 65.409	31 **Ga** 69.723	32 **Ge** 72.64	33 **As** 74.922	34 **Se** 78.96	35 **Br** 79.904	36 **Kr** 83.798
Period 5	37 **Rb** 85.468	38 **Sr** 87.62	39 **Y** 88.906	40 **Zr** 91.224	41 **Nb** 92.906	42 **Mo** 95.94	43 **Tc** (98)	44 **Ru** 101.07	45 **Rh** 102.906	46 **Pd** 106.42	47 **Ag** 107.868	48 **Cd** 112.411	49 **In** 114.818	50 **Sn** 118.710	51 **Sb** 121.760	52 **Te** 127.60	53 **I** 126.904	54 **Xe** 131.293
Period 6	55 **Cs** 132.905	56 **Ba** 137.327	71 **Lu** 174.967	72 **Hf** 178.49	73 **Ta** 180.948	74 **W** 183.84	75 **Re** 186.207	76 **Os** 190.23	77 **Ir** 192.217	78 **Pt** 195.078	79 **Au** 196.967	80 **Hg** 200.59	81 **Tl** 204.383	82 **Pb** 207.2	83 **Bi** 208.980	84 **Po** (209)	85 **At** (210)	86 **Rn** (222)
Period 7	87 **Fr** (223)	88 **Ra** (226)	103 **Lr** (262)	104 **Rf** (261)	105 **Db** (262)	106 **Sg** (266)	107 **Bh** (264)	108 **Hs** (269)	109 **Mt** (268)	110 **Ds** (271)	111 **Rg** (272)	112 **Uub** (285)	113 **Uut** (284)	114 **Uuq** (289)	115 **Uup** (288)	116 **Uuh** (292)	117 **Uus** (294)	118 **Uuo**

Number of protons → 29
Symbol for element → **Cu**
63.546

Average atomic mass in g/mol. For elements having no stable isotope, value in parentheses is approximate atomic mass of longest-lived isotope.

Lanthanoids

57 **La** 138.905	58 **Ce** 140.116	59 **Pr** 140.908	60 **Nd** 144.24	61 **Pm** (145)	62 **Sm** 150.36	63 **Eu** 151.964	64 **Gd** 157.25	65 **Tb** 158.925	66 **Dy** 162.500	67 **Ho** 164.930	68 **Er** 167.259	69 **Tm** 168.934	70 **Yb** 173.04

Actinoids

89 **Ac** (227)	90 **Th** (232)	91 **Pa** (231)	92 **U** (238)	93 **Np** (237)	94 **Pu** (244)	95 **Am** (243)	96 **Cm** (247)	97 **Bk** (247)	98 **Cf** (251)	99 **Es** (252)	100 **Fm** (257)	101 **Md** (258)	102 **No** (259)

Answers to Selected Odd-Numbered Questions and Problems

Chapter 1

1. Undetectable

3. That the sequence is linear, meaning the difference between any two adjacent digits is 1.

5. 12 ways

7. One

9. T, A: reflection symmetry across vertical line passing through letter center. E, B: reflection symmetry across horizontal line passing through letter center. L, S: no reflection symmetry.

11. 9 axes of reflection symmetry, 13 axes of rotational symmetry

13. Two axes of reflection symmetry

15. (a) 1.5×10^{14} mm (b) 12,000 Earths

17. 10^4 gastrotrich lifetimes/tortoise lifetime

19. 10^9 to 10^{10} books

21. (a) Either one order of magnitude or none. Performing $V = \ell^3$ first yields $V_1 = \ell_1^3$, $V_2 = (2\ell_1)^3 = 8\ell_1^3$, which rounds to $10\ell_1^3$ so that $V_2 = 10V_1$, one order of magnitude. (b) Yes, because of the rules of rounding numerical values. For example, if $V_1 = 3.5 \text{ m}^3$, that value would round to an order of magnitude of 10 m³. Then $V_2 = 8V_1 = 28 \text{ m}^3$, which also rounds to an order of magnitude of 10 m³.

23. 10^5 leaves

25. Not reasonable. Because light travels much faster than sound, any thunder peal is delayed compared to the light signal caused by the lightning bolt event. From the principle of causality, the lightning you see after you hear the peal cannot have caused the peal.

27. That the barrier lowers time after time 30 s before a train passes is consistent with a causal relationship between the two events. The single negative result, however, tells you that the lowering of the barrier cannot be the *direct* cause of the passing of the train. More likely, the lowering is triggered when the train passes a sensor quite a distance up the tracks from the barrier and the sensor sends an electrical signal to the lowering mechanism. A malfunction in either the sensor, the electrical connections, or the lowering mechanism would account for the one negative result you observed.

29. $E = mc^2$; E is type of energy described, m is object mass, c is speed of light.

31. If the 30° angles must be interior to adjacent sides, the resulting zigzag pattern gives a distance of 1.0ℓ (to 2 significant digits). If the 30° angles must be exterior to adjacent sides, the result ranges from 3.4ℓ to 3.7ℓ. If a mixture of interior and exterior angles are allowed, the distance ranges from zero (parallelogram) to 2.4ℓ (one interior angle at end of chain).

33. 1.32×10^3 s

35. (a) The position decreases linearly as a function of time, from an initial position $x = 4.0$ m to a final position $x = 0$, reaching this final position at $t = 8.0$ s. (b) $x(t) = mt + b$ with $m = -0.5$ m/s, and $b = 4.0$ m

37. 352 in

39. (a) and (b). In both cases, the density of each piece is the same as the density of the original block.

41. No, because there is a significant difference (14 percent) in their mass densities.

43. Meters

45. (a) 10^{21} kg (b) 10^{25} kg (c) 10^{39} kg

47. (a) 3.00×10^8 m/s (b) $8.99 \times 10^{16} \text{ m}^2/\text{s}^2$ (c) No. Because you should wait until the final answer to round off, the value in part b is $(2.99792 \times 10^8 \text{ m/s})^2 = 8.98752 \times 10^{16} \text{ m}^2/\text{s}^2$ rounded to three significant digits. The square of the value in part a is $(3.00 \times 10^8 \text{ m/s})^2 = 9.00 \times 10^{16} \text{ m}^2/\text{s}^2$.

49. Four significant digits

51. 35,987.1 km

53. 0.17 L. However, in the absence of information about volume measuring devices, mixing a standard one liter is probably best.

55. 7.4×10^{-3} g/s

57. 1.6 m

59. Place two coins on the balance, and hold the third in your hand. If the two coins balance, the one in your hand is the counterfeit. If the two coins do not balance, one must be the counterfeit. Swap the lighter of the two for the coin in your hand. If the two coins on the balance now balance, the counterfeit coin is the one you just removed, and it is lighter than real coins. If the two coins are still unbalanced, the counterfeit is the one that stayed on the balance during the whole experiment, and it is heavier than real coins.

61. 10^{56} mol

63. 2×10^3 boards

65. 10^4 m

67. 10^8

69. 0.349 mm

71. No. Atoms are typically 10^5 times larger than nuclei. If you make the nucleus diameter 500 mm, the atom diameter must be 50 km.

73. No. The swing will never get closer to the ground than about 0.80 m and will never rise above the ground more than about 2 m.

75. (a) 10^{17} kg/m³ (b) 13 orders of magnitude larger than Earth mass density, 14 orders of magnitude larger than water mass density (c) 10^{14} kg

Chapter 2

1. Time interval between adjacent frames and object size

3.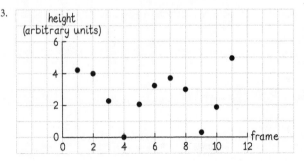

5. (a), (c), (d), (e), and (f)

7. Distance traveled 6.4 km, displacement zero

9. (a) Infinitely many (b) Infinitely many (c) Infinitely many (d) Two (one for each choice of positive direction)

11. If numerical values of time and distance are converted, but the scale of each axis still uses the same numerical labels (that is, "0.40 m" becomes "0.40 in"), then the curve would be much narrower and much taller. This is just a matter of perspective, though. If the scale of each axis is also converted, so that "0.40 m" becomes "16 in," then the shape of the graph is not changed by the conversion of units.

13. +1 block

15. The swimmer swims in the positive x direction at a constant speed (left sloping leg of curve, increasing x values). She stops briefly (horizontal leg, most probably at end of her lane) and then returns to the starting point (right sloping leg, decreasing x values) at a speed slightly lower than her initial speed (this leg not as steep as left leg).

17. Interpolation always gives a continuous path, but there is no reason to expect that the path is accurate everywhere. Suppose you are photographing a clock's pendulum at 1.0-s intervals, collecting data to use in a graph showing the pendulum's position as a function of time. Suppose further that the pendulum takes 1.0 s to swing from left to right and back left again. At this swing speed, the pendulum has just enough time between photographs to swing and return to its initial position, so that the photographs make it appear that the pendulum does not move at all. An interpolation of data points collected from the photographs would show a continuous horizontal line on a position-versus-time graph, which is certainly not correct.

19.

21. (a) $x(t)/q$

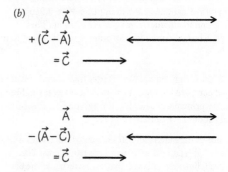

(b) $26qT^3\,\hat{\imath}$

25. (a) 10.2 m/s (b) 10.4 m/s (c) 9.24 m/s (d) 7.233 m/s (e) 6.3 m/s (f) 5.545 m/s

27. (a) Because the images were created at equal time intervals, the spacing between adjacent images is a function of the ball's speed. That the spacing between adjacent images has one value in the first five frames and a different value in the final five frames tells you that the ball moved at one speed at the beginning of the motion and at a different speed at the end of the motion. (b) During the first five frames.

29. (a) Just before instant t_2 and just after instant t_6. (b) From just before instant t_4 until instant t_6, which is where the bottom-curve slope is essentially the same as the top-curve slope.

31. B is closer to C than it is to A.

33. (a) 12 m/s (b) He likely treated the problem as though the cyclist rode at the two speeds for equal time intervals rather than for equal distances, and so just averaged the speeds: (10 m/s + 16 m/s)/2 = 13 m/s.

35. 110 km/h

37. (1) No, because you could walk in either direction and so there are two possibilities for your final location. (2) Yes

39. (a) 3 m (b) 3 m/s (c) 3 m/s

41. (a) $A_x\hat{\imath}$ (b) $A_x\hat{\imath}$ (c) $A_x\hat{\imath}$

43. (a) 4.0 m (b) (+4.0 m) $\hat{\imath}$

45. (a) +0.52 m (b) +0.80 m (c) 0 (d) (+0.28 m)$\hat{\imath}$ (e) (−0.80 m)$\hat{\imath}$ (f) (−0.52 m)$\hat{\imath}$ (g) 0.66 m (h) 0.82 m (i) 1.5 m

47. $\vec{B} = -\vec{A}/2$

49. (a) $\vec{C} - \vec{A}$ (b) $\vec{A} - \vec{C}$

(b)

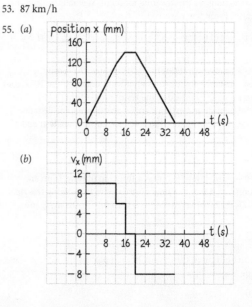

51. (a) (−0.42 m/s) $\hat{\imath}$ (b) 1.3 m/s (c) Because average velocity considers only actual distance between initial and final positions, but average speed considers distance traveled between these two positions; average speed is path-dependent, average velocity is not.

53. 87 km/h

55. (a)

(b)

57. Object A

59.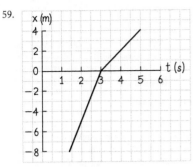

61. (a) 1.4 m/s (b) 10 m/s

63. 6.0×10^2 m

65. At 1.0 s: 45 m/s; at 4.0 s: 91 m/s

67. The fact that A passed B at 2:00 p.m. tells you that initially A was moving faster than 30 m/s. If A continued moving faster than 30 m/s eastward during the entire 1.0-h time interval, there is no way B could have caught up with A at 3:00 p.m. Therefore A must have slowed from a velocity above 30 m/s eastward to a velocity below 30 m/s eastward. Because a car cannot make discontinuous jumps in speed/velocity, B must have had a velocity of 30 m/s eastward at some instant. (Note that the speed could have always been greater than 30 m/s, but the velocity could not always have been greater than 30 m/s eastward.)

69. (a) Average speed of shadow leading edge (b) Yes, at the instant when the car is directly across from the light

71. (a) 21 m/s (b) 48 mi/h

73. (a) $x = -6.0$ m (b) $\vec{x} = (-6.0 \text{ m}) \, \hat{\imath}$ (c) $x = 6.0$ m

75. By a time interval of $0.25(\Delta t)$, where Δt is A's time interval for the race

77. (a) 60 s (b) 3.6×10^2 m

79. (a) Greater than (b) Greater than

81. (a) 1:2 (b) 1:2

83. (a) $+0.39$ m/s (b) $+0.3603$ m/s (c) $\dfrac{x(t = 1.005) - x(t = 0.995)}{0.01 \text{ s}} =$

   $(+0.360003$ m/s$)$, whereas $v_x = \dfrac{dx}{dt} = 3ct^2$ such that

   $v_x(t = 1.0 \text{ s}) = 0.36$ m/s

85. (a) $d/2\Delta t$ (b) $2\Delta t$ (c) The distance traveled by the runner is an infinite series that requires infinitely many terms to approach d, but the time intervals that correspond to these distance intervals also get smaller and smaller in the series. At higher and higher terms in the series, the runner travels almost no distance in each term but does so in a time interval that is almost zero. Because the two effects cancel each other, the runner travels the distance from starting line to finish line in a finite time interval.

87. Tortoise wins by 0.2 mi, even with Hare running at his top speed, 6.0 mi/h. In order to cross the finish line first, Hare must run at 10 mi/h once he gets up from his nap, far above his top speed.

89. (a) $x(t) = -p - qt - rt^2$ (b) $x(t) = (p - 2) + qt + rt^2$

(c) original axes:

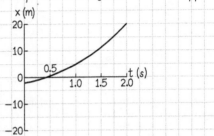

with positive and negative directions flipped:

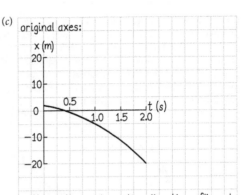

with origin translated:

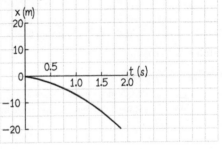

(d) -74 m, $+74$ m, -76 m

(e) -35 m/s, $+35$ m/s, -35 m/s

(f) There is no physical difference because the only things changed are position chosen as origin and direction chosen as positive.

91. You pass 12 empty trucks along the way, with a thirteenth pulling out of the mill just as you enter. The next day, you pass 12 full trucks, with a thirteenth pulling out of the mine just as you enter.

Chapter 3

1. (a) From first dot to fifth dot, evidenced by fact that space between adjacent dots increases for these five dots. (b) From fifth dot to ninth dot, evidenced by fact that space between adjacent dots decreases for these five dots. (c) The answers would be the same because the dots would be designated "first" through "ninth" starting at the right end of the sequence instead of the left end.

3. Not accelerating, indicated by the horse appearing in same position in each frame. With cameras equally spaced and triggered at equal time intervals, the unchanging position in all frames means the horse's speed did not change as the photographs were taken.

5. No. In the position-versus-time graph in the Figure below your car is the solid line and your friend's is the dotted line. Point A, where the lines intersect for the first time, is where your friend passes. To catch up, you accelerate at a constant rate, indicated by the upward bend of the solid line after A. In order to intersect the dotted line again, the slope of the solid line must be steeper than that of the dotted line. This means your speed is greater than that of your friend at B, the position at which you catch up with him.

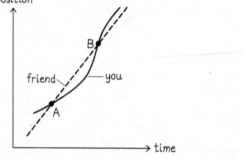

7. Initially you are at rest. When you start to move upward, your velocity has increased in the upward direction. If you take up to be the positive direction of motion, your acceleration is positive as you speed up from rest. This upward acceleration lasts for a short time interval, and soon, you reach the speed at which the elevator is programmed to move. Once that speed is reached, your acceleration is zero as you move at a constant velocity upward. As you approach the 19th floor, the elevator slows down, which makes your acceleration negative. This negative acceleration continues until the elevator stops at your floor.

9. The car that initially had the greater speed.

11. (a) 4.9 m/s (b) 15 m/s (c) 9.8 m/s

13. The curve in Figure 3.6a would still bend downward but not as much. Figure 3.6b would still be a straight line, but its slope would be about half what it is in that graph.

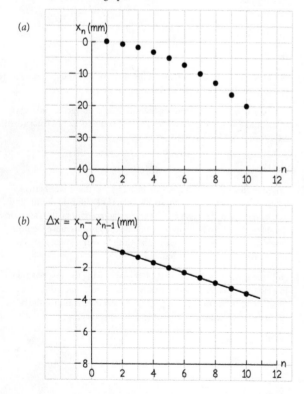

15. (a) Velocity 49 m/s upward, speed 49 m/s (b) Velocity 0, speed 0 (c) Velocity 49 m/s downward, speed 49 m/s (d) Velocity 98 m/s downward, speed 98 m/s

17. (a) Yes. A ball thrown upward stops for an instant at the peak of its path. At this instant, the velocity is zero but the acceleration is $g = -9.8$ m/s^2. (b) Yes. Any object moving at constant velocity has nonzero velocity and zero acceleration.

19. The two techniques cause the snowballs to hit the sidewalk at the same speed.

21. The curve would start out identical to the no-air-resistance case, with a slope of -9.8 m/s^2, but the magnitude of this slope would decrease with time. After some time interval, the curve would become horizontal, indicating a constant speed.

23.

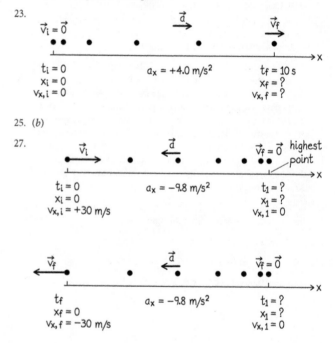

25. (b)

27.

29. (a) 0.33 m/s^2 in direction of motion (b) 6.0×10^2 m

31. (a) 75 mm (b) 6.0×10^{13} m/s^2 in direction of motion

33. (a) You integrate. Determining the area under the curve is equivalent to adding up differential amounts of $v\delta t = \delta x$, and the sum of all such tiny steps is the displacement. (b) 1.0×10^2 m (c) No. In the figure below, the initial and final velocities are both zero, a case in which the equation from Worked Problem 3.3 yields zero for $v_{x,av}$. Yet the graph shows that the object has a positive velocity in the x direction for a significant time interval. Therefore the object must have a displacement in the x direction and its average velocity cannot be zero.

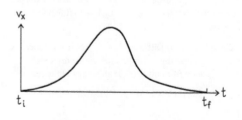

35. (a) 0.20 m downward (b) 0.22 m downward

37. (a) 4.2×10^{15} m/s^2 in direction of motion (b) 2.4 ns

39. (*a*) True. The fact that the curve is a straight line means the rate at which the velocity changes is constant. (*b*) Not necessarily true. The object could have started far enough from the origin that it never passes through position $x = 0$ on a position-versus-time plot. (*c*) True. The velocity is zero at the instant the curve crosses the time axis. (*d*) Not true. The fact that the curve crosses from positive v values to negative v values means the direction of the motion changed.

41. (*a*) 3.3×10^2 m (*b*) 38 s (*c*) 8.6 m/s

43. 13 m

45. 1.0 m

47. Factor of $\sqrt{2}$

49. The ball reaches its maximum height at $t = 3.0$ s, making the trajectory symmetric around that point. Between $t = 2.0$ s and $t = 3.0$ s, the ball moves upward and has a downward acceleration g; it moves some distance in this time interval. Between $t = 3.0$ s and $t = 4.0$ s, the ball, after having zero velocity for an instant, moves downward and has a downward acceleration g. Because the time intervals are equal, the distance the ball moves downward in 1.0 s equals the distance it moves upward in 1.0 s.

51. (*a*) 22 m/s (*b*) 2.3 s

53. (*a*) 0.65 s (*b*) 0.90 s

55. Let $\Delta y_{\Delta t} = \frac{1}{2} g (\Delta t)^2$ be the distance traveled after a time interval Δt and $\Delta y_{\Delta t + 1} = \frac{1}{2} g (\Delta t + 1)^2$ be the distance traveled after time interval $\Delta t + 1$. The difference between these two distances is the distance traveled in the 1-s interval between these two intervals. Call this distance $h_{\Delta t} = g \left(\Delta t + \frac{1}{2} \right)$, and because we are restricting ourselves to time intervals of 1 s, we could also write $h_N = g \left(N + \frac{1}{2} \right)$ where N is an integer number of seconds. The ratio of the distance traveled in the first second to the distance traveled in the Nth second is

$$\frac{h_0}{h_N} = \frac{\frac{1}{2}}{N + \frac{1}{2}} = \frac{1}{2N + 1}.$$

Inserting the first few values for N yields $1/3, 1/5, 1/7, 1/9, \ldots$

57. 14 m

59. (*a*) 29 m/s upward (*b*) 36 m (*c*) 42 m

61. 13.6°

63. (*a*) Child on more-inclined slide (40°) (*b*) Child on more inclined slide (40°)

65. (*a*) 2.0 m/s^2 (*b*) 2.0 m/s^2 (*c*) 12 s (*d*) 20 m/s (*e*) 24 m/s

67. (*a*) 1.5 s (*b*) 3.1 m/s

69. (*a*) $\sqrt{2g \sin(\theta) \ell}$ (*b*) $\sqrt{g \sin(\theta) \ell}$

71. 35°

73. 3.1 m

75. $a_x(t) = 6bt$

77. (*a*) Yes; acceleration constant (*b*) 6.12 m/s in $+x$ direction (*c*) 6.08 m/s in $+x$ direction, 6.16 m/s in $+x$ direction (*d*) 0.400 m/s^2 in $+x$ direction (*e*) 0.400 m/s^2 in $+x$ direction at both instants

79. (*a*) 10.0 m/s^2 in $+x$ direction (*b*) 50.0 m/s in $+x$ direction (*c*) 5.00 m/s^2 in $+x$ direction (*d*) 167 m

81. (*a*) 5.1 m (*b*) 1.8 s

83. (*a*) $a_x(t) = -v_{max} \omega \sin(\omega t)$ (*b*) $x(t) = (v_{max}/\omega) \sin(\omega t)$

85. 63 m

87. (*a*) 6.4×10^5 m/s^2 in direction opposite direction of motion (*b*) 0.25 ms (*c*) 0.18 m

89. (*a*) 2.24 m/s^2 (*b*) 21 m/s (*c*) 1.0×10^2 m

91. (*a*) 44.3 m/s (*b*) 4.52 s

93. (*a*) $(20 \text{ m})\hat{\imath}$, $(29 \text{ m})\hat{\imath}$, $(29 \text{ m})\hat{\imath}$, $(20 \text{ m})\hat{\imath}$ (*b*) $(15 \text{ m/s})\hat{\imath}$, $(4.9 \text{ m/s})\hat{\imath}$, $(-4.9 \text{ m/s})\hat{\imath}$, $(-15 \text{ m/s})\hat{\imath}$ (*c*) 0 (*d*) 12 m/s

95. 9.6×10^2 m/s^2 upward

97. $4g$, or 4×10^1 m/s^2 upward

99. (*a*) 6.0 m/s^2 upward (*b*) 3.3 s

101. (*a*) 11 m/s (*b*) upward (*c*) 5.2 m

103. 1.2 s

105. "Cloud-scraper" goes highest (1.5×10^2 m).

107. $a_1 = \dfrac{2d}{(\Delta t)^2} = 20.2$ m/s^2, $a_2 = \dfrac{v_f^2}{2d} = 11.5$ m/s^2, $a_3 = \dfrac{v_f - v_i}{t} = 15.3$ m/s^2 (*b*) Student 3 calculated the average acceleration, and his value is approximately halfway between the values calculated by students 1 and 2. (*c*) Acceleration was not constant, but students 1 and 2 assumed it was.

109. Don't take the bet. You can throw a stone to a maximum height of 6.7 m.

Chapter 4

1. Puck 2 had twice the initial speed of puck 1.

3. No for object 1, yes for object 2. Friction between two objects opposes relative motion between them, but object 1 speeds up as it travels across the surface, meaning friction cannot account for the change in v_x. Object 2 slows down as it travels across the surface, meaning friction is one valid explanation for the change in v_x. (Though not the only explanation: A hockey stick slowing a puck sliding on ice, for instance, yields the same $v(t)$ curve as that shown for object 2.)

5. Object 2 has three times the inertia of object 1.

7.

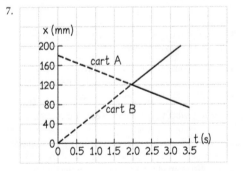

9. (*a*) Car A: upper solid line; car B: lower solid line (*b*) Car A

11. Inertia of A 2.5 times greater than inertia of B

13. Does not change

15. The inertia of just the bottle is the same in each case, but if the contents are included then the full bottle has the greater inertia because the water filling it has a greater inertia than the air filling the "empty" bottle.

17. Graph (a): smooth icy track; one wooden cart, one plastic cart; plastic cart initially at rest, wooden cart initially moving at 1.5 m/s. Graph (b): dusty unpolished track; carts made of same material but we cannot determine whether wood or plastic because we have no information about friction between each cart and surface; carts initially moving in same direction, one at 2.0 m/s and one at 5.0 m/s. Graph (c): rough damaged track; carts made of same material but we cannot determine whether wood or plastic because we have no information about friction between each cart and surface; one cart initially at rest, one initially moving.

19. (a) Extensive (c) No; number of passengers changes as people get on or off at each stop. In principle, people could also die or be born on the bus. (d) Yes, ignoring any deaths or births

21. 32 ways, assuming 5 objects named (person, truck, ball, friend, ground) cannot be subdivided.

23. 0.33 kg

25. 1.0 m/s to left

27. (a) $v_{1x,f} = -0.13$ m/s, $v_{2x,f} = +1.2$ m/s. (b) $\Delta v_{1x} = -1.6$ m/s, $\Delta v_{2x} = +1.2$ m/s. (c) 50 kg (d) $a_{1x} = -3.2$ m/s², $a_{2x} = +2.4$ m/s²

29. Baseball

31. The two cars have the same change in momentum.

33. Yes. Momentum is a vector. Therefore the system has zero momentum if two conditions are met: The carts move in opposite directions and the absolute value of the product of inertia and velocity is the same for the two carts.

35. (a) $p_{1,i} = 0.196$ kg · m/s, $p_{1,f} = 0.131$ kg · m/s (b) $\vec{p}_{2i} = \vec{0}$, $\vec{p}_{2,f} = +0.327$ kg · m/s (c) 1.22×10^3 kg/m³

37. 46 m

39. 1.8 kg · m/s

41. 2.0 m/s

43. (a) No (b) No (c) Yes

45. 2.4 m/s

47. (a) 6 kg · m/s to the right (b) Zero (c) No. The wall does not move because it is attached to the ground or some underlying structure.

49. (a) +1.0 kg · m/s (b) +1.0 kg · m/s (c) Yes

51. (a) $\Delta \vec{p}_A = -8.0$ kg · m/s î, $\Delta \vec{p}_B = +8.0$ kg · m/s î (b) Zero (c) Yes, because change in momentum for system is zero

53. (a) No, provided nothing outside the two-object system interacts with the system. (b) Yes, the object initially moving can come to rest and impart all its momentum to the object initially at rest.

55. (a) It is not possible to predict the velocities of each car using momentum. (b) Yes, the system momentum (combined momenta of both cars) must be the same immediately afterward as before. More specifically, the momentum of both cars together after the collision must be 2000 kg · m/s in the direction of the 1200-kg car's initial motion.

57. Remove your clothing and throw it toward the shore, so that it has a nonzero momentum. You gain equal momentum directed toward the opposite shore and drift toward that shore.

59. 80 kg

61. (a) 0.40 m/s (b) 7.0×10^2 kg · m/s in direction of initial motion (c) higher

63. (a) Before collision, cue ball has momentum directed toward 8 ball and 8 ball has zero momentum. After collision, cue ball has zero momentum and 8 ball has momentum equal in magnitude and direction to momentum of cue ball before collision. (b) Call direction

of motion the $+x$ direction. For the isolated system of two balls, $m_8(v_{8x,f} - v_{8x,i}) = -m_c(v_{cx,f} - v_{cx,i})$. With $v_{8x,i} = 0$, $v_{cx,f} = 0$, and $m_8 = m_c$, this yields $v_{8x,f} = v_{cx,i}$. Because $m_8 = m_c$, this corresponds to $p_{8x,f} = p_{cx,i}$, or zero change in system momentum, consistent with zero impulse and with the answer in (a). Considering each ball separately, the non-zero change in momentum is also equal to the non-zero impulse, because the impulse affecting each ball is equal in magnitude and in the opposite direction, just as the momentum changes of each ball are equal and opposite. Each of the four quantities has magnitude mv.

65. 2.0×10^4 kg

67. (a) $v_{1x,i} = +2.0$ m/s, $v_{1x,f} = 0$ (b) $v_{2x,i} = -0.33$ m/s, $v_{2x,f} = +0.33$ m/s (c) $\Delta p_{1,x} = -2.0$ kg · m/s, $\Delta p_{2,x} = +2.0$ kg · m/s (d) Yes

(e)

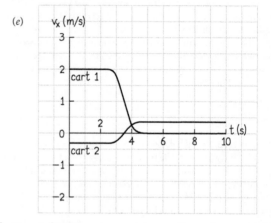

69. $m_{black} = 2m_{red}$

71. 2.0×10^2 kg

73. $p_{golf\,ball}/p_{baseball} = 1/2$

75. 5.6 kg

77.

		initial		final	
golf balls	A O	B O	A O	B O	
velocity	$\xrightarrow{\vec{v}_{A,i}}$	$\vec{v}_{B,i} = \vec{0}$	$\vec{v}_{A,f} = \vec{0}$	$\xrightarrow{\vec{v}_{B,f}}$	
momentum	$\xrightarrow{\vec{p}_{A,i}}$	$\vec{p}_{B,i} = \vec{0}$	$\vec{p}_{A,f} = \vec{0}$	$\xrightarrow{\vec{p}_{B,f}}$	
golf balls & basketball	A O	B ◯	A O	B ◯	
velocity	$\xrightarrow{\vec{v}_{A,i}}$	$\vec{v}_{B,i} = \vec{0}$	$\xleftarrow{\vec{v}_{A,f}}$	$\xrightarrow{\vec{v}_{B,f}}$	
momentum	$\xrightarrow{\vec{p}_{A,i}}$	$\vec{p}_{B,i} = \vec{0}$	$\xleftarrow{\vec{p}_{A,f}}$	$\xrightarrow{\vec{p}_{B,f}}$	

79. $v_{block,f} = \dfrac{m_{bullet}}{m_{block}}(v_{bullet,i} - v_{bullet,f})$

81. When a rocket is launched or a cannonball fired, the projectile has significant forward momentum. Because the momentum of the system is initially zero, after firing there must be momentum in the direction opposite the projectile direction. In a bazooka, material (largely burnt fuel) is expelled out the back, and so the required backward momentum need not come entirely from recoil. In a cannon, there is no outlet for air or debris at the back; consequently, the cannon must recoil with the same magnitude of momentum imparted to the cannonball.

83. In space, the rocket expels a huge number of gas particles at very high speeds. When these gas particles are ejected from the rear of the rocket, the rocket must acquire a forward velocity in order for system momentum to remain constant.

85. The two cars experience the same change in momentum $\Delta\vec{p} = m\Delta\vec{v}$ during the collision. If you are in the car of greater inertia, this momentum change is accomplished with a smaller velocity change. Because change in velocity over time is acceleration, being in the car of greater inertia means your body experiences the smaller acceleration in the collision, which is preferable in avoiding injury.

87. Don't drop the stereo because at the instant it reaches your friend its momentum is 53 kg·m/s downward. This could be harmful to both your friend and the stereo.

89. You get rid of the sandbags to decrease inertia and therefore momentum. If you simply drop them from the basket, your momentum when you reach the ground is 2.66×10^3 kg·m/s downward, below the critical value 2850 kg·m/s at which the basket is damaged. However, if you *throw* the sandbags downward, you increase their downward momentum and therefore decrease your downward momentum, making your momentum when you land far below the critical value.

91. (a) $3v_{ex}/4$ (b) $2v_{ex}/3$ (c) Two-stage, because each time a stage is detached, the inertia that must be accelerated in the next stage is decreased.

Chapter 5

1. (a) 3.0 m/s in negative x direction (b) 4.0 m/s in positive x direction

3. (a) Inelastic (b) Totally inelastic

5. Doubles momentum, quadruples kinetic energy

7. 2.5×10^6 kg

9. $m_A/m_B = 1/4$

11. For same momentum, $K_Y > K_X$. For same kinetic energy, $p_X > p_Y$.

13. The book slows down due to friction, and the book and table heat up slightly as the book's kinetic energy is converted to thermal energy.

15. Cannon: temperature, velocity (due to recoil), momentum. Ball: temperature, velocity, momentum, internal energy (due to slight deformation). Gunpowder: transformational energy (as solid converted to gas when ignited).

17. (a) I choose the system consisting of the two blocks only. It is not isolated; the blocks make contact with the spring outside the system, and this changes the momentum of the system.

(b)

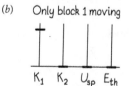

(c) The system starts out with kinetic energy. During the collision of the two blocks, this kinetic energy is changed into thermal energy. As the warmer blocks strike the spring, they momentarily come to a stop as their kinetic energy is changed to internal energy in the spring. Once the spring returns to its equilibrium length, the blocks regain kinetic energy. (d) $\frac{1}{2}v$

19. Kinetic energy of bike or car converted to thermal energy of brake pads and tires

21. The cars convert the same amount of kinetic energy to internal energy.

23. $|\Delta\vec{p}| = 2m|\vec{v}|$; $\Delta K = 0$; the answers are consistent because the change in momentum accounts for the change in velocity direction and the change in kinetic energy accounts for the change in velocity magnitude.

25. 6.3×10^{-3} J

27. (a) 5.0 m/s (b) −5.4 m/s (c) Yes (d) Zero

31. (a) No (b) Yes

33. $v_{1f} = -\dfrac{(m_1 - 2m_2)}{m_1 + m_2}v_{1i}, \quad v_{2f} = \dfrac{1}{2}\left(\dfrac{5m_1 - m_2}{m_1 + m_2}\right)v_{1i}$

35. Inelastic, $m_B = 0.16$ kg

39. $\dfrac{\text{Conversion at 34 m/s}}{\text{Conversion at 25 m/s}} = 1.8$

43. Collision in which initial momenta have same magnitude

45. $\sqrt{\frac{3}{4}}v_{end}$

47. (a) 5.0 m/s (b) No (c) 0.50 J

51. Answers between 1×10^8 and 3×10^8 megatons are reasonable.

53. The coefficients are each other's multiplicative inverse; reversing the time order reverses *initial* and *final* in definition of coefficient, thus inverting it.

55. (a) 0.20 m/s, to left (b) $e = \infty$ (c) 0.20 m/s, to right (d) $e = \infty$ (e) $\Delta K = +200$ J; from chemical energy stored in her body (f) 0.047 Cal

57. (a) 7000 m/s in direction of initial velocity (b) 1.013×10^{10} J

59. $v_{shuttle} = 890$ m/s in direction of initial motion; $v_{rocket} = 790$ m/s in direction of initial motion

61. −0.60 m/s

63. $v_i + \sqrt{\dfrac{3m_B E_{spring}}{2m_A(m_B + m_A)}}$

65. (a)

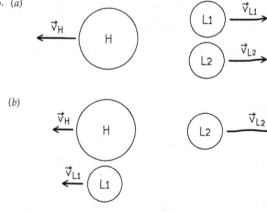

(b)

69. 1 m/s

71. (a) 2.0 m/s to right in Figure P5.70 (b) 0.098 J (c) $\vec{v}_{1f} = 0.66$ m/s to right, $\vec{v}_{2f} = 0.66$ m/s to right (d) 0.33 J (e) $e = 0$, as expected for a totally inelastic collision

77. Magnitude of momentum delivered by water each second is

$$\frac{\Delta p}{t} = \frac{Q^2 \rho}{\pi r^2}.$$ You can determine whether the collision is elastic or

inelastic by comparing the rate at which the ball's momentum changes with time to this momentum magnitude. You expect the collision to be inelastic because water droplets stick to the ball.

Chapter 6

1. Stepping on, move quickly enough to have your speed match the sidewalk speed; stepping off, stop walking as you reach the sidewalk end to minimize your speed relative to the ground.

3. 5.0 m/s in direction of motion of both cars

5. (a) Toward truck (b) Away from truck

7. The truck and the car traveling in the same direction: the truck driver sees the car initially moving backwards at 30 m/s, then accelerating in the direction of the truck travel, finally moving at zero velocity relative to the truck. The car and truck traveling in opposite directions: the truck driver sees the car initially approaching him at 30 m/s, then accelerating in the direction of the truck travel, finally approaching the truck at a speed of 60 m/s. The direction of acceleration is the same in both cases.

9. Before the truck slows, the truck and the cans have the same initial velocity. Because the cans are not attached to the truck, their velocity cannot change when the truck slows; they continue moving in the initial direction of motion until they hit up against the back of the cab.

11. (a) $\vec{p}_{A,i} = 2.5 \times 10^6$ kg·m/s west, $\vec{p}_{B,i} = 2.4 \times 10^6$ kg·m/s west, $\vec{p}_{A,f} = 3.0 \times 10^6$ kg·m/s west, $\vec{p}_{B,f} = 2.0 \times 10^6$ kg·m/s west
(b) $\vec{p}_{A,i} = 1.7 \times 10^6$ kg·m/s east, $\vec{p}_{B,i} = 3.3 \times 10^5$ kg·m/s east, $\vec{p}_{A,f} = 1.2 \times 10^6$ kg·m/s east, $\vec{p}_{B,f} = 8.0 \times 10^5$ kg·m/s east

13. 4.00 m/s, or 12.0 m/s, depending on direction of officer's motion

15. 0.75 m/s

17. (a) +2.3 kg·m/s î (b) +3.8 m/s î

19. Yes, in reference frame moving at speed v toward cart A

23.

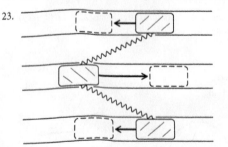

25. (a) 8.0 m/s (b) 5.0×10^4 kg·m/s in direction in which unit moves (c) 8.0 m/s in direction in which unit moves

27. Lightweight object; no

29. Shorter

31. Yes

33. You do not walk fast enough to do this.

35. (a) $\Delta t_{calm} = 2d/v$

37. 4.66×10^3 km

39. Boy's raft; 2.5 m.

41. (a) 0.38 m to right of origin (b) 0.63 m to left of origin (c) 1.38 m to right of origin. The center of mass location must be calculated for only one origin choice; that location can then be expressed relative to the other two origin choices with almost no calculation.

43. If the system's center of mass is not moving at constant velocity, the reference frame from which motion is measured is not inertial.

45.

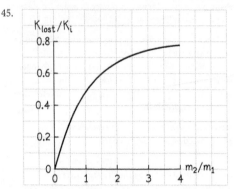

As m_2/m_1 approaches infinity, K_{lost}/K_i approaches 1, meaning all kinetic energy is converted to other forms.

47. μ cannot be larger than m_1: $\mu_{max} = m_1$. Smallest possible value is $\mu_{min} = m_1/2$.

49. Reference frame in which ball is at rest before collision

51. (a) 11 m/s to the right (b) 0.030 kg (c) 60% (d) 1.8 J

53. (a) 9.3 m/s (b) 19 m/s toward each other (c) 0.27 kg (d) 99.7% (e) $\vec{v}_{1f} = 10$ m/s away from you; $\vec{v}_{2f} = 7.4$ m/s toward you

55. Collision between two objects of equal inertia m

57. (a) 0.25 m/s in direction in which ball is thrown (b) 4.6 m/s in direction in which ball is thrown (c) 16 J (d) 16 J

61. (a) 4.4 m/s (b) Before collision: $(1.0$ m/s$)m_{mother}$ toward swimming penguin; after collision: $(2.3$ m/s$)m_{mother}$ toward swimming penguin

63. (a) $\vec{v}_{FG} = \dfrac{\vec{v}_{orange}}{2}\left(\dfrac{2m_{orange} + m_{apple}}{m_{orange} + m_{apple}}\right)$

65. (a) $\vec{v}_{rubber,f} = 18$ m/s west, $\vec{v}_{soft,f} = 8.9$ m/s east. (b) 12-J increase. (c) Observer measures same 12-J conversion from kinetic energy to internal energy. (d) Observer measures same 12-J conversion.

67. (a)   car's frame   (b)   guard's frame

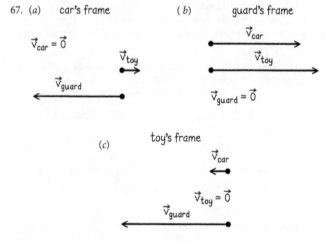

69. 0.86 m/s in the direction man and dog travel

71. (a) Each object has an equal apparent acceleration in your reference frame. (b) The rate of change of momentum of each object is in the same direction, and of magnitude proportional to the object's inertia.

73. Ball: 23 m/s in direction opposite its direction before collision; pot: 1.8 m/s in direction of ball's velocity before collision.

75. (a) 1.52×10^9 kg·m/s in direction in which A1 moves before collision (b) 317 m/s in direction in which A1 moves before collision (e) No dipping down, then rising again in either kinetic energy curve because all kinetic energy is converted to internal energy; none is converted back to kinetic energy after collision; kinetic energy drops to zero and remains there.

77. $\vec{v}_{0.30\,kg,f} = 0.17$ m/s in direction of initial velocity, $\vec{v}_{0.50\,kg,f} = 2.1$ m/s in direction of initial velocity

79. Call disk radius R. Draw horizontal x axis in plane of page, with axis origin at disk center and axis passing through hole center; center of mass is at $x_{cm} = -R/6$.

81. (a) 1.0 m/s (b) 6.9 m (c) 3.7 m from front end of car (d) 3.9 m from front end of car (e) Because speed changes as grain is added, grain is not evenly distributed over length of car.

Chapter 7

1. More than one (one between each piece of bread and salami)

3.

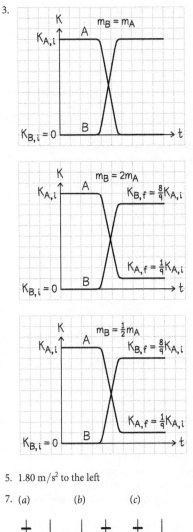

5. 1.80 m/s^2 to the left

7. (a)   (b)   (c)

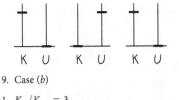

9. Case (b)

11. $K_m / K_{3m} = 3$

13. Trip down

15. (a) Into deforming metal (by breaking and re-forming chemical bonds) and heating it up (b) No, in fact you have to put in more energy to do a similar rearrangement of molecules to fix the slinky.

17. (a)   energy

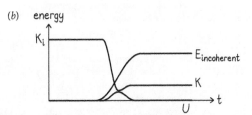

(b)   energy

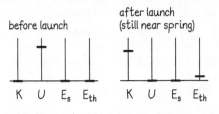

19. (a) System: ball, spring, air, Earth; air resistance not ignored

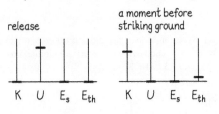

(b) System: ball, air, Earth; air resistance not ignored

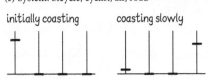

(c) System: bicycle, cyclist, air, road

(d) System: car, air, road, fuel

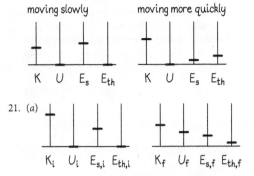

21. (a)

23. Yes. The copper atoms are likely joined to one another by chemical bonds, whereas contact between macroscopic objects typically involves repulsion at a distance. So the copper atoms may be pictured as being more "in contact" than your shoe is with the ground, but only because the atoms in copper are closer together. However, even the chemical bonds between atoms are interactions over a distance.

25. (a) Beginning of flight (b) End of flight

27. (a) All charged particles in the universe would attract one another and collapse into a compact charged center. (b) All charged particles in the universe would repel one another and spread out, making the universe ever more and more diffuse.

29. The strong interaction is responsible for holding atomic nuclei together against the electrical repulsion between protons. These interactions currently balance at a radius of about $10^{-14} - 10^{-15}$ m. If the strong interaction increased in strength by 20 orders of magnitude, but the electrostatic repulsion did not increase, atomic nuclei would be crushed to much smaller radii, perhaps becoming black holes! Atomic size scales are determined by electrical interactions among electrons and nuclei, so atomic sizes would remain more or less unaffected. However, with such a large strength, the attraction between neutrons and protons would be large enough so that nuclei in adjacent atoms could be drawn together. All matter might therefore be crushed. This new strong interaction would still not be large enough to affect inter-planetary distances, where gravity would still dominate.

31. (a) 0.39 kg (b) $\vec{a}_{0.66\,\text{kg}} = 3.2 \times 10^2$ m/s^2 to the left, $\vec{a}_{0.39\,\text{kg}} = 5.4 \times 10^2$ m/s^2 to the right (c) Acceleration ratio and inverse of inertia ratio equal (Chapter 4): $|\vec{a}_{0.66\,\text{kg}}/\vec{a}_{0.39\,\text{kg}}| = 0.59$, $|m_{0.39\,\text{kg}}/m_{0.66\,\text{kg}}| = 0.59$

33. (a) −0.0020 (b) 250 m/s (c) 0.50 m/s

35. (a) 0.14 kg (b) $\vec{a}_{\text{glob,av}} = 25$ m/s^2 to the left, $\vec{a}_{\text{cart,av}} = 6.7$ m/s^2 to the right

37. 0.297 s

39. (a) $\vec{a}_{\text{goalie,av}} = 1.7 \times 10^{-2}$ m/s^2 in puck's initial direction of motion, $\vec{a}_{\text{puck,av}} = 5.3 \times 10^3$ m/s^2 in direction opposite puck's initial direction of motion (b) 90 kg. (c) 1.3×10^2 J

41. Position x_1:

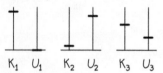

43. (a) Positive (b) Positive

45. 0.20 J

47. (a) 2.9 m/s (b) 3.2 m/s

49. (a) 0.59 J (b) $\vec{v}_{0.36\,\text{kg,f}} = 1.1$ m/s to the left, $\vec{v}_{0.12\,\text{kg,f}}$ 3.0 m/s to the right

51. If air resistance is ignored, the cap reaches your hands at speed v; if air resistance is not ignored, the cap reaches your hands at a speed slightly less than v because some initial kinetic energy is converted to incoherent energy of molecules in the air. Both answers come from the law of conservation of energy.

53. 4.59 km

55. 2.2 m/s

57. (a) 24 m/s (b) 49 J (c) 49 J

59. (a) 0.95 (b) 10 m/s, either upward or downward

61. $v_f = \frac{1}{4}\sqrt{15g\ell}$

63. Configuration (b)

65. 9.4%

67. (c) and (d)

69. (a) 57 J (b) 55 J

71. (a) Before the fall, the system's energy is all potential. During the fall, the system's potential energy is converted to kinetic energy. Just before impact, the system's energy is all kinetic. After impact, the system's kinetic energy has converted to thermal energy as Humpty Dumpty breaks.

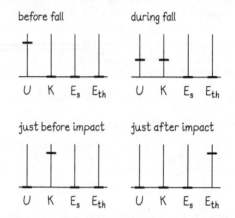

(b) Because conversion of coherent energy (kinetic, potential) into incoherent energy (thermal) is irreversible. If the men try to put Humpty Dumpty together, they constitute source energy. Although this can raise his pieces up to gain (coherent) potential energy, it cannot reverse the irreversible conversion of coherent kinetic energy to incoherent thermal energy. No matter how much source energy the men put in, Humpty Dumpty cannot be put back together.

(c)

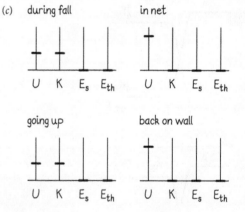

73. No, because some system coherent energy (kinetic) is converted to incoherent energy (mainly sound, small amount thermal energy).

75. 0.092 candy bars

77. Not impossible. The steam engine converts thermal energy (incoherent) to kinetic energy (coherent): Thermal energy causes liquid water to vaporize and expand, and the expanded volume moves pistons.

79. 0.0756 J

81. $a = 0.38$ m/s^2 in the direction of the bicycle's initial motion

83. $\vec{v}_{1-\text{kg,f}} = \left(-\dfrac{2v}{3} - \sqrt{\dfrac{7}{9}v^2 + \dfrac{E}{2m}}\right)\hat{\imath}$,

$\vec{v}_{2-\text{kg,f}} = \left(+\dfrac{v}{3} - \sqrt{\dfrac{7}{9}v^2 + \dfrac{E}{2m}}\right)\hat{\imath}$, where $m = 1.00$ kg, $\hat{\imath}$ points to the right

Chapter 8

1. Neither; vector sum of forces exerted on truck = vector sum of forces exerted on cycle = 0

3.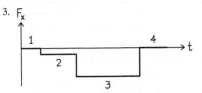

5. Object inertia is constant, which means change in momentum came from change in velocity, but knowing change in velocity does not tell you values of initial and final velocities; both are needed in order to determine change in kinetic energy.

7. (a) Magnitudes equal (b) Magnitudes equal (c) Magnitudes equal

9. (a)–(f) can all exert force.

11. (a) No. The force exerted by the pitcher on the ball results from contact between the pitcher's hand and the ball; once the ball leaves his hand, the pitcher no longer exerts force on it. (b) Drag force is exerted by the air on the ball, gravitational force is exerted by Earth on the ball.

13. No; at the top of the bounce, the cord has stopped exerting upward force but Earth's downward gravitational force is still exerted. The baby was moving upward, and gravitational force is changing the velocity's direction to downward. (The instant of zero velocity is the instant at which the velocity's direction changes from upward to downward.)

15. Because the vector sum of the forces exerted on the refrigerator is not zero. A force opposes your pushing force, probably frictional force exerted by the floor or, if the refrigerator back is against the wall, contact force exerted by the wall.

17. Downward contact force exerted by you on scale and upward contact force exerted by scale on you

19. $\vec{F}_{\text{by floor on you}}$; magnitude decreases

21.

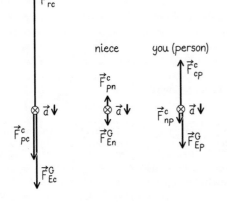

The crate moves because the magnitude of frictional force exerted by the floor on the crate is smaller than the magnitude of the contact force exerted by you on the crate. You do not move because the magnitude of the frictional force exerted by the floor on you is equal to the magnitude of the contact force exerted by the crate on you. (If you try to exert a force exceeding the available friction between your feet and the floor, your feet will slip.)

23. (a)

cabin

niece   you (person)

(b) $\vec{F}^{G}_{\text{En}} = 2.0 \times 10^2$ N downward, $\vec{F}^{c}_{\text{pn}} = 1.8 \times 10^2$ N upward, $\vec{F}^{G}_{\text{Ep}} = 4.9 \times 10^2$ N downward, $\vec{F}^{c}_{\text{np}} = 1.8 \times 10^2$ N downward, $\vec{F}^{c}_{\text{cp}} = 6.2 \times 10^2$ N upward, $\vec{F}^{G}_{\text{Ec}} = 9.8 \times 10^2$ N downward, $\vec{F}^{c}_{\text{pc}} = 6.2 \times 10^2$ N downward, $\vec{F}^{c}_{\text{rc}} = 1.5 \times 10^3$ N upward. Interaction pairs: $\vec{F}^{c}_{\text{pn}} - \vec{F}^{c}_{\text{np}}, \vec{F}^{c}_{\text{cp}} - \vec{F}^{c}_{\text{pc}}$ Gravitational force magnitudes given by mg. Interaction pairs are equal in magnitude, opposite in direction. Vector sum of forces exerted on each object must equal object's inertia times system acceleration (1.0 m/s^2 downward).

25. No; the tension in the upper portion is greater than the tension in the lower portion because the upward tensile force exerted by the upper portion on the lower portion must counteract the downward gravitational force exerted on the lower portion.

27. Forces equal in magnitude

29. 5.30×10^{17} m/s^2 in electron's initial direction of motion

31. Yes. Knowing the history of all the forces exerted on an object allows you to obtain the object's acceleration history and therefore the history of its velocity changes. Coupling this history with the known present position and velocity, you can work backwards to obtain the position and velocity at all previous instants.

33. (a) $\sum F_x(t) = \alpha - \beta t$, where $\alpha = 1.5 \times 10^3$ N and $\beta = 6.0 \times 10^3$ N/s (b) $\sum F_x > 0$ at $t < 0.25$ s, $\sum F_x < 0$ at $t > 0.25$ s, $\sum F_x = 0$ at $t = 0.25$ s

35. 59 m

37. (a) 9.8 N (b) 9.8 N

39. (a) 1500 N (b) 750 N

41. (a) 5.18×10^3 N (b) 3.2×10^2 N

43. (a) Tension equal to magnitude of gravitational force exerted by Earth on hanging block (b) Tension less than magnitude of gravitational force exerted on hanging block

45. (a) 4.9 m/s^2 to the right (b) 8.2 m/s^2 to the right

47. $a = b < d < c$

49. $m_W : m_M : m_P = \frac{1}{2} : 3 : \frac{3}{2}$

51. (a) 1.8×10^3 N/m (b) 0.41 m

53. $k_{\text{combination}} = k_1 k_2 (k_1 + k_2)$, therefore smaller than k_1

55. 60 mm

57. $\vec{a} = \dfrac{dk - gm}{3m}$ downward

59. (a) 5.4×10^2 N/m (b) 2.7 kg (c) 2.1 m/s^2 downward

63. (a) In segment attached to ceiling (b) In segment attached to tassel

65. (a) 4.2×10^4 N·s forward (b) 6.9×10^2 N forward

67. (a) 2.33 m/s (b) 381 N

69. (a) 0.22 N·s upward (b) 9.0 ms (c) 24 N (d) 6.1 N

71. (a) 0.45 N·s (b) 1.5×10^2 N (c) 2.3×10^2 N (d) 1.7 m/s in the direction of the serve

73. (a) 0.70 m/s^2 in direction of push (b) 1.4 m/s^2 in direction of push (c) 0.20 m/s^2 in direction of push

75. (a) $F/3m$ (b) $F/3$ to the right (c) $F/3$ to the left (d) (a) remains $F/3m$, (b) changes to $2F/3$ to the right, (c) changes to $2F/3$ to the left.

77. (a) Zero center-of-mass acceleration (b) $\sum \vec{F}_{\text{car}} = 1.2 \times 10^3$ N in direction car faces, $\sum \vec{F}_{\text{truck}} = 1.2 \times 10^3$ N in direction truck faces (c) 0.80 m/s^2 in direction truck faces

79. (a) 5.0 m/s^2 in direction of 50 N force (b) 18 m/s in direction away from 4.0-kg block

81. As you accelerate the child upward, the magnitude of the upward force you exert on her is greater than the magnitude F_{Ec}^G of the gravitational force exerted by Earth on her. This means that the magnitude of the downward force she exerts on you is also greater than $F_{Ec}^G r$. Hence, as you accelerate her upward, the scale reading increases for an instant or two. Once she is on your shoulders, however, the scale reading is the same as when the two of you stood side by side.

83. (a) $\vec{F}/3000$ kg toward the winch (b) 4.0×10^3 N toward the winch (c) 2.4×10^3 N toward the winch (which is now in front of trailer)

85. (a) 2.7×10^3 N forward (b) 3.0×10^3 N toward the tractor

87. (a) 0.25 m/s² to the right (b) $\vec{a}_{10\,kg\,red} = 1.0$ m/s² in direction of your push, $\vec{a}_{20\,kg} = \vec{a}_{10\,kg\,blue} = \vec{0}$ (c) $\Sigma\vec{F}_{10\,kg\,red} = 4.0$ N in direction of your push, $\Sigma\vec{F}_{20\,kg} = 4.0$ N in direction of your push, $\Sigma\vec{F}_{10\,kg\,blue} = 2.0$ N in direction of your push

89. For a car to stop from a given speed requires a fixed momentum change and therefore a fixed impulse. If we approximate the force magnitude as being constant in time, we can write $F = \Delta p/\Delta t$. If we allow a collision to occur over a greater distance (and therefore a longer time interval) the force magnitude at any given instant is smaller than the force magnitude when the car must stop in a shorter distance. The crumple zone allows more of the car to be destroyed, but it slows the passengers down over a greater distance, thereby exerting smaller-magnitude forces on them.

91. (a) 3.3 kg (b) The greatest tensile force is exerted when the elevator accelerates upward, which means when the elevator is either moving upward and increasing its speed or moving downward and decreasing its speed.

93. (a) 0.33 m/s² in direction of your push (b) $\vec{a}_{10\,kg} = 1.0$ m/s² in direction of your push, $\vec{a}_{20\,kg} = \vec{0}$ (c) 0.33 m/s² in direction of your push

95. The heavy pulley is attached to the beam, the light pulley is attached to the load. Run the rope twice around each pulley. Pull on the rope with force $\frac{9}{32}(m_\ell + m_p)g$.

97. There are at least two possibilities: (1) Use your arm strength to accelerate yourself up the free end of the rope at greater than 1.1 m/s². The tension in the rope will lift your friend off the ground. (2) Tie yourself to the same side of the rope as your friend, and pull on the other (free) end of the rope, lifting both of you with your amazing arm strength and the mechanical advantage of two rope segments to exert tension forces on your combined inertia.

99. The acceleration increases even though the force exerted on the rocket remains constant. In this case $\vec{a} = \vec{F}_{thrust}/m_{rocket}$, but the inertia is the inertia of everything attached to the rocket, including payload and fuel. Because the fuel is being expelled, the inertia is decreasing. This makes the effect of the constant force (the acceleration) increase.

Chapter 9

1. No

3. When you drop the brick from the greater height, the force of gravity is exerted on the brick over a greater distance, thus doing more work on the brick. When more work is done on the brick, it has more kinetic energy when it hits your foot and thus hurts more.

5. Initially, your hand exerts an upward force on the ball. The force displacement is nonzero because the point of application of the force is at the ball and therefore moves. Hence this force does work on the ball. Once you release the ball, the only force exerted on it is the gravitational force. The point of application is again at the ball, which is moving; thus the force displacement is nonzero, and the gravitational force does work on the ball as it rises. At the top of its path the ball reverses its motion and the gravitational force again does work on it because again the force displacement is nonzero. Finally, the laundry exerts an

upward force on the ball as the ball moves downward; this force does work on the ball because again the force displacement is nonzero.

7. No. You push down on the floor, but the floor doesn't move, and so the force displacement is zero; you do no work on the floor. (You rise because your torso and hips push down on your legs, and your leg muscles push up on your torso and hips, lifting them. Your legs do positive work on your upper body.)

9. Both observers are right in their own reference frames.

11. No, work done on a system could also change its potential energy.

13. (c) The block alone should not be used as the system because friction occurs at the block-incline interface and it is not possible to know how much thermal energy produced by friction goes into the block (i.e., into the system) and how much goes into the incline (i.e., out of the system).

15. You push a block up an incline, with the block and incline part of a system that also includes Earth (but not you). The block increases in speed as you push (positive ΔK and positive ΔU), and some energy is lost to friction (positive ΔE_{th}). All these changes constitute work you do on the system (positive W).

17. The downward trip takes longer because the ball's initial kinetic energy is converted to other forms, making the downward speed lower than the upward speed. System 1—ball: Gravity does negative work as the ball rises but does an equal amount of positive work as the ball falls. The air does negative work on the ball both as it rises and as it falls, decreasing the system's energy. System 2—ball, Earth: As the ball rises, kinetic energy is converted to gravitational potential energy, and as the ball falls that potential energy is converted to kinetic energy. The air does negative work on the ball, making the system's final energy lower than its initial energy. System 3—ball, Earth, air: The same kinetic-potential-kinetic interconversion as in system 2, plus collisions between the ball and molecules in the air cause the molecules and ball to heat up, converting some mechanical energy to thermal energy.

19. No, the work magnitudes are the same, but the work done is positive for one ball and negative for the other.

21. The time interval doubles.

23. (a) 8.6×10^2 N (b) 2.4 m/s

27. (a) Yes (b) Gravitational force, tensile force exerted by rope, resistive force exerted by water , normal force exerted by bay floor

29. 13 J

31. (a) 3.1×10^2 N (b) 6.2×10^2 N (c) $(+9.2 \times 10^2$ N$)\hat{\imath}$ where $\hat{\imath}$ points up (d) 1.5×10^2 J (e) 31 J (f) 1.5×10^2 J (g) 0 (h) -1.2×10^2 J

33. (a) 2.5×10^4 N (b) -1.3×10^4 J (c) -1.3×10^4 J

35. (a) 0.30 J (b) 75 mm (c) 0.15 J

37. They require the same amount of work.

39. (a) 2.0 J (b) 2.0 J (c) 1.0 J (d) 1.0 J (e) 1.0 J

41. 3 snowballs

43. $\dfrac{1}{2d}\left(\dfrac{mv^2}{5} - kd^2\right)$

45. They require the same amount of work.

47. 54 J

49. (a) 5.5 m/s (b) Yes, if the dart is fired vertically, some of the spring potential energy is converted to gravitational potential energy as the dart moves upward. Hence, not all the initial energy is converted to kinetic energy, making the vertical launch speed slightly slower than the horizontal launch speed.

51.

	Compression distance				
	0	0.050 m	0.10 m	0.15 m	0.20 m
K (J)	0.59	2.9	4.0	3.8	2.3
U^G (J)	0	−2.9	−5.9	−8.8	−12
U (J)	0	0.63	2.5	5.6	10

53. 6.1 J

55. (a)

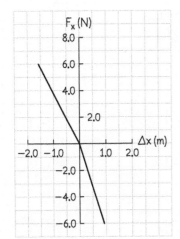

(b) Moves 0.77 m if pushed left, 0.63 m if pushed right (c) 1.2 J

57. 1.3×10^2 W

59. Because the zigzag path is spread out over a greater distance, the climber expends the same quantity of energy over a greater time interval, for a lower average power rating.

61. No. The work increases with time.

63. (a) 0.63 J (b) 1.3 W

65. (a) 9.0 W from the 3.0-N force, 6.0 W from the 2.0-N force (b) 3.0 W (c) Yes. The box is accelerating because the vector sum of the forces exerted on it is nonzero. Because power is equal to the product of force and speed, if the box moves at a higher speed, then the power from the same forces will increase in magnitude.

67. mgh

69. (a) If the initial velocity of the cart is in positive x direction, $\vec{F}_{avg} = -1.0 \times 10^3$ N $\hat{\imath}$ (b) Zero, because the point of application does not move (c) $\Delta K_{cm} = -1.0 \times 10^2$ J

71. (a) 1.9×10^3 N (b) 1.2×10^{-3} candy bars

73. The block is moving at constant speed.

75. (a) With no dissipation, it doesn't matter which way you roll the ball. (b) With energy dissipation, you want to roll the ball down hill A, so that it travels a shorter distance. The shorter path, the less energy dissipated, so the ball has a better chance of having sufficient mechanical energy to get over hill B.

77. Your center of mass must be 0.23 m above the floor. This is not practical.

79. 20 ± 10 N

Chapter 10

1. Parabolic, starting tangent to the vertical axis and curving toward the horizontal axis

3. 0.214 m

5. Ignoring air resistance, the acceleration is downward. Not ignoring air resistance, the acceleration is mostly down and a little bit in the direction opposite the velocity.

7. (a) No (b) Yes

9. (a) Acceleration to right as car speed increases (b) Very small downward acceleration but almost constant speed (c) Downward acceleration with small component to the left as car slows slightly (d) Very small acceleration downward and left, perpendicular to velocity (e) Acceleration upward and left, opposite velocity as car slows (f) Acceleration upward and left, opposite velocity as car stops

11. No

13. Five forces are exerted:

	Parallel to roof ridge	Normal to roof surface	Tangential to roof surface
Gravitational force by Earth, $\vec{F}^G_{Ep}$		X	X
Normal force by roof, $\vec{F}^n_{roof,p}$		X	
Tensile force by left rope, $\vec{F}^c_{left,p}$	X		X
Tensile force by right rope, $\vec{F}^c_{right,p}$	X	X	X
Force of static friction by roof, $\vec{F}^s_{rp}$	X		X

15. Static

17. (a) Force of static friction (b) The magnitude is equal to the magnitude of the gravitational force Earth exerts on the eraser. (c) No, unless you push with insufficient force to hold the eraser up at all. (d) It decreases to zero.

19. (a)

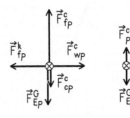

(b)

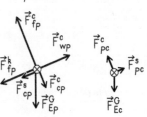

21. The normal force does positive work on the saw as the board and saw are lifted, no work as they are transported horizontally, and negative work as they are lowered onto the sawhorses; the algebraic sum of these work values is zero. The force of static friction does no work on the saw as the board and saw are lifted, positive work as their speed increases from zero to carrying speed, negative work as their speed decreases from carrying speed to zero at the sawhorses, and no work as they are lowered onto the horses; the algebraic sum of these work values is zero.

23. (*a*) 28° (*b*) 0.54

25. (*a*) They have the same speed at the bottom, but the child on the steeper slide arrives first. (*b*) The child on the steeper slide moves faster.

27. (*a*) $1.0\hat{\imath} + 4.0\hat{\jmath}$ (*b*) 4.1 units

29. (*a*) (30, −53°) (*b*) (18, −24)

31. 1.7 h

33. (*A*, ω*t*)

35. (*a*) 0.93 km (*b*) 1.0 m/s at 31° north of east (*c*) 1.4 m/s

37. (*a*) One (*b*) Two (clockwise and counterclockwise equilateral triangles) (*c*) Three (*d*) N-1 distinct patterns for N arrows

39. Path (*a*) is the best representation. Path (*b*) is a poor representation because it ends up pointing directly downward, indicating no horizontal component to the velocity; as long as it moves, the cantaloupe always has a horizontal velocity component. Path (*c*) has two big issues: no vertical acceleration at first, then abrupt acceleration at the upper right corner.

41. 0.116 m

43. (*a*) 0.40 s (*b*) 1.2 m/s

45. (*a*) Never (*b*) Never (*c*) *t* = 0.70 s

47. A position that is more than half the range

49.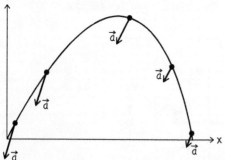

51. 6.0 m/s

53. (*a*) 1.5 s (*b*) 1.4 m (*c*) $v_{x,f}$ = 13 m/s, $v_{y,f}$ = −7.6 m/s (*d*) Yes

55. 15 m/s

57. (*a*) $\vec{a} = (-g\sin\phi)\hat{\jmath}$ (*b*) $\vec{v}(t) = (v_i\cos\theta)\hat{\imath} + (v_i\sin\theta - gt\sin\phi)\hat{\jmath}$
(*c*) $\Delta y = \dfrac{v_i^2\sin^2\theta}{2g\sin\phi}$ (*d*) $\Delta x = \dfrac{2v_i^2\sin\theta\cos\theta}{g\sin\phi}$

59. Assuming elastic collisions, (*a*) *v*/16 (*b*) *mv*/16 in the original direction of motion

61. (*a*) v_1 = 0.28 m/s, v_2 = 0.44 m/s (*b*) No

63. (*a*) $\vec{v}$ = 4.0 m/s at θ = 44° (*b*) 69 mm

65. −7.2 m²

67. (*a*) 23° (*b*) 35 units²

69. (*a*) 2.0 J (*b*) 79°

71. (*a*) 2.5 m/s (*b*) 49 mm

73. (*a*) 13 m/s (*b*) 34

77. (*a*) 1.0 m/s (*b*) 4.9 kJ (*c*) 2.0 m/s (*d*) 4.9 kJ

79. Pulling

81. μ_s = 0.40, μ_k = 0.20

83. (*a*) 4.3×10^2 N (*b*) 43 kJ

85. (*a*) 11 N (*b*) 13 N

87. (*a*) 3.4 s (*b*) 11 s (*c*) 1.5×10^2 m

89. 1.0 m

91. (*a*) 0.12 m (*b*) 0.15 m

93. (*a*) 14 m/s (*b*) 13 m/s (*c*) 13 m

95. 22 kW

97. 53 m/s

99. range

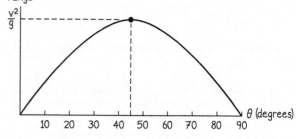

101. (*a*) 8.0×10^2 m (*b*) $(-20 \text{ m/s})\hat{\jmath}$ (*c*) -4.0×10^2 m

103. (*a*) $(1.49 \text{ N})\,\hat{\imath} + (5.33 \times 10^{-3} \text{ N})\,\hat{\jmath}$ (*b*) 55.5 J

105. 75°

107. In order for a 100-kg pair to reach the top at a maximum speed of 5.0 m/s, the counterweight must have an inertia of 6.6×10^1 kg. For a 200-kg pair, the counterweight inertia must be 1.3×10^2 kg. The plan won't work. Either the 200-kg pair will not be accelerated or the 100-kg pair will be accelerated to a speed higher than 5.0 m/s.

109. (*a*) $y(x) = (\tan\theta)x - \dfrac{g}{2v^2\cos^2\theta}x^2$ (*b*) 23 m/s (*c*) 70 N

111. 51 mm

Chapter 11

1. Innermost track

3. The distance around the curved track is shorter in the inner lane, meaning the distance the passing car has to travel in order to pass is shorter in the inner lane than it would be in an outer lane.

5.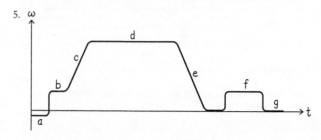

7. $p = 2, q = -1$

9.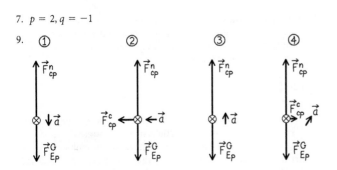

11. As the spinner rotates, the water and lettuce, because of their inertia, tend to move in a straight line tangent to the spinner circumference. Because it cannot fit through the holes in the spinner wall, the lettuce can't move in a straight line. The contact force exerted on it by the wall keeps it inside. Water drops can pass through the holes and do so, separating from the lettuce and leaving it dry. Initially, the drops might be held to the lettuce by cohesive forces, but as the spinner speeds up, these forces are insufficient to keep the drops moving in a circle, and they spin out of the spinner.

13. Ignoring friction between the car and track, the car climbs up the right wall as it enters the left turn. Because the student's body and the metal chunk climb this wall by the same amount as the car, the chunk stays between his knees, just as it was before the ride began.

15. (a)

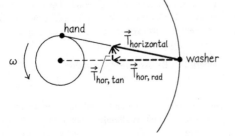

(b) Tensile force exerted by string. Acceleration has a radial and a tangential component. (c) Ignoring air resistance: hand stays at circle center; tensile force is directed toward circle center and acceleration has no tangential component.

17. Because the body's rotational inertia is greater in the layout position than in the tucked position. The radius of the circular path the head and feet travel during the flip is larger in the layout position than in the tucked position. Because the body remains airborne for roughly the same time interval in either position, the gymnast must have much greater kinetic energy in the layout position to complete the backflip.

19. (a) No, the inertia of the bowling ball is so much greater than that of the baseball that even placing the rotation axis on the outer surface of the baseball would not make it as difficult to spin as the bowling ball. (b) Yes. You could choose to revolve the baseball around an axis that passes no closer than, say, 5 m to the baseball, while choosing an axis passing just centimeters from the edge of the bowling ball. The rotational inertias are $I_{bowl} = m_{bowl}r_{bowl}^2$ and $I_{base} = m_{base}r_{base}^2$, where r is distance from either ball to the axis of revolution. Choose an arbitrary location for this axis and place the two balls at distances r_{bowl} and $r_{base} \gg r_{bowl}$ from the axis. Once the inequality $r_{base} \gg r_{bowl}$ is sufficiently large to make the difference between m_{bowl} and m_{base} insignificant, $I_{base} > I_{bowl}$.

21. (a) Rotational inertia decreases. (b) Carousel rotational speed increases.

23. $0.10 \text{ s}^{-1}, 1.5 \times 10^{-4} \text{ s}^{-1}$

25. $8.7 \times 10^{-3} \text{ s}^{-2}$

27. Figure P11.27(b)

29. (a) $3mg \sin \theta$ (b) $3mg$

31. (a) $5.95 \times 10^{-3} \text{ m/s}^2$ (b) $3.55 \times 10^{22} \text{ N}$ toward the center of mass of the Earth–sun system, which is essentially the center of the sun.

33. 19.6 m/s^2

35. (a) 58 s^{-1} (b) 2.9×10^2 (c) 19 m/s (d) 96 m

37. (a) $\sqrt{2g(h-d)}$ (b) $mg\left(1 + \dfrac{2(h-d)}{R}\right)$ (c) $\sqrt{2g(h-d-R)}$ (d) $mg\left(\dfrac{2(h-d-R)}{R}\right)$ (e) $g\left(\dfrac{2(h-d-R)}{R}\right)$

39. (a) 18 m/s^2 (b) 0 (c) The vertical component of the normal force exerted by the cone on the ball (d) 0.92 m

41. 31 J

43. (a) $12 \text{ kg} \cdot \text{m}^2/\text{s}$ (b) $4.0 \text{ kg} \cdot \text{m}^2/\text{s}$

45. In order to continue moving in a circle at constant speed along with the pail, the water must have centripetal acceleration. This acceleration must be due to some force directed toward the center of the circle. When you whirl the pail rapidly, the forces exerted on the water are the force of gravity and a large contact force exerted by the bottom of the pail. When you whirl the pail at just the right speed, the gravitational force alone is sufficient to keep the water from spilling out. If you whirl too slowly, the acceleration due to gravity is larger than the necessary centripetal acceleration and the water spills out.

47. (a) $\dfrac{4v_i}{5\ell}$ (b) $\left(-\dfrac{3v}{5}\right)\hat{i}$ where $\hat{i}$ points in the direction of $\vec{v}_i$

49. 3.0 s^{-1}

51. $\omega_{\vartheta,i}/2$

53. $2mr^2 \sin^2 \theta$

55. $\frac{5}{3} mR^2$

57. 0.16 s^{-1}

59. (a) $\frac{1}{2} mR^2$ (b) $\frac{1}{12} ma^2$

61. The day would lengthen.

63. 20 to $35 \text{ kg} \cdot \text{m}^2$, depending on your inertia

65. $2.0 \times 10^2 \text{ s}^{-1}$

67. $\frac{13}{8} mR_{outer}^2$

69. $0.28 \text{ kg} \cdot \text{m}^2$

71. $8.2 \times 10^{-2} \text{ J}$

73. (a) $\dfrac{2m\ell^2}{3}$ (b) $\dfrac{m\ell^2}{6}$

75. $0.25 \text{ kg} \cdot \text{m}^2$

77. (a) $0.535°$ (b) $0.517°$

79. The liquid inside the egg continues to rotate once you stop the egg. When stopped and released, viscous forces between the liquid and shell soon cause the shell to move along with the liquid, causing the entire egg to spin. In a hard-boiled egg, there is no liquid to continue rotating once you stop the egg. When you stop the outside of the hard-boiled egg, you stop everything.

81. (a) No work is done. (b) At the lowest point

83. (a) Force independent of r (b) Force proportional to $1/r^2$ (c) Force proportional to r

85. $\dfrac{6m_b v_b}{(3m_d + 4m_b)\ell_d}$

87. The acceleration due to gravity at her head is about 6.5 m/s². To avoid lightheadedness, you figure that the acceleration due to gravity at her head must be within 5% of the value at her feet. To accomplish this, the radius of the cylinder must be no less than 40 m.

89. You should maintain a constant tension of at least 74 N in the string while you unwind the entire string.

91. $\omega(x) = \dfrac{\sqrt{\left(\frac{3}{4}v\right)^2 - \frac{3}{2}g\left(\sqrt{d^2 - 4dx - 4x^2} - d\right)}}{d}$

Chapter 12

1. You can exert a greater torque by exerting a greater force tangential to the lid. The coefficient of static friction between the rubber and the lid is likely to be greater than the coefficient of static friction between your bare hand and the lid.

3. Torque is a better tightening specification because giving the specification in terms of the force exerted on the wrench you use does not provide a unique specification for how tight you fasten the bolts. You could use a wrench of any length, and the force necessary to get the correct tightness would be different for each different wrench length.

5. c and e

7. Option a. The baton's center of mass is closer to the larger sphere, making the lever arm distance between your hand and the center of mass longer in option a than in option b. The longer lever arm distance gives you finer control.

9. $\tau_B < \tau_A < \tau_C < \tau_D$

11. $C_A/C_B = 1/4$

13. The stick does not rotate, which means the torques caused by the contact forces exerted on it by your two fingers cancel each other. The farther a finger is from the stick's center of mass, the greater its lever arm distance and the smaller the contact force it exerts on the stick. So as you begin sliding your fingers, any slight difference in lever arm distance causes the finger farther from the center of mass—the left finger, say—to exert a smaller contact force and so slide more easily than the right finger. Once your left finger moves far enough toward the center of the stick to make the right lever arm distance greater than the left lever arm distance, the right finger exerts the smaller contact force and so speeds up, but only until its lever arm distance is less than that of the left finger. This tradeoff continues until the fingers meet, always at the 0.5-m mark.

15. c

17. (a)

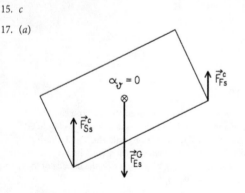

(b) The son carries the greater share of the load. (c) They would carry equal loads in the case of a sheet of plywood.

19. As the painter climbs, he moves farther from the point where the ladder contacts the carpeting. This gives him a greater lever arm distance, meaning that as he climbs he causes a greater torque around the axis running through the contact point.

21. $\tan^{-1}\left(\dfrac{1}{2\mu_s}\right)$

23. In the United States, the threading of nearly all bolts, screws, and nuts is such that a clockwise rotation tightens and a counterclockwise rotation loosens. From the perspective of the mechanic looking at his or her work, clockwise rotation is comparable to rightward motion and counterclockwise rotation is comparable to leftward motion. (Picture your hand placed on the 12 on a clock face: moving to the 1 is to the right, moving to the 11 is to the left.) Note that this clockwise-counterclockwise convention is consistent with the right-hand rule. With a nut on a bolt, for instance, the direction of the torque is the direction that the nut should move (down the body of the bolt to tighten, for example).

25. Positive x direction

27. 90° around the y axis followed by −90° around x axis

29. (a) 0.75 m from either end of the rod (b) 0.30 m from the heavier bucket

31. $8.2 \times 10^{-1}\,\text{s}^{-1}$

33. You fall backwards. The axis around which you are free to rotate (your toes) is right up against the wall. Your center of mass is not right up against the wall; it is near the (back-to-front) center of your body. Hence the force of gravity exerted on you causes a torque that tends to rotate you backwards about your toes.

35. $10^{-10}\,T_E$, where T_E is Earth's period of rotation, 24 h.

37. (a) 45 N (b) 30 N

39. If there are no external torques on the helicopter, its angular momentum must remain constant. With only a main rotor, the body of the helicopter would therefore rotate in the direction opposite the direction in which the rotor rotates. The purpose of the tail rotor is to exert a force on the air surrounding the craft, causing an external torque that keeps the body from rotating.

41. (a) $17\,\text{s}^{-1}$ (b) $1.2 \times 10^2\,\text{J}$ (c) The additional energy comes from work done by the skater's muscles as she pulls her arms and weighted hands in toward her body. This force is not perpendicular to the motion because the hands and weights spiral in toward the center of her body.

43. (a) Stays the same (b) increases (c) increases

45. (a) The center of mass is a distance $\ell/3$ from the ball. (b) $v_f = v_i/3$ in the direction of the ball's initial motion. (c) $\omega_f = v/\ell$

47. (a) $7/17\,\omega$ clockwise (b) −0.42

49. The object continues to roll without slipping. Nothing changes when the coefficient of friction increases. Only the maximum possible force of static friction increases, not the actual force of static friction exerted.

51. (a) $3.5\,\text{m/s}^2$ (b) 4.2 N

53. $\sqrt{3}/6$

55. The two cans reach the bottom at the same instant.

57. $t_h/t_s = \sqrt{25/21}$

59. (a) $\dfrac{2}{7}g$ (b) $\dfrac{2}{5}g$

61. 1.7×10^{-1} J

63. 1.4 m

65. 0.15 MJ

67. 5.9 s^{-2}

69. 43 s^{-1}

71. (a) 5.0 J (b) 5.0 J (c) 7.6×10^2 s^{-1}

73. (a) 3.4 m/s (b) $T = \dfrac{mv_i^2 r_i^2}{r^3} = 2.8$ N (c) 2.3×10^{-1} J

75. $54°$

77. (a) Because $L = mrv_i$, treat the cube as a particle located at the cube's center, and insert $r = d/2$. This yields $L = mdv_i/2$. (b) At the instant of collision, the point of application of the contact force exerted by the lip on the cube is at the axis of rotation. The lever arm distance for this force is zero and thus this force cannot cause a torque about the axis. Hence there is no external torque on the cube and its angular momentum must be constant. (c) $3g/4d$ (d) $\sqrt{\dfrac{16gd}{3\sqrt{2}}}$

79. To change your angular momentum, there must be a torque on you. Otherwise your body continues moving in a straight line and you fall off the bike.

81. (a) 30 N·m (b) 26 N·m (c) 21 N·m (d) 15 N·m (e) 0 (f) 19 N·m

83. Writing $\vec{A} = A_x \hat{\imath} + A_y \hat{\jmath}$ and $\vec{B} = B_x \hat{\imath} + B_y \hat{\jmath}$, you can compute the vector product one component at a time, noting that for any two components along the same axis the vector product is always zero. Thus you have $\vec{A} \times \vec{B} = A_x B_y \hat{k} + A_y B_x (-\hat{k}) = (A_x B_y - A_y B_x)\hat{k}$.

85. (a) 20 N·m in the direction opposite the direction of motion (b) 68 N·m in the direction of motion

87. (a) 3.0 s (b) 4.9 rev

89. 0.37 N·m

91. $\hat{\jmath}$

93. (a) The engine is connected to the rear wheels, and so the force that accelerates the car forward is exerted at the bottom of the rear wheels. Because the line of action of this force goes below the center of mass of the car, the force causes a torque on the car that tends to lift the front wheels off the road. (b) With front-wheel drive, the force that accelerates the car forward is exerted at the bottom of the front wheels. The line of action of this force also goes below the center of mass of the car causing a torque on the car, but now the rear wheels are pushed into the road.

95. (a) 7.8×10^2 N (b) 6.0×10^2 N (c) 8.6×10^2 N and 6.6×10^2 N

97. 1×10^4 s^{-1}

99. The torque is the gravitational force exerted on the cyclist times the lever arm distance, which is the length of the metal rod attaching each pedal to the bicycle. For a typical human ($m = 75$ kg) and bicycle (lever arm distance 0.3 m), this yields a torque of 10^2 N·m.

101. (a) 5.3 m/s^2 (b) 0.27

103. 4.0 m

105. (a) 3.1×10^2 N (b) 5.5×10^2 N

107. (a) 2.5 m/s^2 (b) 9.1 s^{-1} (c) 9.1 s^{-1} (d) 22 N (e) 60 W

109. The yo-yo accelerates downward, and the magnitude of the acceleration is $\dfrac{g}{1 + a/2b}$.

Chapter 13

1. The acceleration due to gravity increases linearly with radius.

3. 18 km

5. 6 : 1

7. $\dfrac{m_1}{m_2} = 1$

9. Torque can be interpreted as the second time derivative of the same area whose first derivative represents angular momentum.

11. (a) Yes, when you jump the scale shows a higher number at first. (b) No, the magnitude of the gravitational force exerted by Earth on you has not changed.

13. (a) 9.8 m/s^2 downward (b) 1.6 m/s^2 downward (c) Conclusion would not change.

15. The airplane moves downward at 2g. During the time interval in which this motion takes place, the person is in free fall, accelerating downward at g. This means that, relative to the plane, he is accelerating *upward* at g! This relative motion of plane and person is exactly like the person falling onto his head from an upside-down position on solid ground.

17. At least two possibilities to obtain a second scale reading: (1) Hold the tube horizontally and mark the unstretched (0 g) position, or (2) Add a second identical bob to find the 2 g position.

19. (a) The milk climbs the sides of the bowl, and the milk surface becomes concave. (b) Either a massive hemisphere placed near the milk or the combination of a toroid around the bowl and a massive object beneath the bowl.

21. 6.7×10^{-15} N

23. $\dfrac{4}{9}$

25. $3 \times 10^{11}g$

27. 3.2 km, 32 km, 3.5×10^2 km

29. 1×10^1 h

30. (a) Force exerted by Sun (b) $F_{SE}^G / F_{ME}^G = 1.8 \times 10^2$

31. 1.05×10^{18} kg

33. $Gm_{test}^2 \sqrt{\left(\dfrac{1}{d^2} - \dfrac{2d}{(d^2 + \ell^2)^{3/2}}\right)^2 + \left(\dfrac{2\ell}{(d^2 + \ell^2)^{3/2}}\right)^2}$

35. $\dfrac{Gm_E r}{R_E^3}$

37. No. A 70-kg person can jump high enough to bring his center of mass to a height of 1.0 m to 1.5 m. That means the legs can exert forces capable of increasing the gravitational potential energy by about 10^3 J On the surface of Toro, this person's gravitational potential energy is -1.9×10^3 J, meaning he is bound to Toro by more energy than he can deliver in a jump.

39. Closer to object 1; specifically, a distance $(\sqrt{2} - 1)d$ from object 1 and a distance $(2 - \sqrt{2})d$ from object 2

41. (a) $\dfrac{Cm_E m_m}{2h^2}$ (b) $\sqrt{\dfrac{Cm_E}{h^2}}$

43. 9.4×10^2 km

45. 2.3×10^{30} N·m^2

47. (a) $\vec{0}$ (b) -1.00×10^{-12} J/g (c) -5.0×10^{-13} J

49. Over a larger range

51. Elastic

53. $19 \, \text{km/s}$

55. Being in very low orbit means that the radial distance from the satellite to the center of the moon is approximately the moon radius R_{moon}. The projectile reaches a distance $2R_{\text{moon}}$ from the moon's center, which is a height R_{moon} above the moon surface.

57. $v_{\text{comet}}/v_{\text{Mercury}} = \sqrt{2}$

59. $\sqrt{2C/a}$

61. $7.5 \, \text{km/s}$

63. (a) $2.2 \times 10^{-7} \, \text{s}^{-1}$ (b) $89 \, \text{km/s}$

67. To the right in the figure

69. $\dfrac{Gm_{\text{ring}}m_{\text{obj}}s}{(R_{\text{ring}}^2 + s^2)^{3/2}}$

70. (a) $0.54 \dfrac{Gm_{\text{inner}}m_{\text{obj}}}{R^2}$ (b) $0.83 \dfrac{Gm_{\text{inner}}m_{\text{obj}}}{R^2}$ (c) 0

71. (a) $-\dfrac{2Gm_{\text{part}}m_{\text{disk}}}{R^2}\left(1 - \dfrac{y}{\sqrt{R^2 + y^2}}\right)\hat{\jmath}$

73. From a theoretical standpoint, it does not matter. However, there may be logistical considerations, such as how much atmosphere you must traverse before reaching deep space, where air resistance is negligible. With these secondary considerations, it is best to launch vertically.

75. The acceleration vector is directed towards one focus of the ellipse. The tangential component could be greater than the perpendicular component of acceleration when the satellite is crossing a semiminor axis, provided $e^2 > \frac{1}{2}$. If the eccentricity is much greater, this condition could be satisfied elsewhere in the orbit. However, it can never be satisfied when the satellite is crossing a semimajor axis.

77. For $R_{\text{planetoid}} \approx 5 \, \text{m}$, mass density must be $6 \times 10^9 \, \text{kg/m}^3$.

79. $4.24 \times 10^7 \, \text{m}$ above the surface of Jupiter

81. Satellite is $2.7 \times 10^2 \, \text{km}$ above Earth's surface.

83. (a) $\rho_{\text{max}} = \dfrac{3H^2}{8\pi G} = 9.6 \times 10^{-27} \, \text{kg/m}^3$ (b) The estimate is about the same as what we found for part (a). As it is, the universe seems balanced between being open and being closed. If there were no dark matter or dark energy in the universe, it would be much less dense than estimated, and we would expect it to be open.

Chapter 14

1. (b), (e), (f)

3. A, 33 μs after noon; B, 67 μs after noon; C, 75 μs after noon; D, 94 μs after noon.

5. (a) Later (b) Same time (c) Earlier

7. c_0

9. $1.4 \times 10^2 \, \text{m}$

11. Straight calculation shows the speed of each end larger than the speed of light. This cannot happen because the concept of a rigid object is an approximation that breaks down under such extreme conditions: The rod would bend into a spiral shape so that no portion of it moves faster than the speed of light.

13. Longer than.

15. $1.4 \times 10^3 \, \text{m}$

17. $2.88 \times 10^3 \, \text{s}$

19. $0.5 \, \text{km}^2$

21. Zero

23. Energy, mass, and inertia

25. $3.59 \times 10^6 \, \text{m}$

27. (a) Lightlike (b) Lightlike (c) Timelike (d) Timelike

29. $v_A = 0.48c_0$, $v_B = 0.96c_0$

31. $0.99c_0$

33. $(1 - 2.47 \times 10^{-7})c_0$

35. (a) $8.00 \, \text{km}$ (b) $6.14 \times 10^{-5} \, \text{s}$

37. 2.13

39. (a) $7.62 \times 10^3 \, \text{km}$ (b) $1.27 \times 10^4 \, \text{km}$

41. (a) $3.625 \times 10^{14} \, \text{m}$ (b) $8.108 \times 10^{15} \, \text{m}$

43. (a) $59.5°$ (b) Length 5.00 m, wingspan 8.00 m, opening angle $77.3°$.

47. (a) $x = 0$ (b) $t = 0$ (c) $x = 1.77 \times 10^8 \, \text{m}$ (d) $t = 0.591 \, \text{s}$

49. (a) $5.93 \times 10^3 \, \text{s}$ (b) $1.43 \times 10^{12} \, \text{m}$ (c) $4.70 \times 10^3 \, \text{s}$

51. (a) $11.3°$ (b) $24.6°$

53. (a) 1.00 (no increase) (b) 1.64

57. $9.46 \times 10^{-20} \, \text{kg} \cdot \text{m/s}$

59. Defining the direction of motion of the 150-kg probe to be the $+x$ direction, $\vec{v}_{150 \, \text{kg}} = (+0.764c_0)\,\hat{\imath}$, $\vec{v}_{250 \, \text{kg}} = (-0.578c_0)\,\hat{\imath}$

61. (a) $\gamma_C > \gamma_B > \gamma_A$ (b) $K_C > K_B > K_A$ (c) $|\vec{v}_C| > |\vec{v}_B| > |\vec{v}_A|$ (d) $p_C > p_B > p_A$

63. $1.73 \times 10^{12} \, \text{J}$; $E_{1 \, \text{kg U}}/E_{1 \, \text{kg coal}} = 5.8 \times 10^4$

65. $E_1 = \dfrac{m_1 c_0^2}{\sqrt{1 - \dfrac{(m_1 - m_2 - m_{\text{orig}})(m_1 + m_2 - m_{\text{orig}})(m_1 - m_2 + m_{\text{orig}})(m_1 + m_2 + m_{\text{orig}})}{(m_1^2 - m_2^2 + m_{\text{orig}}^2)^2}}}$

$p_1 = \dfrac{m_1 c_0 \sqrt{(m_1 - m_2 - m_{\text{orig}})(m_1 + m_2 - m_{\text{orig}})(m_1 - m_2 + m_{\text{orig}})(m_1 + m_2 + m_{\text{orig}})}}{\sqrt{(m_1^2 - m_2^2 + m_{\text{orig}}^2)^2 - (m_1 - m_2 - m_{\text{orig}})(m_1 + m_2 - m_{\text{orig}}) \times \sqrt{(m_1 - m_2 + m_{\text{orig}})(m_1 + m_2 + m_{\text{orig}})}}}$

67. (a) $v = (1 - 8.98 \times 10^{-9})c_0$ (b) $1.40 \times 10^4 \, \text{GeV}/c_0^2$ or $2.49 \times 10^{-23} \, \text{kg}$

69. (a) $3.01 \times 10^{-10} \, \text{J}$ (b) $9.0 \times 10^8 \, \text{m}$

71. 30.1 m, $24.2°$ away from vertical.

73. Yes, an observer in any reference frame moving along the perpendicular bisector of a line drawn between the two events sees the events as simultaneous.

75. (a) $0.986c_0$ (b) $91.1 \, \text{s}$

77. If Orion's initial position is corrected for light travel time, the station will have just under 45 minutes to evacuate, so no re-write is required, just some hurry. If Orion's position is not corrected for travel time, so that the ship is seen at one location but has continued to travel toward the station while the light signal is in transit, there is no hope and a rewrite is definitely in order.

79. You can complete the race in the shortest time interval (measured in the Earth reference frame) by flying at speed $c_0/\sqrt{2}$.

Chapter 15

1. Least blurry at highest and lowest wing positions because at these positions vertical motion of wings is instantaneously zero.

3.

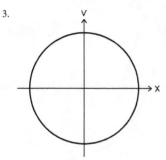

5. $0.5 < x < 3.5$

7. 5 s

9. Motion is periodic motion because it repeats itself over time but is not simple harmonic motion because its position and velocity cannot be described by a simple sine or cosine function. As yo-yo rises and falls, not all of its potential energy is converted to translational kinetic energy; some of it becomes rotational kinetic energy.

11. 127 Hz

13. Three harmonics

15. $\frac{4}{\pi} \sum\limits_{n=1}^{\infty} \frac{1}{2n-1} \sin\left[(2n-1)\frac{2\pi t}{T}\right]$, where T is the period of one square "oscillation"

21. $x(t) = A \sin\left(\frac{2\pi t}{T} + \phi_i\right)$

$v_x(t) = \frac{2\pi A}{T} \cos\left(\frac{2\pi t}{T} + \phi_i\right)$

$a_x(t) = -\left(\frac{2\pi}{T}\right)^2 A \sin\left(\frac{2\pi t}{T} + \phi_i\right)$

23. (a) Yes (b) $-\pi/2$

29. 0.30 J

33. 0.69

35. 1/3

37. (a) Increase (b) It decreases.

39. (a) Yes (b) No (c) Yes (d) Yes (e) No (f) No (g) If the cup is glued to the table, the answers do not change. If the cup is free to move, then the coffee would not fly out of the cup even if the cup flew into the air in free fall (at least until it hit the table again).

41. (a) 0.059 m (b) 2.7 s^{-1} (c) 4.6 mJ (d) 2.6 N/m (e) 5.6 rad
(f) $x(t) = A \sin(\omega t + \phi_i)$ where $A = 0.059$ m, $\omega = 2.7$ s^{-1},
$\phi_i = 5.6$ rad

43. 0.062 m

45. (a) 300 N/m (b) $x(t) = A \sin(\omega t + \phi_i)$, where $A = 0.020$ m,
$\omega = 71$ s^{-1}, $\phi_i = 1.6$

47. 0.060 m

49. 0.25 m

51. Pendulum on left

53. $v = \sqrt{2g\ell(\cos \vartheta_{max} - \cos \vartheta)}$

55. (a) 9.11×10^{-4} kg·m^2 (b) 0.766 s

57. (a) 0.15 rad (b) 0.10 m/s

59. 0.90 s

61. $\Delta T = -\frac{1}{12}\frac{m_{rod}}{m_{bob}} + \frac{11}{288}\left(\frac{m_{rod}}{m_{bob}}\right)^2$ plus higher order terms

63. ω_d increases.

65. (b) 4.24 Hz (c) 0.0800 s (d) 2.13 rad

67. (a) 25 s (b) Instant $t = 18$ s

69. (a) 5.00 s^{-1} (b) 2.00 kg/s (c) $y(t) = Ae^{-tb/2m} \sin(\omega_d t + \phi_i)$ where $A = 0.100$ m, $b = 2.00$ kg/s, $m = 0.500$ kg, $\omega_d = 4.58$ s^{-1}

71. (a) 0.58% (b) 0.69

73. (a) $2\sqrt{mk}$ (b) Damping occurs so quickly that the spring returns to equilibrium position before being fully compressed. In the car, this means the system returns quickly to normal level rather than oscillating for a long time interval; the negative aspect is that springs do not absorb road-bump shocks as well as a spring system having $b \le b_{crit}$.

75. $x(t) = Ae^{-t/2\tau} \sin(\omega t + \phi)$ where $A = 67$ mm, $\tau = 7.2$ s, $\omega = 2\pi$ s^{-1}, and $\phi = 3\pi/2$

77. (a) Energy increases by factor of 4. (b) Maximum speed increases by factor of 2. (c) Period does not change.

79. $f_{half}/f_{whole} = \sqrt{2}$

83. 0.14 kg·m^2

85. (a) 0.522 kg·m^2 (b) 0.129 kg·m^2 (c) 1.74 s

87. $mv^2/6$

89. You cut the wire to a length equal to the distance the ball stretches vertical spring.

91. Your mass is 71.4 kg.

Chapter 16

1. Yes, water can carry both transverse and longitudinal waves.

3. (a)

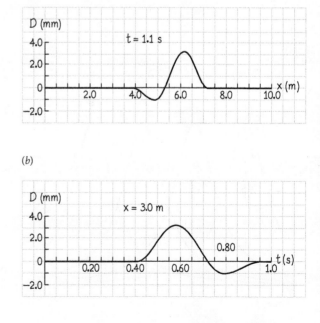

(b)

5.

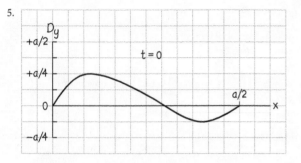

7. The definition is the same as for harmonic periodic wave: number of cycles per second executed by each medium particle.

9. The first crate must have struck when the cable was under minimal tension, resulting in low wave speed; the second crate must have struck when the cable was under significant tension, resulting in high wave speed. The tension change was probably the result of the ship's drifting away from the dock in the time interval between the two incidents.

13. (a) 0.10 m (b) 0.20 m (c) 0.30 m

15. Zero

17. Reflected wave not inverted

19. (a) Thinner string

(b)

21.

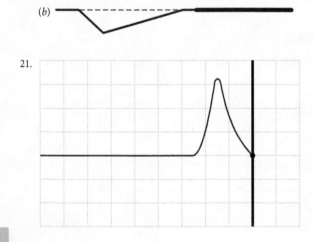

23. 30 m

25. (a)

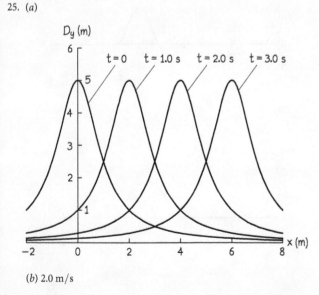

(b) 2.0 m/s

27. (a) $f(x, t) = \dfrac{a}{b^2 + (x - ct)^2}$, where $c = 1.75$ m/s

(b)

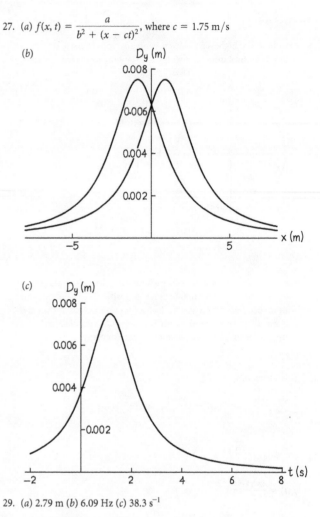

(c)

29. (a) 2.79 m (b) 6.09 Hz (c) 38.3 s^{-1}

31. 382 m/s in negative x direction

33. (a) 0.50 m (b) 5.7 × 10^2 s^{-1} (c) 90 Hz (d) 0.011 s

35. 0, 0.16 m, 0.32 m from tank edge

37. $f/5$

39. (a) 110 Hz (b) At frequencies n(110 Hz), where n is any integer

41. $A = 3.00 \times 10^{-2}$ m for both components; components travel in opposite directions at 1.20 m/s.

43. (a) 0.60 m (b) 10 mm in the y direction

(c) $f(x,t) = (0.010 \text{ m}) \sin\left(\dfrac{2\pi}{0.60 \text{ m}}x + \dfrac{\pi}{2}\right) \cos\left(\dfrac{2\pi}{0.60 \text{ s}}t\right)$

45. 0.0578 m

47. 4.4 kg

49. (1) Shorten string by pinching off part of it; (2) replace string with one having lower linear mass density; (3) increase string tension.

51. 22 m/s

53. Fundamental frequency decreases by factor of 4

55. 4.62 × 10^6 N

57. 1.22 kW

59. (a) No change in power required. (b) Power required increased by factor of 16. (c) Power required decreased by factor of 0.25.

61. 2.3 × 10^5 J

63. 14.3 m/s

65. (a) $f(x,t) = a \sin(bx - qt)$, where $a = 0.0725$ m, $b = 2.09$ m^{-1}, $q = 377$ s^{-1} (b) 89.6 W

67. The fact that the speed at which the surfer moves forward toward the wave base equals the speed at which the wave moves forward.

71. (a) No, because the pulse needs a nonzero time interval to travel the length of the rope. (b) No, again because the pulse needs a nonzero time interval to travel the length of the bar, though the pulse speed is much greater in the bar than in the rope.

73. $\Delta t_B = 0.87 \Delta t_A$

75. (a) 0.51 m/s (b) 12 s

77. (a) 0.500 m (b) 260 Hz (c) $f(x,t) = A \sin\left[\dfrac{2\pi}{\lambda} x\right] \cos[\omega t]$, where $A = 0.0200$ m, $\lambda = 0.500$ m, $\omega = 1.63 \times 10^3$ s^{-1}

79. 1.9 m/s

81. For the pulse to travel end to end through a rope of length ℓ, $\Delta t = 2\sqrt{\ell/g}$.

Chapter 17

1. The approaching train emits waves that travel through the air and the track; those traveling through the air spread out spherically, those traveling in the track remain (largely) confined to the track, making the vibrations they cause detectable at greater distance. Also, the speed of vibrations through steel is greater than the speed of sound through air.

3. Yes, as long as the sound waves are free to spread out spherically from the source (professor's mouth). However, large lecture halls are often designed to have sound waves reflect off the walls and ceiling; in such cases, the amplitude may not drop off as $1/r$.

7. Because the bat feels air compressions created by your shout.

9. (a)

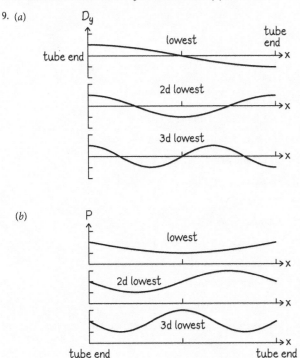

11. Nodal lines become antinodal lines, and vice-versa.

13. Because waves reflecting off the wall behind the speakers can travel to parts of the room that might otherwise be at the nodes.

15. The ripples are two-dimensional surface waves. The vibration causes the cup interior to act like a chain of sources. Because waves propagate away from sources, the wavefronts are parallel to the cup interior and therefore circular.

17. (a) $\theta = \sin^{-1}\left[\dfrac{(m + \frac{1}{2})c}{df}\right]$, $m = 0, 1, 2, \ldots$

   (b) $\theta = \sin^{-1}\left[\left(m + \dfrac{1}{2} - \dfrac{\phi}{2\pi}\right)\dfrac{c}{df}\right]$, $m = 0, 1, 2, \ldots$

19. The sound waves she emitted diffracted around the corner and reached your ears.

21. (c) Nodal line locations in (a) are antinodal line locations in (b); antinodal line locations in (a) are nodal line locations in (b).

23. 5.0×10^{-6} W/m^2

25. 35 dB

27. 4.8 dB

29. 0.60 mW

31. (a) 3.2×10^{-3} W/m^2 (b) 7.9 W

33. 67 dB

35. (a) 70 dB (b) 6.0×10^2 W (c) 1.1×10^3 whales

37. The possible intensities at point R are $\dfrac{P}{4\pi}\left(\dfrac{1}{9\lambda} - \dfrac{1}{d}\right)^2$ where $d = 7.5\lambda, 8.5\lambda, 9.5\lambda$, or 10.5λ. The possible intensities at point Q are $\dfrac{P}{4\pi}\left(\dfrac{1}{6\lambda} + \dfrac{1}{d}\right)^2$ where $d = 4\lambda, 5\lambda, 6\lambda, 7\lambda$, or 8λ.

39. You hear both frequencies because the ear cannot resolve beats above $\Delta f = 20$ Hz.

41. 194 Hz, 198 Hz

43. $C < B < D < A$

45. 2 Hz, 4 Hz, 6 Hz

47. 6.6 Hz

49. Shift magnitude decreases.

51. 405 Hz

53. (a) 3 m/s (b) 34 m/s (c) 172 m/s

55. (a) 299 Hz (b) 298 Hz

57. (a) 450 Hz (b) 350 Hz

59. (a) 50 pulses (b) 6.2 s

61. 16 m/s away from whistle

63. 800 Hz

65. 4.7×10^2 m/s

67. 18.0 km/h

69. 50.3°

71. The reasoning is invalid because it is based on the boom being created at only one instant, the instant the plane attains Mach 1 speed. The boom is continuous at all speeds above Mach 1.

73. (a) 28° (b) 0.82 m

75. 19 m

77. No

79. (a) $f_1 = 399.8$ Hz, $f_2 = 409.8$ Hz (b) 10.0 Hz

81. Hyperbola

83. $f_b = 12.4$ Hz

85. Your current setup would only allow you to pick up radio stations 3.4 km down the road. You might try using a larger dish.

Chapter 18

1. 3.33 N

3. (a) $P_{C(top)} < P_{A,av} < P_{B,av} < P_{C(bottom)}$ (b) $F_{C(top)} < F_A < F_B < F_{C(bottom)}$

5. (a) $\vec{F}_{\ell w}^c$ at A directed to the right (b) No direction; pressure is scalar (c) $\vec{F}_{w\ell}^c$ at B directed upward (d) $\vec{F}_{\ell p}^c$ directed downward when piston pushed (e) $\vec{F}_{\ell p}^c$ directed upward when piston pulled (f) Answers (d), (e)

7. $\dfrac{1}{20}$

9. $45Gm_{planet}^2/64\pi R^4$

11. 25 N

13. (a) 125 kg/m^3 (b) Yes. (c) 1.75×10^7 kg

15. Water levels are identical.

17. Four friends

19. $\rho_1/\rho_2 = 2$

21. 2.99×10^{-3} m^3

23. (a) 0.133 kg/m^3 (b) He/H$_2$ = 0.479/0.521 = 0.919

25. 5.21 m/s

27. $v_B > v_A$, $P_B < P_A$, diameter at B < diameter at A

29. The speed of the air outside the window is greater than the speed of the air inside, making the outside pressure lower than the inside pressure, so that the smoke is pulled out of the car.

31. (a) 3.56 m/s (b) 16.4 s

33. 2.53 N

35. (a) $T_B < T_C < T_A$ (b) $P_A = P_B = P_C$

37. 2.92 mm

39. Wetting: $R_{tube} = R_{men} \cos\theta_c$; nonwetting: $R_{tube} = -R_{men}\cos\theta_c$

43. To top of tube

45. 6.3×10^4 N

47. (a) 1.5×10^4 N (b) 2.2×10^4 N (c) Because capsule mass increases as water enters through the leak

51. (a) 25 km (b) No, because at that height air resistance would not be negligible and because for water passing through such a small opening, viscosity would affect flow rate.

53. $F = P_{atm}wh/2 + gwh^2\rho/6$

55. $P = P_{atm} + mg/\pi R^2$

57. $\dfrac{P_A/P_B}{P_{A'}/P_{B'}} = 1.0$

59. 9.9×10^2 N

61. (a) 4.7×10^5 Pa (b) 80 m

63. 759 kg/m^3

69. 21.6 m/s

71. $v_2 = \sqrt{\dfrac{2gh}{1 - \left(\frac{d_2}{d_1}\right)^4}}$

73. 93%

75. (a) 4.84 m/s (b) 0.0974 m^3/s (c) 1.38 m/s

77. 2.3×10^{-5} kg

79. 2.05×10^{-7} m^3/s

81. 4.66 μJ

83. 5.43 m/s

85. $R_2/R_1 = \sqrt[4]{2}$

87. (a) 7.52 days (b) 51.5 years

89. $Q_2 = Q_1/256$

91. 6.09 m

93. (a) 1.68×10^3 N (b) 1.09×10^3 N

97. 4.88×10^{24} kg

99. $T_A = 269$ N, $T_B = 419$ N

101. (a) 0.0608 Hz (b) 0.0542 Hz

Chapter 19

1. (a) 1/13 (b) 4/13

3. 6.31×10^{-7} s

5. (a) 24 configurations (b) 624 configurations

7. 1/4

9. (a) HHHHH and HTHTH equally likely (b) Heads-up three times

11. 11 s

13. 3/10

15. $v_{av,N_2}/v_{av,O_2} = 1.069$

17. 1/14

19. 158 m/s

21. (a) 3.32×10^{-22} J (b) 102 m/s

23. (a) 1 basic state (b) 7 basic states

25. (a) 20 basic states (b) 64 basic states

27. 5 particles

29. 88 times

31. 9.79 times more likely

33. (a) C (b) A and E (c) 16 (d) 1/4

35. (a) 6 basic states (b) 30 basic states

37. 1.67×10^6 basic states

39. (a) No (b) No (c) Yes

41. The system containing 15.0-mm beads has 1.09 times more entropy.

43. 3.00×10^{18} particles

45. $S_B > S_C > S_D > S_E > S_A$

47. (a) 1.13×10^{15} (b) 34.7

49. 8 particles

51. 90 K

53. (a) 11.2 m/s (b) 12.5 m/s

55. 9

57. $\dfrac{7}{2}N\dfrac{1}{E_{th}} + \dfrac{2}{15}NE_{th}^{-13/15}$

59. 453 m/s

61. 1.1×10^4 m/s

63. (a) 5.05×10^{-20} J (b) $K_{particle}/K_{bacterium} = 1.0 \times 10^9$, $K_{particle}/K_{slug} = 1.0 \times 10^{-12}$

65. $m_B = 36m_A$

67. 181 kg·m/s

69. (a) Pressure due to helium 95.44%, pressure due to krypton 4.560%

71. (a) 4.13 m/s (b) 2.56×10^{-3} m/s

73. +0.432

75. $+8.73 \times 10^{24}$

77. $+3.50 \times 10^{23}$

79. +1.30

81. Increased by factor of 3.16

83. 8.59 K

85. (a) 2.50×10^{24}, mixed state (b) Zero

87. 1.07×10^9 basic states

89. $+2.08 \times 10^3$

91. (a) 3.69×10^{-25} kg (b) 6.38×10^{-21} J

93. 0.64%. Uranium-235

95. (a) 95.8 K (b) 1.19×10^{-21} J

97. (a) 18.6 (b) 4.31

99. 94.7 km

101. (a) 0.447 (b) 0.200

103. This is an unsafe container; its estimated life is less than 5 hours.

Chapter 20

1. Positive

3. (a) Neither (b) Quasistatic (c) Both

5. Ignoring collisions between molecules, the upper limit is about 10^3 cycles/s, because the piston must move more slowly in the x direction than the gas molecules. You can increase this frequency by increasing the gas temperature, by reducing the stroke length, or by using less massive gas particles.

7. (a) 100 K (b) 100 °C (c) 180 °F

11. (a) 22.1 °C (b) Yes

13. 2.14×10^3 °C

15. 1.5×10^7 J

17. 4.4×10^{14} J

19. (a) 1.46×10^{10} J (b) 1.5×10^2 km

21. 0.19 °C

23. 5.3×10^{-22} J (b) 6.11×10^{-21} J

25. 403 J/K³·kg

27. B

29. 0

31. $T_A = 314$ K, $T_B = 176$ K, $T_C = 102$ K

33. $W_{on\ gas} = -P_i V_i$

35. -5.0×10^2 J

37. 0.0459 m

39. 14.1 kJ

41. 0

43. (a) 0.062 K, assuming $\rho_{air} = 1.2$ kg/m³ (b) 5.2×10^5 J

45. 1.09×10^{23} atoms

47. 2.68×10^3 J

49. Reason 1: Because $C_P = C_V + k_B$, $C_P/C_V > 1$ always, regardless of number of degrees of freedom. Reason 2: 6/9 corresponds to $d = 6/11$, which is not valid because d must be integer.

51. -2.70×10^3 J (b) $+2.70 \times 10^3$ J

53. $\dfrac{P_1 V_1 T_2}{T_1 V_3}$

55. (a) 928 J (b) 928 J

57. $W = -Nk_B T \ln\left(\dfrac{V_f - nb}{V_i - nb}\right) - an^2\left(\dfrac{1}{V_f} - \dfrac{1}{V_i}\right).$

$W(a = b = 0) = -Nk_B T \ln\left(\dfrac{V_f}{V_i}\right)$

59. 5.07×10^4 Pa

61. $4N(\ln 3)$

63. $C_P = 2.5k_B$

65. 1.9×10^2 K

67. (a) $d = 3$ (b) Particles are monatomic.

69. $W = (21/20)P_i V_i$

71. (a) 5.08×10^4 J (b) 1.36 km

73. 2.4×10^{23}

75. (a) °F (b) Either °F or °C

77. -5.28×10^3 Pa

79. In the process undergone by sample A, because $Q_A = 6Nk_B T_{tp}$ and $Q_B = 0$, $Q_A > Q_B$ by $6Nk_B T_{tp}$.

81. Half a dozen tubes, but better plan on 10 because of assumptions made.

Chapter 21

1. (a)

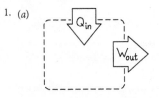

(b) System energy does not change; system entropy increases. (c) No

3. $\Delta S_3 < \Delta S_1 < \Delta S_2$

5. 425 J

7. (a) 9.6 J (b) 5.5×10^6 J (c) 2.8×10^4 kg

9. Material 2

11. 1.34×10^3 K

15. 4.09×10^3 J

17. (a) Reservoir 1 (b) Yes; device A

19. Cycle in (a)

21. 1.8 J

23. $\Delta S_{dev} = 0$, $\Delta S_{env} = 1.25 \times 10^{26}$

25. 1.0×10^{22}

27. 0.268

29. 18.8 MJ

31. $Q_{in} = 195$ J, $\eta = 0.44$

33. 0.396

35. System is reversible.

37. (a) 16 (b) 6.1

39. (a) 6.9 (b) 12 (c) 1.6×10^7 J

41. 3.1 kJ

43. 163 °C

45. $P_1 = 58.2$ kPa, $P_2 = 19.4$ kPa, $P_3 = 2.33$ kPa, $P_4 = 6.99$ kPa, $V_3 = 1.07$ m^3, $V_4 = 0.356$ m^3

47. 187 K

49. (a) 215 W (b) 6.28

51. 4.15×10^3 J

53. $\left(\dfrac{\Delta S}{\Delta t}\right)_{ocean} = -3.4 \times 10^{23}$ s^{-1}, $\left(\dfrac{\Delta S}{\Delta t}\right)_{cabin} = +3.4 \times 10^{23}$ s^{-1}

55. (a) 228 s (b) 6.38 (c) 1.93×10^5 J (d) -4.43×10^{25} (e) $+3.1 \times 10^{24}$ (not zero, because not all parts of the process are reversible).

57. 0.15

59. 0.0149

61. 431 K

63. 1.09×10^3 W

65. 7

67. 1.14×10^{24}

69. 4

71. (a) 478 K (b) 0.562 MJ

73. 2.2%

75. (a) 10.8 W (b) 1.17 W

77. (a) 0.71 (b) 12 km

79. (a) $COP_{cooling} = \dfrac{1}{\eta} - 1$ (b) $COP_{heating} = \dfrac{1}{\eta}$ (c) $COP_{cooling} > 0$, $COP_{heating} > 1$

81. (a) 20.5 kJ (b) 13.7 kJ

83. Five degrees of freedom

85.

	Car 1, Brayton cycle	Car 2, Carnot cycle
Efficiency	0.415	0.500
Work per cycle per unit mass (J/kg)	4.2	5.1
Power per unit mass (W/kg)	34	5.1
Speed after 11.5 s (m/s)	28	11
Drag force per unit mass due to air resistance at top speed[1] (N/kg)	1.2	0.33
Top speed[1] (m/s)	29	16

[1]Assuming drag force proportional to v^2.

Chapter 22

1. 9.8×10^{-4} N upward

3. 7.55 N downward

5. Any object carrying the third type of charge either would be attracted to both the T strip and the B strip or would be repelled by both of them.

7. (a) Stick C to a flat surface, then press A down on top of C such that the two pieces overlap along only half their lengths. Next press B down on top of the half of C that is not covered by A, so that B and C also overlap along only half their lengths. Holding A and B by the ends not stuck to C, remove A and B from C. The ends that were stuck to C have the same charge and repel each other. (b) No. Charge is a conserved quantity. This means that as A and B acquire a surplus charge of one type from C, C is left with a surplus of the opposite type of charge and so is attracted to A and B.

9. (a) 10^{-4} m^2, comparable to area of a fingernail (b) 2.6×10^{-5} m^2, making estimate off by one order of magnitude

11. The wriststrap allows any small amount of surplus charge that might build up on the technician to immediately discharge to the ground. This prevents a buildup of static charge and so eliminates any possibility of a spark.

13. Lightning occurs when there is an enormous surplus of one type of charge built up in clouds. The clouds then exert an attractive force on oppositely charged particles at Earth's surface. Once a large amount of charge collects on the ground where a person is standing, the charge moves into the person's body and travels to the head and along each strand of hair. Because each strand carries the same type of charge, the strands repel each other and stand out away from the person's head.

15. (a) 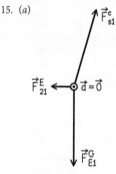 (b) 1.41×10^{-3} N directed away from clip exerting the force (c) No; that the strings form an angle tells you that the clips repel each other, meaning they carry the same type of charge, and so no discharge is possible.

17. (a) Place B and C on same side of A. (b) Place B and C on opposite sides of A.

19. Attractive

21. pith ball 1   pith ball 2

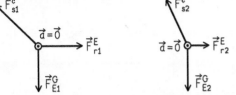

23. (a) The sphere rolls toward the rod. (b) If the quantity of the positive charge on the sphere is very small, polarization of the charge carriers in the sphere is the dominant effect and the sphere rolls toward the rod. If the quantity of the positive charge on the sphere is large, the sphere rolls away from rod.

25. (a) $F_A^E < F_C^E < F_B^E$ (b) $F_A^E < F_C^E < F_B^E$ (c) $F_B^E < F_C^E < F_A^E$

27. The polarized charge distribution in a larger chunk induces polarization in a smaller chunk. The two polarized chunks are therefore attracted to each other, collide, and cohere.

29. 1.02×10^{-10} N, repulsive

31. (a) $F_x^E = -3.6 \times 10^{-4}$ N, $F_y^E = 0$ (b) $F_x^E = 0$, $F_y^E = 1.0 \times 10^{-3}$ N

33. $-3.78 \, \mu C$

35. $\dfrac{F^E}{F^G} = 1.35 \times 10^{20}$

37. (a) 4 units (b) 8 units

39. 8.51×10^{-6} C

41. (a) $F_{12}^E / 8$ (b) Yes

43. (a) 1.6×10^{-5} N

(b, c)

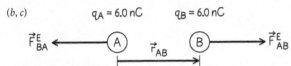

$q_A = 6.0$ nC $q_B = 6.0$ nC

45. $2.0 \, \mu C$ and $4.0 \, \mu C$

47. 2 electrons.

49. (a) The balls are initially attracted to each other due to polarization of the uncharged ball. Once they touch, they share charge and repel each other. When they come to rest, the two strings make the same angle with the vertical.

(b) $q = \sqrt{\dfrac{d^3 mg}{2k\sqrt{\ell^2 - d^2/4}}}$

51. Increased

53. 0.015 N directed along negative x axis

59. $\dfrac{\sqrt{2}}{2} + \dfrac{1}{4} \approx 0.952$

61. 1/8

63. (a)   (b)

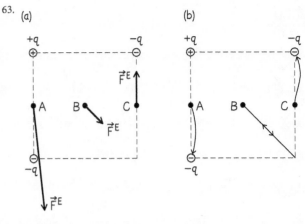

65. $3.0 \, \mu C$

69. At $y = 10$ mm or $y = 40$ mm

71. Electrons in a piece of metal do not settle because gravitational forces exerted on them are negligible relative to electric forces exerted on them. Thus the difference between gravitational potential energy of an electron at the top of the piece and gravitational potential energy of an electron at the bottom of the piece is infinitesimally small.

73. 2.0×10^{-3} N upward

75. (a) 2.4×10^{-2} N directed along the positive y axis (b) 2.4×10^{-2} N directed along the negative y axis

77. -36 nC $- 36$ nC

81. 47.1 N/m

83. At $5\pi/4$

85. (a) 8×10^{23} electrons. (b) 1×10^5 C (c) 2×10^{14} N (d) No

87. (a)

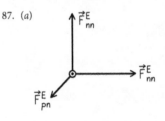

(b) 3.0×10^{-5} N along the line pointing from corner D to corner B and forming a 45° angle with side DC

91. The electric field is zero only at the center of the ring. Consider a location in the plane of the ring that is off-center. Call the distance from the location to the closest segment of the ring r_1 and call the distance to the farthest location on the ring r_2. Rather than picturing conical surfaces passing through the off-center location (as in Newton's and Priestley's arguments) you use a roughly triangular pie-slice off to either side of the location. If the charge is distributed evenly along the ring, the relationship between the charge q_1 on the smaller pie crust and the charge q_2 on the larger pie crust is $\frac{q_1}{r_1} = \frac{q_2}{r_2}$. The sum of the electric fields at the location due to the large and small pie crusts is $\vec{E} = \vec{E}_1 + \vec{E}_2 = k\left(\frac{q_1}{r_1^2} - \frac{q_2}{r_2^2}\right)$ in the direction of the larger pie crust. Using the charge ratio above, this simplifies to $\vec{E} = \frac{kq_2}{r_2}\left(\frac{1}{r_1} - \frac{1}{r_2}\right)$ in the direction of the larger pie crust. This is only zero if the two distances to the edges are equal (meaning the location is in the center of the ring).

Chapter 23

1. 5.93×10^{-3} N/kg

5. No, because the kilogram portion of the unit *newton* is cancelled in gravitational-field units but not in electric-field units. Gravitational: N/kg = (kg $\cdot$ m/s^2)/kg = m/s^2; electric: N/C = (kg $\cdot$ m/s^2)/C

7.

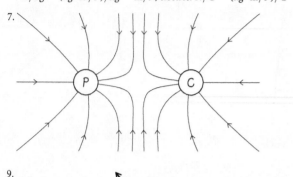

9.

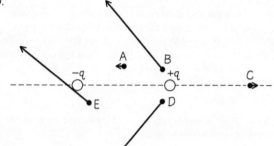

11.

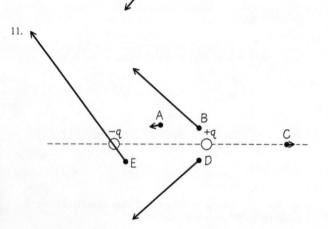

13. $|E|_c < |E|_a = |E|_d < |E|_b < |E|_e$

15. Very uniform because to a good approximation all points in the room are the same distance from Earth's center. Because the gravitational fields due to all other objects around you are extremely small, these fields cause negligible nonuniformity.

17. $\vec{F}^E = 5.0 \times 10^{-4}$ N south, 2.4×10^{-4} N west, 9.2×10^{-5} N downward

19. 84 N/C vertically upward

21. At (4.7 mm, 0, 0)

23. 6.8×10^5 N/C

25. (a) 0 (b) 2.5×10^2 N/C directed from A to B

27. (a) 4.0×10^{-10} N directed from the origin to the proton
(b) 2.5×10^9 N/C 2 directed from the origin to (4.00 mm, 3.00 mm)

29. (a)
(b)

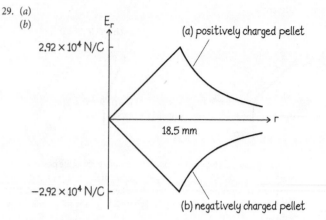

35. The beads are at $(0, y_0, z_0)$, $(0, -y_0, z_0)$, $(0, -y_0, z_0)$, $(0, -y_0, -z_0)$ and $a^2 = y_0^2 + z_0^2$. The electric field on the *x* axis is

$$\vec{E} = \sum_q \frac{kq}{x^2 + a^2}\hat{r}_{qx}. \text{ The unit vectors are}$$

$$\frac{1}{\sqrt{x^2 + a^2}}[(x, -y_0, -z_0), (x, y_0, -z_0), (x, y_0, z_0), (x, -y_0, z_0)], \text{ so}$$

$$\vec{E} = \sum_q \frac{kq}{x^2 + a^2}\hat{r}_{qx} = \frac{4kqx}{(x^2 + a^2)^{3/2}}\hat{i}.$$

37. (a) 2.17×10^3 N/C directed along positive *x* axis (b) At (-144 mm, 0)

39. (a) 0 (b) $\dfrac{4kq}{3a^2}$ directed away from the triangle's center

(c) $\dfrac{kq}{a^2}\left(1 + \dfrac{1}{\sqrt{2 + \sqrt{3}}}\right)$ directed upward

43. Treating the bonds as ionic yields $|\vec{p}_{H_2O}| 1.1 \times 10^{-29}$ C $\cdot$ m, 1.8 times the measured value; these bonds cannot be ionic.

51. $\lambda\ell^2$

53. 3.4×10^{-5} C

61. 8.2 mm

63. (a) Bottom plate (b) 2.0×10^{-8} C/m^2

65. (a) $E_y = \dfrac{k\lambda}{y}$ (b) $\tan^{-1}\dfrac{E_y}{E_x} = \tan^{-1}(-1) = 135°$

67. $E_x = \dfrac{kQ}{\ell}\left(\dfrac{1}{d} - \dfrac{1}{\sqrt{\ell^2 + d^2}}\right)$, $E_y = \dfrac{kQ}{d}\left(\dfrac{1}{\sqrt{\ell^2 + d^2}}\right)$

71. Any substance heats up when the kinetic energy of its molecules increases. In liquid water, the polar water molecules tend to align with the positive region of each molecule next to the negative region of neighboring molecules, and the molecules have a natural frequency associated with their oscillation around that equilibrium position. The transmitter in a microwave oven produces an oscillating electric field that matches that natural frequency. This increases the kinetic energy of the water molecules in a food placed in the oven, and the food is heated. Being nonpolar, oil molecules have a natural oscillation frequency different from that of liquid water, so the frequency of the microwaves is not a good match to the natural frequency of the oil molecules. The oil molecules in a food sample therefore do not increase their oscillation period, which means their kinetic energy does not increase and the food does not heat up. Because the water molecules in ice are constrained, their natural frequency differs from that of liquid water. Thus the frequency of the microwaves (that of liquid water) does not match that of water molecules in a sample of frozen food. Therefore the kinetic energy of the molecules does not increase, and the food does not heat up.

75. (a)

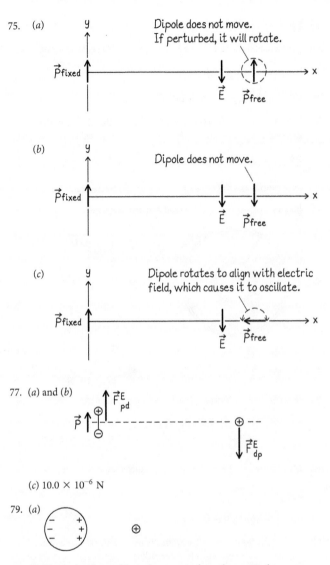

Dipole does not move.
If perturbed, it will rotate.

(b)

Dipole does not move.

(c)

Dipole rotates to align with electric field, which causes it to oscillate.

77. (a) and (b)

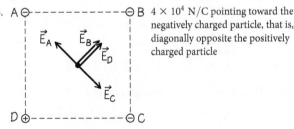

(c) 10.0×10^{-6} N

79. (a)

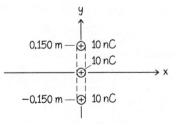

(b) The molecule would accelerate away from the positively charged particle.

81. 2.69×10^{-45} C$^2 \cdot$ m/N

83.

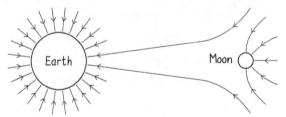

4×10^4 N/C pointing toward the negatively charged particle, that is, diagonally opposite the positively charged particle

85. (a) $\left(\frac{d}{2}, 0\right)$ (b) No such position exists.

87. (a) 6.4×10^{-27} N $\cdot$ m (b) 0

91. (a)

(b) 4.5×10^3 N/C. (c) 16% (d) Approximate the rod as five charged particles evenly spaced along the rod, each carrying one-fifth of a 30-nC charge.

95. $\dfrac{3kq}{\pi R^2}$

Chapter 24

1. (a) From origin to (0.6, 1.2) (b) From (0.6, 1.2) to origin

3. No

5. (a) The particle accelerates in the direction of $\vec{E}$. (b) The initial speed is different, but the trajectory does not change. (c) The component of the initial velocity parallel to $\vec{E}(v_i \cos \theta)$ increases the particle's speed; the component of the initial velocity perpendicular to $\vec{E}(v_i \sin \theta)$ changes trajectory from linear to parabolic. (d) In (a), the particle accelerates in the direction opposite the direction of $\vec{E}$. In (b), the particle initially moves in the direction of $\vec{E}$, then reverses course and travels in the direction opposite the direction of $\vec{E}$. In (c), the trajectory changes from linear to parabolic.

7. (a) Accelerates horizontally to the right (b) Accelerates horizontally to the left (c) Accelerates horizontally to the left (d) Accelerates to the right along the path that curves toward the negative end of the dipole (e) Accelerates to the right along the path that curves toward the negative end of the dipole

11. The quarter covers one or more charged particles carrying a combined negative charge equal in magnitude to 7/17 of the charge on the positively charged particle shown to the right of the quarter.

13. (a) With gravitational field lines defined as pointing in the direction of the gravitational force exerted on any object having mass, the Earth–moon gravitational field is as shown in the figure. (b) Both objects must carry negative charge. (c) All gravitational forces are attractive, but electric forces can be attractive or repulsive. Gravitational field lines always terminate on all objects in a field; electric field lines emanate from positively charged objects and terminate on negatively charged objects.

15. At lower right, where electric field line density is greatest

17. $E_B > E_A > E_C$

19. Treat the plate as infinite and lying horizontally in the xy plane. Because the arrangement is reflection symmetric about the xz and yz planes, the electric field can have only the E_z component. For the finite-sized plate, this symmetry is broken as you move away from the plate, but for the infinite plate, the symmetry argument holds for any distance from the plate. This means the field line density is constant around plate (the lines never bend toward or away from any region of space) and the electric field is uniform.

21. (a) $\Delta t_{C \to D} < \Delta t_{B \to C} < \Delta t_{A \to B}$ (b) No change as long as the pellets do not leave the electric field.

23. The field line density is greater near B by factor of 1.6.

25. $A = B = C$

29. The charge inside the closed surface must equal the charge on 4 protons, $+4e$. All that can be said about the number of particles over which this charge distributed is that the number must be even and there must be 4 or more particles.

33. (a) No (b) The relationship still applies to charged dipoles.

35. $+\Phi/6$

37. Many other shapes are equally useful, such as a cubic or rectangular box centered on a plate.

39. (a) $E_0/4$ (b) E_0 (c) $E_0/4$

41. Yes, because both the charge enclosed by the surfaces and the flux through the two surfaces are proportional to the area of the slab that is enclosed.

43. (a) $-q$ on cavity 1 inner surface; $+2q$ on cavity 2 inner surface (b) $-q$ on outer surface

45. Because metal is an electrical conductor, it remains in electrostatic equilibrium even when placed in an external electric field. The electric field inside a metal box is therefore zero and any device inside the box is not exposed to the electric field.

47. (a) $+2q$ (b) $-2q$ (c) $+q$ (d) Zero charge on outer surface of inner shell, zero charge on inner surface of outer shell, charge $+q$ on outer surface of outer shell

49. $-9q$

51. (a) $-2q$ (b) $-q$
    (c)

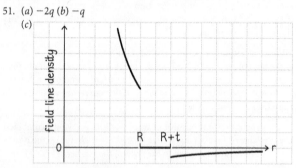

53. (a) Yes, by orienting the sheet such that the angle between the electric field direction and the direction normal to sheet is 78°. (b) No

55. (a) $6.8 \times 10^5 \, \text{N} \cdot \text{m}^2/\text{C}$ (b) $6.8 \times 10^5 \, \text{N} \cdot \text{m}^2/\text{C}$

57. $\Phi_{E, \text{right side } (a)} = \Phi_{E, \text{right side } (b)} = \Phi_{E, \text{right side } (c)}$

59. (a) $+2q$ (b) $-5q$

61.

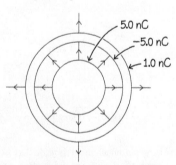

5.0 nC
−5.0 nC
1.0 nC

(b) $\sigma_{\text{solid}} = 1.1 \times 10^2 \, \text{nC/m}^2$ of positive charge, $\sigma_{\text{inner}} = 40 \, \text{nC/m}^2$ of negative charge, $\sigma_{\text{outer}} = 5.5 \, \text{nC/m}^2$ of positive charge (c) The electric field is directed away from the center and has magnitude:

$$E = \begin{cases} 0, & r \le 60 \text{ mm} \\ \dfrac{kq_1}{r^2}, & 60 \text{ mm} < r < 100 \text{ mm} \\ 0, & 100 \text{ mm} \le r \le 120 \text{ mm} \\ \dfrac{kq_2}{r^2}, & r > 120 \text{ mm} \end{cases}$$

where $q_1 = 5.0$ nC and $q_2 = 1.0$ nC

63. (a) $-4.0 \, \text{N} \cdot \text{m}^2/\text{C}$ (b) -3.5×10^{-11} C

65. (a) Yes; use a cylindrical Gaussian surface. (b) No (c) Yes; use a spherical Gaussian surface.

67. (a) $\dfrac{\lambda \ell}{4\epsilon_0}$ (b) Increase

69. (a) 12 field lines directed from the particle to the cube exterior
    (b) 2 field lines (c) $3.4 \times 10^5 \, \text{N} \cdot \text{m}^2/\text{C}$ (d) $5.6 \times 10^4 \, \text{N} \cdot \text{m}^2/\text{C}$
    (e) Answers (b) and (d) change.

71. (a) $\dfrac{q}{\epsilon_0}$ (b) $\dfrac{q}{\epsilon_0}$ (c) Technique using Gauss's law.

73. (a) 1.9×10^2 N/C directed away from sphere (b) 8.5×10^2 N/C directed away from sphere (c) 7.8×10^2 N/C directed away from sphere

75. (a) $E(r < a) = 0$, $\vec{E}(a < r < b) = \dfrac{2k\lambda_a}{r}$ directed radially away from

    long central axis, $\vec{E}(r > b) = \dfrac{2k(\lambda_a + \lambda_b)}{r}$ directed radially away from

    long central axis (b) 5.0 nC/m of negative charge

    (c)

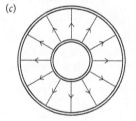

77. (a) $\sigma_{\text{inner}} = 4.8 \, \mu\text{C/m}^2$ of negative charge, $\sigma_{\text{outer}} = 3.4 \, \mu\text{C/m}^2$ of positive charge (b) 5.5×10^5 N/C (c) 0 (d) 2.7×10^5 N/C

79. $\vec{E}(r \le a) = \dfrac{\rho_0 r}{3\epsilon_0}$ directed away from sphere;

    $\vec{E}(a \le r \le b) = \dfrac{\rho_0 a^3}{\epsilon_0 r^2}\left[\frac{1}{12} + \frac{1}{4}\left(\frac{r}{a}\right)^3\right]$ directed away from sphere;

    $\vec{E}(r \ge b) = \dfrac{\rho_0 a^3}{\epsilon_0 r^2}\left[\frac{1}{3} + \frac{1}{4}\left(\frac{b^4}{a^4} - 1\right)\right]$ directed away from sphere

81. Either -3λ or $+9\lambda$

83. (a) 7.1×10^{-10} C (b) 20 N/C (c) 21 N/C

85. (a) 2 shells (b) Inner shell: electrically neutral, thick, made of conducting material, inner radius R, outer radius $2R$; outer shell: carries charge $-2q$, thin, made of nonconducting material, radius $3R$

87. 0.040 m

89. (a) $q_{\text{part}} = \dfrac{49}{64} q_{\text{sphere}}$ (b) $x = \dfrac{R}{4}$, $x = \dfrac{16}{15}R$

91. (a) $\vec{E}(r < R) = \dfrac{\rho_0 r^2}{4\epsilon_0 R}$ directed away from sphere,

    $\vec{E}(r > R) = \dfrac{\rho_0 R^3}{4\epsilon_0 r^2}$ directed away from sphere

    (b) $\vec{E}(r < R) = \dfrac{\rho_0}{4\epsilon_0}(\frac{4}{3}r - R)$ directed away from sphere,

    $\vec{E}(r > R) = \dfrac{\rho_0 R^3}{12\epsilon_0 r^2}$ directed away from sphere

    (c) $\vec{E}(r < R) = \dfrac{\rho_0}{4\epsilon_0}(\frac{4}{3}r - 2R)$ directed away from sphere,

    $\vec{E}(r > R) = \dfrac{\rho_0 R^3}{6\epsilon_0 r^2}$ directed toward sphere

93. No, in electrostatics (as long as the charged particles in the electric field are not suddenly accelerated) electric fields have no kinks.

95. The acceleration is constant and independent of d: $a = \sigma q/2m\epsilon_0$ away from sheet.

97. (a)

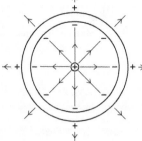

(b) $\sigma_{\text{inner shell surface}} = 24 \text{ nC/m}^2$ of negative charge, $\sigma_{\text{outer shell surface}} = 17 \text{ nC/m}^2$ of positive charge.

(c) $\vec{E}(r < R_{\text{inner}}) = \dfrac{kq}{r^2}$ directed from center to shell

$E(R_{\text{inner}} < r < R_{\text{outer}}) = 0$

$\vec{E}(r > R_{\text{outer}}) = \dfrac{kq}{r^2}$ directed away from shell outer surface

(d)

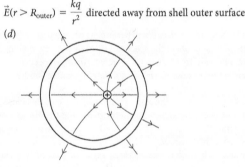

99. 1.3 nC/m^2 of negative charge

101. (a) $E_D > E_A = E_B = E_C$ (b) $E_A > E_D > E_C > E_B$

103. (a) $\vec{E}(-a < x < a) = \dfrac{\rho_0}{2\epsilon_0 a}(a^2 - x^2)$ in $-x$ direction; $E = 0$ everywhere outside slab.

(b) To left of 1, $\vec{E} = \rho_0 t/\epsilon_0$ in $-x$ direction; inside 1,

$\vec{E}(x) = \left(\dfrac{\rho_0}{2\epsilon_0 a}(a^2 - x^2) + \dfrac{\rho_0 t}{\epsilon_0}\right)$ in $-x$ direction, between 1 and 2,

$\vec{E} = \dfrac{\rho_0 t}{\epsilon_0}$ in $-x$ direction; inside left half of 2, $\vec{E}(x) = \dfrac{\rho_0}{\epsilon_0}(d - x)$

in $-x$ direction; inside right half of 2, $\vec{E}(x) = \dfrac{\rho_0}{\epsilon_0}(x - d)$ in

$+x$ direction; to right of 2, $\vec{E} = \dfrac{\rho_0 t}{\epsilon_0}$ in $+x$ direction

105. $f = \dfrac{1}{2\pi}\sqrt{\dfrac{k|q_s|q_p}{mR^3}}$

107. Your wire should be positively charged at linear charge density $5 \times 10^2 \text{ nC/m}$.

Chapter 25

1. The greatest electric potential energy is when the direction of the dipole moment is antiparallel to the direction of the electric field; the least is when the direction of the dipole moment is parallel to the direction of the electric field.

3. (a) 1-kg ball (b) 3-kg ball

5. (a) $K_p = 2K_d = K_\alpha$ (b) $p_p = p_d = p_\alpha/2$ (c) $v_p = 2v_d = 2v_\alpha$
   (d) $\Delta x_p = 2\Delta x_d = 2\Delta x_\alpha$ (e) $\Delta U_p^E = 2\Delta U_d^E = \Delta U_\alpha^E$

7. $\Delta U^E = 2qEd$

9. $2W$

11. From B to A

13. $3W$

15. (a) Remained the same (b) Increased (c) $V_B - V_A < 0$

17. (a) Increase (b) Decrease (c) Answer (a) would be "remain the same"; answer (b) would not change.

19. $W_{(a)} = W_{(b)} < W_{(c)} < W_{(d)}$

21. Yes, such as at the location where $E = 0$.

23. The equipotential surfaces are infinitely long cylindrical shells.

25.

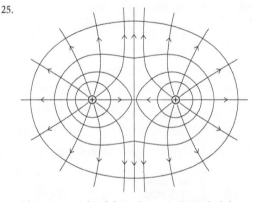

(a) Region to right of charged particle (b) To the left
(c) Outermost line

27. (a) No (b) No

29. (a) 6.7 V (b) 2.0×10^{-8} J (c) 2.0×10^{-8} J

31. (a) 1.5×10^{-7} J (b) 0 (c) -3.8×10^{-8} J (d) -7.0×10^{-8} J

33. (a) 2.7×10^2 V (b) 1.9×10^2 V

35. (a) Negative (b) $\dfrac{q^2}{4\pi_0 d}(\sqrt{2} - 4)$

37. $W_A = W_B = W_C = W_D$.

39. (a) 51 V (b) 25 V (c) Zero

41. (a) $x = -d$ and $x = +5d$ (b) $y = \pm\sqrt{5}d$ (c) Nowhere (other than infinity)

43. (a) Negative (b) 3.0 V/m directed along the $+x$ axis
   (c) 5.3×10^{-11} C/m^2

45. (a)

(b) 5.0×10^3 V/m (c) -8.0×10^{-17} J when the system is the electron and plates (d) $+8.0 \times 10^{-17}$ J when the system is the electron only and the electric field is external to the system (e) 8.0×10^{-17} J

47. (a) Positive (b) Particle 2 could carry charge $q_2 = 6q_1$ and be at $x_2 = 2d$, and it could carry charge $q_2 = 6q_1/5$ and be at $x_2 = -2d/5$.

49. (a) 24 V (b) 17 V (c) 11 V

51. (a) 6.0×10^2 V (b) -1.3×10^3 V (c) -4.2×10^3 V

53. (a) Zero (b) $V = \dfrac{q}{\pi\epsilon_0}\ln\left(\dfrac{\sqrt{2} + 1}{\sqrt{2} - 1}\right)$

55. $V = \dfrac{-q}{4\pi\epsilon_0 \ell}\ln\left[\dfrac{\ell + \sqrt{\ell^2 + y^2}}{y}\right] + \dfrac{q}{4\pi\epsilon_0(y - y_p)}$

57. $V = \dfrac{c}{8\epsilon_0}\left[2R\sqrt{R^2 + x^2} + x^2\ln\left(\dfrac{x^2}{(R + \sqrt{R^2 + x^2})^2}\right)\right]$

59. $E = B$; $-x$ direction.

61. (a) $\begin{array}{l}V(x = 3.0000) = 8.99\text{ V}\\V(x = 3.0100) = 8.96\text{ V}\end{array}$ (b) decreases, $\dfrac{\Delta V}{\Delta x} = -2.98\text{ V/m}$
    (c) $E(x = 3.0000) = 2.99\text{ V/m}$. This has the opposite sign, as expected, and is close to the approximate value obtained in part b.
    (d) $E(x = 3.0000, y = 0.0100) = 3.00\text{ V/m}$. Within the precision of the data, this is the same as the result found in part c, which is not surprising because the distance from the particle to the points in parts c and d are the same to within the precision of the data.

63. (a) B (b) F
    (c)

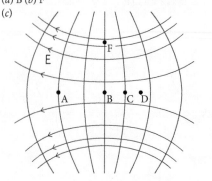

65. (a)

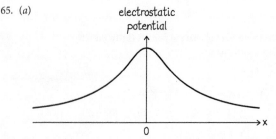

electrostatic potential

    (b) At $x = 0$ (c) 0

67. (a) Positive (b) Positive

69. (a) -6000 V/m (b) $(A/x^2)+B$, where $A = 2000\text{ V}\cdot\text{m}$,
    $B = -1500\text{ V/m}$ (c) $A+Bx$, where $A = -2000\text{ V/m}$ and
    $B = 6000\text{ V/m}^2$ (d) 0

71. (a) 25 mm (b) 1.3×10^2 mm

73. (a) $q_{\text{sphere}} = -2q_{\text{shell}}/5$ (b) $q_{\text{sphere}} = -q_{\text{shell}}$

75. In order for 92 protons to stay together in nucleus, negative energy from strong interaction must equal positive electric potential energy, 4.8×10^{-10} J for the entire nucleus. Alternatively, each proton must be held inside the nucleus by a force of magnitude of approximately 300 N.

Chapter 26

1. Charges are equal in magnitude and opposite in sign.

3. Very large

5. 34.1 J

7. $\pm 1.35 \times 10^{-6}$ C

9. Greater electric field magnitude with battery connected;
   $E_{\text{batt connected}}/E_{\text{batt disconnected}} = 2$

11. $q_1 = q_2$

13. Because the potential difference between the plates is maintained at some value by battery, $V_{\text{cap}} \neq 0$ is always true. This potential
    difference can be written $V_{\text{cap}} = \int_{+}^{-} \vec{E} \cdot d\vec{\ell}$. If the electric field magnitude

outside the plates were zero, there would be a path from one plate to the other such that $\int_{+}^{-} \vec{E} \cdot d\vec{\ell} = 0 = V_{\text{cap}}$, which can never be true. Hence the electric field magnitude outside the plates can never be zero.

15. q

17. (a) $+q/2$ (b) $+q$

19. Many answers are possible. (a) The dielectric and the conductor both cause surface charge to accumulate on the slab. At a constant potential difference, both slabs increase the charge on the capacitor. For an isolated capacitor, both slabs decrease V_{cap} and decrease E between the plates. (b) With the conductor, E between the plates is zero; with the dielectric, E between the plates is lower than E outside the plates by not zero. The charge that accumulates on the slab is free on the conductor but bound on the dielectric. The dielectric increases the breakdown threshold but the conductor does not.

21. (a) $E_1 > E_2$ (b) $V_1 > V_2$ (c) $U_1^E > U_2^E$

23. $1.3q$

25. (a) 1:1 (b) 3:2

27. The conducting slab does not help because its presence increases the electric field magnitude in the space not filled by the slab, making the air in that region more likely to break down. Also, charge carriers can travel across the conducting slab, a motion not possible (under normal conditions) in a dielectric.
    Increasing the plate separation does not help because this increases both the potential difference between the plates and the distance over which the potential changes. These two effects cancel when determining the electric field magnitude. (This argument is valid only when the plate areas are much greater than the separation distance. If the plate separation is made very large, the electric field magnitude in the region between the plates could decrease.)

29. Stay the same

31. 2.8×10^{-17}

33. 4.0×10^{-8} C/m^2

35. 2.77×10^{-2} m

37. 9.3 mm

39. (a) $d = \dfrac{2R_{\text{inner}}R_{\text{outer}}}{R_{\text{inner}} + R_{\text{outer}}}$ (b) $d = \dfrac{2R_{\text{inner}}R_{\text{outer}}}{R_{\text{inner}} + R_{\text{outer}}}$ (c) $d = \sqrt{R_{\text{inner}}R_{\text{outer}}}$,
    $d = \sqrt{R_{\text{inner}}R_{\text{outer}}}$

41. (a) a, N/C$^2 \cdot$ m^2; b, m^2 (b) $C = \dfrac{1}{a\left(\dfrac{(128\text{ m}^3)}{3} + (8\text{ m})b\right)}$

43. 2.97×10^{-5} J

45. $8U_1^E$

47. (a) $C_2 > C_1 > C_3$ (b) $q_2 > q_1 > q_3$ (c) $E_2 = E_1 > E_3$ (d) $U_2^E > U_1^E > U_3^E$
    (e) $u_{E,2} = u_{E,1} > u_{E,3}$

49. (a) $\dfrac{3q^2}{448\pi^2\epsilon_0 R^4}$ (b) $\dfrac{q^2(\ln 2)}{12\pi^2\epsilon_0 \ell^2 R^2}$

51. (a) $d/4$ (b) Not possible, because the isolated plates have no source of charge, regardless of the separation distance. (c) $4d$ (d) Not possible, because the energy density is independent of the plate separation.

53. (a) Generally no, but you could say that the dielectric constant of a conductor approaches infinity as conductivity increases. (b) 0 (because any arbitrarily small electric field separates charge carriers)

55. (a) Increase the plate area, decrease the plate separation distance, insert the dielectric that has a higher dielectric constant, change the geometry in some cases. (b) No

57. (a) $C_2 = \kappa C_1$ (b) $q_2 = \kappa q_1$ (c) $U_2^E = \kappa U_1^E$ (d) $E_2 = E_1$
    (e) $u_{E2} = \kappa u_{E1}$

59. (a) $4/3$ (b) If the capacitor is isolated, then there is no change to the bound charge. If the capacitor remains connected to a battery, then the bound charge is reduced to $6/7$ of its initial value.

61. 1.1×10^5 V/m

63. 18.3 V

65. $F/\kappa_{distilled\ water} = F/80.2$

67. (a) $9Q/2$ (b) $3/2$

69. (a) The model shows that increasing the separation distance increases the elastic potential energy stored in the electric field between the objects just as stretching the elastic band increases the elastic potential energy stored in the band. (b) The analogy suggests that electric field lines run from a positively charged object to a negatively charged object along the shortest possible path (so as to minimize energy), which is not true.

71. (a) $V_1 = V_2$ (b) $q_1 = 4q_2$.

73. Decreasing the volume occupied by the charge would always lower energy. There is no way to hold positive and negative charge carriers apart using only electrostatic interactions.

75. $\dfrac{q^2}{A\epsilon_0}$

77. With slabs $d/2$, $d/4$, and $d/5$ inserted, 95% of the gap between the plates is filled with a conductor. Because the electric field in the plates is zero, the entire potential difference now occurs over the remaining gap, which is 5% of the original gap width, and the electric field increases by factor of 20.

Chapter 27

1. North

3. Horizontally, with all north poles at one disk flat face and all south poles at opposite disk flat face

5. Either magnet attracts the unmagnetized bar, but neither magnet repels it. Try all possible two-bar pairings, making sure in each pairing to flip one of the bars and check both orientations. When you are holding a pair that repel each other, you are holding the two magnets, making the remaining bar the unmagnetized one.

9. (a) 0 (b) $-\Phi_{north}$ (c) 0 (d) 0

11. The magnet experiences (1) torque that rotates it until the line directed from S to N is parallel to the magnetic field and (2) the force accelerating it in the direction of the magnetic field, toward the region of the highest field line density.

13. No. In order to match everywhere, patterns must match at their sources. Electric field lines begin on positively charged particles and terminate on negatively charged particles, whereas magnetic field lines never begin nor end, with no way for these source differences to be reconciled into one field line pattern.

15. $\tau_{(a)} = \tau_{(b)} < \tau_{(e)} < \tau_{(c)} = \tau_{(d)}$

17. (a) To the left (b) Into page

19. (a) Yes (b) Yes; wire P

21. (a) Counterclockwise (b) Side 2 downward, side 3 to the left, side 4 upward

23. To the observer in the Earth reference frame, no magnetic force is exerted on S. To the observer in the reference frame M$'$ moving parallel to M's path but at half the speed of M (as measured from the Earth reference frame), both M and S have nonzero velocity in reference frame M$'$ and there is magnetic force exerted on S.

27. 0.26 T

29. 1.96 A

31. (a) 1.6×10^{19} electrons (b) In $-x$ direction. (c) 0.50 N/m
    (d)

33. 0.52 A

35. (a) Out of page ($-y$ direction) (b) Into page ($+y$ direction)
    (c) Upward ($+z$ direction) (d) To the right ($+x$ direction)
    (e) Not possible

37. (a) 14.1 A into page (b) $I_{max} = 42.6$ A

39. $\Phi_{B(a)} = \Phi_{B(b)} = \Phi_{B(e)} < \Phi_{B(c)} = \Phi_{B(d)}$

41. 19°

43. 6.0 Wb

45. (a) 0.30 T in the $-y$ direction (b) In the $-z$ direction

47. (a) $\omega = 3.6 \times 10^7$ s^{-1}, $T = 1.7 \times 10^{-7}$ s (b) 2.7×10^7 m/s
    (c) 2.4×10^{-12} J

49. (a) 2.1×10^{-4} m (b) $\omega = 6.2 \times 10^{10}$ s^{-1}, $T = 1.0 \times 10^{-10}$ s
    (c) 1.3×10^7 m/s

51. 0.68 kV

53. (a) Negative (b) 1.1×10^{-4} m/s (c) 5.9×10^{28} m^{-3}

55. $(0, 0.023$ m, 0.016 m$)$

57. 18 μV with the left side at the higher potential

59. (a) $+x$ (b) $-x$

61. $0.23c_0 = 7.0 \times 10^7$ m/s

63. $T_{new,1} = T$, $T_{new,2} = 2T$, $T_{new,3} = T$

65. $B_x = 0.10$ T, $B_y = 0.10$ T, $B_z = -0.15$ T.

67. (a) 1.7×10^8 m/s (b) 1.6×10^{-4} m downward

69. Label magnets A, B, C. Hold magnet A fixed and mark one of its poles X. Now see which pole of magnet B attracts pole X of magnet A and which pole of magnet C attracts pole X of magnet A. Now you have identified a pole of B and a pole of C that interact with A in the same way, meaning these B and C poles have the same polarity (either both N or both S; you do not know which, but it does not matter). Now bring this pole of B and this pole of C together to see whether like poles attract or repel each other. Seeing them repel each other should convince your colleague.

71. The external magnetic field exerts no force on wire.

Chapter 28

1. There is no magnetic force exerted on the particle because the particle is at rest relative to the magnets.

3. (a)–(d) All four magnetic fields are directed into the plane of the loop from above.

5. There is a repulsive electrostatic force that obeys Coulomb's law. There is also an attractive magnetic force. Which of these forces is stronger depends on the speed of the electrons. The gravitational force exerted on each electron by Earth is much smaller than the Coulomb force, and the gravitational force exerted on each electron by the other is much smaller still.

7. (a) One location (b) One location (c) Two locations

9. $\vec{F}^B_{12} = 0$, $\vec{F}^B_{21}$ is downward in plane of page

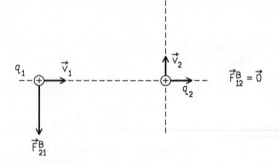

11. At the center of the loop

13. $\vec{B}_1$, $\vec{B}_2$ out of page; $\vec{B}_3$, $\vec{B}_4$ into page

15. If a current loop appears "small" then we are observing it from a distance much greater than the loop size. At this distance, the B field from a square or circular current loop is the same. A sketch of the field lines around each loop would also appear identical (a dipole field). As we approach the square loop, at a distance r from a corner, the field would be stronger than at a distance r from the side of a circular loop. A more exact analysis would require more information about the loops.

17. The magnetic field of a spinning disk of uniform charge may be thought of as a superposition of the magnetic fields due to many circular current loops with progressively larger radii. At the center of the spinning disk, the magnetic field from all current loops will reinforce each other, so the magnetic field here will be largest. Because all the current in a current loop is a distance R from the center, whereas some of the current in a disk is near the center, you expect the magnetic field at the center of the spinning disk to exceed the magnetic field at the center of the comparable current loop. As you move progressively outward from the center of the spinning disk, the magnetic field from the inner current loops will oppose the magnetic field from the outer current loops, decreasing the magnetic field strength with respect to that at the center of the disk. Therefore, in the plane of the disk, you expect the off-axis magnetic field of the spinning disk to decrease more rapidly than the off-axis magnetic field in the plane of the current loop. At the edge of the spinning disk, the magnetic field should be significantly smaller than for the current loop.

19. (a) Positive x direction (b) Negative x direction (c) Negative x direction

21. Because both particles have spin, they both produce magnetic fields, and each particle interacts with the field produced by the other. Because the electron is orbiting the proton, it acts like a tiny current loop, which also produces a magnetic field, and both particles interact with that field. The moving electron is also subject to a magnetic force due to the proton's magnetic field.

23. Clockwise

25. (a) Counterclockwise (b) Clockwise (c) Into page

27. Clockwise when viewed while standing on positive z axis and looking toward origin

29. (a) Positive y direction (b) Negative y direction (c) Negative x direction (d) Negative z direction (e) None

31. (a) $F^B_{on\,1}$ toward top of page; $F^B_{on\,2}$ out of page; $F^B_{on\,3}$ toward bottom of page; $F^B_{on\,4}$ into page (b) Into page (c) Vertical with side 1 on top

33. (a) Yes, it would be different, because the particle at rest would not be subject to a magnetic force if it were not spinning. (Since it is spinning, it experiences a torque that tends to align its magnetic moment with

the applied magnetic field.) (b) The electromagnetic field produced by the particle as it moves under the influence of the applied electric and magnetic fields would also be different if the particle were not spinning, because it would lack the component due to its magnetic moment.

35. (a) $3I$ (b) Negative

37. $e < a = b = f < c < d$

39. $|I_1| = |I_2| = |I_3|$; I_1, I_3 out of page, I_2 into page

41. Greater than zero

43. (a) $\oint_A = \oint_B$ (b) Path A (c) Path B is longer than path A but farther from the wire so the magnetic field is smaller and makes a nonzero angle with the path. These differences cancel because the dot product multiplies only the portion of the magnetic field and path length that are parallel. The line integral is independent of the path as long as identical currents are encircled.

45. 2.5 A

47. (a) 1.2×10^2 A (b) 0.32 mT

49. 2.6 A

51. (a) 4.4×10^{-6} T (b) 1.9×10^{-6} T (c) 1.9×10^{-6} T

(d)

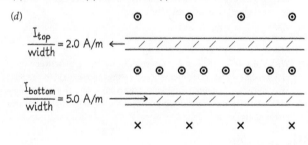

53. (a) $B = \begin{cases} 0, & r < R \\ \dfrac{\mu_0 I}{2\pi r}, & r \geq R \end{cases}$

(b)

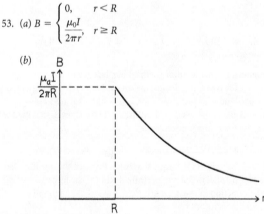

55. 6.28×10^{-3} N/m² downward

57. 1.6×10^{-19} C

59. 2.8×10^3 windings/m

61. In a coordinate system in which the magnetic field generated by the solenoid is in the positive x direction and the wire is displaced in the negative y direction, the magnetic field at the solenoid center is 5.7×10^{-5} T directed 10° from the positive x axis toward the positive z axis. It does not matter whether the wire is inside or outside the solenoid.

63. (a) 1.0×10^{-6} T (b) Zero (c) Zero

65. $B = \dfrac{\mu_0 n R_{toroid} I}{r}$

67. Because the circle forming the toroid outer edge is significantly larger than the circle forming the toroid inner edge, the windings are spread over a larger circumference near the outer edge than near the inner

edge. This means that the magnetic field magnitude B_1 at position 1 should be different from the magnetic field magnitude B_2 at position 2. The same argument applies to positions 3 and 4. If the toroid is perfectly symmetric, $B_1 = B_3$ and $B_2 = B_4$. Checking whether or not these equalities hold in this toroid is a good check of the unit's uniformity and symmetry.

69. 1.2×10^{-2} A

71. 2.5×10^2 A to the right

73. 6.1×10^{-8} T out of page

75. 1.5×10^{-7} T

77. With the velocity direction defined as the positive x direction and 15 mm distance below the path being in the negative y direction, the magnetic field is 3.6×10^{-15} T in the positive z direction.

79. $\vec{B} = \dfrac{|\vec{E}|}{c^2} \vec{v} \times \hat{r}$

81. $F^B_{12} = \dfrac{\mu_0 q_p^2 v_1 v_2}{4\pi r^2}$, $\quad F^B_{21} = \dfrac{\mu_0 q_p^2 v_1 v_2 (\sin 135°)}{4\pi r^2}$

83. 0.53 m

85. (a) $\vec{0}$ (b) 9.6×10^{-35} N in negative x direction

87. (a) Yes, in positive y direction (b) Yes, in negative x direction (c) No

89. 1.2×10^{-5} N away from wire 2

91. 33 A

93. 531 turns, inner radius 0.020 m, outer radius 0.080 m. The magnetic field magnitude per ampere ranges from 1.3×10^{-3} T at the outer radius to 5.3×10^{-3} T at the inner radius.

Chapter 29

1. (a) There is no effect on the charge carriers because the rod moves parallel to the magnetic field. (b) The is charge separation because the motion is perpendicular to the magnetic field. If the rod moves in the $+y$ direction, a positive charge accumulates on the side of the rod facing the $+x$ axis, and a negative charge accumulates on the side facing the $-x$ axis. If the rod moves in the $-y$ direction, a positive charge accumulates on the side facing the $-x$ axis, and a negative charge accumulates on the side facing the $+x$ axis.

3. The airplane should fly perpendicular to the magnetic field, with the wings oriented with their width perpendicular to the magnetic field and to the plane's velocity.

7. (a) Yes (b) Varies with time

9. Circular shape; one winding

11. In the Earth reference frame, you are moving quickly through Earth's magnetic field. Because your motion is not perfectly parallel to the field direction (Avignon is southeast of Paris, and in that region Earth's magnetic field has a component directed toward the planet's center), a magnetic force is exerted on charge carriers in the rod. In an inertial reference attached to the train, the changing magnetic field produces an electric field that causes charge separation in the rod.

13. Concentric circles centered on the long axis of the pipe

15. Hold the magnet above the loop with the south pole facing the loop, move the magnet toward loop. Hold the magnet above the loop with the north pole facing the loop, move the magnet away from the loop. These are two examples; there are other ways.

17. The clockwise induced current occurs whenever the straight-wire current increases: $t = 0$ to $t = \pi/2\omega$, $t = 3\pi/2\omega$ to $t = 5\pi/2\omega$, ... The zero induced current occurs at instants when the straight-wire current is maximum or minimum: $t = \pi/2\omega, 3\pi/2\omega, 5\pi/2\omega$....

The counterclockwise induced current occurs whenever the straight-wire current decreases: $t = \pi/2\omega$ to $t = 3\pi/2\omega$, $t = 5\pi/2\omega$ to $t = 7\pi/2\omega$, ...

19. 3.0 V

21. 4.2×10^{-4} A

23. 1.0×10^2 windings

25. 9.4×10^{-6} m^2

26. 6.9×10^{-3} V

27. 10 A

29. (a) $\Phi(t) = \pi R^2 B_0 e^{-t/\tau}$; decreasing (b) $\epsilon(t) = \dfrac{\pi R^2 B_0}{\tau} e^{-t/\tau}$

    (c) Clockwise when viewed from the origin along the $+z$ direction

31. 3.6×10^{-2} V

33. (a) 0.24 V (b) Contact touching disk edge

35. 0.029 s

39. 0.080 T/s

41. (a) 3.0×10^{-2} V/m (b) 7.5×10^{-2} V/m (c) Counterclockwise

43. $B(t) = 2Ct^3$

45. Yes

47. 3.0 H

49. (a) $\epsilon_{\text{ind}}(t) = -LI_{\max}\omega\cos(\omega t)$ (b) Increasing (c) Opposing (d) Inductance prevents changes in current from happening instantly. When the current in a circuit containing an inductor tends to increase the emf across the inductor, the inductor acts to oppose the emf increase.

51. (a) 5.0×10^{-7} H (b) Your friend missed the fact that you cannot have 40 windings with the wire and rod described; the correct value is $N \approx 20$. He then used wire length rather than solenoid length for ℓ in the equation and wire radius rather than solenoid inner radius in calculating solenoid cross-sectional area.

53. 11 J

55. 3.5 J

57. 2.0×10^5 J, 1.0×10^4 W

61. -6.7×10^{-4} V, where the minus sign indicates that the induced emf opposes the increase in current.

63. 1.3×10^2 J

65. (a) 0.0075 T (b) 0.0020 H (c) 0.0089 J (d) 0.0089 J

67. (a) $2B\pi v^2 t$ (b) Clockwise viewed looking into the page.

69. 4.4×10^{-4} V

71. 1.2 m/s

75. 5×10^4 A

77. The induced emf is around 3 mV. The faster the tape runs, the faster the magnetic field changes direction. This typically corresponds to a higher frequency for the sound waves, although it may also affect their amplitude (because the faster change in flux induces a greater emf).

Chapter 30

1. Increasing

3. There is no magnetic field surrounding the capacitor.

5. (a) To the left (b) Increasing to the left (c) Clockwise when viewed from the position to the right of the right plate

7. (a) Yes (b) Yes (c) No

9. No; the electric field lines would bend but not kink because kinking is a characteristic of a sudden onset of motion.

11. (a) No, not in the reference frame in which the positive and negative charge carriers have the same linear charge density. (b) Yes (c) Yes (d) No

15. Upward

17. (a) From down to up (b) Into page to left of P, out of page to right of P (c) In-out of page.

19. Because no radiation is emitted along the long axis. The towers laid horizontally along, say, the north-south line would emit waves detectable east and west of the towers but not north or south of them.

21. Negatively charged

23. 1.9×10^{-5} T

25. 3.2×10^{-5} T

27. (a) 5.6×10^{-4} A
(b)

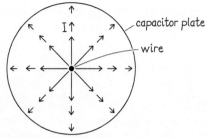

29. (a) $E(t) = It / \pi R^2 \epsilon_0$ (b) 0.22 A (c) 0 (d) Answer (c) is different from answer (b) because the flat circular surface in Figure P30.29b has charge carriers flowing through it, whereas the flat circular shell surface in Figure P30.29a has displacement current only, with no charge carriers moving through it. Answer (b) is not 2.0 A because I_{disp} exists everywhere between the plates but the circular surface occupies only a part of this region. Answer (c) is not 2.0 A because the open cylindrical shell surface intersects a current-carrying conductor twice: where the wire passes through the closed end and where the cylinder passes through the capacitor plate. So all the charge carriers that pass into the cylinder pass back out again, resulting in zero current.

31. 3.6×10^{-11} T

37. AM wavelengths, 0.3 km to 3.0 km; FM frequencies, 3×10^7 Hz to 3×10^8 Hz.

39. 26 ms

41. For the dipole antenna, the likely frequency is around 1.9 GHz.

43. Around 280 nm, which is UV light

45. 6.3×10^{10} Hz

47. 2.46×10^{-2} N/C

49. The light emitted by an incandescent bulb spreads out over a spherical surface of increasing radius, but the angular spread of a laser beam is extremely small. The result is that the intensity of the laser light 100 m from the source is essentially the same as the intensity 1 m from the source. Over this same distance, the intensity of the incandescent bulb drops by a factor of 10^{-4}.

53. 0.020 s

55. (a) $E_{max} = 2.4 \times 10^1$ N/C, $B_{max} = 8.2 \times 10^{-8}$ T
(b) $E_{max} = 4.9 \times 10^{-2}$ N/C, $B_{max} = 1.6 \times 10^{-10}$ T (c) 24 V at 100 m, 49 mV at 50 km.

57. 6.0×10^2 W

59. Assuming the light spreads out spherically, it can be seen 9×10^2 km from the source, a result you know from experience does not make sense.

61. (a) $+z$ direction (b) 50 W (c) $+y$ direction (I) 6.3 mm,
5×10^{10} Hz (I) $\vec{E}(x, y, z, t) = E_{max} \sin^2(kz - \omega t)\hat{i}$,
$\vec{B}(x, y, z, t) = B_{max} \sin^2(kz - \omega t)\hat{j}$, where $k = 1000$ m^{-1},
$\omega = 3.0 \times 10^{11}$ s^{-1}, $E_{max} = 1.9 \times 10^2$ N/C, $B_{max} = 6.5 \times 10^{-7}$ T

63. 177 W/m^2

65. 1.66 m

67. $\lambda_{2.45 \text{ GHz}} = 0.122$ m, antenna length 61.2 mm; $\lambda_{915 \text{ MHz}} = 0.328$ m, antenna length 164 mm.

69. 2.7×10^9 W/m^2

71. $S = 2.2 \times 10^{10}$ W/m^2, $B_{rms} = 9.6 \times 10^{-3}$ T, $E_{rms} = 2.9 \times 10^6$ N/C

73. 50 W/m^2

75. At a distance of 50 from each device, the intensity relationships are $I_{phone} = 3.5 I_{oven}$ and $I_{headset} = 0.0080 I_{oven}$. With the headset, however, you have to add the intensity contributed by the cell phone at your waist, approximately $I_{waist} = 0.088$ W/m^2, meaning the headset intensity is $I_{headset} + I_{waist} = 0.17$ W/m^2. This is two orders of magnitude smaller than the intensity 50 mm from a microwave oven and 200 times smaller than the intensity 50 mm from a cell phone: a drastic improvement.

   Because intensity depends quadratically on the rms value of the magnetic field ($S : B_{rms}^2$), the rms value of the magnetic field you are exposed to using a headset is one order of magnitude smaller than when holding a cell phone to your ear.

   The wavelength of the 824.6-MHz radiation from a cell phone is 0.36 m, just a little longer than the head is wide. This tells you that standing waves within the skull are not an issue.

Chapter 31

1. 3×10^{24}

3. $a = b = e = f = j > g = h = c = d$

5.

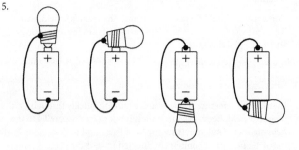

9. Your friend is correct that charge does not flow across the gap, meaning there is no current. There is however a displacement current. The electric field between the plates allows positive and negative charges to influence each other across the gap. Also, we know from our detailed study of capacitors that they can certainly discharge. If the air gap prevented charge from ever flowing from the plates, then no capacitor could ever discharge.

11. (a) No, only B, C, and D light up. (b) $C > B = D > A$

13. (a) No (b) Yes

15. $\Delta E_A = 1.5$ J, $\Delta E_B = 3.0$ J, and $\Delta E_C = 4.5$ J

17. A, B, and C are in parallel. E and F are also in parallel.

19.

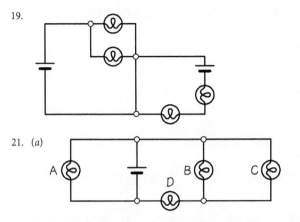

21. (a)

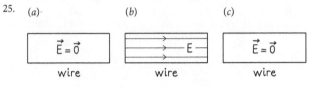

(b) Yes, all bulbs light up. (c) A is the brightest, B and C are tied for the dimmest. (d) B and C are in parallel, and none are wired in series.

23. Lights in a house are wired in parallel with very few exceptions.

25. (a)   (b)   (c)

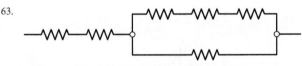

29. 1.0 m when made of nichrome, and 89 m when made from copper

31. 5.7 N/C

33. 1.2×10^3 m for the 4-gauge, and 19 m for the 22-gauge

35. 3.29×10^{-14} s

37. (a) Decrease (b) increase (c) decrease

39. 1.25×10^{10} protons

43. 2.77×10^{13} J

45. 0.90 A clockwise

47. (a) 9.0×10^{-2} A clockwise (b) 6.1×10^{-3} A counterclockwise (c) 1.1×10^{-1} A counterclockwise

49. $\epsilon = 6$ V and $R_{batt} = 1\ \Omega$

51. 3.0 Ω

53. (a) 0.57 A clockwise (b) $V_{ab} = 7.1$ V, $V_{bc} = 0$, $V_{cd} = -3.7$ V, $V_{da} = -3.4$ V

55. (a) 1.2×10^3 Ω (b) 1.0×10^{-2} A (c) $V_a = 12$ V, $V_b = 10$ V, and $V_c = 1$ V

57. 10 Ω

59. 3.1 Ω

61. −1.24 %

63.

65. (a) 750 Ω (b) 3.0 V (c) The current is 0.020 A down through the 1500 Ω resistor, 0.020 A to the right across the 900 Ω resistor that is along the top wire, 0.010 A down through the 1200 Ω resistor, and 0.010 A downward through both the 900 Ω and the 300 Ω resistors along the far right.

67. $I_1 = 2.0 \times 10^{-2}$ A, $I_2 = 1.5 \times 10^{-2}$ A, $I_3 = 5.0 \times 10^{-3}$ A

69. (a) 2.8 Ω (b) Let I_n denote the current across resistor number n. $I_1 = 5.0$ A, $I_2 = 2.0$ A, $I_3 = 2.0$ A, $I_4 = 1.0$ A, $I_5 = 1.0$ A, and $I_6 = 5.0$ A.

71. 0.085 A

73. The resistance of the entire string is $N\left(\dfrac{1}{R_b} + \dfrac{1}{R_a}\right)^{-1}$. If one bulb goes out the remaining bulbs will become dimmer.

75. 17 Ω

77. $I_1 = 0$, $I_2 = 0.67$ A but opposite the direction shown, $I_3 = 1.3$ A, $I_4 = 0.67$ A but opposite the direction shown, and $I_5 = 0.67$ A

79. (a) 1.3 A (b) 7.0 V

81. (a) $P_1 = 16$ W, $P_2 = 11$ W (b) $P_{Circuit} = 27$ W (c) $P_1 = 2.6$ W, $P_2 = 3.8$ W, and $P_{Circuit} = 6.4$ W

83. (a) $I_1 = 1.0$ A and $\Delta V = 5.00$ V, $I_2 = I_3 = I_4 = 0.333$ A, and $\Delta V_2 = \Delta V_3 = \Delta V_4 = 1.7$ V (b) $P_1 = 5.0$ W, $P_2 = P_3 = P_4 = 0.566$ W (c) ϵ_1 supplies a power of 10 W and ϵ_2 uses power at a rate of 3.30 W.

85. The current through all the outer resistors (250 Ω, 100 Ω, 50 Ω, and 200 Ω) is 0.25 A. The current through the center (75 Ω) resistor is zero. $Q_{cap} = 1.5$ mC

87. The power dissipated is 1.5 kW. Using a higher potential difference means you can deliver the same amount of power to a city at a lower current. Using the lower current means less power is dissipated in the transmission lines leading into the city.

89. Power is delivered by the 12 V battery at a rate of 0.24 W, by the 9 V battery at a rate of 0.14 W, by the two 1.5 V batteries at a rate of 7.5 mW each. The total power delivered by all batteries is 0.39 W. Energy is dissipated in the 300 Ω resistor at a rate of 0.12 W, in the 1000 Ω resistor at a rate of 0.23 W, in the 1200 Ω resistor at a rate of 0.030 W, and in the 600 Ω resistor at a rate of 0.015 W. The total power dissipated by the resistors is 0.39 W. This makes perfect sense, since all the energy provided to the circuit each second by the batteries has to go somewhere. In this case it goes into thermal energy in the resistors.

91. The resistance increases by a factor of 15, or 135 Ω.

93. There may be many correct answers. Examples are electrolytic solutions, solid state ionic conductors, etc.

95. 187 Ω

97. (a) 9.0 V (b) 18.0 V

99. We would add a resistor in parallel to those already in the circuit. This reduces the overall resistance of the circuit. We would add a resistor of large area like the top resistor.

101. The maximum current you can pull from the battery is 0.10 A. This happens when you fill the gap with a resistor that has such a small resistance that it is practically zero (like adding an ideal conductor). In that case, current would bypass the 100 Ω resistor in parallel with the conductor and the total resistance of the circuit would just be 100 Ω from the resistor that is not in series with anything. The smallest the current could ever be is 0.05 A. This happens when you close the gap with a resistor that has such a huge resistance that current is essentially prohibited from traversing it (or you could just leave the gap there, with nothing closing it). In that case the total resistance of the parallel arrangement would just be 100 Ω, and the total resistance of the circuit would be 200 Ω.

103. Let I_n be the current through resistor R_n. Then $I_{battery} = I_1 = I_2 = I_7 = 6.1$ A, $I_3 = I_4 = I_5 = 3.0$ A, and $I_6 = 0$. The charge on the 30 μF capacitor is 1.8×10^{-4} C. The charge on the 20 μF capacitor is also 1.8×10^{-4} C.

105. *Principles* equation 31.9 refers to the movement of electrons in a solid. In that case it is an electron that is carrying charge and leading to conduction of a current. In seawater, the particle that carries charge is never a dissociated electron, but rather an entire ion. Even the lightest possible ion (H^+) is about 2000 times heavier than an electron, and the ions in water are typically from salts of much heavier ions. Hence, even if equation 31.9 were valid, it would not be the mass of the electron in the denominator, but the mass of the ion. This leads you to a much lower conductivity.

Chapter 32

1. $B_{rms} = \dfrac{\mu_0 n I_{max}}{\sqrt{2}}$

3. 0.25 s, 0.75 s, 1.25 s, ...

5. X could certainly contain a resistor, perhaps in series with an inductor or another capacitor. Y could also contain a resistor if there is a source of alternating current maintaining a fixed maximum potential difference.

7. $\dfrac{3}{4} U^E$

9. 4.11 nC

11.

13.

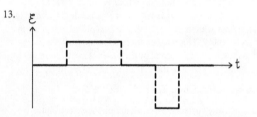

15. The circuit contains only a 9.0 Ω resistor and an AC source operating at a frequency that obeys $f = \left(\frac{1}{8} + n\right)$ Hz, where n is any integer.

17. (a) We draw the figure assuming that the capacitor is initially uncharged.

(b)

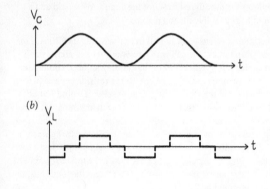

19. 1.2×10^{23}

21. Before doping, there are no free charge carriers in pure silicon (assuming no crystal impurities and very low temperatures). Hence the addition of even a small number of free (conducting) electrons is quite noticeable.

23. (a) Either of the doped semiconductors will conduct a current much better than the undoped silicon. (b) *n*-type (c) None

25. B

27. No

29. No

31. (a) B to A (b) A to B (c) A is *n*-type, and B is *p*-type (d) A may contain Phosphorous, and B may contain Boron

33. ABCD, ABC, ABD, ACD, BCD, AC, AD, BC, or BD

35.

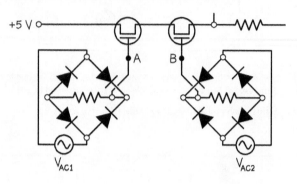

37. $3.3\ S^{-1}$

39. (a) 1.0 A (b) The current amplitude increases linearly with the source frequency.

41. (a) 15.2 V (b) 3.60 V

43. The device lags behind the source emf (or leading the emf by more than $\pi/2$ radians, but this is less likely).

45. $R = 1.41\ \Omega$ and $\omega = 70.7\ s^{-1}$

47. 4.50 V

49. (a) −121 rad, or −69.3° (b) $V_C = 2.64$ V, $V_R = 34.9$ V, and $\phi = -0.0756$ rad, or −4.33°

51. 1.56 mH

53. (a)

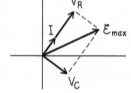

(b) −5.95° or −0.104 rad

55. 3.13 H

57. 43 Ω

59. (a)

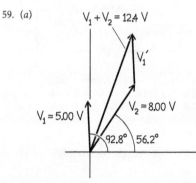

(b) $V = 12.4$ V, $\phi = 41.5°$, $v_{sum}(t = 0.0500$ s$) = 8.28$ V. These values are in very good agreement with the results from using phasors.

61. 1.0×10^3 s^{-1}

63. 8.7×10^{-6} F

65. $\omega_{0f} = \omega_{0i}$

67. $L = 3.00 \times 10^{-4}$ H and $R = 12.5$ Ω

69. (a) 5.59×10^3 s^{-1} (b) 6.00 A (c) 4.14 A

71. $C = 2.23 \times 10^{-9}$ F. The radio could be made more selective by lowering the resistance.

73. 50.8 mW

75. 4.00 W

79. $\cos(\phi) = 0.981$, $\phi = -11.3°$, $Z = 102$ Ω, $\epsilon_{rms} = 21.2$ V, $I_{rms} = 0.208$ A, and $P_{av} = 4.33$ W

81. (a) 6.0 W (b) 6.4 W

85.
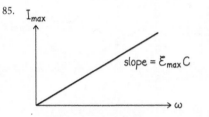

87. (a) (A, B) could be (Y, Y), (Y, N), (N, Y), or (N, N). The output is N for all combinations except (Y, Y), for which the output is Y. (b) The possible inputs for (A, B) are the same as in part (a): (Y, Y), (Y, N), (N, Y), or (N, N). Now the output is Y for all combinations except (N, N) for which the output is N.

89. (a) $f = 120$ Hz (b) $\phi = 85.7°$ or 1.50 radians

91.
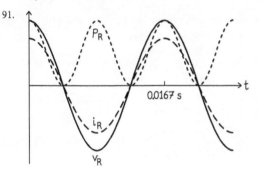

93.
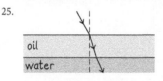

95. You can arrange the diodes and capacitors as shown below. This setup is called a "voltage doubler", or more generally a "voltage multiplier".

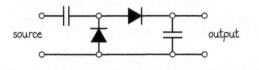

Chapter 33

1. (a) Light from all sources (a–h) strikes A. (b) Light from six sources (c–h) strikes B.

7. The bright spot would be a circle. The position of the circle may fluctuate as variations in the candle's flame cause the brightest spot to move slightly. The boundary of the circle would not be sharp, as light comes from a 1-3 cm region of flame, rather than a single point source.

9.
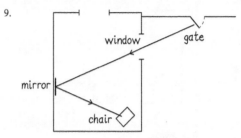

13. Assume you are looking into a mirror at the distant object behind you. Call the distance from you to the distant object d_o, call the distance from you to the mirror d_m, call the height of the distant object h_o, and call the height of the mirror h_m. Then $h_{m,min} = \dfrac{h_o d_m}{d_m + d_o}$.

15. You could demonstrate the difference between a real image and a virtual image by casting a real image onto a screen. Then look at an object in a mirror and place a screen on the mirror's surface. Note that no visible image appears on the screen. Hence, the image is not being formed at the mirror's surface.

19. The shadow is smaller when the tub is filled with water than when the tub is empty.

21. Shallower

23. Case A: (a) Light travels faster in material 2. (b) Light originates in material 2. Case B: (a) Light travels faster in material 1 (b) Light originates in material 2. Case C: (a) One cannot tell in which material light moves more quickly from examining a ray that is incident normal to the interface. (b) One cannot tell in which material the light originates from examining a ray that is incident normal to the interface.

25.
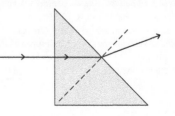

27. The light will pass straight through the vertical edge into the prism. Light cannot undergo total internal reflection when it strikes the diagonal edge. Rather, light will exit the diagonal edge and bend toward the line normal to that diagonal edge. This is shown below.

29. Place a second prism next to the first. Invert the second prism, so that its vertex points downward as shown below.

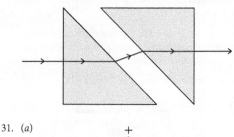

31. (a)

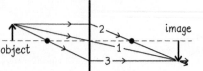

(b) Real (c) Inverted (d) It shrinks.

33. The object is held closer to the lens than the focal point, such that the lens is not able to focus the light down to a single point.

35. The image is on the same side as the object (opposite side from your eyes). If the image is magnified, the lens is converging. If the image is reduced, the lens is diverging.

37. (a)

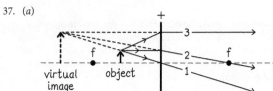

(b) Virtual (c) Upright (d) It becomes larger.

39. (a)

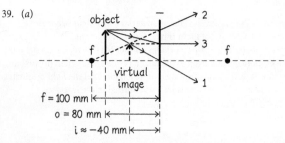

(b) Virtual (c) Upright (d) Smaller than the object

41. $f_{diverging} = 100$ mm and $f_{converging} = 200$ mm

43. Diamond

45. $f = 5.66 \times 10^{14}$ Hz and $\lambda = 321$ nm

47. 46.9°

49. (a) The wavelength is reduced by 1.333 to $\lambda = 404$ nm. (b) The frequency does not change. It remains 5.58×10^{14} Hz. (c) The speed is reduced by 1.333 to 2.25×10^8 m/s. (d) The angle from normal is reduced to 40.5°. (e) The wavelength, frequency, and speed would not be altered by changing the angle of entry. The refracted angle would change to 0°; the light will continue on parallel to the normal line.

51. (a) 56.1° (b) 53.6° (c) 21.7 mm

55. 54°

57. (a) $\sin^{-1}(\sqrt{n^2 - 1})$ (b) $\sqrt{2}$

59. 3.3 m

61. For a diverging lens, the focal length is negative. Using the lens equation (*Principles* equation 33.16), we can write $\frac{1}{i} = \frac{1}{f} - \frac{1}{o}$. The object distance is always positive. The only way for a real image to be formed is it the image distance is also positive. But clearly both terms on the right hand side of the above equation are negative. Hence $\frac{1}{i} < 0$, from which it immediately follows that $i < 0$. Since the image distance is always negative for a diverging lens, a diverging lens cannot form a real image.

63. 105 mm

65. 50 mm

67. (a) −240 mm (b) 1.60

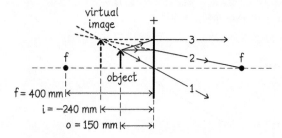

69. (a) −143 mm (b) 0.714 (c)

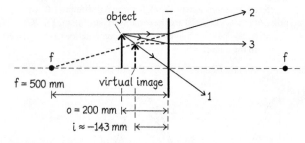

71. 1.5 diopters

73. (a) $\dfrac{dM_\theta}{M_\theta + 1}$ (b) $\dfrac{d}{M_\theta + 1}$

75. (a) 0.64 m (b) −5.1 (c) Inverted

77. The image will be virtual, inverted, and enlarged.

79. (a) 181 mm to the right of the right-most lens (b) Upright (c) Real (d) 0.625

81. This would require an objective lens with a focal length of 999.6 mm and an eyepiece lens with a focal length of 0.383 mm. The eyepiece focal length would be very difficult to achieve, and is not likely to be found in a home telescope. It would be much easier to use a longer telescope, and allow for a more complex setup involving multiple lenses and/or mirrors.

83. 333 mm

85. The image appears 392 mm behind mirror. But because the image is reduced, it occupies a much smaller fraction of your field of view than the car itself would. The images occupies roughly the same angular spread in your field of view as a car (object) that is 51 m away.

87. (*a*) 6.09 mm (*b*) Real (*c*) Inverted (*d*)

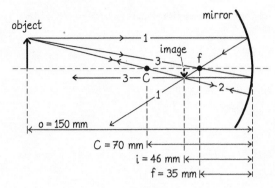

89. 0.40 m

91. 1.00 MM

95.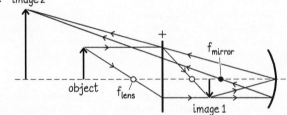

97. $R_2/R_1 = 3$

99. 470 mm

101. 0.10 m

103. 1.2

105. 200 mm

107. (*a*) 80 mm (*b*) 1.4

109. (*a*) Converging (*b*) Neither converging nor diverging (*c*) Diverging

111. You can only see light when it is reflected off of some object. In the air, there is no mechanism by which the laser light can be reflected to your eye. However, if you sprinkle powder into the path of the beam, the particles can scatter/reflect light to your eyes and the beam becomes partly visible.

113. 0.021 s

115. (*a*) This could be used to form a real image that is the same size as the original object. (*b*) This could be used to make light emanating from a points source travel in a straight line without spreading. (*c*) This could be used to focus light down to a single point, such as for heating a small region of space.

117. If the image is upright the object is 33 mm from the lens. If the image is inverted, the object is 67 mm

119. (*a*) Dispersion (*b*) It can be minimized, but not removed completely. (*c*) No

121.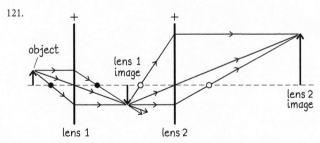

123. (*a*) 43.0° (*b*) 24.4°

125. Use a converging lens with a focal length of 33.48 mm. Place the lens a distance 33.64 mm in front of the film holder. This will cause an image to be cast on the screen 7.316 m in front of the lens, and the image will be three times larger than your initial attempt.

Chapter 34

1. There are many possible answers. Any material consisting of tiny pinholes or gaps is acceptable, such as the fabric of an umbrella. One can also observe diffraction at very sharp edges, such as that of a razor blade.

3. The wave properties of light predict that the center of the pattern should be bright. Since all rays diffracting around the edge of the circular obstacle are equidistant from the center, all the waves should strike the center in phase, and therefore interfere constructively.

5. Sound is also a wave and diffracts around barriers in a fashion similar to light. But the relevant wavelengths of sound waves and light waves are different by many orders of magnitude. Diffraction of a light wave around an object as thick as a tree is negligible, whereas the diffraction of sound around a tree is considerable.

7. 17.1°

9. The criteria to determine the highest order bright fringe visible is $m \le \dfrac{w}{\lambda N}$. Then the total number would be $2m_{max} + 1$.

13. (*a*) 33.0°

(*b*) $\sin^{-1}\left(\dfrac{\lambda}{d_{\text{orig}} + A\sin(\omega t)}\right)$

$= \sin^{-1}\left(\dfrac{546 \times 10^{-9}\text{ m}}{(1.0 \times 10^{-6}) + (0.25 \times 10^{-6})\sin((100\text{ s}^{-1})t)}\right)$

(*c*) $\dfrac{3\pi}{200}$ s, which is approximately 4.7×10^{-2} s (*d*) $\dfrac{\pi}{200}$ s, which is approximately 1.6×10^{-2} s (*e*) Only A, λ, and d_{orig} affect the values of the maximum and minimum angles, although ω affects the time at which these maximum values are achieved.

15. Farther apart

17. 8.717×10^{-10} m

19. 10^{-35} m

21. Yes, the electron has a nonzero chance of reaching the detector in all cases. But the chance may be very small if the obstacle is wide.

23. 6.65×10^{-15} m

25. 5.20×10^3 m/s

27. 5.84×10^{20}

29. 1.34×10^{16} photons per second, assuming that all the power refers to the output power as opposed to internal power use from the batteries, and assuming the photons are not scattered or absorbed by any medium on their way to the wall.

33. (*a*) 3 bright fringes (*b*) 0.165 m

35. 423 nm

37. $\Delta y_{1g} = 0.173$ m, $\Delta y_{2g} = 0.434$ m, $\Delta y_{1b} = 0.135$ m, and $\Delta y_{1g} = 0.307$ m

39. (*a*) $\Delta\theta = 0.11°$ (*b*) No

41. 0.154 m

43. 1.04 m

45. 7.942×10^3 slits

49. 608 nm and 434 nm

53. 2.37

55. 9.5×10^{-5} m

57. 6.25 m

59. 0.10 m

61. Many numerical answers are possible depending on the exact wavelength of light, the width of the door, and the distance from the door to the far wall of the cabin. But the crux of the answer is that the pattern will be extremely small, too small to observe with the naked eye, and too small to observe even with instruments if light from other sources is present. One would not even call this a diffraction pattern. As an example, let us assume that the light has a wavelength of 700 nm, that the door is 1.0 m wide, and that the distance from the door to the far wall of your cabin is 10 m. This would result in a first order dark fringe that is 7.0 μm from the central bright spot.

63. 5.3 mm

65. (a) 1.39×10^{-5} m (b) 78.4°

69. 226 nm

71. 4.03 μm

73. The minimum resolvable angular separation is between $(1.48 \times 10^{-2})°$ and $(2.47 \times 10^{-4})°$, depending on the wavelength being used.

75. 2.59 mm

77. $y_{r,\text{water}} = \dfrac{y_{r,\text{vac}}}{n} = \dfrac{y_{r,\text{vac}}}{1.33}$

81. 5.82 m

83. Yes, the lights are likely to be resolvable.

85. (a) The kinetic energy is reduced by a factor of 1/4. (b) There is no change; frequency is fixed.

87. 2.5 pm

89. 304 nm

91. 4.5×10^{-19} J or 2.8 eV

93. 8.8×10^{-19} J

95. 1.22×10^{15} Hz

97. (a) $\dfrac{\lambda_e}{\lambda_{ph}} = 3.49 \times 10^{-3}$ (b) $E_{ph}/K_e = 2.06 \times 10^5$, photon has more energy.

101. 0.0459°

103. 600 nm

107. 5.2×10^{-5} m

109. (a) The pattern will appear compressed. (b) The pattern will become brighter, but will be geometrically unchanged. (c) The number of photons per second is now greater than the initial number of photons per second.

111. 0.097

113. (a) 2.65×10^7 m/s (b) 2.74×10^{-11} m (c) Yes, the first order bright spot would be diffracted to an angle of 12.9°. So the diffraction pattern should be quite easily detected.

117. 3.75×10^{-4} mm

119. No, the width must be much greater than 1 m to get close to utility with the visible spectrum.

Credits

Unit conversion factors

Length

1 in. = 2.54 cm (defined)

1 cm = 0.3937 in.

1 ft = 30.48 cm

1 m = 39.37 in. = 3.281 ft

1 mi = 5280 ft = 1.609 km

1 km = 0.6214 mi

1 nautical mile (U.S.) = 1.151 mi = 6076 ft = 1.852 km

1 fermi = 1 femtometer (fm) = 10^{-15} m

1 angstrom (Å) = 10^{-10} m = 0.1 nm

1 light − year (ly) = 9.461×10^{15} m

1 parsec = 3.26 ly = 3.09×10^{16} m

Volume

1 liter (L) = 1000 mL = 1000 cm^3 = 1.0×10^{-3} m^3
    = 1.057 qt (U.S.) = 61.02 in.^{3}

1 gal (U.S.) = 4 qt (U.S.) = 231 in.^{3} = 3.785 L = 0.8327 gal (British)

1 quart (U.S.) = 2 pints (U.S.) = 946 mL

1 pint (British) = 1.20 pints (U.S.) = 568 mL

1 m^3 = 35.31 ft^3

Speed

1 mi/h = 1.4667 ft/s = 1.6093 km/h = 0.4470 m/s

1 km/h = 0.2778 m/s = 0.6214 mi/h

1 ft/s = 0.3048 m/s = 0.6818 mi/h = 1.0973 km/h

1 m/s = 3.281 ft/s = 3.600 km/h = 2.237 mi/h

1 knot = 1.151 mi/h = 0.5144 m/s

Angle

1 radian (rad) = 57.30° = 57°18′

1° = 0.01745 rad

1 rev/min (rpm) = 0.1047 rad/s

Time

1 day = 8.640×10^4 s

1 year = 365.242 days = 3.156×10^7 s

Mass

1 atomic mass unit (u) = 1.6605×10^{-27} kg

1 kg = 0.06852 slug

1 metric ton = 1000 kg

1 long ton = 2240 lbs = 1016 kg

1 short ton = 2000 lbs = 909.1 kg

1 kg has a weight of 2.20 lb where g = 9.80 m/s^2

Force

1 lb = 4.44822 N

1 N = 10^5 dyne = 0.2248 lb

Energy and work

1 J = 10^7 ergs = 0.7376 ft · lb

1 ft · lb = 1.356 J = 1.29×10^{-3} Btu = 3.24×10^{-4} kcal

1 kcal = 4.19×10^3 J = 3.97 Btu

1 eV = 1.6022×10^{-19} J

1 kWh = 3.600×10^6 J = 860 kcal

1 Btu = 1.056×10^3 J

Power

1 W = 1 J/s = 0.7376 ft · lb/s = 3.41 Btu/h

1 hp = 550 ft · lb/s = 746 W

1 kWh/day = 41.667 W

Pressure

1 atm = 1.01325 bar = 1.01325×10^5 N/m^2 = 14.7 lb/in.^{2} = 760 torr

1 lb/in.^{2} = 6.895×10^3 N/m^2

1 Pa = 1 N/m^2 = 1.450×10^{-4} lb/in.^{2}